P9-DBK-541

# Engineering

The brightness of the future depends
upon the diligence and imagination with which the engineering student
pursues his studies today. Opportunities for the engineering graduate
are unlimited since the expanding frontiers of knowledge permit investigation
of an ever-increasing array of discoveries.

# Engineering

## AN INTRODUCTION TO
## A CREATIVE PROFESSION

**George C. Beakley**

Professor of Engineering, Arizona State University

**H. W. Leach**

Instrumentation Engineer, Bell Helicopter Company

**The Macmillan Company**　**Collier-Macmillan Limited**
**New York**　**London**

WISCONSIN STATE UNIVERSITY
PLATTEVILLE

Fifth Printing, 1969

Earlier editions entitled *Elementary Problems in Engineering* copyright 1949 and 1951 by H. W. Leach and George C. Beakley. Earlier edition entitled *Engineering: The Profession and Elementary Problem Analysis* © copyright 1960 by H. W. Leach and George C. Beakley. Material reprinted from *The Slide Rule* copyright 1953 by H. W. Leach and George C. Beakley. Material reprinted from *Engineering Analysis* © 1959 by H. W. Leach and George C. Beakley.

Figures 14–1, 14–13, 14–14, 14–22, 14–23, 14–25, 14–26a, b, c, d, 14–27a, b, 14–28, 14–29a, b, 14–30, 14–32, 14–36a, b, c, 14–39a, b, c, d, 14–42, 14–44, 14–45, 14–47a, b, 14–49, 14–50, 14–52, 14–53, 14–54, 14–55, 14–56, 14–57, 14–58, 14–59, 14–60, 14–61, 14–62, 14–63, 14–64, 14–65, 14–66, 14–67, 14–68, 14–69, 14–70, 14–71, 14–72, 14–73, 14–74 are from Katz: *Technical Sketching and Visualization for Engineers,* copyright 1949 by The Macmillan Company. Used with permission of The Macmillan Company and the author, Hyman H. Katz.

Figure 14–2 is from Katz: *Handbook of Layout and Dimensioning for Production,* copyright 1957 by The Macmillan Company. Used with permission of The Macmillan Company and the author, Hyman H. Katz.

Library of Congress catalog card number: 67–16047

The Macmillan Company, New York

Collier-Macmillan Canada, Ltd., Toronto, Ontario

Printed in the United States of America

# Preface

As the frontiers of science are advanced and the work of the engineer assumes an increasingly important role in our modern society, the teaching concepts for engineering courses are undergoing continual change to keep abreast of technological developments. Recent reports by committees from the American Society for Engineering Education have shown that the high schools have assumed the responsibility for teaching the basic courses in the sciences and mathematics with sufficient comprehensiveness to enable the first year college engineering student to begin his more advanced mathematical and technical courses immediately.

Considerable experimentation is under way throughout the United States with regard to the type of engineering material that is best suited for young engineering students to study. At the moment, the courses of study that are gaining in popularity are (a) informational courses that introduce the student to the profession of engineering, (b) engineering problems and analysis courses that give the student some practice in engineering problem solving, and (c) introduction to engineering design courses that give the student a sense of "personal involvement" in undertaking real engineering tasks. Each type of course has its advantages and disadvantages. In many instances it will be appropriate to organize a course that draws material from each of the areas. The authors have prepared this text to meet the needs of all three types of courses—a task that, to their knowledge, has not been attempted before under a single cover. Ample material has been included for a full year's study, if this is desired. Text materials not assigned in class may be used for individual study and for reference purposes. We hope that this text will make possible a greater variety of course offerings at the elementary level than may have been available before.

The format of this text is such that the student can record points of emphasis and certain class notes and questions directly as they occur without the use of extra notepaper. Marking pens may be used for highlighting sentences or phrases, and the use of colored ink for underlining is recommended. For the student to get the most out of the text he should "live in it." If he does, the book will have a "lived in" appearance.

In order to give the student an understanding of the types of problems that are likely to be encountered in the practice of engineering, a large number of varied situations are described in problems throughout the book. Some of the problems are straightforward, and appropriate data are given to permit a unique solution. In other problems, data are given in general terms, sometimes with insufficient data so that the student must add information, and sometimes with an overabundance of data from which the student must select that which he needs. In all cases, the problems are designed to introduce the student to the realm of engineering study at the beginning of his college career, to offer him work with engineering concepts, and to confront him with situations in which decisions must be made where a number of choices exist.

The problem solving method introduced in the authors' previous textbooks has been expanded to include more of the creative phases of engineering. It is not enough just to manipulate numbers in engineering work; the engineer must be able to see applications of scientific principles, to develop designs that are based upon abstract principles, and to assume the lead in formulating imaginative solutions to unfamiliar problems. Every effort is made here to motivate the student to think imaginatively and constructively, and also to present material that will provide the best introduction to a career in engineering.

For additional classroom material, a workbook of problems is available on request directly from the authors to supplement the problems given in the text. These problems are prepared to require a minimum of layout work so that more time is available to the student for practice in problem analysis and computation.

The authors are interested in learning the opinions of those who read this book concerning its utility and serviceability in meeting the needs for which it was written. Improvements that are suggested will be incorporated in later editions.

In preparing this book, the authors have been aided not only by reviews and criticisms of previous editions but also by comments and suggestions from numerous engineering professors and practicing engineers in industry throughout the United States. In particular, the professional colleagues of the authors at Arizona State University and Bell Helicopter Company have been most influential in giving this book a unique blend of the *academic* and the *industrial* viewpoints. Other professional colleagues from industry have made equally significant contributions that are acknowledged where appropriate throughout the text. In particular we wish to thank the following people for their suggestions and reviews: Professors Theodore Allen, Jr.; Donald D. Autore; David D. Bedworth; John F. Bregar; Jack A. Collins; Richard L. Ditsworth; Leon W. Florschuetz; Harold Fry; C. B. Gambrell, Jr.; John B. Hawley; Louis A. Hill, Jr.; Charles D. Hoyt, Jr.; Daniel F. Jankowski; Robert D. Kersten; Earl Logan, Jr.; Darryl E. Metzger; O. B. Moan; Merle C. Nutt; Thornton W. Price; A. Alan B. Pritsker; Castle O. Reiser; Warren Rice; Earl R. Robbins; Wilbur C. Schoeller; Jack E. Stadmiller; Alfred B. Stafford; Peter K. Stein; Lee P. Thompson, Dean; Truet B. Thompson; Brian A. Thomson; James W. Turnbow; Charles S. Walker; and Charles E. Wallace, all of the College of Engineering Sciences of Arizona State University, and in addition Kenneth Christiansen, Bell

Helicopter Company; Jeannie Hill; George Eckstein, Remington Arms Company, Inc.; Myron S. Allen, President, Technical Service Research; Sidney J. Parnes, State University of New York at Buffalo; Amos H. Hoff, Phoenix College; William Wokum, Human Engineering Laboratories, Department of the Army; Carl Eyring, P.E., Salt River Project; J. W. Haefele, The Procter & Gamble Co.; C. Lester Hogan, Motorola Semiconductor Products Division; J. P. Guilford, University of Southern California; Donald W. MacKinnon, University of California; Colonel Bert J. Decker, United States Air Force; Morris O. Edwards, Stanford Research Institute; John Beakley, University of New Mexico; and Frank E. Edlin, Solar Energy Society.

The portion of Chapter 13 relating to the use of digital computers was prepared by William Babcock of the General Electric Company. Hyman H. Katz, President of the American Institute of Engineering and Technology, has been most helpful in making available to the authors several of his original sketches for use in Chapter 14, "Technical Sketching." The use of these figures is acknowledged on the copyright page of this text. Several photographs and drawings have been reproduced from "An Introduction to IBM DP Systems." These are reprinted by permission © 1960 by International Business Machines Corporation. The chapter on engineering systems, Chapter 18, includes the description of two complex engineering systems from today's technological environment. One, the exciting account of man's venture into outer space, has been contributed by Paul E. Purser and Maxime A. Faget of the National Aeronautics and Space Agency. The other, the story of the development and production of solid-state integrated circuits, has been prepared by Motorola Semiconductor Products Division of Phoenix, Arizona. In Chapter 19, "The Engineering Design Process," the authors have described in some detail the story of the design of the first safety razor. We are grateful to the Gillette Safety Razor Company of Boston, Massachusetts, for making available to us numerous historic documents and company records. Gene Nightengale of the United States Air Force Academy faculty prepared the majority of the material for Chapter 20, "Decision Processes in Design." His work is gratefully acknowledged. The authors are also indebted to Nils O. Myklestad, Professor of Engineering at Arizona State University, who edited Chapter 11, "Unit Systems and Dimensional Analysis," and supplied some of its content.

Electronic computer-produced drawings and graphs are frequently used by the engineer to supplement his problem analysis. Many of these, although geometric in form, aesthetically are very pleasing to look at and to consider. In many respects they can be made into exciting patterns such as those observed in nature. Patterns in nature are precise and yet no two of them are identical. Nature's masterfulness may lie not in her repeatability but in her randomness. So in working with artistic design by computer one must attempt to imitate the orderly actions of nature on the one hand by programming into the computer certain precise mathematical relationships that describe laws of nature in order to provide pattern and stability, and at the same time give the computer an almost mischievous capability of randomness —either wildly rampant randomness or discretely controlled randomness. The latter frees the final pattern obtained and provides an elusive and almost unexpected quality, and in some cases an eerie or ethereal touch. Such is the case with several computer-produced designs that have been used as the cover and frontispiece of this text. These designs are the result of the work of Donald Robbins and Leigh Hendricks of the Sandia Corporation, Albuquerque, New Mexico, who have made them available for this specific use. We are grateful to them for permission to reproduce these examples of their work.

To the many others who have given the authors the benefit of their experience by making recommendations as to format and content, we wish to express our sincere gratitude.

G. C. B.
H. W. L.

# Contents

Contents

x

# PART ONE
## ENGINEERING – A CREATIVE PROFESSION

The pyramids of Egypt exemplify man's desire to create and build enduring monuments. (Ewing Galloway)

# Chapter 1

# Engineering – The Story of Man's Developing Civilization

When did engineering begin? Who were the first engineers? What were the objectives of work by the early engineers? Answers to these questions and others concerning the beginning of engineering appear in the fragments of historical information available to us. In fact the beginnings of civilization and the beginnings of engineering are coincident. As early man emerged from caves to make homes in communities, he adapted rocks and sticks as tools to aid him. Simple as these items may seem to us today, their useful employment suggests that the creative ideas which emerged in the minds of early man were developed into useful products to serve the recognized needs of the day. Some served as tools in the struggle for existence of an individual or group, and others were used for protection against wild animals or warlike neighbors. Early engineering was therefore principally either civil or military.

Down through the ages, the engineer has been in the forefront as a maker of history. His material accomplishments have had as much impact on world history as any political, economic, or social development. Sometimes, his accomplishments have stemmed from the pressures of need from evolving civilizations. At other times, his abilities to produce and meet needs have led the way for civilizations to advance. In general, the engineers do the things required to serve the needs of the people and their culture.

Basically, the role of the engineer has not changed down through the centuries. His job is to take knowledge and make practical use of it. He converts scientific theory into useful application; and in so doing, he provides for man's material needs and well being. From era to era, only the objectives that he has pursued, the techniques of solution that he has used, and the tools of analysis at his disposal have changed.

It is helpful to review the past to gain insight to the driving forces of science and to learn of the men who developed and applied these principles. A review also will reveal certain facts concerning the discovery and use of fundamental scientific principles. Primarily, science builds its store of knowledge on facts which, once determined, are from then on available for further discovery. This principle is in contrast to the arts, since, for example, the ability of one person to produce a beautiful painting does not make available to others his skills in producing paintings.

Outstanding characteristics of engineers through the centuries have been a willingness to work and an intellectual curiosity about the behavior of things. Their queries about "Why?," "How?," "With what?," and "At what cost?" have all served to stimulate an effort to find desirable answers to many types of technological problems.

Another characteristic associated with engineers is the ability to "see ahead." The engineer must have a fertile imagination, must be creative, and must be ready to accept new ideas. Whether an engineer lived at the time of construction of the pyramids or has only recently graduated in nuclear engineering, these characteristics have been an important part of his intellectual makeup.

The following sections present a brief picture of the development of engineering since the dawn of history and outline the place that the engineer has held in various civilizations.

## THE BEGINNINGS OF ENGINEERING: 6000 B.C.–3000 B.C.

The beginning of engineering can be considered to have occurred probably in Asia Minor or Africa some 8000 years ago. About this time, man began to cultivate plants, domesticate animals, and build permanent houses in community groups. With the change from a nomadic life came requirements for increased food production. Among the first major engineering projects were irrigation systems to promote crop growing. Increased food production permitted time for men to engage in other activities. Some became rulers, some priests, and many became artisans, whom we may call the first engineers.

Early achievements in this era included methods of producing fire at will, melting certain rocklike materials to produce copper and bronze tools, invention of the wheel and axle, development of a system of symbols for written communication, origination of a system of mathematics, and construction of irrigation works.

Early records are so fragmentary that only approximate dates can be given for any specific discovery, but evidences of the impact of early engineering achievements are readily discernible. For example, in setting up stable community life in which land was owned, men had to provide both for irrigation and for accurate location and maintenance of boundaries. This necessity stimulated the development of surveying and of mathematics. The moving of earth to make canals and dams required computations, and to complete the work meant the efforts of many men had to be organized and directed. As a result, a system of supervisors, foremen, and workers was established that formed the beginnings of a class society.

In this society, craftsmen became a distinct group producing useful items such as pottery, tools, and ornaments that were desired by others. As a result, trade and commerce were stimulated and roads were improved. Some 5000 years ago man first used the wheel and axle to make the first two-wheeled carts drawn by animals.

In order to record the growing accumulation of knowledge about mathematics and engineering, the early engineer needed a system of writing and some type of writing material. In the Mesopotamian region, soft clay was used on which cuneiform characters were incised. When baked, the clay tile material was used for permanent documents, some of which are legible even today (see Illustration 1–1). In the Nile Valley, a paperlike material called *papyrus* was made from the inner fibers of a reed. In other parts of Asia Minor, treated skins of animals were used to form parchment. Occasionally, slabs of stone or wood were used as writing materials. The type of writing that developed was strongly influenced by the writing

Mesopotomia, often called the "Cradle of civilization," could also be said to have nurtured engineering in its infancy. Clay tablets, such as the ones shown on this page, have been unearthed which show city plans, irrigation, and water supply systems, and what appears to be, road maps. Although no engineering tools have been discovered among the remains of ancient Mesopotamia, the evidence unearthed of their remarkable architectural construction indicates that they used measuring tools, which, even though primitive, aided in producing engineering of a high degree for this period. Their cities, with their water supply, irrigation systems, and road networks, were among the wonders of the ancient world.

Many outstanding contributions of mathematics were made by the Mesopotamians. It has been proven that they had knowledge of the sexagesimal system, in which they divided the circle into 360 degrees, the hour into 60 minutes and the minute into 60 seconds.

Map of caravan routes, mountains, cities, and water.

Clay tablet of a city plan.

City planning and building.

Irrigation *systems* were extensive.

**Illustration 1–1.** Mesopotamia, often called the cradle of civilization, also may be said to have begun engineering. Excavations have revealed their extensive architecture, irrigation systems, roads, and land planning. In this picture is shown a party of surveyors using tools for measurement which, for the period, were remarkably accurate. (Courtesy Maddox and Hopkins.)

**Illustration 1–2.** Ancient builders employed engineering principles in the construction of their structures. Clay plumb bobs, such as the one pictured here being used by Babylonian builders, have been unearthed recently by archeologists. (Courtesy W. S. Dickey Clay Mfg. Co.)

material available. For example, the incised characters in soft clay differed significantly from the brush strokes used in writing on papyrus.

In engineering work, a source of energy is necessary. This requirement led to the enslavement and use of numbers of humans as primary sources of energy. The construction of all early engineering works, whether they be Oriental, Mediterranean, or American Indian, have been accomplished principally by human labor. It was not until near the end of the period of history known as the Middle Ages that mechanical sources of power were developed.

## ENGINEERING IN EARLY CIVILIZATIONS: 3000 B.C.–600 B.C.

After about 3000 B.C., enough records were made on clay tablets, on papyrus and parchment, on pottery, and as inscriptions on monuments and temples to provide us with information about ancient civilization. These records show that urban civilizations existed in Egypt, Mesopotamia, and the Indus Valley and that a class society of craftsmen, merchants, soldiers, and government officials was a definite part of that civilization.

In Mesopotamia, clay tablets have been uncovered which show that Babylonian engineers were familiar with basic arithmetic and algebra. From these writings we know that they routinely computed areas and volumes of land excavations. Their number system, based on 60 instead of 10, has been handed down through the centuries to us in our measures of time and angle. Their buildings were constructed principally of baked brick. Primitive arches were used in some of their early hydraulic works. Bridges were built with stone piers carrying wooden stringers for the roadway. Some roads were surfaced with a naturally occurring asphalt, a construction method not used again until the nineteenth century.

It was in Egypt that some of the world's most remarkable engineering was performed (see Illustration 1–3). Beginning about 3000 B.C. and lasting for about a

In ancient Egypt warfare and strife delayed the development of engineering; however, with the unification of Upper and Lower Egypt, the science of measurement and construction made rapid progress. Buildings, city planning, and irrigation systems show evidence of this development. Good judgment and reasonable engineering design resulted in sound and durable structures. The Pyramids are engineering marvels both in design and construction.

That the Egyptians advanced mathematics is attested to by papyrus scrolls, dating back to 1500 B.C., which show that the Egyptians had knowledge of the triangle and were able to compute areas and volumes. They also had a device to obtain the azimuth from the stars.

The annual floods of the Nile afforded ample practice in measurement surveying. This may well have been the first example of the importance of re-surveys. The rope used as a measure was first soaked in water, dried, and then coated heavily with wax to insure constant length. Probably some crude surveying instruments were devised, but none have been found.

Resetting boundaries after the Nile floods.

Early geometric application.

**Illustration 1–3.** In Egypt the science of measurement and construction developed rapidly. The pyramids are engineering marvels both in design and construction. Papyrus scrolls show that the Egyptians had knowledge of the triangle and were able to compute areas and volumes. (Courtesy Maddox and Hopkins.)

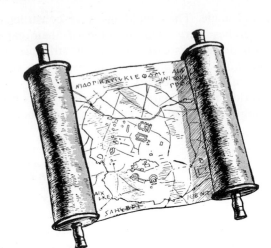

The outstanding progress made by the Ancient Grecians in architecture and mathematics and their contribution to the advancement of engineering demand our admiration.

Aristotle contended that the world was a spheroid. He stated that observations of the various stars showed the circumference of the earth to be about 400,000 *stadia* (400,000) miles.

Erathosthenes, of Cyrene, observed that the sun's rays, when perpendicular to a well at Alexandria, cast a shadow equal to one fiftieth of a circle at Syene (Aswan) five hundred miles away. Thus he established that the circumference of the earth was fifty times five hundred miles or 25,000 miles.

The Greeks constructed many buildings and structures of large size, which show engineering skill and excellent architectural design. One tunnel, which was built to bring water to Athens, measured eight feet by eight feet and was forty-two hundred feet in length. The construction of such a tunnel necessitated extremely accurate alignment both on the surface and underground.

**Illustration 1—4.** The Greeks constructed many buildings of unusual beauty which show a high degree of engineering skill and architectural design. Their cities had municipal water supplies that required dams and aqueducts to bring water from the mountains. This picture shows a builder laying out a building foundation, using a divided circle, a plumb bob, and a knotted rope. (Courtesy Maddox and Hopkins.)

hundred years, the Pyramid Age flourished in Egypt. The first pyramids were mounds covered with stone, but the techniques progressed rapidly until the Great Pyramid was begun about 2900 B.C. Stones for the structures were cut by workmen laboriously chipping channels in the native rock, using a ball made of a harder rock as a tool. By this method, blocks weighing 15 tons or more were cut for use in building. The Egyptian engineers apparently used only the lever, the inclined plane, the wedge, and the wheel in their construction efforts (see Illustration 1–4).

Although early construction tools were primitive, the actual structures, even by today's standards, are outstanding examples of engineering skill in measurement and layout. For example, the base of the Great Pyramid is square within about one inch in a distance of 756 feet, and its angles are in error by only a few minutes despite the fact that the structure was built on a sloping rocky ledge.

The Egyptian engineers and architects held a high place in the Pharaoh's court. Imhotep, a designer of one of the large pyramids, was so revered for his wisdom and ability that he was included as one of the Egyptian gods after his death. Not only were the Egyptian engineers skilled builders, they were also skilled in land measurement. Annual overflows of the Nile River obliterated many property lines and a resurvey of the valley was frequently necessary. Using geometry and primitive measuring equipment, they restored markers for land boundaries after the floods receded.

The Egyptians also were skilled in irrigation work. Using a system of dikes and canals, they reclaimed a considerable area of desert. An ancient engineering contract to build a system of dikes about 50 miles long has recently been discovered.

Although the skill and ingenuity of the Egyptian engineers were outstanding, the culture lasted only a relatively short time. Reasons which may account for the failure to maintain leadership are many, but most important was the lack of pressure to continue development. Once the engineers formed the ruling class, little influence could be brought to bear to cause them to continue their creative efforts. Since living conditions were favorable, after an agricultural system was established, little additional engineering was required. The lack of urgency to do better finally stifled most of the creativity of the engineers and the civilization fell into decay.

## SCIENCE OF THE GREEKS AND ROMANS: 600 B.C.–A.D. 400

The history of engineering in Greece had its origins in Egypt and the East. With the decline of the Egyptian civilization, the center of learning shifted to the island of Crete and then about 1400 B.C. to the ancient city of Mycenae in Greece.

To the engineers of Mycenae were passed not only the scientific discoveries of the Egyptians but also a knowledge of structural building materials and a language that formed the basis of the early Greek language. These engineers subsequently developed the corbeled arch and made wide use of irrigation systems.

From the Mycenaean engineers, the Greeks of Athens and Sparta borrowed many of their developments. In fact, the engineers of this period were better known for the intensive development of borrowed ideas than for creativity and invention. Their water system, for example, modeled after Egyptian irrigation systems, showed outstanding skill in the use of labor and materials, and these Greeks established technical procedures that have endured for centuries (see Illustration 1–4).

Greece was famous for its outstanding philosophers. Significant contributions were made by men such as Plato, Aristotle, and Archimedes. In the realm of abstract thought, they perhaps have never been equaled, but at that time extensive use of their ideas was retarded because of the belief that verification and experimentation, which required manual labor, was fit only for slaves. Of all the contributions of the Greeks to the realm of science, perhaps the greatest was the discovery that nature has general laws of behavior which can be described with words.

The best engineers of antiquity were the Romans. Within a century after the death of Alexander, Rome had conquered many of the eastern Mediterranean countries, including Greece. Within two more centuries Rome had dominion over most of the known civilized areas of Europe, Africa, and the Middle East. Roman engineers liberally borrowed scientific and engineering knowledge from the conquered countries for use in warfare and in their public works. Although in many instances they lacked originality of thought, Roman engineers were superior in the application of techniques (see Illustration 1–5).

From experience Rome had learned the necessity for establishing and maintaining a system of communications to hold together the great empire. Thus Roman roads became models of engineering skills. By first preparing a deep subbase and then a compact base, the Romans advanced the technique of road construction so far that some Roman roads are still in use today. At the peak of Roman sovereignty, the network of roads comprised over 180,000 miles stretching from the Euphrates Valley to Great Britain.

In addition, Roman engineers were famous for the construction of aqueducts and bridges. Using stone blocks in the constructing of arches, they exhibited unusual skill. An outstanding example of this construction is the famous Pont du Gard near Nîmes, France, which is 150 feet high and over 900 feet long. It carries both an aqueduct and a roadway.

By the time of the Christian era, iron refining had developed to the extent that iron was being used for small tools and weapons. However, the smelting process was so inefficient that over half of the metallic iron was lost in the slag. Except in the realm of medicine, no interest was being shown in any phase of chemistry.

Despite their outstanding employment of construction and management techniques, the Roman engineers seemed to lack the creative spark and imagination necessary to provide the improved scientific processes required to keep pace with the expanding demands of a far-flung empire. The Romans excelled in law and civil administration but were never able to bring distant colonies fully into the empire. Finally, discontent and disorganization within the empire led to the fall of Rome to a far less cultured invader.

## ENGINEERING IN THE MIDDLE AGES: FIFTH TO SIXTEENTH CENTURIES

After the fall of Rome, scientific knowledge was dispersed among small groups, principally under the control of religious orders. In the East, an awakening of technology began among the Arabs but little organized effort was made to carry out any scientific work. Rather, it was a period in which isolated individuals made new discoveries or rediscovered earlier known scientific facts.

It was during this time that the name *engineer* first was used. Historical writings

The Romans excelled in the building of aqueducts. Many of these carried water for great distances with perfect grade and alignment. The key design in this type of construction was the arch which was also used in bridges, tunnels, buildings, and other construction.

Evidence of the Romans' knowledge and understanding of basic geometric principles is further shown by their River and Harbor construction and the scientific approach to navigational problems.

Sanitary systems, paved roads, magnificent public buildings, water supply systems, and other public works still in evidence today, stand as monuments to the Roman development of engineering as a key to the raising of the standard of living.

The rise of the Roman Empire was attributable to the application of engineering principles applied to military tactics. Invincibility of the Roman legions was the result not only of the valor of the fighting men but also, and perhaps more strongly, to the genius of the Roman military engineers.

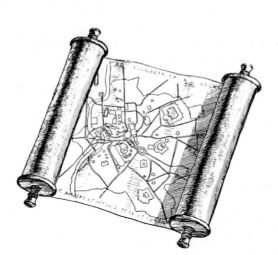

**Illustration 1–5.** The rise of the Roman Empire was attributed to the application of engineering principles to military tactics. This picture shows a construction party as they build a section of the famous Roman highways. Notice the heavy foundations which exist to this day. (Courtesy Maddox and Hopkins.)

of about A.D. 200 tell of an *ingenium,* an invention, which was a sort of battering ram used in attacks on walled defenses. Some thousand years later, we find that an *ingeniator* was the man who operated such a device of war—the beginning of our modern title, *engineer.*

Several technical advances were made late in this period. One important discovery involved the use of charcoal and a suitable air blast for the efficient smelting of iron. Another advance was made when the Arabs began to trade with China and a process of making paper was secured from the Chinese. Within a few years the Arabs had established a paper mill and were making paper in large quantities. With the advent of paper, communication of ideas began to be reestablished. Also in Arabia, the sciences of chemistry and optics began to develop. Sugar refining, soap making, and perfume distilling became a part of the culture. The development of a method of making gun powder, probably first learned from China about the fourteenth century, also had rapid and far reaching results.

After centuries of inaction, the exploration of far away places began again, aided greatly by the development of a better compass. With the discovery of other cultures and the uniting of ideas, there gradually emerged a reawakening of scientific thought.

With the growth of Christianity, an aversion arose to the widespread use of slaves as primary sources of power. This led to the development of water wheels and wind mills and to a wider use of animals, particularly horses, as power sources.

About 1454, Gutenberg, using movable type, produced the first books printed on paper (see Illustration 1–6). This meant that the knowledge of the ages, which previously had been recorded laboriously by handwriting, now could be disseminated widely and in great quantities. Knowledge which formerly was available only to a

**Illustration 1–6.** The invention of printing by using movable type meant that scientific information could be made available to many more people. Here Johann Gutenberg is examining a proof sheet, the first ever produced from movable type. (The Bettman Archive.)

few, now was spread to scholars everywhere. Thus the invention of paper and the development of printing served as fitting climaxes to the Middle Ages.

Seldom has the world been blessed with a genius such as that of Leonardo da Vinci (1452–1519). Although still acclaimed today as one of the greatest of all artists, his efforts as an engineer, inventor, and architect are even more impressive. Long after his death his designs of a steam engine, machine guns, a camera, conical shells, a submarine, and a helicopter have been proven to be workable.

Galileo (1564–1642) was also a man of great versatility. He was an excellent writer, artist, and musician, and he is also considered as one of the foremost scientists of that period. One of his greatest contributions was his formulation of what he considered to be the scientific method of gaining knowledge (see Illustration 1–7).

**Illustration 1–7.** Galileo is considered one of the foremost scientists of his time. Many inventions and discoveries have been credited to him, including the first telescope. By using his telescope, Galileo discovered the moons around the planet Jupiter. This picture shows Milton in the observatory of Galileo looking through a telescope. (The Bettman Archive.)

## THE REVIVAL OF SCIENCE: SEVENTEENTH AND EIGHTEENTH CENTURIES

Following the invention of printing, the self-centered medieval world changed rapidly. At first, the efforts to present discoveries of Nature's laws met with opposition and in some cases even hostility. Slowly, however, freedom of thought was permitted and a new concept of *testing to evaluate a hypothesis* replaced the early method of establishing a principle solely by argument.

Four men in this period made discoveries and formulated laws which have proved to be of great value to engineering. They were Boyle, who formulated a law relating pressures and volumes of gases, Huygens who investigated the effects of gravitational pull, Hooke who experimented with the elastic properties of materials, and Newton who is famous for his three laws of motion. All of the early experimenters were hampered by a lack of a concise vocabulary to express their ideas. Because of this many of the principles were expressed in a maze of wordy statements.

During this period, significant advancements were made in communication and transportation. Canals and locks were built for inland water travel and docks and harbors were improved for ocean commerce. Advances in ship design and improved methods of navigation permitted a wide spreading of knowledge that formerly had been isolated in certain places.

The search for power sources to replace human labor continued. Water power and wind power were prime sources, but animals began to be used more and more. About this time, the first attempts to produce a steam engine were made by Papin and Newcomen. Although these early engines were very inefficient, they did mark the beginning of power from heat engines.

An important industry was made possible in this period by the development of spinning and weaving machinery by such men as Jurgen, Hargreaves, Crampton, and Arkwright. This period also marked a general awakening of science after the Dark Ages. Individual discoveries, although they usually were isolated, found their way into useful products within a short period of time because of the development of printing and the improvements in communication.

**Illustration 1—8.** During the eighteenth century scientific research began to provide more answers to men's questions concerning natural laws. In this picture, Foucault, who devised a pendulum to demonstrate the effect of the earth's rotation, shows his new development to a group of scientists of that time. (The Bettman Archive.)

The basic discoveries in this era were made by men who were able to reject old, erroneous concepts and search for principles that were more nearly in accord with Nature's behavior (see Illustration 1–8). Engineers in any age must be equally discerning if their civilization is to advance.

## BEGINNINGS OF MODERN SCIENCE: NINETEENTH CENTURY

Early in the nineteenth century, two developments provided an impetus for further technological discoveries. The two developments were the introduction of a method, developed by Henry Cort, of refining iron and the invention of an efficient steam engine by James Watt. These developments provided a source of iron for machinery and power plants to operate the machinery.

As transportation systems began to develop, both by water and by land, a network of railroads and highways were built to tie together the major cities in Europe and in the United States (see Illustration 1–9).

**Illustration 1–9.** This remarkable picture, taken in 1877 when the high Secrettown trestle in the Sierra Nevada mountains of California was being filled in with dirt by the Central Pacific, now the Southern Pacific Railway, shows the meager tools with which the builders had to work in blasting a trail over and through the rugged mountains for the rails of the first transcontinental railroad. In those days there were none of the power implements that are so common to modern construction. Scrapers were not even used in the grading. Dynamite had been invented but was not in general use during the years the railroad was being built in 1863–69. Chinese "coolies" did the work with pick and shovel, one-horse dump carts, wheel barrows, and back power. At times it was necessary to lower the workmen over cliffs in baskets to ledges where they could level off a grade in the mountainside. (Courtesy Southern Pacific Company.)

In this period, the awakening of science and engineering truly had begun. Now, although people were slow to accept new ideas, knowledge was not rejected as it had been in earlier centuries. Colleges began to teach more and more courses in science and engineering, and it was here that the fuse was lighted for an explosion of discoveries in the twentieth century.

One of the most important reasons for the significant development of technology in this period was the increasingly close cooperation between science and engineering. It began to become more and more evident that discoveries by research scientists could be used to develop new articles for commerce. Industry soon began to realize that money spent for research and development eventually returned many times its value.

## TWENTIETH CENTURY TECHNOLOGY

As the twentieth century came into being, a number of inventions emerged that were destined to have far-reaching effects on our civilization. The automobile began to be more widely used as better roads were made available. The inventions of Edison and DeForest of electrical equipment and electron tubes started the widespread use of power systems and communication networks. Following the demonstrations by the Wright brothers that man could build a machine that would fly, aircraft of many types developed rapidly.

These inventions, typical of many basic discoveries that were made early in the century, exemplify the spirit of progress of this period. So fast has been the pace of discovery, with one coming on the heels of another, that it is difficult to evaluate properly their relative importance, although we certainly can realize their impact on our way of life.

Until late in the nineteenth century, engineering as an applied science was divided into two principal groups, civil and military. Mining and metallurgy was the first group to be recognized as a separate branch and the American Institute of Mining and Metallurgical Engineers was founded in 1871. In 1880, the American Society of Mechanical Engineers was founded, and in 1884 the American Institute of Electrical Engineers (now the Institute of Electrical and Electronic Engineers) was founded. In 1908, the American Institute of Chemical Engineers was founded and since then a number of other branch societies have been founded with objectives peculiar to specialized fields of engineering endeavor.

An outstanding characteristic of this century is the increased use of power. In 1966, it was estimated that the average family in the United States used about 5000 kilowatt hours of energy per year.[1] This would be equivalent to the work of about 65 laborers per day to supply just the household power requirements. This is a considerable advance from the days of the Egyptians and Greeks.

Following World War II, the political, economic, and scientific disorganization in the world caused the emigration of many outstanding educators, scientists, and engineers to the United States. Here they have been able to expand their knowledge and skills and to aid generally in advancing our own understanding of the basic natural laws on which the improved techniques of the future will be based.

[1] Edison Electric Institute, Vol. 34, No. 7, Oct. 4, 1966.

**Illustration 1—10.** Engineering today is exemplified by the teamwork of engineers, scientists, and technicians. In this photograph, such a team is shown preparing to simulate an orbital mission and to record the results of the test. (Courtesy McDonnell Aircraft Corporation.)

## ENGINEERING TODAY

Broadly speaking, modern engineering had its beginnings about the time of the close of the Civil War. Within the last century, the pace of discovery has been so rapid that it can be classed as a period within itself. In these modern times, engineering endeavor has changed markedly from procedures used in the time of Imhotep, Galileo, or Ampere. Formerly, engineering discovery and development were accomplished principally by individuals. With the increased store of knowledge available and the widening of the field of engineering to include so many diverse branches, it is usual to find groups or teams of engineers and scientists working on a single project. Where formerly an individual could absorb and understand practically all of the scientific knowledge available, now the amount of information available is so vast that an individual can retain and employ at best only a part of it.

Within fairly recent times, two developments have produced profound changes in our way of life. These developments are nuclear power and the electronic digital computer. Apparently, these concepts are still in their early stages of development, but historians of the future may well refer to our present time as the *nuclear age* or the *computer age*. The engineer, of course, has been a principal developer of these concepts because of the need for their capabilities.

In this age, as in any age, the engineer must be creative and must be able to

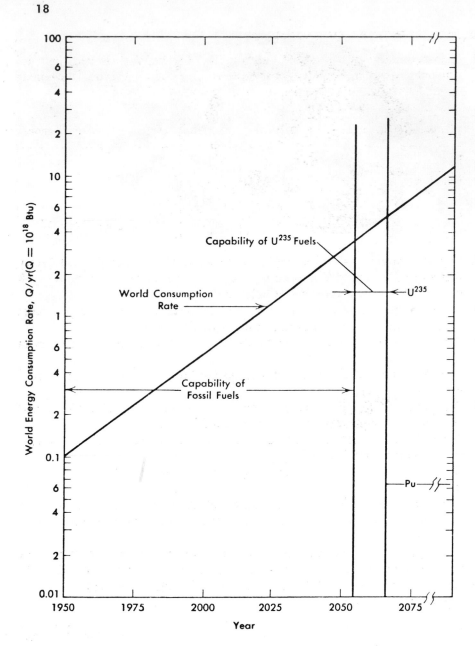

**Figure 1–1.** Estimated world energy consumption in future years.[2]

visualize what may lie ahead (see Figure 1–1). He must possess a fertile imagination and a knowledge of what others have done before him. As Sir Isaac Newton is reputed to have said, "If I have seen farther than other men, it is because I have stood on the shoulders of giants." The giants of science and engineering still exist. All any person must do to increase his field of vision is to climb up on their shoulders.

[2] A. S. Coffinberry, *The Metal Plutonium,* University of Chicago Press, Chicago (1961), p. 336.

## PROBLEMS ON HISTORY OF ENGINEERING

**1–1.** Prepare a chart as a series of columns, showing happenings and their approximate dates in a vertical time scale for various civilizations, beginning about 3000 B.C. and extending to about 1200 A.D.

| CHINESE | MIDDLE EAST | EGYPTIAN | GREEK | ROMAN | WESTERN EUROPE |
|---|---|---|---|---|---|
|  |  |  |  |  |  |

**1–2.** Prepare a brief essay on the possible circumstances surrounding the discovery that an iron needle when rubbed on a lodestone and then supported on a bit of wood floating on water would point to the north.

**1–3.** Determine from historical references the approximate number of years that major civilizations existed as important factors in history.

**1–4.** What were the principal reasons for the lack of advancement of discovery in Greek science?

**1–5.** Explain why the development of a successful horsecollar was a major technological advancement.

**1–6.** Draw to some scale a typical cross section of the "Great Wall" of China, and estimate the volume of rock and dirt required per mile of wall.

**1–7.** Trace the development of a single letter of our alphabet from its earliest known symbol to the present.

**1–8.** Describe the details of preparing papyrus from reed-like plants which grew in Egypt.

**1–9.** Describe the patterns of behavior and accomplishments of ancient engineers that seem to have made successful civilizations, and to have prolonged their existence.

**1–10.** Prepare lists of prominent persons who contributed outstanding discoveries and developments to civilization during the period from A.D. 1200 to A.D. 1900 in the fields of (*a*) mathematics, (*b*) astronomy, (*c*) electricity, (*d*) mechanics, and (*e*) light.

| PERSON | DATE | MAJOR CONSTRUCTION |
|---|---|---|
|  |  |  |

## ENGINEERING — A CREATIVE PROFESSION

**1–11.** List the ten most significant engineering achievements of the twentieth century.

**1–12.** Beginning with 3000 B.C., list the twenty-five most significant engineering achievements.

**1–13.** Based upon your knowledge of world history, describe the probable changes that might have occurred had the airplane not been invented until 1970.

**1–14.** Describe the precision with which the pyramids of Egypt were constructed. How does this precision compare with that of modern office buildings of over 50 stories in height?

**1–15.** Trace the development of the power producing capability of man from 3000 B.C. to the present.

## BIBLIOGRAPHY

DeCamp, L. S., *The Ancient Engineers*, Doubleday, Garden City, (1963).

Dobrovolny, Jerry S., *Engineering History and Western Civilization*, McGraw-Hill, New York, (1962).

Finch, James Kip, *Engineering and Western Civilization*, McGraw-Hill, New York, (1951).

Finch, James Kip, *The Story of Engineering*, Anchor Books, Doubleday, Garden City, N.Y., (1960).

Fleming, A. P. and H. J. Brocklehurst, *A History of Engineering*, Black, London, (1925).

Forbes, R. J., *Man The Maker*, Abelard-Schuman, New York, (1958).

Jenkins, Rhys, *Links in the History of Engineering and Technology from Tudor Times*, Cambridge U. P., New York, (1936).

Kirby, R. S., Sidney Withington, and A. B. Darling, *Engineering in History*, McGraw-Hill, New York, (1956).

Klemm, Friedrich, *A History of Western Technology*, M.I.T. Press, Cambridge, Mass., (1964).

Parsons, William Barclay, *Engineers and Engineering in the Renaissance*, Williams & Wilkins, Baltimore, (1939).

Sarton, George, *A History of Science: Ancient Science Through the Golden Age of Greece*, Harvard U. P., Cambridge, Mass., (1952).

Walker, Charles R., *Modern Technology and Civilization*, McGraw-Hill, New York, (1962).

White, Lynn, "Technology and Invention in the Middle Ages," *Speculum*, Vol. 15, (1940), pp. 141–159.

Wolf, A. A., *A History of Science, Technology and Philosophy in the Eighteenth Century*, Macmillan, New York, (1939).

# Chapter 2

# The Engineer's Role in a Technological Society

Some students become interested in a career in engineering at an early age—perhaps even in elementary school. Often the spark of excitement has been provided by some neighbor, friend, or member of the family who is an engineer. Teachers and school counselors also perform a valuable service in providing students with literature pertaining to engineering as a profession; however, it is not uncommon for many freshmen or sophomore college students to ask themselves the question, "Do I really want to be an engineer?" This is not surprising since there is a general misunderstanding in the United States today concerning the role played by the engineer in our modern technical society.

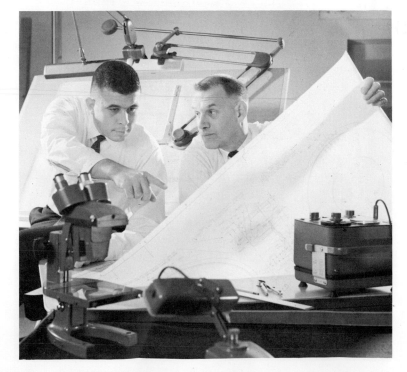

**Illustration 2–1.** The engineer is responsible for creative and imaginative design. This includes every step in the design process from the origination of the idea to the finished product. Here an engineer is discussing necessary changes in a design with a draftsman in his design group. (Courtesy Eastman Kodak Company.)

## THE SCIENTIFIC TEAM

In the expanding realm of science and technology, the engineer is a member of a three-part team of technical specialists. These specialists are engineers, scientists, and technicians. Although their spheres of activity overlap, they tend to fit into specific roles appropriate to their interests and areas of work. Since high school graduates sometimes decide to enter one of these fields without understanding the training, qualifications, and type of work each specialist requires, let us consider a brief description of each field.

### The Engineer

The engineer is concerned primarily with the application of discoveries to benefit mankind. It is his objective to design, plan, develop, and construct usable devices that employ scientific principles. In this role, he must understand the laws and principles of science in order to be able to take new discoveries and to make practical applications of them. For example, recent discoveries in biology have made it possible for engineers, with the assistance of medical doctors, to develop new devices that may add materially to our ability to treat certain diseases and defects of the human heart.

**Illustration 2–2.** The scientist engages in basic research to discover fundamental facts that form the basis for natural laws. In this picture, scientists are studying uranium metal with an electron microscope where they achieve magnification as high as 200,000 ×. (Courtesy National Lead Company of Ohio.)

### The Scientist

The primary objective of the scientist is to discover, to expand the fields of knowledge, to correlate observations and experimental data into a formulation of laws, to learn new theories and explore their meanings, and to broaden the horizons of science into the unknown. In general, the scientist is less concerned with the practical application of discoveries than with adding to the sum total of human knowledge.

### The Technician

In many cases, much of the actual fabrication of devices designed by engineers is performed by technicians. These persons are specialists, usually in a specific field, where manual skill is needed. They may be draftsmen, electronic technicians, laboratory technicians, cost estimators, equipment operators, or service and maintenance specialists. Usually, the technician, although he may have studied some courses in engineering, has only general training in mathematics and science. The technician frequently performs the manual part of engineering concerned with experimental models, troubleshooting, filling in details of design, recording data while laboratory tests are being conducted, and helping in subprofessional work. The technician's role should not be confused with the work of a craftsman or mechanic. The craftsman or mechanic have specific manual skills, acquired usually over a long period of apprenticeship and they are much less concerned with the scientific, mathematical, or engineering features of a design. Rather, their interest is in using their manual skills to produce a part that will show their competence as craftsmen.

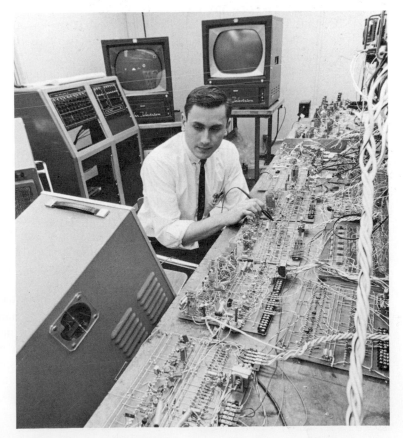

**Illustration 2–3.** The technician assists the engineer by constructing, testing, and operating equipment that the engineer has designed. Here a technician is checking an intricate electronic circuit that is to be used in a video systems display. (Courtesy United Aircraft Corporation.)

## THE ROLE OF THE ENGINEER

It is generally known that engineering has made possible the many material things that now make our lives more enjoyable and provide extra time for recreation and study. It is also an accepted belief that the engineer will continue to provide innovative and creative designs for the purpose of easing the burdens of man's physical toil and to convert the materials and forces of Nature to the use of all mankind; however, when the time comes to make a choice of careers, each student finds himself groping for an answer to the question, "As an engineer, how would *I* fit into this picture?"

First, we must realize that one does not become an engineer solely by studying a few courses. Engineering education is more than the ability to know when to manipulate a set of formulas, to know where to search in an armful of reference books, or to get accurate answers from a slide rule or computer; it is also a state of mind. Through experience and training the engineer must be able to formulate problem statements and must conceive design solutions that many times involve novel ideas and creative thought processes. He must also exercise judgment and restraint, must design with initiative and reliability, and must be completely honest with himself and with others. These qualities should all mature as the student engineer advances from elementary to graduate-level studies.

### What Skills Does the Engineer Need?

The public expects all engineers to be competent technically. The profession has through the years built up a record of producing things that work. No one expects a company to produce TV tubes that spontaneously explode, or a bridge that falls down, or an irrigation ditch that has the wrong slope. In fact, the technological failures of engineering are so rare that when they do occur, they usually are front page news.

The engineering curriculum followed in college is designed to instill technical competence. The grading system generally used in college rewards acceptable solutions and penalizes inferior or unworkable solutions to practical problems. The subjects studied are not easy, and usually those persons who do not adapt themselves to the discipline of study and who do not accept the ideas of the exactness of Nature's laws will not complete a college engineering course. This discipline has paid handsome dividends. The consistency of quality in the engineering graduate over many years has given the public a confidence that must not be destroyed.

It should also be realized, however, that the completion of a college course is not the end of study for an engineer. The pace of discovery is so rapid today that, even with constant study, the engineer barely can keep abreast of technological improvements. If the engineering graduate should resolve not to continue his technical study, he would be far behind in technology within five years and probably would be completely out of step within ten years.

The engineer, then, must be capable of dealing with technological problems—not only those which he may have been trained to handle in college but also new and unfamiliar situations which arise as a result of new discoveries. Of course, it is obvious that college courses can present problem areas only in general terms. Upon a base of fundamental principles, the engineer is expected to provide solutions to new problem situations.

### After College What Are the Opportunities?

A question that arises frequently in the mind of an engineering student is "What if I start out in engineering and decide to change to another course of study?" Let us examine some of the possibilities. Normally an engineering student will follow engineering as a profession. However, many students change their mind during their college career or after graduation. Many authorities agree that engineering courses are excellent training for a great variety of careers, and records reveal that perhaps as many as 40 per cent of people on a management level have engineering educations. One of the basic and most valuable training concepts of an engineering education is that *engineering students are taught to think logically.* This means that if a career decision is made not to follow engineering as a profession, the training and experience gained in engineering courses still will prepare a person for a wide variety of occupations.

What will the future hold for the serious student who proposes to make engineering his career? *First,* employment will be no problem. For the foreseeable future more engineers will be needed than the colleges can supply. The rigor of the college courses usually removes those who are unable or unwilling to stick with a problem until they come up with a reasonable answer. Those who graduate in engineering usually are well qualified technically and, in addition, are well-rounded in their knowledge of nonengineering courses.

*Second,* he will enjoy the profession. A sampling of questionnaires sent to engineers in large industrial concerns shows that those with several years experience almost unanimously enjoy their work. They like the opportunities for advancement, the challenges of new and exciting problems to be solved, the friendships gained in contacts with people with diverse backgrounds, and the possibilities of seeing their ideas develop into working realities. The engineer will find that as a profession, the salary scale is among the higher groups, and his individual income usually is determined largely by the quality of his own efforts.

*Third,* engineering provides unlimited opportunities for creative design. As has been mentioned before, the pace of discovery is so great that the need for the application of discoveries provides countless places where the engineer with initiative and creative ability can spend his time in development. Also, in applications which are old and well known, the clever engineer can devise new, better, and more economical ways of providing the same services. For example, although roads have been built for centuries, the need for faster and more efficient methods of road building offers a continuing challenge to engineers.

Sometimes nontechnical people say that engineers are too dogmatic, that they think of things as being either positive or negative. To a certain extent this is true because of the engineer's training. He is educated to give realistic answers to real problems and to make the answers the most practical that he can produce. Within his knowledge of Nature's laws, the engineer usually can obtain a precise solution to a given problem, and he is always willing to defend his solution. To a nontechnical person accustomed to arriving at a solution by surmise, argument, and compromise, the positive approach of the engineer frequently is distressing. Part of the postgraduate training of an engineer is learning to convince nontechnical people of the worth of a design. The ability to reason, to explain by using simple applications, and to have patience in presenting ideas in simple terms that can be understood are essential qualities of the successful engineer.

The engineer does not claim to be a genius. However, by training, he is a leader. Because he has a responsibility to his profession and to his community to exercise that leadership, he should establish a set of technical and moral standards that will provide a wholesome influence upon all levels of his organization and upon his community as a whole.

## PROBLEMS ON THE ENGINEER'S ROLE

**2–1.** Interview an engineer and write a 500 word essay concerning his work.

**2–2.** Survey the job opportunities for engineers, scientists, and technicians. Discuss the differences in opportunity and salary.

**2–3.** Discuss the role of the engineer in government.

**2–4.** Frequently technical personnel in industry are given the title "engineer" in lieu of other benefits. Discuss the difficulties that arise as a result of this practice.

**2–5.** Write an essay on the differences between the work of the engineer, the scientist, and the technician.

**2–6.** Write an essay on the differences between the education of the engineer, the scientist, and the technician.

**2–7.** Interview an engineering technician and write a 500 word essay concerning his work.

**2–8.** Discuss the role of the engineering technician in the aircraft industry.

**2–9.** Investigate the opportunities for employment of electronic technicians. Write a 500 word essay concerning your findings.

**2–10.** Investigate the differences in educational requirements of the engineer and the technician. Discuss your conclusions.

## BIBLIOGRAPHY

Love, Albert and James Saxon Childers, *Listen to Leaders in Engineering,* Tupper and Love, Atlanta, Ga., (1965).

Love, Albert and James Saxon Childers, *Listen to Leaders in Science,* Tupper and Love, Atlanta, Ga., (1965).

O'Dea, William T., *The Meaning of Engineering,* Museum Press, London, (1961).

Rapport, Samuel and Helen Wright, *Engineering,* New York. U. P., New York, (1963).

Taylor, Lloyd W., *Physics, The Pioneer Science,* Houghton Mifflin, Boston, (1941).

Whinnery, John R., *The World of Engineering,* McGraw-Hill, New York, (1965).

# Chapter 3

# The Work of the Engineer

During the years that he is in college, an engineering student will study courses in many subject areas. He will study language courses to better prepare himself in organizing and presenting ideas effectively, mathematics courses to learn the manipulation of symbols as an aid in problem solving, social science courses to help him better find his place in society as an informed citizen, and various technical courses to gain an understanding of natural laws. In his study of technical courses, he will become familiar with a store of factual information that will form the basis for his engineering decisions. The nature of these technical courses, in general, determines the major field of interest of the student. For example, he may decide to concentrate his major interest in some particular field such as civil, chemical, industrial, or mechanical engineering.

The college courses also provide training in learning facts and in developing powers of reasoning. Since it is impossible to predict what kind of work a practicing engineer will be doing after graduation, the objective of an engineering education is to provide a broad base of facts and skills upon which the engineer can practice his profession.

It usually is not sufficient to say that an engineer is working as a *civil engineer*. His work may vary over a wide spectrum. As a civil engineer, for example, he may be performing research on materials for surfacing highways, or he may be employed in government service and be responsible for the budget preparation of a missile launch project. In fact, there are many things that a practicing engineer will be called upon to do which are not described by his major course of study. The *type* of work that the engineer may do, as differentiated from his major field of specialization, can be called "engineering function." Some of these functions are research, development, design, production, construction, operations, sales, and management.

It has been found that in some engineering functions, such as in the management of a manufacturing plant, specialization is of lesser importance, whereas in other functions such as research in transistor theory, specialization may be extremely important. In order to understand more fully the activities of a practicing engineer, let us examine some of these functions.

## RESEARCH

Today research is one of the more glamorous functions of engineering. In this type of work the engineer delves into the nature of matter, exploring processes to use engineering materials, and searching for reasons for the behavior of the things that make up our world. In many instances the work of the scientist and the engineer who are engaged in research will overlap. The work of scientists usually is closely allied with research. The objective of the research scientist is to *discover truths*. The objective of the research engineer on the other hand usually is directed toward the practical side of the problem: not only to discover but also *to find a use for the discovery*.

The research engineer must be especially perceptive and clever. He must be able to work patiently at tasks never before accomplished and must be able to recognize and identify phenomena previously unnoticed. As an aid to training an engineer to do research work, some colleges give courses in research techniques. However, the life of a research engineer can be quite disheartening. Since he is probing and exploring in new areas, much of his work is trial and error, and outstanding results of investigation usually occur only after long hours of painstaking and often discouraging work.

Until within the last few decades, almost all research was solo work by individuals. However, with the rapid expansion of the fields of knowledge of chemistry, physics, and biology, it became apparent that groups or "research teams" of scientists and engineers could accomplish better the aims of research by pooling their efforts and knowledge. Within the teams, the enthusiasm and competition

**Illustration 3–1.** Research is an important type of work performed by an engineer. In this work he enjoys basic scientific principles in the discovery and application of new knowledge. This engineer is experimenting with an arrangement to study optical heterodyning, using two single frequency lasers tuned 5 megacycles apart. (Courtesy Spectra-Physics.)

provides added incentive to push the work forward, and since each person is able to contribute from his specialty, discovery is accelerated.

As has been indicated, a thorough training in the basic sciences and mathematics is essential for a research engineer. In addition, an inquiring mind and a great curiosity about the behavior of things is desirable. Most successful research engineers have a fertile and uninhibited imagination and a knack of observing and questioning phenomena that the majority of people overlook. For example, one successful research engineer has worked on such diverse projects as an automatic lawnmower, an electronic biological eye to replace natural eyes, and the use of small animals as electric power sources.

Most research engineers secure advanced degrees because they need additional training in basic sciences and mathematics, and in addition, this study usually gives them an opportunity to acquire useful skills in research procedures.

## DEVELOPMENT

After a basic discovery in natural phenomena is made, the next step in its utilization involves the development of processes or machines that employ the principles involved in the discovery. In the research and development fields, as in many other functions, the areas of activity overlap. In many organizations, the functions of research and development are so interrelated that the department performing this work is designated simply as a research and development (R and D) department.

The engineering features of development are concerned principally with the actual construction, fabrication, assembly, layout, and testing of scale models, pilot models, and experimental models for pilot processes or procedures. Where the research engineer is concerned more with making a discovery that will have commercial or economic value, the development engineer will be interested primarily in producing a process, an assembly, or a system *that will work*.

The development engineer does not deal exclusively with new discoveries. Actually the major part of his work will involve using well-known principles and in employing existing processes or machines to perform a new or unusual function. It is in this region that many patents are granted. In times past, the utilization of basic machines, such as a wheel and axle, and fundamental principles including Ohm's Law and Lenz' Law, have eventually led to patentable articles such as the electric dynamo. On the other hand, within a very short time after the announcement of the discovery of the laser in 1960, a number of patents were issued on devices employing this new principle. Thus the lag between the discovery of new knowledge and the use of that knowledge has been steadily decreasing through the years.

In most instances the tasks of the development engineer are dictated by immediate requirements. For example, a new type of device may be needed to determine at all times the position in space of an airplane. Let us suppose that the development engineer does not know of any existing device that can perform the task to the desired specifications. Should he immediately attempt to invent such a device? The answer, of course, is, "Usually not." First, he should explore the files of available literature for information pertaining to existing designs. Such information may come from two principal sources. The first source is library material on processes, principles, and methods of accomplishing the task or related tasks. The second source is manufacturer's literature. It has been said humorously that there is no need to re-invent the wheel. A literature search may reveal a device that can accomplish the task with little or no modification. If no device is available that will do the work, a system of existing subassemblies may be set up and joined to accomplish the desired result. Lacking these items, then the development engineer must go further into basic literature, and using results from experiments throughout the world, formulate plans to construct a model for testing. Previous research points a way to go, or perhaps a mathematical analysis will provide clues as to possible methods.

The development engineer usually works out his ideas on a trial or "breadboard" basis, whether it be a machine or a computer process. Having the parts or systems somewhat separated facilitates changes, modifications, and testing. In this process, improved methods may become apparent and can be incorporated. When the system or machine is in a workable state, the development engineer must then refine it and package it for use by others. Here again ingenuity and a knowledge of human nature is important. A device that works satisfactorily in a laboratory when manipulated by skilled technicians, may be hopelessly complex and unsuited for field use. The development engineer is the important man behind every push button.

The training of an engineer for development work is similar to the training that the research engineer will expect to receive. However, creativity and innovation are perhaps of more importance, since the development engineer is standing between the scientist or the research engineer and the members of management who provide money for the research effort. He must be able to recognize the economic value of certain processes over others in achieving a desired result, and he must be able to convince other people that his conclusions are the ones that should be accepted. A comprehensive knowledge of basic principles of science and an inherent cleverness in making things work are essential skills for the development engineer.

## DESIGN

In our modern way of life, mass production has given us cheaper products and has made more articles available than ever before in history. In the process of producing these articles, the design engineer enters the scene just before the actual manufacturing process begins. After the development engineer has assembled and tested a device or a process and it has proved to be one that is desirable to produce for a mass market, the final details of making it adaptable to produce will be handled by a design engineer.

In his role of bridging the gap between the laboratory and the production line, the design engineer must be a versatile individual. He should be well grounded in basic engineering principles and in mathematics, and he must not only understand the capabilities of machines but also the temperament of the men who operate them. He must be conscious also of the relative costs of producing items, for it will be his design that will determine how long the product will survive in the open market. Not only must the device or process work, it must also be made in a style and at a price that will attract customers.

As an example, let us take a clock, a simple device widely used to indicate time.

**Illustration 3–2.** Development engineers use the results of basic research and convert them into models and prototypes for full-scale testing and evaluation. This full-scale mock-up of the Westinghouse deep sea research vehicle, "Deep Star", enables development engineers to determine the best location for equipment. The box-like structures represent battery cases and the cylinders indicate the location of the ballast tanks. (Courtesy Westinghouse Underseas Division.)

It includes a power source, a drive train, hands, and a face. Using these basic parts, engineers have designed spring driven clocks, weight driven clocks, and electrically driven clocks with all variations of drive trains. The basic hands and face have been modified in some models to give a digital display. The case has been made in many shapes and, perhaps in keeping with the slogan "time flies," it has even been streamlined! In the design of each modification the design engineer has determined the physical structure of the assembly, the esthetic features of it, and the economics of producing it.

Of course the work of the design engineer is not limited solely to performing engineering on mass produced items. Design engineers may work on items such as bridges or buildings in which only one of a kind is to be made. However, in such work he still is fulfilling the design process of adapting basic ideas to provide for making a completed product for the use of others. In this type of design the engineer must be able to use his training, in some cases almost intuitively, to arrive at a design solution which will provide for adequate safety without excessive redundancy. The more we learn about the behavior of structural materials, the better we can design without having to add additional materials to cover the "ignorance factor" area. Particularly in the aircraft industry, design engineers have attempted to use structural materials with minimum excess being allowable as a safety factor. Each part must perform without failure, and every ounce of weight must be saved. Of course to do this, fabricated parts of the design must be tested and retested for resistance to failure due either to static loads or to vibratory fatiguing loads. Also, since surface roughness has an important bearing on the fatigue of life of parts which are subjected to high stress repeated loads, much attention must be given to specifying in designs that surface finishes must meet certain requirements.

Since design work involves a production phase, the design engineer is always considering costs as a factor in our competitive economy. One of the ways in which costs can be minimized in manufacture or construction is to use standard parts, and standard sizes and dimensions for raw material. For example, if a machine were designed using nonstandard bolt threads or a bridge designed using nonstandard steel I-beams, the design probably would be more expensive than needed to fulfill its function. Thus, the design engineer must be able to coordinate the parts of his design so that it functions acceptably and is produced at minimum cost.

The design engineer soon comes to realize also that there usually is more than one acceptable way to solve a design problem. Unlike an arithmetic problem with fixed numbers which give one answer, his problem can have many answers and many ways of obtaining a solution, *and all may be acceptable.* In such case his decision becomes a matter of experience and judgment. At other times it may become just a matter of making a decision one way or the other. Regardless of the method used, his solution to a problem should be a conscious effort to provide the *best* method considering fabrication, costs, and sales.

What are the qualifications of a design engineer? He, of course, must be creative. His every design will embody a departure from what has been done before. At the same time, he is constrained by the reality of the physical properties of materials and by economic factors. Therefore, he must be thoroughly knowledgeable in fundamental engineering in a rather wide range of subjects. In addition, he must

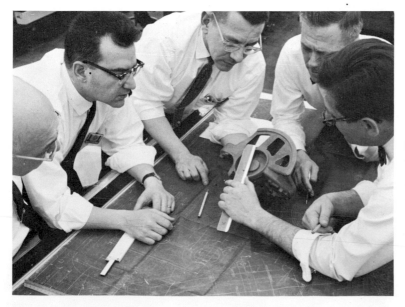

**Illustration 3–3.** The design engineer coordinates the activities of many people as he guides a product through its various stages of development. (Courtesy Sperry Gyroscope Company.)

be familiar with basic principles of economics, both from the standpoint of employing people and using machines. As he progresses upward into supervisory and management duties, the employment of principles of psychology and economics become of even more importance. For this reason design engineers usually will have more use for management courses than will research or development engineers.

## PRODUCTION AND CONSTRUCTION

In the fields of production and construction, the engineer is more directly associated with the technician, mechanic, and laborer. The production or construction engineer must take the design engineer's drawings and supervise the assembly of the object as was conceived and illustrated by drawings or models.

Usually a production or construction engineer is associated closely with the process of estimating and bidding for competitive jobs. In this work, he employs his knowledge of structural materials, fabricating processes, and general physical principles to estimate both time and cost to accomplish tasks. In construction work the method of competitive bidding is usually used to award contracts, and the ability to reduce an appropriate amount from an estimate by skilled engineering practices may mean the difference between a successful bid and one that is either too high or too low.

Once a bid has been awarded, it is usual practice to assign a "project engineer" as the person who assumes overall responsibility and supervision of the work from the standpoint of materials, labor, and money. He will have other production or construction engineers working under his direction who will be concerned with more specialized features of the work such as civil, mechanical, electrical, or chemical engineering. Here the engineer must complete the details of the designers' plans. He must provide the engineering for employment of special tools needed for the work. He must also set up a schedule for production or construction, and he must be able to answer questions that technicians or workmen may raise concerning features of the design. He should be prepared to advise design engineers concerning desirable modifications that will aid in the construction or fabrication processes. In addition, he must be able to work effectively with construction or production crafts and labor unions.

Preparation of a schedule for production or construction is an important task of the engineer. In the case of an industrial plant, all planning for the procurement of raw materials and parts will be based upon this production schedule. An assembly line in a modern automobile manufacturing plant is one example which illustrates the necessity for scheduling the arrival of parts and subassemblies at a predetermined time. As another example, consider the construction of a modern multistory office building. The necessity for parts and materials to arrive at the right time is very important. If they arrive too soon, they probably will be in the way, and if they arrive too late, the building is delayed, which will cause an increase in costs to the builder.

Qualifications for a production or construction engineer include a thorough knowledge of basic engineering principles. In addition, he must have the ability to visualize the parts of an operation, whether it be the fabrication of a solid-state computer circuit or the building of a concrete bridge. From his understanding of

**Illustration 3—4.** In production, an engineer is responsible for insuring that all phases of the assembly are conducted so that each part of the finished product will perform according to design specifications. In this picture, the final assembly of H—1 rocket engines is being carried out. In clusters of eight, these engines will provide 1,600,000 pounds of thrust for the Saturn space vehicle. (Courtesy Rocketdyne, A Division of North American Aviation, Inc.)

the operations involved, he must be able to arrive at a realistic schedule of time, materials, and manpower. Therefore, emphasis should be placed upon courses in engineering design, economics, business law, and psychology.

### OPERATIONS

In modern industrial plants, the number and complexity of machines, the equipment and buildings to be cared for, and the planning needed for expansion has brought out the need for specialized engineers to perform services in these areas. If a new manufacturing facility is to be constructed, or an addition made to an existing facility, it will be the duty of a plant engineer to perform the basic design, prepare the proposed layout of space and location of equipment, and to specify the fixed equipment such as illumination, communication, and air conditioning. In some cases, the work of construction will be contracted to outside firms, but it will be the general responsibility of the plant engineer to see that the construction is carried on as he has planned it.

**Illustration 3—5.** The construction engineer is responsible to see that a project is carried out as it was designed. Usually he is working with large projects where weather and terrain are complicating factors. Construction work requires the exercise of all the capabilities of the engineer. This picture shows the upstream surface of the intake structure of Ghana's Akosombo dam on the Volta River, which will make the fourth largest reservoir in the world (3,275 square miles). (Courtesy Kaiser Engineers.)

After a building or facility has been built, the plant engineer and his staff are responsible for maintenance of the building, equipment, grounds, and utilities. This work varies from performing routine tasks, to setting up and regulating the most complex and automated machinery in the plant.

The plant engineer must have a wide knowledge of several branches of engineering in order to perform these functions. For land acquisition and building construction, he will need courses in civil engineering; for equipment and machinery he will need mechanical training; for power he will need mechanical and electrical backgrounds, and for the specialized parts of the plant, his knowledge may need to be in such fields as chemical, metallurgical, nuclear, petroleum, or textile engineering.

In many plants, particularly in utility plants, the engineer also is concerned with operation of the plant. It is his duty to see that boilers, generators, turbines, and accessory equipment are operated at their best efficiency. He should be able to compare costs of operating under various conditions, and he attempts always to set schedules for machines so that best use will be made of them. In the case

**Illustration 3—6.** In the operation of a plant, the engineer must make certain that all parts of the plant remain in service. In this picture, a periodic check is being made of a large transformer to detect any signs of possible breakdown. (Courtesy James G. Biddle Company.)

of chemical plants, he also will attempt to regulate the flows and temperatures at levels that will produce the greatest amount of desired product at the end of the line.

In his dual role as a plant and operations engineer, he will be constantly evaluating new equipment as it becomes available to see whether additional operating economies can be secured by retiring old equipment and installing new types. In this, he frequently must assume a salesman's role in order to convince management that it should discard equipment that, apparently, is operating perfectly and spend money for newer models. Here the ability to combine facts of engineering and economics are invaluable.

Plant engineering of course will be associated closely with production engineering processes. The production engineer will create needs for new machines, new facilities, and new locations. The plant engineer will correlate such things as the building layout, machine location, power supplies, and materials handling equipment so that they best will serve the needs of production.

The general qualifications of plant and operations engineers have already been mentioned. They must have basic knowledge of a wide variety of engineering fields such as civil, chemical, electrical, and mechanical, and also they must have specialized knowledge of areas peculiar to their plant and its operation. In addition, the plant and operation engineer must be able to work with men and machines and to know what results to expect from them. In this part of their work, a knowledge of industrial engineering principles is valuable. In addition, it is desirable to have basic understanding and knowledge of economics and business law. In this work, in general, training in detailed research procedures and abstract concepts is of lesser importance.

## SALES

An important and sometimes unrecognized function in engineering is the realm of applications and sales. As is well known, the best designed and fabricated product is of little use unless a demand either exists or has been created for it. Since many new processes and products have been developed within the past few years, a field of work has opened up for engineers in presenting the use of new products to prospective customers.

Discoveries and their consequent application have occurred so rapidly that a product may be available about which even a recent graduate may not know. In this case, it will fall to the engineer in sales who has intimate knowledge of the principles involved to go out and educate possible users so that a demand can be created. In this work, the engineer must assume the role of a teacher. In many instances he must present his product primarily from an engineering standpoint. If his audience is composed of engineers, he can "talk their language" and answer their technical questions, but if his audience includes nonengineers, he must present the features of the product in terms that they can comprehend.

In addition to his knowledge of the engineering features of his own product, the sales and application engineer must also be familiar with the operations of his customer's plant. This is important from two standpoints. First, he should be able to show how his product will fit into the plant, and also he must show the economics involved to convince the customer that he should buy it. At the same time, the engineer must point out the limitations of his product and the possible changes necessary to incorporate it into a new situation. For example, a new bonding material may be available, but in order for a customer to use it in an assembly of parts, a special refrigerator for storage may be necessary. Also the customer would need to have emphasized the necessity for proper cleaning and surface preparation of the parts to be bonded.

A second reason that the sales and application engineer must be familiar with a customer's plant operation is that many times new requirements are generated here. By finding an application area in which no apparatus is available to do the work, the sales engineer is able to report back to his company that a need exists and that a development operation should be undertaken to produce a device or process to meet the need.

Almost all equipment of any complexity will need to be accompanied by introductory instructions when it is placed in a customer's plant. Here the application engineer can create good will by conducting an instruction program outlining the capabilities and limitations of the equipment. Also, after the equipment is in service, maintenance and repair capabilities by competent technical personnel will serve to maintain the confidence of customers.

The sales and applications engineer should have a basic knowledge of engineering principles and should, of course, have detailed knowledge in the area of his own products. Here the ability to perform detailed work on abstract principles is of lesser importance than the ability to present one's ideas clearly. A genuine appreciation of people and a friendly personality are desirable personal attributes.

**Illustration 3–7.** In sales, the engineer must be able to describe a technical product to customers and show how they will benefit from using the latest developments. (Courtesy Eastman Kodak Company.)

In addition to basic technical subjects, courses in psychology, sociology, and human relations will prove valuable to the sales and applications engineer.

Usually an engineer will spend several years in a plant learning the processes and the details of his plant's operation and management policies before starting out to be a member of the sales staff. Since the sales engineer represents his company in the mind of the customer, he must present a pleasing appearance and give a feeling of confidence in his engineering ability.

## MANAGEMENT

Results of recent surveys show that the trend today is for corporate leaders in the United States to have backgrounds in engineering and science. In a survey of some 600 large industrial firms, twenty technical and engineering colleges and universities have four or more of their graduates serving as board chairmen, presidents, or senior vice presidents in these firms.

It has been predicted that within ten years, the *majority* of corporation executives will be men who are trained in engineering and science, as well as in business and humanities, and who can bridge the gap between these disciplines.

Since the trend is toward more engineering graduates moving into management positions, let us examine the functions of an engineer in management.

The basic functions of the management of a company are largely similar whether the company objective is dredging for oyster shells or building diesel locomotives or digital computers. These basic functions involve using the capabilities of the company to the best advantage to produce a desirable product in a competitive economy. The use of the capabilities, of course, will vary widely depending upon the enterprise involved.

The executive of a company, large or small, has the equipment in the plant, the labor force, and the financial assets of the organization to use in conducting the plant's operations. In management, he must make decisions involving all three of these items.

In former years it was assumed that only persons trained and educated in business administration should aspire to management positions. However, now it has been recognized that the education and other abilities which make a good engineer also provide the background to make a good management executive. The training for correlating facts and evaluating courses of action in making engineering decisions can be carried over to management decisions on machinery, men, and money. In general, the engineer is technically strong but may be quite naïve in the realm of business practicability. Therefore, it is in the business side of an operation that the engineer usually must work harder to develop his skills.

The engineer in management is concerned more intimately with the long range effects of policy decisions. Where the design engineer considers first the technical phases of a project, the engineer in management must consider how a particular decision will affect the men who work to produce a product and how the decision will affect the people who provide the financing of the operation. It is for this reason that the management engineer is concerned less with the technical aspects of his profession and relatively more with the financial, legal, and labor aspects.

This does not imply that engineering aspects should be minimized or deleted.

**Illustration 3—8.** The engineer is an important part of the management team. Due to the complexity of today's society, the engineer in management must be able to relate the technical aspects of a problem with economic and human factors in management decisions. (Courtesy Universal Oil Products Company.)

Rather the growing need for engineers in management shows that the type and complexity of the machines and processes used in today's plants requires a blending of technical and business training in order to carry forward effectively. Particularly is this trend noted in certain industries such as aerospace and electronics, where the vast majority of executive managerial positions are occupied by engineers and scientists. As other industries become automated, a similar trend in those fields also will become apparent.

The education that an engineer in management receives should be identical to the basic engineering education received in other engineering functions. However, a young engineer can usually recognize early in his career whether or not he has an aptitude for working with men and directing their activities. If the young engineer has the ability to "sell his ideas" and to get others to work with him, he probably can channel his activities into managerial functions. He may start out as a research engineer, a design engineer, or a sales engineer, but the ability to influence others to his way of thinking, a genuine liking for people, and a consideration for their responses, will indicate that he probably has capabilities as a manager.

Of course, management positions are not always executive positions, but the ability to apply engineering principles in supervisory work involving large numbers of men and large amounts of money is a prerequisite in management engineering.

## OTHER ENGINEERING FUNCTIONS

A number of other engineering functions can be considered that do not fall into the categories previously described. Some of these functions are testing, teaching, and consulting.

As in the other functions, there are no specific curricula leading directly toward these types of work. Rather a broad background of engineering fundamentals is the best guide to follow in preparing for work in these fields.

In testing, the work resembles design and development functions most closely. Most plants maintain a laboratory section that is responsible for conducting engineering tests of proposed products or for quality control on existing products. The test engineer must be qualified to follow the intricacies of a design and to build suitable test machinery to give an accelerated test of the product. For example, in the automotive industry, not only are the completed cars tested, but also individual components such as engines, brakes, and tires, are tested on stands to provide data to improve their performance. The test engineer must be able also to set up quality control procedures for production lines to insure that production meets certain standards. In this work, mathematics training in statistical theory is helpful.

A career in teaching is rewarding for many persons. A desire to help others in their learning processes, a concern for some of their personal problems, and a thorough grounding in engineering and mathematics are desirable for those considering teaching engineering subjects. In the teaching profession, the trend today

**Illustration 3–9.** Testing is an important part of the design process. Design concepts must be verified and improvements recommended as a result of the evaluation of engineering tests. In this picture, test engineers are conducting a whirl test of a new helicopter design using closed circuit TV to monitor the test operation. (Courtesy Sikorsky Aircraft.)

is toward the more theoretical aspects of engineering, and a person will usually find that teaching is more closely allied with research and development functions than with others. Almost all colleges now require the faculty to obtain advanced degrees, and a person desiring to be an engineering teacher should consider seriously the desirability of obtaining a doctorate in his chosen field.

More and more engineers are going into consulting work. Work as an engineering consultant can be either part time or full time. Usually a consulting engineer is a person who possesses specific skills in addition to several years of experience. He may offer his services to advise and work on engineering projects either part time or full time.

Frequently two or more engineers will form an engineering consulting firm that employs other engineers, technicians, and draftsmen and will contract for full engineering services on a project. The firm may restrict engineering work to rather narrow categories of work such as the design of irrigation projects, power plants, or aerospace facilities, or a staff may be available that is capable of working on a complete spectrum of engineering problems.

On the other hand, a consulting engineer can operate alone. His firm may consist of a single individual with skills such that, in a minimum time, he is able to advise and direct an operation to overcome a given problem. For instance, he may be employed by an industrial plant. In this way the plant may be able to more

Illustration 3–10. Teaching is a rewarding activity of engineering. Frequently the engineering professor is the first person to introduce the student to the ethics and responsibilities of the profession. (Courtesy General Electric Company.)

economically solve a given problem, particularly if the required specialization is seldom needed by the plant.

As may be inferred, a consulting engineer must have *specific* skills to offer, and he must be able to use his creative ability to apply his skills to unfamiliar situations. Usually these skills and abilities are acquired only after several years of practice and postgraduate study.

For a person who desires self-employment together with its business risks but also with the opportunity for financial reward, consulting work is an inviting part of the engineering profession.

## ENGINEERING FUNCTIONS IN GENERAL

As described in previous paragraphs, training and skills in all functions are basically the same; that is, fundamental scientific knowledge of physical principles and mathematics. However, it can be seen that research on one hand and management on the other require different educational preparations.

For work in research, emphasis is on theoretical principles and creativity, with little emphasis on economic and personnel considerations. On the other hand, in management, primary attention is given to financial and labor problems and relatively little to abstract scientific principles. Between these two extremes, we find the other functions with varying degrees of emphasis on the research oriented or managerial oriented concepts.

Figure 3–1 shows an idealized concept of this distribution. Bear in mind that this diagram merely depicts a trend and does not necessarily apply to specific instances.

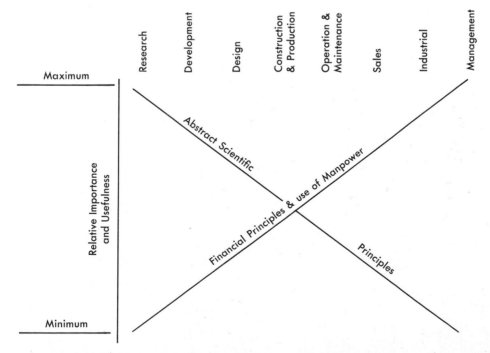

**Figure 3–1.** Application of principles in various engineering functions.

To summarize the functions of the engineer, we can say that in all cases he is a problem solver. Whether it be a mathematical abstraction that may have an application to a nuclear process or a meeting with bargaining group at a conference table, it is a problem that must be reduced to its essentials and the alternatives explored to reach a solution. The engineer then must apply his knowledge and inventiveness to select a reasonable method to achieve a result, even in the face of vague and sometimes contradictory data. That the engineer has been able, in general, to accomplish this is proven by a long record of successful industrial management and productivity.

## PROBLEMS ON WORK OF THE ENGINEER

**3–1.** Discuss an important scientific breakthrough of the past year that was brought about by an engineering research effort.

**3–2.** Discuss the differences between engineering research and engineering development.

**3–3.** Interview an engineer and estimate the percentage of his work that is devoted to research, development, and design.

**3–4.** Discuss the importance of the engineer's design capability in modern industry.

**3–5.** Investigate the work functions of the engineer and write a brief essay describing the function that most appeals to you.

**3–6.** Discuss the importance of the sales engineer in the total engineering effort.

**3–7.** Interview an engineer in management. Discuss the reasons that many engineers rise to positions of leadership as managers.

**3–8.** Compare the engineering opportunities in teaching with those in industry.

**3–9.** Investigate the opportunities for employment in a consulting engineering firm. Discuss your findings.

**3–10.** Discuss the special capabilities required of the engineer in construction.

## BIBLIOGRAPHY

Smith, R. J., *Engineering As A Career,* McGraw-Hill, New York, (1962).

Williams, Clement C. and Erich A. Farber, *Building An Engineering Career,* McGraw-Hill, New York, (1957).

# Chapter 4

# Engineering Careers
# of Challenge

Much of the change in our civilization in the past hundred years has been due to the work of the engineer. We hardly appreciate the changes that have occurred in our environment unless we attempt to picture the world of a few generations ago without automobiles, telephones, radios, electronics, transportation systems, supersonic aircraft, automatic machine tools, electric lights, television, and all the modern appliances in our homes. In the growth of all these things the role of the engineer is obvious.

Development in the field of science and engineering is progressing so rapidly at present that within the last ten years we have acquired materials and devices that are now considered commonplace but which were unknown to our parents. Through research, development, and mass production, directed by engineers, ideas are made into realities in an amazingly short time.

The engineer is concerned with more than research, development, design, construction, and the operation of technical industries, however, since many are engaged in businesses that are not primarily concerned with production. Formerly, executive positions were held almost exclusively by men whose primary training was in the field of law or business, but the tendency now is to utilize engineers more and more as administrators and executives.

No matter what kind of work the engineer may wish to do, he will find opportunities for employment not only in purely technical fields but also in other functions such as general business, budgeting, rate analysis, purchasing, marketing, personnel, labor relations, and industrial management. Other opportunities also exist in such specialized fields of work as teaching, writing, patent practice, and work with the military establishment.

Although college engineering curricula contain many basic courses, there will be some specialized courses available that are either peculiar to a certain curriculum or are electives. These specializations permit each student to acquire a particular proficiency in certain subjects so that, for example, he can be designated as an electrical, civil, chemical, mechanical, or industrial engineer.

Education in the application of certain subject matter to solve technological problems in a certain engineering field constitutes engineering specialization. Such training is not for manual skills as is the case in trade schools, but rather is planned to provide preparation for research, design, operation, management, testing, maintenance of projects, and other engineering functions in any given specialty.

The principal engineering fields of specialization that are listed in college curricula and that are recognized in the engineering profession are described in the following sections.

## AEROSPACE AND ASTRONAUTICAL ENGINEERING

Within the past few years many changes have taken place to alter the work of the aeronautical engineer—not the least of which is man's conquest of outer space. Principal types of work vary from the design of guided missiles and spacecraft to analyses of aerodynamic studies dealing with the performance, stability, control, and design of various types of planes and other devices that fly. Most of such activity is concerned with the design, development, and performance testing of supersonic commercial transports and their associated propulsion systems.

Although aerospace engineering is one of the newer fields, it offers many possibilities for employment. The rapidly expanding network of airlines, both national

**Illustration 4–1.** An aeronautical engineer working with an industrial model of a jet aircraft makes final adjustments of mounting and instrumentation prior to test in a supersonic wind tunnel. (Courtesy North American Aviation, Inc.)

and international, provide many openings for the engineering graduate. Since the demand for increasing numbers of aircraft of various types exists, there are opportunities for work in manufacturing plants and assembly plants and in the design, testing, and maintenance of aircraft and their component parts. The development of new types of aircraft, both civilian and military, requires the efforts of well-trained aeronautical engineers, and it is in this field that the majority of positions exist. Employment opportunities exist for specialists in the design and development of fuel systems using liquid oxygen propellants and solid propellants. Control of the newer fuels involves precision valving and flow sensing at very low and very high temperatures. Air traffic control is a problem that is becoming increasingly more complex, and trained people are needed here. The design of ground and airborne systems that will permit operation of aircraft under all kinds of weather conditions is also a part of the work of aeronautical engineers.

The aerospace engineer works on designs that are not only challenging and adventuresome but also designs that play a major role in determining the course of present and future world events.

## AGRICULTURAL ENGINEERING

The courses in agricultural engineering are designed for the student who is interested in a career in the application of engineering principles to the field of agriculture. The curriculum prepares a student for design or sales work with farm equipment, machinery, and buildings; superintendency of farms and ranches where

**Illustration 4–2.** Agricultural engineers apply fundamental engineering principles of analysis and design to improve our methods of food production and land utilization. In this picture, agricultural engineers at a research center make evaluations and comparisons of farm machines and tillage devices to provide improved performance. (Courtesy International Harvester Company.)

machinery and buildings, irrigation, drainage, and erosion control are important parts of their management; teaching or extension work with various agricultural colleges; engineering work with landholding or management companies or with the government on soil conservation and other projects having engineering applications. The agricultural engineer must also be familiar with such diverse subjects as metallurgy, hydraulics, and sanitation.

Many agricultural engineers are employed by companies that serve agriculture, and some are employed by firms that serve other industries. Development, advertising, and sales work with manufacturers of farm equipment and machinery provide openings for agricultural engineers. State agricultural colleges and their extension services and experiment stations employ many agricultural engineers, as do federal agencies.

In order that the agricultural engineer may understand the problems of agriculture and the application of engineering methods and principles to their solution, instruction is given in agricultural subjects as well as in basic engineering. Agricultural research laboratories are maintained at schools for research and instruction using various types of farm equipment for study and testing. The young man who has an analytical mind and a willingness to work, together with an interest in the engineering aspects of agriculture, will find the course in agricultural engineering an interesting preparation for his life's work.

**Illustration 4–3.** The architectural engineer may work either in an engineering firm or in an architectural firm. As part of a team of engineers, he combines fundamental principles of architecture and engineering in the design of structures to harmonize beauty and utility. The architectural engineer shown in this picture has designed a new lightweight high-strength extruded aluminum set of structural members which permit rapid construction of prefabricated housing units. (Courtesy Alcoa.)

## ARCHITECTURAL ENGINEERING

The architectural engineer is primarily interested in the selection, analysis, design, and assembly of modern building materials into structures that are safe, efficient, economical, and attractive. The education he receives in college is designed to teach him how best to use modern structural materials in the construction of tall buildings, manufacturing plants, and public buildings.

The architectural engineer is trained in the sound principles of engineering and at the same time is given a background which enables him to appreciate the point of view of the architect. The architect is concerned with the space arrangements, proportions, and appearance of a building, whereas the architectural engineer is more nearly a structural engineer and is concerned with safety, economy, and sound construction methods.

Opportunities for employment will be found in established architectural firms, in consulting engineering offices, in aircraft companies, and in organizations specializing in building design and construction. Excellent opportunities await the graduate who may be able to associate himself with a contracting firm or who may form a partnership with an architectural designer. In the field of sales an interesting and profitable career is open to the individual who is able to present his ideas clearly and convincingly.

## CHEMICAL ENGINEERING

Chemical engineering is responsible for new and improved products that affect every person. Consequently, chemical engineers must be able to apply scientifically the principles of chemistry, physics, and engineering to the design and operation of plants for the production of materials that undergo chemical changes during their processing.

The courses in chemical engineering cover inorganic, analytical, physical, and organic chemistry in addition to the basic engineering subjects; and the work in the various courses is designed to be of a distinctly professional nature and to develop capacity for original thought. The industrial development of our country makes large demands on the chemical engineer. The increasing uses for plastics, synthetics, and building materials require that a chemical engineer be employed in the development and manufacture of these products. While well trained in chemistry, the chemical engineer is more than a chemist in that he applies the results of chemical research and discovery to the use of mankind by adapting laboratory processes to fullscale manufacturing plants.

The chemical engineer is instrumental in the development of the newer fuels for turbine and rocket engines. Test and evaluation of such fuels and means of achieving production of suitable fuels are part of the work of a chemical engineer. This testing must be carefully controlled to evaluate the performance of engines before the fuel is considered to be suitable to place on the market.

Opportunities for chemical engineers exist in a wide variety of fields of manufacture. Not only are they in demand in strictly chemical fields but also in nearly all types of manufacturing. The production of synthetic rubber, the uses of petroleum products, the recovery of useful materials from what was formerly considered waste products, and the better utilization of farm products are only a few of the

**Illustration 4–4.** Chemical engineers work with elaborate chemical apparatus to study minute detail of materials in order to reveal structural secrets that cannot be uncovered by any other means. Here a chemical engineer makes an adjustment on an involved distillation apparatus used in the photographic industry. (Courtesy Eastman Kodak Company.)

tasks that will provide work for the chemical engineer. Although the first professional work of a graduate chemical engineer may be in production, other opportunities exist in the fields of engineering design, research and development, patents, and sales engineering.

## CIVIL ENGINEERING

Civil engineering is one of the oldest branches of the engineering profession and deals with the art and science of directing the great sources of power in nature for the use and convenience of man. Specialization has brought the grouping of engineers into electrical, mechanical, chemical, etc.; but underlying all these groups is the work of the civil engineer.

Civil engineering covers such a broad field that it has been divided into several branches. The major subdivisions are: construction, soil mechanics and foundations, transportation, municipal and sanitary, surveying and mapping, and hydraulic engineering. Construction engineering deals with the design and supervision of construction of bridges, buildings, tunnels, and dams. Soil mechanics and foundations investigations are useful not only in civilized areas but are also vital for successful conquest of areas ranging from Antarctica to the moon. Transportation engineering includes the planning, design, and construction of roads, streets, and thoroughfares. Municipal and sanitary engineering is concerned with the planning of urban centers for the growth and development of business and residential areas and the design and construction of water supply systems, sewerage systems, and systems for the disposal of wastes. Surveying and mapping deals with the measurements of distances over the earth's surface and the location of structures, rights of way, and property boundaries. Hydraulic engineering is concerned with the improvement of water resources, harbor and river development, flood control, irrigation, and drainage.

Civil engineers engage in technical, administrative, or commercial work with manufacturing companies, construction companies, transportation companies, and power companies. Other opportunities for employment exist in consulting engineering offices, in city and state engineering departments, and in the various bureaus of the federal government.

**Illustration 4–5.** An important phase of civil engineering is the planning for orderly growth and development of urban areas to include transportation systems. This picture shows a four-level interchange in downtown Los Angeles where several freeways intersect. Such freeways play an increasingly important role in making it possible to handle tremendous volumes of traffic in minimum time. (Courtesy State of California Department of Public Works.)

## ELECTRICAL ENGINEERING

Electrical engineering is concerned, in general terms, with the utilization of electric energy, and it is perhaps more far-reaching in its contacts with human endeavor than any of the other branches of engineering. Electricity used in one form or another reaches nearly all our daily lives and is truly the servant of mankind. Electrical engineering is divided into broad fields such as information systems, automatic control, and systems and devices.

**Illustration 4–6.** The electrical engineer works with many types of apparatus, both electronic and mechanical. In this picture, engineers make adjustments on circuits during closed-loop simulation testing of automatic controls for a steel mill. The solid state circuit control cabinets in the background, and the control desks in the foreground, provide feedback sensing and information display for operation. (Courtesy Allis-Chalmers.)

A need arose after World War II for improved information systems. Electronic computers were designed to help fill this need. The increase in the complexity of computers has created a need for specialists in the field who can adapt existing knowledge of mechanical and electrical devices to extend the capabilities of computers.

Computers can provide answers to specific sets of questions. However, engineers have designed them for a variety of purposes, and computers drastically reduce the time necessary to explore a variety of concepts of a design or to control the multitude of processes within a manufacturing plant.

The electrical engineer is concerned with the application of sound engineering principles, both mechanical and electrical, in the design and construction of computers. He must be familiar with the basic requirements of a computer so that he can design to provide for the necessary capabilities. In addition he must strive to build a machine that will furnish solutions of greater and greater problem complexity and at the same time have a means of introducing the problem into the machine in as simple a manner as possible.

Although there are relatively few companies that build elaborate computing machines, employment possibilities in the design and construction part of the industry are not limited. Many industrial firms, colleges, and governmental branches have set up computers as part of their capital equipment, and opportunities exist for employment as computer applications engineers who serve as liaison between computer programmers and engineers who wish their problems evaluated on the machines. Of course, in a field expanding as rapidly as computer design, increasing numbers of employment opportunities become available. More and more dependence will be placed on the use of computers in the future, and an engineer educated in this work will find ample opportunity for advancement.

The automatic control of machines and devices, such as autopilots for spacecraft and missiles, has become a commonplace requirement in today's technically conscious society.

Automatic controlling of machine tools is an important part of modern machine shop operation. Tape systems are used to furnish signals to serve units on automatic lathes, milling machines, boring machines, and other types of machine tools so that they can be programmed to perform repeated operations. Not only can individual machines be controlled but also entire power plants can be operated on a program system. The design of these systems is performed usually by an electrical or mechanical engineer.

Energy conversion systems, where energy is converted from one form to another, also are a necessity in almost every walk of life. Power plants are constituted to convert heat energy from fuels into electrical energy for transmission to industry and homes. In addition to power systems, communication systems are a responsibility of the electrical engineer. Particularly in communications the application of modern electronics have been most evident. The electrical engineer who specializes in electronics will find that the majority of communication devices employ electronic circuits and components.

Other branches of electrical engineering that may include power or communication activities, or both, are illumination engineering, which deals with lighting using electric power; electronics, which has applications in both power and communications; and such diverse fields as x-ray, acoustics, and seismograph work.

Employment opportunities in electrical engineering are extremely varied. Electrical manufacturing companies use large numbers of engineers for design, testing, research, and sales. Electrical power companies and public utility companies require a staff of qualified electrical engineers, as do the companies which control the networks of telegraph and telephone lines and the radio systems. Other opportunities for employment exist with oil companies, railroads, food processing plants, lumbering enterprises, biological laboratories, chemical plants, and colleges and universities. The aircraft and missile industries use engineers who are familiar

with circuit design and employment of flight data computers, servomechanisms, analog computers, vacuum tubes, transistors, and other solid-state devices. There is scarcely any industry of any size that does not employ one or more electrical engineers as members of its engineering staff.

The engineering graduate must be familiar with the various sciences, but it is especially desirable that he be well versed in the fundamental principles of physics, chemistry, and mathematics. A thorough understanding of the underlying phenomena is necessary if the engineer is to direct the forces of nature to the best advantage. In addition to basic science courses, the electrical engineer will take courses in machinery, electronics, communication, and wave phenomena. As in other engineering courses, the demand for breadth and culture is met by studies in history, literature, economics, English, and public speaking.

## INDUSTRIAL ENGINEERING

The field of industrial engineering is a wide and all-inclusive one dealing with the design and installation of manufacturing systems. Whereas other branches of engineering tend to specialize in some particular phase of science, the realm of

Illustration 4–7. The industrial engineer in this picture is checking his engineering calculations of critical path scheduling, using a photograph showing the progress of construction of a power plant. The photo behind him shows that the steel framework has been erected and that boiler tubing is now being installed. His next step is to estimate the duration of the remaining jobs and to calculate the critical cost factor of each. (Courtesy Eastman Kodak Company.)

industrial engineering may include parts of all engineering fields. The industrial engineer then will be more concerned with the larger picture of managment of industries and production of goods than with the detailed development of processes.

The work of the industrial engineer is rather wide in scope, so it is difficult to designate any specializations that the industrial engineer may choose. His general work is with men and machines, and as a result he is trained in both personnel administration and in the relations of men and machines to production.

The industrial engineer must be capable of preparing plans for the arrangement of plants for best operation and then of organizing the workers so that their efforts will be coordinated to give a smoothly functioning unit. In such things as production lines, the various processes involved must be perfectly timed to insure smooth operation and efficient use of the worker's efforts. In addition to coordination and automating of manufacturing activities, the industrial engineer is concerned with the development of data processing procedures and the use of computers to control production, the development of improved methods of handling materials, the design of plant facilities and statistical procedures to control quality, the use of mathematical models to simulate production lines, and the measurement and improvement of work methods to reduce costs.

Opportunities for employment exist in almost every industrial plant and in many businesses not concerned directly with manufacturing or processing goods. In many cases the industrial engineer may be employed by department stores, insurance companies, consulting companies, and as engineers in cities. The industrial engineer is trained in fundamental engineering principles, and as a result may also be employed in positions which would fall in the realm of the civil, electrical, or mechanical engineer.

The courses prescribed for the student of industrial engineering follow the pattern of the other branches of engineering by starting with a thorough foundation in the engineering sciences. The engineering courses in the later semesters will be of a more general nature, and the curriculum will include such courses as economics, psychology, business law, personnel problems, and accounting principles.

## MECHANICAL ENGINEERING

Mechanical engineering deals with power and the machines used to generate power and apply it to useful processes. In general, the mechanical engineer works with systems, subsystems, and components that have motion. The range of work that may be classed as mechanical engineering is wider than that in any of the other branches of engineering, but it may be grouped generally under two heads: work that is concerned with power-generating machines, and work that deals with machines that transform or consume this power in accomplishing their particular tasks.

Some of the general subdivisions of mechanical engineering are as follows: Power or combustion engineers deal with the production of power from fuels. Design specialists may work with parts that vary in size from the microscopic part of the most delicate instrument to the massive parts of heavy machinery. Railway engineers work with the complex railway equipment that is part of our transportation system. Automotive engineers work constantly to improve the vehicles and engines that we now have. Heating, ventilating, air conditioning, and refrigeration

**Illustration 4–8.** The mechanical engineer may be called upon to design a wide variety of complex machines like the one shown here which operates on air bearings. This "weightlessness simulator" permits an astronaut to float in mid air. It also is used in studying the spacecraft design requirements for astronauts who will fly orbital laboratories and other future space craft. (Courtesy General Dynamics/Convair.)

engineers deal with the design of suitable systems for making our buildings more comfortable and for providing proper conditions in industry for good working conditions and efficient machine operation.

Employment may be secured by mechanical engineering graduates in almost every type of industry. Manufacturing plants, power-generating stations, public utility companies, transportation companies, airlines, and factories, to mention only a few, are examples of organizations that need mechanical engineers. Experienced engineers are needed in the missile and space industries in the design and development of such items as gas turbine compressors and power plants, air-cycle cooling turbines, electrically and hydraulically driven fans, and high-pressure refrigerants. Mechanical engineers are also needed in the testing of airborne and missile fuel systems, servovalves, and mechanical-electrical control systems. In addition, an engineer may be employed for research endeavor as a university professor, or in the governments of cities, states, and the nation.

The courses in mechanical engineering include courses both in power and in machine principles. Courses include thermodynamics, fluid mechanics, design, energy conversion, electricity and electronics, vibrations, and heat transfer. In the senior year elective courses may enable one to specialize in any of the various fields of mechanical engineering.

## METALLURGICAL ENGINEERING AND MATERIALS SCIENCE

Metallurgical engineering may be divided into two branches. One branch deals with the location and evaluation of deposits of ore, the best way of mining and concentrating the ore, and the proper method of refining the ore into the basic metals. The other branch deals with the fabrication of the refined metal or metal alloy into various machines or metal products.

The metallurgist performs pure and applied research on vacuum melting, arc melting, and zone refining to produce metallic materials having unusual properties of strength and endurance. In addition the metallurgist in the aircraft and missile industries is called upon to recommend the best materials to use for special applications and is frequently called on to give an expert opinion on the results of fatigue tests of metal parts of machines.

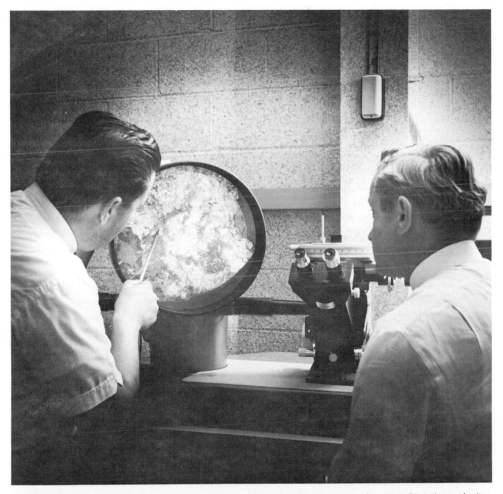

**Illustration 4–9.** Materials and metallurgical engineers are specialists in their knowledge of the properties of mineral, metallic, and man-made materials. Here, engineers are using a metallograph to study an enlarged picture of a specimen to investigate the material structure of a newly developed alloy. (Courtesy Sperry Gyroscope Company.)

In addition to the two branches listed above, ceramic engineering is frequently included as a branch of this type of engineering. Requirements for the design of inorganic materials that will be flexible at $-60°$ Celcius or have strength at $2000°$ Celcius have given impetus to the study of ceramic engineering. In addition some materials may need to have properties that will not be changed by exposure to high concentrations of radioactivity. Use is made of the newer techniques of sintering in the field of high-temperature inorganic materials, some of which are unusual blends of ceramic and metallic materials. An example of one of the newer uses of ceramics in industry is in the manufacture of the parts of turbine and rocket engines that are exposed to hot gases. These frequently are protected with refractory ceramic materials developed by research teams.

The engineer who has specialized in materials science is in great demand today because of the urgent need for man-made composites—the joining of two or more different materials for the purpose of gaining advantageous characteristics or overcoming disadvantageous ones of each.

## NUCLEAR ENGINEERING

Nuclear engineering is one of the newest and most challenging branches of engineering. Although much work in the field of nucleonics at present falls within the realm of pure research, a growing demand for people educated to utilize recent discoveries for the benefit of mankind has led several colleges and universities to offer courses in nuclear engineering. The nuclear engineer is familiar with the basic principles involved in both fission and fusion reactions; and by applying fundamental engineering concepts, he is able to direct the enormous energies involved in a proper manner. Work involved in nuclear engineering includes the design and operation of plants to concentrate nuclear reactive materials, the design and operation of plants to utilize heat energy from reactions, and the solution of problems arising in connection with safety to persons from radiation, disposal of radioactive wastes, and decontamination of radioactive areas.

The wartime uses of nuclear reactions are well known, but of even more importance are the less spectacular peacetime uses of controlled reactions. These uses include such diverse applications as electric power generation and medical applications. Other applications are in the use of isotopes in chemical, physical, and biological research, and in the changing of the physical and chemical properties of materials in unusual ways by subjecting them to radiation.

Recent advances in the knowledge of controlled nuclear reaction have enabled engineers to build power plants that use heat from reactions to drive machines. Submarine nuclear power plants, long a dream, are now a reality, and experiments are being conducted on smaller nuclear power plants that can be used for airborne or railway applications.

At present, ample opportunities for employment of nuclear engineers exist in both privately owned and government-operated plants, where separation, concentration, or processing of nuclear materials is performed. Nuclear engineers are also needed by companies that may use radioactive materials in research or processing involving agricultural, medical, chemical, metallurgical, and petroleum products.

**Illustration 4–10.** The nuclear engineer is a member of one of the newer branches of engineering. As part of his work, he explores all possible methods of utilizing nuclear energy for the benefit of mankind. This picture shows the installation of the cover plates of a nuclear reactor after it has been fueled. (Courtesy Allis Chalmers.)

## PETROLEUM ENGINEERING

Petroleum engineering deals with all phases of the petroleum industry, from the location of petroleum in the ground to the ultimate delivery to the user. Petroleum products play an important part in many phases of our everyday life in providing our clothes, food, work, and entertainment. Because of the complex chemical structure of petroleum, we are able to make an almost endless number of different articles. Owing to the wide demand for petroleum products, the petroleum engineer strives to satisfy an ever-increasing demand for oil and gas from the ground.

The petroleum engineer is concerned first with finding deposits of oil and gas in quantities suitable for commercial use, in the extraction of these materials from the ground, and the storage and processing of the petroleum above ground. The petroleum engineer is concerned with the location of wells in accordance with the findings of geologists, the drilling of wells and the myriad problems associated with the drilling, and the installation of valves and piping when the wells are completed. In addition to the initial tapping of a field of oil, the petroleum engineer is concerned with practices that will provide the greatest recovery of the oil, considering all possible factors that may exist many thousand feet below the surface of the earth.

**Illustration 4–11.** One of the tasks of the petroleum engineer is to locate oil deposits and to devise methods for oil recovery. In some cases deposits lie in places which are remote from easy accessibility. This picture shows an oil-drilling rig in the bayou country of Louisiana. Other drilling locations are in the open waters of the Gulf of Mexico and in the Pacific Ocean off the California coast. These offshore locations may be a considerable distance from shore and frequently are serviced by helicopter. (Courtesy Shell Oil Co.)

After the oil or gas has reached the surface, the petroleum engineer will provide the means of transporting it to suitable processing plants or to places where it will be used. Pipe lines are providing an ever-increasing means of transporting both oil and gas from field to consumer.

Owing to the expanding uses for petroleum and its products, the opportunities for employment of petroleum engineers are widespread. Companies concerned with the drilling, producing, and transporting of oil and gas will provide employment for the majority of engineers. Because of the widespread search for oil, employment opportunities for the petroleum engineer exist all over the world; and for the young man wishing a job in a foreign land, oil companies have crews in almost every country over the globe. Other opportunities for employment exist in the field of technical sales, research, and as civil service employees in the national government.

The curriculum in petroleum engineering includes courses in drilling methods, engines, oil and gas recovery, storage and transportation, and geology.

## PROBLEMS ON ENGINEERING CAREERS OF CHALLENGE

**4–1.** Discuss the changing requirements for aerospace and astronautical engineers.
**4–2.** Investigate the opportunities for employment in agricultural engineering. Discuss your findings.

**4–3.** Write a short essay on the differences in the utilization and capability of the architectural engineer and the civil engineer who has specialized in structural analysis.

**4–4.** Interview a chemical engineer. Discuss the differences in his work and that of a chemist.

**4–5.** Assume that you are employed as an electrical engineer. Describe your work and comment particularly concerning the things that you most like and dislike about your job.

**4–6.** Explain why the demand for industrial engineers has increased significantly during the past ten years.

**4–7.** Write a 200 word paper describing the challenging job opportunities in engineering that might be particularly attractive for young ladies.

**4–8.** Explain the importance of mechanical engineers in the electronics industry.

**4–9.** Describe the changes that might be brought about to benefit mankind by the development of new engineering materials.

**4–10.** Investigate the need for nuclear and petroleum engineers in your state and report on your findings.

## BIBLIOGRAPHY

BURSTALL, AUBREY, *A History of Mechanical Engineering,* M.I.T. Press, Cambridge, Mass., (1963).

CRESSY, EDWARD, *A Hundred Years of Mechanical Engineering,* Macmillan, New York, (1937).

*Electric Development from 600 B.C.,* National Manufacturers Association, New York, (1946).

GODDARD, ROBERT H., "A Method of Reaching Extreme Altitudes," Smithsonian Institution Publication, No. 2540, Washington, D.C., (1919).

GOLZE, ALFRED R., *Your Future in Civil Engineering,* Richards Rosen Press, Inc., New York, (1965).

KELLY, MERVIN J., "Should You Be An Electronics Engineer?," *Career Opportunities,* New York Life Insurance Co., September, 1962.

PINCHES, HAROLD E., *Introduction to Agricultural Engineering,* Ann Arbor, Mich., (1942).

POLLACK, PHILIP, *Careers and Opportunities in Engineering,* Dutton, New York, (1959).

RUTHERFORD, ERNEST R., *The Newer Alchemy,* Macmillan, New York, (1951).

STEINMAN, DAVID B., *The Builders of the Bridge,* Harcourt, New York, (1945).

STRAUB, HANS, *A History of Civil Engineering,* M.I.T. Press, Cambridge, Mass., (1964).

TIMOSHENKO, STEPHEN P., *History of the Strength of Materials,* McGraw-Hill, New York, (1953).

WELLS, ROBERT, *What Does a Civil Engineer Do?,* Dodd, New York, (1960).

# Chapter 5

# The Professional Role
# of the Engineer

The word "professional" is used in many ways and has many meanings. It can be used in the sense of the skill of a professional actor who receives pay for his efforts as distinguished from an amateur who performs more for the joy of performing. It can be used in the sense of a type of work as in describing a professional job of house painting done by an experienced painter. Also, it can be used merely to describe a degree of effort or line of conduct over a period of time as used in the expression "a professional beggar." However, in the sense that engineers would employ the word "professional," it should be restricted to a particular and specialized group of people, identified by distinguishing characteristics, that separate its members from nonprofessionals.

Within the last century, three groups have emerged with the title "learned professions." These professional groups are law, medicine, and theology. These groups came into being gradually over a long period of time and had certain characteristics in common, among which were higher levels of educational achievement and a sincere desire for performing a service for people. There is no formal naming of a person or group of persons to professional status, nor is there a schedule or procedure to follow to achieve recognition as a professional. Rather the group itself sets standards of training, skills, achievement, and service in order to call itself a professional group, and the public accepts the group's evaluation of itself.

Who is a professional? As generally used in the sense of the learned professions, a professional person is one who applies certain knowledge and skill, usually obtained by college education, for the service of people. In addition, a professional person observes an acceptable code of conduct, uses discretion and judgment in dealing with people, and respects their confidences. Also, professional persons usually have legal status, use professional titles, and associate together in groups. Although engineering has met most of these criteria for a long time, it has been only within the last few decades that legal status has been conferred upon the engineering profession.

## THE ENGINEER AS A PROFESSIONAL PERSON

Knowledge and skill above that of the average person is a characteristic of the professional man. Where a workman will have specific skills in operating a particular machine, a professional person is considered to be able to apply fundamental principles that are usually beyond the range of the average workman. The knowledge of these principles as well as the skills necessary to apply them distinguishes a professional man. The engineer because of his education in the basic sciences, mathematics, and engineering sciences, is capable of applying basic principles for such diverse things as improving the construction features of buildings, developing processes that will provide new chemical compounds, or designing tunnels to bring water to arid areas.

An important concept in the minds of most persons is that a professional person will perform a service for people. This means that service must be considered ahead of any monetary reward that a professional man may receive. In this respect, the professional person should, by himself, recognize a need for personal services and seek ways to provide a solution to these needs. Almost all engineering is performed to fill a need in some phase of our society. It may be to develop better appliances for the household, or to provide better transportation facilities, or to make possible a better life in regions of unfavorable climate.

Discretion and judgment also characterize a professional person. In most

**Illustration 5–1.** This building houses the headquarters of a majority of the major engineering societies in the United States. In addition to offices for the societies it also has space for conference rooms, auditoriums, exhibits, and the engineering societies library. (Courtesy United Engineering Center Project.)

situations, a choice of several methods to accomplish a given task will be available. The engineer must consider the facts available and the principles that apply and make decisions based upon these rather than upon expediency. Consideration must be given not only to the mechanical aspects of a solution but also to the effects that a particular decision will have upon the persons concerned.

A professional person is one in whom confidence can be placed. This confidence is not only in his skill and ability but is also a confidence that his knowledge of his client's business or trade information or personal matters will not be divulged improperly. The engineer works in a relation of confidence to his client or employer not to divulge trade secrets or to take any advantage of his knowledge that may harm the client or employer. The public, in general, will have confidence that the engineer's design of buildings, bridges, or power systems will be adequate and safe to use. The engineer must not fail the public in this responsibility.

All professionals adhere to a code of ethical conduct. This code of ethics outlines the standards to which members of the group subscribe and gives an understanding of what the public can expect in its relationship with the profession. The code of ethics also serves as a guide to the members of the profession in their conduct and relations with each other. In engineering, the professional society is the National Society of Professional Engineers. A general code of ethics for professional engineers has been set up by the Society. This code is given on page 66.

Usually, professionals will band themselves together for the mutual exchange of ideas, to improve their knowledge, and to learn new skills and techniques. Meeting and discussing problems with others in the same field of endeavor affords an opportunity for the stimulation of thought to improve learning and skills. In addition to the National Society of Professional Engineers, which is primarily concerned with the *professional* aspects of the whole field of engineering, engineers have organized certain technical societies in their fields of specialization. Examples of these are the Institute of Electrical and Electronic Engineers, the American Society of Civil Engineers, and the American Society of Mechanical Engineers.

Legal status usually is a characteristic of a professional. A medical doctor, for example, has certain rights and privileges afforded by law. Legal recognition of a professional group is afforded by a procedure of certification, licensing, or registration. In all States, a registration law is in effect which provides for legal registration of an engineer following submission of evidence of education and technical ability. Registration confers the legal title of "engineer" to the recipient, and he may use the initials "P.E." after his name to denote his registration as a "Professional Engineer."

## PROFESSIONALISM

Professionalism is an individual state of mind. It is more than developing skills and acquiring knowledge. It is a way of thinking and living. The mere acquisition of knowledge may make a person a more skilled laborer or clerk but knowledge alone does not promote a desire to serve people. In the realm of service, the engineer joins the other learned professional groups with a concept of doing always what is honest and right rather than what is the legal minimum.

Professionalism is not inherent in a person's nature. It, like technical skills, must be taught. While the student is still in college, the meanings of professional conduct and responsibility should be learned and the beginnings of a professional attitude established. Obviously a person will not be a professional engineer upon graduation, but the fundamental concepts required should be established so that as the engineering graduate goes into employment, he can continue rather than begin his professional advancement.

In college courses in engineering, some professors will promote ideas of professionalism as they teach their courses. For example, in laboratory work, an *honest* reporting of facts and an intelligent evaluation of results is a necessary part of professional training.

After graduation, opportunities for public service will present themselves. The engineer, as part of his professional responsibility, should seek and accept places of service in schools, community government, religious organizations, and charitable groups. Not only will he be able to contribute his talents to these causes, but also he will enhance his own outlook by contacts with both professional and nonprofessional persons. Each individual engineer should recognize within himself the need for a professional attitude and assume the ultimate responsibility for upholding this concept.

It may be argued by some that professionalism is an abstract concept and that engineers deal only in real quantities. This generalization is not completely correct, for in the creative part of engineering, the ideas always come from a realm of abstraction. For example, if a requirement arises for a source of electric power to serve a community, the need for an engineering service constitutes a problem that the engineer must solve. A power plant may need to be designed. The location, size, and fuel sources constitute parts of the problem about which assumptions must be made. All this is in the realm of abstraction. When the basic assumptions are made, engineering surveys, tests, plans, and measurements are made to define particular parts of the construction. This, of course, is in the realm of reality. However, we recognize that in the design and construction of the plant, assumptions always must be made about features or conditions that cannot be subjected to definite measurements. Thus, we see by this example that the engineer must be able to operate both in the realm of abstraction and in the realm of reality.

To sum up professionalism, engineering is a profession insofar as it meets these characteristics of a professional group.

1. Knowledge and skill in specialized fields above that of the general public.
2. A desire for public service and a willingness to share discoveries for the benefit of others.
3. Exercise of discretion and judgment.
4. Establishment of a relation of confidence between the engineer and client or the engineer and employer.
5. Acceptance of overall and specific codes of conduct.
6. Formation of professional groups and participation in advancing professional ideals and knowledge.

With these as objectives, the student should pursue his college studies and his training in his employment so as to meet these characteristics within their full meaning and take his or her place as a professional engineer in our society.

## CODE OF ETHICS*

Preamble

The Engineer, to uphold and advance the honor and dignity of the engineering profession and in keeping with high standards of ethical conduct:

*Will be honest and impartial, and will serve with devotion his employer, his clients, and the public;*
*Will strive to increase the competence and prestige of the engineering profession;*
*Will use his knowledge and skill for the advancement of human welfare.*

Section 1—The Engineer will be guided in all his professional relations by the highest standards of integrity, and will act in professional matters for each client or employer as a faithful agent or trustee.

*a. He will be realistic and honest in all estimates, reports, statements, and testimony.*

*b. He will admit and accept his own errors when proven obviously wrong and refrain from distorting or altering the facts in an attempt to justify his decision.*

*c. He will advise his client or employer when he believes a project will not be successful.*

*d. He will not accept outside employment to the detriment of his regular work or interest, or without the consent of his employer.*

*e. He will not attempt to attract an engineer from another employer by unfair methods.*

Section 2—The Engineer will have proper regard for the safety, health, and welfare of the public in the performance of his professional duties. If his engineering judgment is overruled by nontechnical authority, he will clearly point out the consequences. He will notify the proper authority of any observed conditions which endanger public safety and health.

*a. He will regard his duty to the public welfare as paramount.*

*b. He shall seek opportunities to be of constructive service in civic affairs and work for the advancement of the safety, health, and well-being of his community.*

*c. He will not complete, sign, or seal plans and/or specifications that are not of a design safe to the public health and welfare and in conformity with accepted engineering standards. If the client or employer insists on such nonprofessional conduct, he shall notify the proper authorities and withdraw from further service on the project.*

Section 3—The Engineer will not advertise his work or merit in a self-laudatory manner, and will avoid all conduct or practice likely to discredit or unfavorably reflect upon the dignity or honor of the profession.

*a. Circumspect advertising may be properly employed by the engineer to announce his practice and availability. Only those media shall be used as are necessary to reach directly an interested and potential client or employer, and such media shall in themselves be dignified, reputable, and characteristically free of any factor or circumstance that would bring disrepute to the profession or to the professional using them. The substance of such advertising shall be limited to fact and shall contain no statement or offer intended to discredit or displace another engineer, either specifically or by implication.*

*b. Telephone listings shall be limited to name, address and telephone number either under or with each branch listing in which he qualifies.*

*c. He will not allow himself to be listed for employment using exaggerated statements of his qualifications.*

*d. He will not use his professional affiliations or public office to secure personal advantage and will avoid any act tending to promote his own interest at the expense of the dignity and standing of the profession.*

*e. He will not actively participate in strikes, picket lines, or other collective coercive action.*

* Adopted by the National Society of Professional Engineers, 1966.

Section 4—The Engineer will endeavor to extend public knowledge and appreciation of engineering and its achievements and to protect the engineering profession from misrepresentation and misunderstanding.

*a. He shall not issue statements, criticisms, or arguments on matters connected with public policy which are inspired or paid for by private interests, unless he indicates on whose behalf he is making the statement.*

Section 5—The Engineer will express an opinion of an engineering subject only when founded on adequate knowledge and honest conviction.

*a. The Engineer will insist on the use of facts in reference to an engineering project in a group discussion, public forum, or publication of articles.*

Section 6—The Engineer will undertake engineering assignments for which he will be responsible only when qualified by training or experience; and he will engage, or advise engaging, experts and specialists whenever the client's or employer's interests are best served by such service.

Section 7—The Engineer will not disclose confidential information concerning the business affairs or technical processes of any present or former client or employer without his consent.

*a. While in the employ of others, he will not enter promotional efforts or negotiations for work or make arrangements for other employment as a principal or to practice in connection with a specific project for which he has gained particular and specialized knowledge without the consent of all interested parties.*

Section 8—The Engineer will endeavor to avoid a conflict of interest with his employer or client, but when unavoidable, the Engineer shall fully disclose the circumstances to his employer or client.

*a. The Engineer will inform his client or employer of any business connections, interests, or circumstances which may be deemed as influencing his judgment or the* quality of his services to his client or employer.

*b. When in public service as a member, advisor or employee of a governmental body or department, an Engineer shall not participate in considerations or actions with respect to services provided by him or his organization in private engineering practice.*

*c. An Engineer shall not solicit or accept an engineering contract from a governmental body on which a principal or officer of his organization serves as a member.*

*d. He shall not accept an assignment the results of which he will act upon as a member of a public body.*

Section 9—The Engineer will uphold the principle of appropriate and adequate compensation for those engaged in engineering work.

*a. He will not undertake or agree to perform any engineering service on a free basis, except for civic, charitable, religious, or eleemosynary nonprofit organizations when the professional services are advisory in nature.*

*b. He will not undertake work at a fee or salary below the accepted standards of the profession in the area.*

*c. He will not accept remuneration from either an employee or employment agency for giving employment.*

*d. When hiring other engineers, he shall offer a salary according to the engineer's qualifications and the recognized standards in the particular geographical area.*

*e. If, in sales employ, he will not offer, or give engineering consultation, or designs, or advice other than specifically applying to the equipment being sold.*

Section 10—The Engineer will not accept compensation, financial or otherwise, from more than one interested party for the same service, or for services pertaining to the same work, unless there is full disclosure to and consent of all interested parties.

*a. He will not accept financial or other considerations, including free engineering* designs, from material or equipment suppliers for specifying their product.

*b. He will not accept commissions or allowances, directly or indirectly, from contractors or other parties dealing with his clients or employer in connection with work for which he is responsible.*

Section 11—The Engineer will not compete unfairly with another engineer by attempting to obtain employment or advancement or professional engagements by competitive bidding, by taking advantage of a salaried position, by criticizing other engineers, or by other improper or questionable methods.

*a. The Engineer will not attempt to supplant another engineer in a particular employment after becoming aware that definite steps have been taken toward the other's employment.*

*b. He will not offer to pay, either directly or indirectly, any commission, political contribution, or gift, or other consideration in order to secure work, exclusive of securing salaried positions through employment agencies.*

*c. He shall not solicit or submit engineering proposals on the basis of competitive bidding. Competitive bidding for professional engineering services is defined as the formal or informal submission, or receipt, of verbal or written estimates of cost or proposals in terms of dollars, man days of work required, percentage of construction cost, of any other measure of compensation whereby the prospective client may compare engineering services on a price basis prior to the time that one engineer, or one engineering organization, has been selected for negotiations. The disclosure of recommended fee schedules prepared by various engineering societies is not considered to constitute competitive bidding. An engineer requested to submit a fee proposal or bid prior to the selection of an engineer or firm subject to the negotiation of a satisfactory contract, shall attempt to have the procedure changed to conform to ethical practices, but if not successful he shall withdraw from consideration for the*

proposed work. These principles shall be applied by the Engineer in obtaining the services of other professionals. When engaged in work in foreign countries in which the practice is to require the submission of tenders or bids for engineering services, the Engineer shall make every reasonable effort to seek a change in the procedure in accordance with this section, but if this is not successful the Engineer may submit tenders or bids as required by the laws, regulations or practices of the foreign country.

*d. He shall not solicit or accept an engineering engagement on a contingent fee basis if payment depends on a finding of economic feasibility, or other conclusions by the engineer.*

*e. While in a salaried position, he will accept part-time engineering work only at a salary or fee not less than that recognized as standard in the area.*

*f. An engineer will not use equipment, supplies, laboratory, or office facilities of his employer to carry on outside private practice without consent.*

Section 12—The Engineer will not attempt to injure, maliciously or falsely, directly or indirectly the professional reputation, prospects or practice of another engineer, nor will he indiscriminately criticize another engineer's work in public. If he believes that another engineer is guilty of unethical or illegal practice, he shall present such information to the proper authority for action.

*a. An Engineer in private practice will not review the work of another engineer for the same client, except with the knowledge of such engineer, or unless the connection of such engineer with the work has been terminated.*

*b. An Engineer in governmental, industrial or educational employ is entitled to review and evaluate the work of other engineers when so required by his employment duties.*

*c. An Engineer in sales or industrial employ is entitled to make engineering comparisons of his products with products by other suppliers.*

Section 13—The Engineer will not associate with or allow the use of his name by an enterprise of questionable character, nor will he become professionally associated with engineers who do not conform to ethical practices, or with persons not legally qualified to render the professional services for which the association is intended.

*a. He will conform with registration laws in his practice of engineering.*

*b. He will not use association with a nonengineer, a corporation, or partnership, as a "cloak" for unethical acts, but must accept personal responsibility for his professional acts.*

Section 14—The Engineer will give credit for engineering work to those to whom credit is due, and will recognize the proprietary interests of others.

*a. Whenever possible, he will name the person or persons who may be individually responsible for designs, inventions, writings, or other accomplishments.*

*b. When an engineer uses designs supplied to him by a client, the designs remain the property of the client and should not be duplicated by the engineer for others without express permission.*

*c. Before undertaking work for others in connection with which he may make improvements, plans, designs, inventions, or other records which may justify copyrights or patents, the engineer should enter into a positive agreement regarding the ownership.*

*d. Designs, data, records, and notes made by an engineer and referring exclusively to his employer's work are his employer's property.*

Section 15—The Engineer will cooperate in extending the effectiveness of the profession by interchanging information and experience with other engineers and students, and will endeavor to provide opportunity for the professional development and advancement of engineers under his supervision.

*a. He will encourage his engineering employees efforts to improve their education.*

*b. He will encourage engineering employees to attend and present papers at professional and technical society meetings.*

*c. He will urge his engineering employees to become registered at the earliest possible date.*

*d. He will assign a professional engineer duties of a nature to utilize his full training and experience, insofar as possible, and delegate lesser functions to subprofessionals or to technicians.*

*e. He will provide a prospective engineering employee with complete information on working conditions and his proposed status of employment, and after employment will keep him informed of any changes in them.*

## PROBLEMS ON THE PROFESSIONAL ROLE OF THE ENGINEER

**5–1.** Discuss the factors that are common to all professions.

**5–2.** Investigate the laws of the state that pertain to serving as an expert engineering witness in court. What would you need to do to qualify as such a witness?

**5–3.** What engineering fields of specialization are recognized by the state registration board for licensing as professional engineers?

**5–4.** Using the Code of Ethics as a guide, discuss the procedures that professional engineers in private practice may utilize to attract clients.

**5–5.** Discuss the value of humanities and social studies courses in relation to the work of the professional engineer in industry.

**5–6.** Investigate the need for graduate engineering education for the engineer in private practice.

**5–7.** List the reasons why it is important for engineers in education to become registered professional engineers.

**5–8.** Engineer Brown, P.E., is approached by Engineer Smith (non-registered) who offers a fee of $100.00 to Brown if he will "check over" a set of engineering plans and affix his professional P.E. seal to them. Describe Brown's responsibilities and actions.

**5–9.** Discuss the reasons why a professional person such as a registered engineer, an attorney, or a physician will not bid competitively on the performance of a service.

**5–10.** In interviewing for permanent employment, a senior student in a California engineering school agreed to visit on two successive days a company in Chicago and a company in Detroit. Upon his return home both companies sent him checks to cover his expenses including round-trip airfare. Discuss the appropriate actions that should have been taken by the student.

**5–11.** The majority of all engineering designs require some extension of the engineer's repertoire of scientific knowledge and analytical skills. How can the engineer determine whether or not this extension lies beyond the "training and experience" referred to in Section 6 of the Code of Ethics?

**5–12.** Engineer Jones, P.E., is the only registered engineer living in Smileyville. Two individuals, Green and Black, approach him with regard to employing his services in estimating the cost of constructing a small dam that would make it possible to reclaim 500 acres of swampland that is now owned by the city but will soon be offered for sale to the highest bidder. Jones learns that both individuals will be bidding against each other to purchase the acreage. Discuss Jones' responsibilities and actions.

**5–13.** Engineer White is approached by several of his neighbors to urge him to announce his candidacy for City Mayor. In previous months the city administration has been accused of "selling rezoning authorizations" and of "enhancing personal fortunes" through the sale of privileged information pertaining to the location of the new proposed freeway. Discuss the course of action that you would recommend for White.

**5–14.** Engineer Williams and Contractor Smart have been good friends for several years. In March Smart is to begin construction on a multi-story building that Williams designed. On Christmas a complete set of children's play equipment (swings, slides, gymnastic bars, etc.) is delivered to Williams' house—compliments of the Smart Construction Company. What course of action do you recommend for Williams?

## BIBLIOGRAPHY

ALGER, PHILIP, N. A. CHRISTENSEN and STERLING P. OLMSTED, *Ethical Problems in Engineering,* Wiley, New York, (1965).

CROSS, HARDY, *Engineers and Ivory Towers,* McGraw-Hill, New York, (1952).

HOOVER, THEODORE J. and JOHN CHARLES LOUNSBURY FISH, *The Engineering Profession,* Stanford U. P., Stanford, Calif., (1950).

MANTELL, MURRAY I., *Ethics and Professionalism in Engineering,* Macmillan, New York, (1964).

# PART TWO
## PREPARATION FOR A CAREER IN ENGINEERING

The engineer of tomorrow must rise to challenges in the future with the same degree of competence as the engineer of today has done in meeting the challenge of space exploration. Pictured here is another successful launch of a Saturn space vehicle as it lifts off into earth orbit. (Courtesy Chrysler Corporation.)

# Chapter 6

# Education for a Career
# of Change

## AN ENVIRONMENT OF CHANGE

Man has always lived in an environment of change. As he has been able to add to his storehouse of technical knowledge, he has also been able to change his economic structure and his sociological patterns. For centuries the changes that took place during a lifetime were hardly discernible. Beginning about 1600, the changes became more noticeable; and today technological change is literally exploding at an exponential rate. Although a description of this accelerated expansion by empirical means will suffice for general purposes, it is interesting to contemplate one's future if a growth curve relationship such as $k = a\,(i)^t$ is followed (Figure 6–1).

In Figure 6–1, engineering and scientific knowledge is assumed to be doubling every fifteen to twenty years. Experience with other growth curves of this nature indicates that at some point a threshold will be reached and the rate will begin to decline. However, in considering the expansion of technology, no one can say with certainty when this slowing down is most likely to occur. National and international factors certainly must be taken into account.

We have many ways of measuring the increase in engineering knowledge and in the number of engineers. For example, the world supply of engineering and scientific manpower has been following a consistent growth pattern since the mid-seventeenth century. With this supply doubling approximately every fifteen years, it is easy to see that approximately 90 per cent of the engineers and scientists who have ever lived *are alive today*. The total number of scientific journals founded, the number of doctorates granted in engineering, the growth of a tomato vine, the growth of the United States population, and many other relationships which vary with time also tend to follow an exponential growth pattern.[1] Of course, they do not all grow at the same rate as that illustrated in Figure 6–1.

[1] Derek J. De Solla Price, *Little Science, Big Science,* Columbia U. P., New York, (1963), p. 11.

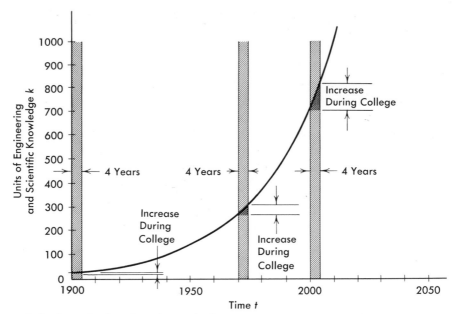

**Figure 6–1.** Growth of engineering and science.

Similar factors are working to provoke changes in educational goals and patterns. In 1900, for example, the engineering student studied for four years to earn his baccalaureate degree, and he saw relatively little change take place in his technological environment during this period. Today, however, due to the accelerated growth pattern of engineering and scientific knowledge, many significant changes will have taken place between his freshman and senior years in college. In fact, complete new industries will be bidding for the services of the young graduate that were not even in existence at the time he began his freshman year of college. This is particularly true of the engineering student who continues his studies for a masters or a doctorate. It is also interesting to contemplate that at the present rate of growth, engineering and scientific knowledge will have doubled within 20 years after graduation. This places a special importance on continuing lifetime studies for all levels of engineering graduates.

These growth patterns, which are promoting change in all phases of society, are also causing educators and leaders in industry to reappraise existing educational practices with a view to increasing their scope and effectiveness. From time to time these changes, while not revolutionary, often provoke a sense of progress that shocks those who received their formal education a scant generation before.

## THE EDUCATION OF THE ENGINEER

Engineering students who will be best prepared for a career of change should have better than average abilities in the following areas:

1. An ability to think with imagination and insight.

2. An ability to understand scientific principles and to apply analytical methods to the study of natural phenomena.

3. An ability to conceive, organize, and carry to completion appropriate experimental investigations.

4. An ability to synthesize and to design.[2]

In general, engineering programs in colleges and universities have concentrated upon providing a broad based education that is not closely aligned to a specific state-of-the-art. This has been necessary because for one to acquire even a small part of all the factual knowledge now available, a continuous memorization process would be required. It is, therefore, more appropriate to learn the basic laws of nature and certain essential facts that contribute to an understanding of problem solving. Emphasis must be placed upon developing mature minds and in educating engineers who can *think*. A means of condensing and concentrating the material to be learned is also of paramount importance. A powerful way of doing this is to employ mathematical techniques that can describe technical situations. For this reason mathematics is a most effective tool of the engineer and its mastery early in one's college career will allow for more rapid progress in such subjects as engineering mechanics, physics, and electrical circuit analysis. In a similar way, if a student learns the principles of physics, this knowledge will bind together such diverse engineering developments as magnetic materials, gas discharges, semiconductors, and dielectric and optical properties of materials. Similarly there is no substitute for a mastery of the fundamental principles of other sciences such as chemistry and biology.

Naturally, the education of an engineer must not end upon graduation from college. The pace of discovery is too great to consider any other course of action than to study and keep abreast of the expanding realm of science and technology. Therefore, in addition to learning fundamental principles of science and engineering in college, the student must develop an intellectual and technical curiosity that will encourage him to continue study after graduation.

In his work the engineer is faced constantly with situations in which problems appear where data are incomplete or perhaps where no prior similar experience is known. In such situations the engineer finds that he must make decisions in the face of uncertainty. He will be forced to draw upon his background of fundamental knowledge and frequently to engage himself in research or experimentation to ascertain or verify his conclusions. In obtaining such answers, however, it may be found that a contradictory situation exists to the one previously assumed to be present. It may also be that a specialized knowledge of several complex disciplines is required. In such cases a team effort may be used to advantage. In working with a team, the engineer must have an awareness of the broad relations existing between specialized sections of the team, and he must be able to integrate the in-depth knowledge of specialists into a summary that will clearly define the problem and provide the necessary answers.

The general objectives toward which an engineer must direct his educational goals are: (a) an ability to communicate with his fellowmen, (b) a facility for applying the principles of mathematics to his surroundings, (c) an awareness of the social and political implications of his technological achievements, (d) a skill in coordinating the efforts of others, (e) a mastery of the fundamental laws of

[2] Joseph Kestin, Brown University *Engineer*, No. 7, May, 1965, p. 11.

nature as explained by science, and (f) a capability to recognize and define problems and then apply available knowledge and skills to the economic solution of those problems.

### Communication

The engineer must be able to pass his knowledge and ideas to others, and conversely he must be able to receive information from others. Various types of communication used to describe ideas involve the use of mathematical expressions, skills in oral and written languages, graphical presentations, and communication with computing machines. Education in these techniques is a minimum requirement for a free interchange of ideas.

### Mathematics

Since mathematical tools are very important instruments of the engineer, an understanding of various mathematical principles furnishes a means of providing in symbolic form a pattern of reasoning and deduction essential to scientific thought. In addition to training in logical thought processes, an understanding of mathematics forms a basis for employment of computing machines to aid in the solution of complex problems.

### Social Sciences and Humanities

The engineer must deal with objects and theory and also with people. Although his technical training may teach him the manipulation of complex machines, unless he also is competent in dealing with people, his education is lacking much that is needed for a professional person. A fundamental knowledge of people, from both historical and modern behavioral studies, is required to understand their reactions and traits. In addition to a study of people, an engineer must be familiar with literature, geography, political science, economics, and philosophy in order to aid in providing satisfactory technical decisions. Too often the importance of social sciences and humanities is not realized until the engineer is several years out of college. In such cases he frequently finds that it is desirable and necessary to take additional courses in order to improve his ability in dealing with people.

### Management

The engineer seldom works by himself. In team efforts he frequently finds that he is directing the work of such diverse groups as economists, physicists, sociologists, mathematicians, accountants, technicians, draftsmen, and psychologists. He must not only be aware of their individual capabilities, but he also must be able to lead them in a coordinated effort in solving the particular problem that has been undertaken. In addition he must have a clear understanding of business principles, personnel management, fiscal procedures, and human and labor relations.

### Science and Engineering

The basic educational needs for an engineer lie in the field of science. They may range from the biological sciences through the whole realm of physical sciences. From the knowledge of fundamental scientific principles, the student can see a pattern of understanding emerge from which he may select the parts needed to make an application of the principles to solve a problem. Since change will be a routine part of the engineer's environment, it is important that the curriculum be designed around a core of engineering sciences such as solid mechanics, energy conversion, electrical science, materials science, fluid mechanics, and mass and energy transfer. However, the process of instructing a student in the integration of a wide mass of knowledge is extremely difficult. One approach frequently used is to confront him with situations in which the data needed for decisions are fragmentary and to encourage him to draw on his own resources to complete the picture. When confronted with such problems the engineering student must realize that in practice the answer is seldom clear-cut and the best that one can hope for is to arrive at a solution which will accomplish the desired result with the fewest unfavorable side effects. Optimization and the evaluation of alternatives guide in the decision process. Here the engineer interrelates and correlates as many factors as possible to provide a good solution while realizing that none of the factors may be the optimum which he would like to have. Since the day, centuries ago, when the first engineers were actively engaged in their work, engineers always have applied their creative abilities to manipulate the materials and forces in nature available to them for the purpose of obtaining designs useful to man. Although technology will continue to change in the years ahead, the role of the engineer will not change.

## CHALLENGES OF THE FUTURE[3]

For the foreseeable future, opportunity for the engineer will continue to expand at an exponential rate. Barring a national catastrophe or world war, available knowledge, productivity, and the living standard will probably continue to increase. For this reason man's resources must also continue to be available in larger and larger quantities, particularly with regard to water, energy, material, information, land, and air. Certainly it is hoped that man's appreciation for moral and esthetic values will continue to deepen and keep pace with this technological explosion.

Engineering scientists as well as applied scientists must continue to seek and to find ways to convert the new discoveries of science to beneficial human use as rapidly as possible. In the past, such efforts have made major contributions to the advancement of civilization. In the future, the success of these efforts will be vital to the survival of a crowded, resource-poor world.

Gordon and Helmer[4] used the opinions of 23 scientific and engineering experts, in a very interesting systematically conducted exercise, to name and to date the anticipated scientific and engineering breakthroughs. Thirty-one breakthroughs were named. Several examples are listed here with the median dates forecast for their accomplishment.

1. 1970 Economically feasible desalination of sea water.
2. 1971 Development of new synthetic materials for ultralight construction.

[3] Role of the Engineer in A.D. 2000, *An Engineering Master Plan Study for the University of California,* 1965. Predictions from this report are used liberally here with permission.
[4] Gordon, T. J. and Olaf Helmer, *Report on a Long-Range Forecasting Study,* The Rand Corporation, Santa Monica, Calif., September 1964.

3. 1980 Operation of a central data-storage facility with wide access for general or specialized information retrieval.

4. 1985 Stimulated emission (lasers) in x- and gamma-ray region of the spectrum.

5. 1987 Controlled thermonuclear power.

6. 1989 Economically useful exploitation of the ocean bottom through mining (other than off-shore oil drilling).

7. 1990 Feasibility of limited weather control to substantially affect regional weather at acceptable cost.

8. 1990 Economic feasibility of commercial generation of synthetic protein for food.

9. 2000 Economically useful exploitation of the ocean through farming, producing at least 20 per cent of the world's food.

10. 2020 Man-machine symbiosis, enabling man to extend his intelligence by direct electromechanical interaction between his brain and a computing machine.

11. 2050 Control of gravity through some form of modification of the gravitational field.

12. 2075 Two-way communication with extraterrestrials.

13. 2100 Economic feasibility of commercial manufacture of many chemical elements from subatomic building blocks.

14. 2600 Feasibility of education by direct information recording on the brain.

The above report contains similarly obtained forecasts in other areas such as progress in space, the world of 2000, and war and its prevention.

Because of the accelerated growth in engineering and technology, graduate degrees in engineering are likely to become prerequisites for a large majority of those in the engineering profession. Emphasis will shift more and more to the "design of complex systems which are capable of enabling man to use existing machines and structures more efficiently." This same "accelerating accumulation of knowledge will probably force deeper specialization for many members of the engineering profession." The doctorate degree will then not be an unusual goal for a large percentage of engineers.

## BIBLIOGRAPHY

*An Engineering Master Plan Study for the University of California,* Engineering Advisory Council, (1965).

BROSCHART, CHARLES B., *The Young Engineer,* Exposition Press, New York, (1953).

ESTRIN, HERMAN A., *Higher Education In Engineering and Science,* McGraw-Hill, New York, (1963).

NOURSE, ALAN E. and JAMES C. WEBBERT, *So You Want To Be An Engineer,* Harper, New York, (1962).

O'NEILL, JOHN JOSEPH, *Engineering The New Age,* Ives Washburn, New York, (1949).

PUTNAM, P. C., *Energy In The Future,* Van Nostrand, Princeton, (1953).

"The Long Range Demand for Scientific and Technical Personnel," National Science Foundation Study, (1961).

# Chapter 7

# Study Habits of the Engineer

## FROM HIGH SCHOOL TO COLLEGE

Students who have enrolled in a college or university for the first time often ask, "Is there a difference between a high school course and a college course?" and "Will I need to make any adjustments in my study habits, now that I have enrolled in college?"

The answer to both of these questions is probably *yes,* but let us examine some of the reasons why this may be so.

First, in high school you were competing against the *average* of high school students. However, of the total numbers graduating from high school in the United States each year, fewer than one-third go to college. Thus, you are now competing with the average of *very good* high school students.

The study habits and learning process that you used in high school may not be adequate to cope with the increased requirements of college courses because of both the limited time available and the large quantity of material to be covered. A refinement of your study habits or perhaps a complete change in study habits may be necessary to enable you to keep up with the demands of new course material.

Many students, as they enter college, do not realize what will be expected of them. In general they are expected to bring basic skills in mathematical manipulation, in reading rapidly and comprehending, and in possessing a broadbased vocabulary. Engineering educators have observed that a high school graduate who has the ability to *read* and *add* also possesses the capability to succeed in a college engineering program. In high school, much time was taken in class to outline and drill on the daily assignments. In college, relatively less time is taken in class, and much more study and preparation is expected from the student outside of class. The student is largely on his own, and his time can be used to a considerable extent as he sees fit. It can be used efficiently and profitably or it can be dissipated without plan and, in effect, be wasted.

Without parental urging or strong encouragement from teachers, the student must adopt personal methods of study that will produce desirable results. Specifically he must budget his time to permit adequate preparation for each course. There must be more than a casual desire to improve study habits. Positive steps must be taken to insure effective study and learning conditions. It is for this reason that the following topics are included as suggestions to aid in improving the students effectiveness in study.

## PRECLASS STUDY

The object of study is to learn. Mere idle reading is not study. Particularly in scientific and technical courses, extreme attention to detail is necessary. With the learning process in mind, let us examine some basic principles.

1. The material must be organized into appropriate learning units. Random facts and concepts are more difficult to learn than facts which are related. For example, in learning the names of the bones of the body it is easier to remember the names if groups such as the arm or leg bones are studied as a unit.

2. Attempt to form the correct pattern of facts on the first try. This is necessary to eliminate the need for "unlearning" and relearning factual material. In the case of research or exploratory study, trial and error methods are necessary and frequently incorrect assumptions are made. However, by conscious effort to use reasoning and to incorporate other correct facts, false assumptions are minimized.

3. Correct errors immediately and reinforce correct learning responses. Experiments have shown that immediate confirmation of correct learning is more effective in remembering than when the confirmation is delayed. For example if a mathematics problem is solved and its correctness immediately verified, the principle involved in the solution is retained better than if the verification is delayed.

4. Relate realistic experiences with the facts. Experiments have demonstrated that most people learn and retain information better if it is related in some way to their experiences. For example, an abstract idea such as "democracy" is difficult to present as a realistic picture unless the student has some related background of government upon which to draw a conclusion. On the other hand a description of a new type of internal combustion engine may be simple to present to an experienced automobile mechanic because of his related experience with similar devices.

5. Give concise meanings to the facts. Particularly in scientific work the meanings of words may not always be clear. Frequently we misunderstand one another because we each may give different meanings to the same word. The use of dictionaries, encyclopedias, and reference books is therefore necessary to gain a common understanding of new words.

6. Practice, review and provide application for facts. Education specialists believe that facts are not actually learned until at least one perfect recitation or response is completed. After this has been accomplished, review and repeated use of the facts will greatly aid retention. Research also has shown that if the review is broken into spaced periods, retention and recall are increased (sometimes as much as doubled) over the retention when the reviewing is all done at one sitting. One should be alert to applications for the ideas being learned. This will help to relate

them to previous experience and to place them into a pattern where they will become bricks in a wall of knowledge upon which other ideas can be added.

7. Evaluate the adequacy of the learning: A self-evaluation of the understanding of the new ideas which have been presented is one of the most valuable learning experiences in which a student can participate. Memorizing facts does not encourage self-evaluation. However, the ability to apply principles and *to use* facts is one important way in which a person can evaluate the adequacy of learning. For example, after studying a portion of text material in a physics book, are you able at once to apply the facts and principles discussed to the solution of related problems?

The realm of factual information available is so tremendous that a student should acquire at first only the essential and basic facts in a particular field of study. From this set of basic facts, the student then enlarges or details his information into more specialized subjects. For example, the electrical engineering student should begin his study of electricity with an inspection of basic principles, such as Ohm's law, before beginning to consider the design of amplifiers.

## SETTING THE STAGE

Provide a designated study area. It is desirable to find a place where you can concentrate and where other people will not bother you. Unfortunately distractions frequently abound in large study areas and interfere with study schedules. Other people in your home or your dormitory may have conflicting schedules and may not be concerned with respecting your own study periods. Radios, TV, and "bull sessions" are always, inviting diversions from study. For this reason many students

**Illustration 7–1.** The library is an excellent place to study since it is quiet, and numerous reference works are readily available. (Courtesy Monsanto Company.)

find that libraries afford good study areas because of the absence of distractions and the ready availability of reference materials. Although a secluded spot is not always essential for study, for most people it does require a conscious effort to reject distracting sounds and backgrounds in order to concentrate.

The best place to study is usually at a desk or table, not on a bed. The effort of sitting helps to keep most people alert and in a mood for study. Good lighting is especially helpful and it is desirable for the whole study area to be illuminated, rather than a small portion of the area. Studies have shown that it is less fatiguing on the eyes if sharply defined regions of light and dark are excluded from the immediate study area. In addition, the work area should be large enough so that reference materials can be kept close at hand.

## PREPARE A SCHEDULE

Time is one of the most important factors to be considered in college study. In every course there is usually more material assigned than can be studied in detail in the time available. In addition outside activities will always compete for the use of a student's time. Athletic events, social and educational programs, recreational activities, and unscheduled meetings with other people seem to disrupt the best laid plans. The student must realize that these contradictory conditions for study will always exist. Positive steps must be taken to insure that the time for study is not taken away piecemeal by nonessentials.

In preparing a daily schedule, the question arises concerning the amount of time to allocate for study. Several rule-of-thumb principles are in common use, but the individual's capabilities in learning each specific subject will necessarily need to be the final guide. A recent survey of a cross section of students at a large university showed that the greatest number of students spent an average of 28 to 32 hours of study per week. Engineering students usually spend considerably more than this amount. Actually the number of hours of study is not always the most significant criterion to be used. Rather *how well* one studies is the factor that counts most. The results of study as shown by grades and by one's own personal satisfaction in doing a good job are usually the best indicators of the effective use of time.

A positive and direct approach to a schedule is necessary in the same way that a budget is necessary to manage the fiscal affairs of a business. No commercial enterprise can long exist that does not plan ahead for meeting expenses as they arise. In a similar way a student should prepare a budget of time for his school work and adhere to it, unless circumstances definitely indicate that it should be altered. Not only should the daily time be budgeted on a weekly basis, but also extra time must be allocated for major quizzes, term papers, and final examinations. It has been found, for instance, that the majority of the better students budget their time so that final examinations do not have to be prepared for on a frantic last minute rush. Study skills, no matter how effective, will not be of much value if a student's time is not properly scheduled so that they can be employed.

Scheduling helps to allocate more time to the more difficult courses and to assign less time to the less demanding courses. It also helps to space the available study time so that it will be distributed in a manner to aid in better retention. (Refer to the sixth principle of learning on page 80.)

**Illustration 7–2.** It is very important that the student's place for study be well arranged, adequately lighted, and free from distraction. (Courtesy Chicago Bridge & Iron Co.)

## STUDYING TO LEARN

Studying to learn is a skill that can be developed just as other skills are developed. All good golfers do not use exactly the same stance or swing, yet they all accomplish a reasonably consistent pattern of results. In like manner, all good students may employ slightly different techniques of study and still accomplish an acceptable learning pattern. However, despite individual differences, in any activity a general set of principles can be found that will produce good results, whether it be golf or studying. Some of these principles for study are discussed below.

1. Remove or minimize distractions.
2. Arrange all necessary pencils, reference books, notebooks, note paper, and other supplies before beginning.
3. Put your full attention on the work at hand, and insist that your brain work accurately and rapidly. If the brain is not employed to its full capacity, it will tend to let other thoughts enter to distract it from the task at hand. Read with a purpose—to extract details from the printed page and to comprehend important ideas.

4. Practice reading as fast as feasible. This does not mean skipping from word to word randomly, but rather training the eyes and brain to group words, phrases and even lines of reading material and to understand the thoughts therein. Many good books are available on how to improve your reading speed for comprehension. Time spent in learning this skill will aid immensely in the faster grasping of ideas.

5. Study as though you were going to teach someone else the subject matter. This will provide motivation for learning and also will encourage self-appraisal of the adequacy of learning as discussed in the seventh principle of learning on page 81.

6. Plan for review and repetition of the assignment. Principle of learning number six on page 80 points out the desirability of spaced periods of review.

The suggested methods and practices described above have been found to aid most students in their learning and the majority of good students follow the general outline of these practices.

## PREPARATION FOR CLASS RECITATION

A plan of study for each course is necessary to gain the greatest return in learning from your investment of study time. The plan will vary with the teacher, the textbook, the nature of the course, and the type of recitation and examination that is expected. However, before considering suggestions for specific types of courses, we should investigate study techniques that are applicable in general to all subjects.

Learning proceeds best from the general to the specific. It is therefore recommended at the beginning of a course to first skim the chapter and topic headings of the text without reading in detail any of the discussion material. This is done to get an overview of the whole organization of the book. Notice the order in which the topics appear and how the author has arranged the ideas to proceed from one to another. Next, read the lesson quickly to gain an insight into the nature of the material to be covered. Do not attempt to learn details nor to analyze any but the most emphasized points. If there is a summary, read it as part of your lesson survey to prepare you with background material that will be useful in understanding details.

Second, after a rapid survey of the material to be studied, start at the beginning of the assignment with the idea in mind that you will make notes during your study. Remember, you are going to learn as though you would have to teach the lesson content to someone else. Mere superficial reading here will not suffice. The notes can take various forms. They may include summaries of important facts, definitions of words, sample problems or examples, answers to questions, sketches, diagrams, and graphs. A better mental picture is formed and retained if the hand and eye work together on an idea and if you are forced to participate more actively and completely in the learning process.

These notes should be made in semipermanent form, not on random scraps of paper. Bound notebooks or loose-leaf notebooks can be used, but it is important that the notes be organized and retrievable. In addition to separate notes, it is helpful to underline key words and phrases in the text. Don't worry about the appearance of the book. However, do not overdo the underlining; it is better to note the crucial words and phrases so that they are more obvious for review than to underline whole sentences and paragraphs. Usually from three to eight words per paragraph will point out the central idea that has been presented.

Third, reread and review the lesson assignment and prepare your own questions and answers to the topics. At first this may seem to be an unnecessary step but it will pay dividends. Attempt, if possible, to foresee the questions the instructor may ask later concerning the material. Your notes on these predictions can be invaluable at examination time. Check to see that you have noted all of the important details and related facts that bring out the main ideas. Particularly in the technological courses, you can do this easily, since much of the material is completely factual.

Fourth, if given an opportunity, plan to participate in the classroom recitation. Force yourself, if necessary, to volunteer to recite. Recitation is a form of learning and it aids in acquiring ideas from others. If the class does not afford an opportunity for recitation, recite the lesson in your room. Review and recitation are the best methods for making a final check of your retention of information. Tests show that you begin to forget even while learning, but if you participate in some form of recitation as soon after study as possible, the retention of facts may be increased by as much as 50 per cent.

Recitation is an effective way of self-appraisal of learning. Just reading a book is not enough to convince anyone—yourself included—that you have learned what you should. When you study, break the topics into groups, and upon completion of each group of topics, as a summary close the book and see if you can recite the important facts either mentally or in writing. When you can repeat them satisfactorily then continue; if you cannot repeat them, for further study, go back and pick out the ones that you have missed. It is particularly important to recite if the subject matter consists of somewhat disconnected material such as names, dates, formulas, rules, laws, or items. If the material to be studied is more narrative in style and well organized, the recitation time can occupy a small part of the study period, but it should never be left out altogether.

The general principles above apply to all courses, but certain study plans will apply better to one course than to another. We shall examine study plans for several types of courses in more detail.

## TECHNICAL COURSES

In this type of course your study plan should be to direct your study toward understanding the meanings of words and toward grasping the laws and principles involved. In order to understand the words, a dictionary, encyclopedia, and reference books are necessary. The first step is to write down definitions of unfamiliar terms. Remember also that a word does not always have the same meaning in different courses. For example, the word "work" as used in economics has a meaning quite different from the word "work" as used in physics.

When the definitions of words are obtained, study for complete understanding. Texts in technical courses tend to be concise and extremely factual. A technique of reading must be adopted here for reading each word and fitting it into its place in the basic idea. Except for the initial survey reading of the lesson, do not skim rapidly through the explanations, but rather read to locate the particular ideas in each paragraph. If example problems are given, try working them yourself without reference to the author's solution.

After definitions and basic ideas are studied, apply the principles to the solution of problems. It has been said by students that it is impractical to study for examinations where problems are to be solved because you are unable to predict the problem questions. This statement is not correct, for you can predict the principles which will be used in solving the problems. For example in chemistry, a vast number of compounds can be used in equation-balancing problems. However, a very few basic principles are involved. If the principle of balancing is learned, all problems, regardless of the chemical material used are solved the same way. The objective of this part of study then is to determine the few principles involved and the few problem patterns that can be used. After this, all problems, regardless of their number arrangement and descriptive material, can be classified into one of the problem patterns for which a general method of solution is available. For instance, a problem in physics may involve an electrical circuit in which both current and voltage are known and an unknown resistance is to be determined. Another problem may suggest a circuit containing a certain resistance and with a given current in it. In this case a voltage is to be found. The problems are worded differently, but a general principle involving Ohm's Law applies to each situation. The same problem structure is used in each case. The only difference appears in where the unknown quantity lies in the problem pattern.

Do not become discouraged if you have difficulty in classifying problems. One of the best ways to aid in learning to classify problems is to work an abundance of problems. It is then likely that any examination problem will be similar to a problem that you have solved before.

Learn to analyze each problem in steps. Examine the problem first for any operations that may simplify it. Sometimes a change in units of measure will aid in pointing toward a solution. Try rewriting the problem in a different form. Frequently in mathematical problems, this is a useful approach. Write down each step as the solution proceeds. This approach is particularly helpful if the solution will involve a number of different principles. If a certain approach is not productive, go back and reexamine the application of the principles to the data. For problems which have definite answers, these techniques usually will provide a means for obtaining a solution.

It usually is better in studying technological courses to divide the study periods into several short sessions, rather than one continuous and long study period. For most people a period of incubation (where the idea is allowed to soak into the subconscious) is helpful in grasping the new ideas presented. After returning to do subsequent study, make a quick review of the material previously studied, and look at the notes you have prepared to provide continuity for your thinking.

## LITERATURE COURSES

Most writings classed as literature are written to be interesting and to entertain. For this reason, not as much attention to detail and to individual words is needed as is required in technological books. Usually the ideas are presented descriptively and are readily distinguished. However, the interpretation of the ideas may vary from person to person, and it is with this in mind that the following suggestions are given.

Examine the ideas not only from your point of view but also from the point of view of your teacher. Try to find out from his discussions and examinations the pattern of thought toward which he is directing you, and study the things *in which he is interested*.

Consciously look for these items while you read prose: The setting, central characters (note the realism or symbolism of each), the theme, the point of view of the author (first person, omniscent, etc.), the author's style of writing, the tone, and the type of the writing. For poetry, the ideas may be more obscure, but certain things may be noted. For example, the authors' style, the type of verse, the rhyme scheme, the theme, the symbols, allusions, images, similes, metaphors, personifications, apostrophes and the alliterations are all basic and important parts to the study of poetry.

## SOCIAL SCIENCE COURSES

These courses can be very dry and dull but with the proper attitude on the part of the student, they can be very interesting and most satisfying. Most texts use a narrative style in presenting the material and, as a consequence, the assignment should be surveyed quickly for content and then more in detail for particular ideas. Here the use of notes and underlining is invaluable, and summaries are very helpful to aid in remembering the various facts.

If the course is history, government, sociology, psychology, or a related subject, consider that it contains information that is necessary to help you as a citizen. A knowledge of these subjects will aid you in dealing with other people and it will give you background information to aid in the evaluation of material that has been specifically designed to influence and control people's thinking. Study the course for basic ideas and information and, unless the instructor indicates otherwise, do not exaggerate the importance of detail and descriptive information.

These principles apply also to courses in economics, statistics, and related courses except that they frequently are treated on a more mathematical basis. Here a combination of techniques described above together with problem solving procedures can be helpful. Again, since the volume of words usually is quite large, it is necessary to use notes and summaries to keep the ideas in a space to be handled easily.

## LANGUAGE COURSES

Many techniques have been developed to aid in learning foreign languages. In the absence of specific study guides from your instructor, the following procedures have been found to be helpful.

Learn a vocabulary first. Study new foreign words and form a mental image of them with a conscious effort to think in the new language. As you study, practice putting words together, and, if the course includes conversation, say the words aloud. Space your vocabulary study and review constantly, always trying to picture objects and actions in the new language rather than in English.

Rules of grammar are to be learned as any rule or principle: first as statements and then by application. Reading and writing seem to be the best ways of aiding retention of grammar rules. Read a passage repeatedly until it seems natural to see or hear the idea in that form. Write a summary in the language, preferably in a form that will employ the rules of grammar which you are studying. Unfortunately, there is no way to learn a new language without considerable effort on your part. Even English, our native tongue, when studied as a subject, gives some students trouble. However, many students have said that they really understand basic English much better after having taken a foreign language.

## CLASSROOM LEARNING

The discussion so far has been concerned with learning by study. An equally effective and more widely used method of learning is by listening. From earliest childhood you have learned by listening and imitating. Do not stop now but rather use the classroom to supplement your home study. You will find that things are covered in classroom work that you do not find in your texts. The interchange of ideas with others stimulates your thinking and retention processes. The classroom can also be a place to practice and to demonstrate your learning and problem solving skills before the examination periods.

The skill of listening seldom is used to the fullest extent: If your attention is only partly on the lecture, the part missed may make a major difference in your grade. Use the time in class to evaluate your instructor, find out what he will expect of you, watch for clues for examination questions, and make notes to be used for later study. If you plan to make the classroom time profitable, you will find it also will be enjoyable.

Come to class with a knowledge of the assignment to be discussed. The instructor then can fill in your knowledge pattern rather than be presenting entirely new material. This saves time in taking notes also because the notes are needed only for amplification rather than as semiverbatim recording. If a point arises at variance with your knowledge from study, you have an opportunity to question it. Prior study also permits you to predict what the instructor will say next. This serves as a valuable psychological device to hold your attention throughout the class period.

Note taking during class is a skill that can be learned. The inexperienced will try to take notes verbatim and thus get so involved in writing that they cannot listen for ideas. Usually, they cannot write fast enough to copy all of the words anyway. Rather than take notes verbatim, practice your listening skills and evaluate the critical points in the lecture. A few critical points will be amplified with descriptive materials. Practice taking down these critical points in your own words. Such note taking serves to keep your attention focused and to encourage a better understanding of the principles being discussed. If you do not understand the points completely, make notes for later study or for questioning the instructor.

If the course is such that you can, recite during the class period. Push your shyness aside, and place your ideas and information before the class. It stimulates your thinking and retention, it will help to clear up obscure points, and will give you much needed practice in hearing your voice in the presence of others.

**Illustration 7–3.** Adequate study gives confidence when reciting in class. (Courtesy Sperry Gyroscope Co.)

Attention and listening during a class period together with participation either in recitation or in anticipating what the instructor will cover next, will save you hours of study time outside the classroom.

## PREPARATION FOR THEMES, PAPERS, AND REPORTS

The purpose of writing is to transmit information. For an engineer, this is a valuable means of communicating his ideas to others and the practicing engineer takes pride in the conciseness and adequacy of his reports. No matter how good your ideas may be, if you cannot communicate them to others, they are of little value. Since part of the work of an engineer is writing reports and papers, the opportunity to learn and to practice this skill in school should be exploited. There are many good books on composition and manuals on writing that will help you. For this reason the suggestions given here are to be considered as supplementary helps in the preparation of written work.

In general, good writing involves good grammar, correct spelling and an orderly organization of ideas. The basic rules of grammar should be followed and a logical system of punctuation used. If in doubt as to the application of a somewhat obscure rule in grammar, either look it up or reword your idea in a more conventional manner. Punctuation is used to separate ideas and should follow, in general, the pauses you would use if you were reading the material aloud. Usually, reports are written in an impersonal manner; seldom is the first person used in formal writing.

Little needs to be said about spelling except to say, spell correctly. There is so little room for choice in spelling that there is no excuse for a technical student to misspell words. If you don't know how to spell a word, look it up in a dictionary or reference book and remember how to spell it correctly thereafter.

The last characteristic of good writing is a clear orderly organization of ideas. They may take several forms depending upon the type of writing. For themes, usually a narrative or story form is used in which a situation is set up, possibly with characters, and a story is told or a condition is described. Engineering papers and reports generally are concerned with technical subjects. Therefore they describe the behavior of objects or processes, or they provide details of events in technical fields. Frequently, the first paragraph summarizes the thoughts in the whole report in order to give the reader a quick survey without his having to skim through the manuscript first. Following paragraphs outline the contents in more detail. They frequently end with graphs, drawings, charts, and diagrams to support the conclusions reached.

In preparation of written work, some research usually is needed. In order to aid in keeping the notes for the material in usable form, it is helpful to record abbreviated notes from research works on cards in order that the arrangement of the writing of the paper can be made in a logical order. Usually in compiling information, you do not know how much will be used so the notes on cards provide a flexibility of choice that is a great aid in the final organization of the paper. The cards can be 3″ by 5″ or 4″ by 6″, with the latter usually being the better choice because of more available space.

An outline of the material to be discussed or described is necessary, even for brief reports. An outline insures a more logical arrangement of ideas and helps to make the writing follow from concept to concept more smoothly.

Write a draft copy first and plan on making alterations. Write first to get your ideas down on paper, and then go over the copy to improve the rough places in grammar, spelling, punctuation, and wording. If possible, wait a short time before taking these corrective steps to get a more detached and objective approach to the suggested changes. When the rework of the draft has been made, copy it over neatly, still maintaining a critical attitude on the mechanics of the writing. It is helpful if the final draft can be typed, but if not, you will find that good handwriting or lettering frequently makes a favorable impression upon the person who grades your paper.

## PREPARATION FOR EXAMINATIONS

Have you ever felt after taking an examination (for which you studied) that everything you studied was inappropriate? Perhaps you used the wrong techniques in studying for the examination. Certain rules have been found to be very useful in preparation for tests of any kind. The type of preparation you make is often more important in the final grading than how long you spend in preparation. Let·us discuss some of these rules that have been found to be effective.

Start preparing for tests the day the course starts. You know that they will be assigned, so do not close your eyes to this fact. From the very first, start studying two things: (1) the big overall ideas of the course, and (2) the instructor. Keeping these two things in mind will help you to learn while in class and while studying. This will also mean shorter reviews before tests.

Keep writing reminders of important points—as notes in margins of your books, as flagged notes in class, or as short statements while studying. Use nontext material as it becomes available, such as outlines, old tests, and information from students who have taken the course.

It is not unethical to study the instructor. After all, he is a person qualified to present the subject matter, and, because of his training and experience, frequently you will learn much more from him than you will from any text. From a study of the instructor, you can follow his pattern of lesson organization and find out what he wants from you. In your preparation, attempt to think and study along these lines. Close attention in class frequently will give major clues pertaining to the nature of future examination questions.

Make a final review of the subject matter. This should be a planned review and not a "last ditch" cramming session. Schedule it in several short sessions and do these things: First, review the general organization of the material before the final class periods of the semester in order to take advantage of the instructor's summaries and reviews. Second, set up the major topics or ideas and associate them with specific facts or examples. In the case of problem courses, this is the time to work out and review sample problems that will illustrate laws or principles. Third, study for more detailed information and to complete the areas of uncertainty. If the first two phases of the review have been adequate, this last phase should take relatively little time.

Predict the type of test that will be given. If the test is to be an essay type, practice outlining key subject matter, summarizing important concepts, comparing or contrasting trends, and listing factual data. This may seem to be an excessive amount of work, but if you have noted the points the instructor has stressed during the course, you can narrow the field considerably. However, a word of caution here: do not try to outguess the instructor; it usually will not pay. Study the topics you honestly feel are important, and avoid unjustified evaluation of different concepts in hope that there will not be questions on them. Remember that on this type of test not only are the ideas to be recalled but also the organization and sequence of the ideas is important.

For objective or short answer type tests, follow the three-step program of study given above giving more attention to relating key ideas to specific items of information. Here, short periods of highly concentrated study usually are to be preferred. Think about each idea long enough to form mental pictures and precise answers, but guard against merely memorizing words. Frequently sketches and diagrams will aid in retaining a mental picture of a concept.

If the test is to be a problem solving test, review first the principles that may be encountered in a problem. Work at least one sample problem that will illustrate the principle. Ask yourself, "If there is a change in the quantity to be solved for, can I still place this problem in the correct problem solving pattern?" This is important because, although the variation in problem statements is infinite, the applicable principles and consequently the problem patterns are relatively few.

What if you have more than one examination on the same day? Most students have found it better to do the last review on the subject that comes first. A quick check of notes than can be made before the next examination begins. An old but useful maxim states that the best preparation for taking tests is to practice the things you will need to do on the test.

## TAKING EXAMINATIONS

We shall assume that a primary objective in taking an examination is to make a high grade on it. Your grade will be based on what you put down on the test paper—not on what you know. It is crucially important then to get the correct sampling of your knowledge on record. Sometimes students fail, not because of lack of knowledge, but rather because of lack of skill in proving on the test paper that they do understand the material.

In taking any examination, be prepared. The ability to think clearly is of most importance, but the ability to recall facts is also very important. Enter the examination room with a feeling of confidence that you have mastered the subject and, while waiting for the questions to be distributed, be formulating plans for taking the test so that your mind will not be blocking itself with worry.

If the test is an objective type, turn quickly through the pages and note the kinds of questions; true-false, multiple choice, matching, completion. Make a rapid budget of time, and read the directions for answering the questions. If there is no penalty for guessing, answer every question; otherwise plan to omit answers to questions on which you are not reasonably sure. Be certain you understand the ground rules for marking and scoring so that you will not lose points on technicalities.

A basic principle of taking any examination is: *Answer the easy questions first.* If time runs out, at least you have had an opportunity to consider the questions you could answer readily; and usually an answer to an easy question counts as much as an answer to a difficult question. Do not carry over thoughts from one question to another. Concentrate on one question at a time and do not worry about a previous answer until you return to it on the next trial. It helps to relax for a moment between questions and get a fresh breath, and to help dismiss one set of thoughts before concentrating on another. Look for key words that may point to whether a statement is true or false. Usually statements are worded so that a key word or phrase tips the balance one way or the other. In case of doubt, try substituting a similar word into the statement and see whether it may aid in identification of truth or falsity. When you go back over the examination, do not change your answers unless you have obviously misread the questions or you are reasonably certain your original answer is incorrect. Tests have shown that your first response to a question on which you have some doubt is more likely to be correct than not.

If the test is an essay type, again read quickly through the questions, budget your time and answer the easy questions first. It is helpful to plan to put an answer to each question on a separate sheet of paper unless the answer obviously will be short. The one-answer-per-page system permits easy addition of material after your initial trial. Watch your time schedule, since it is easy to write so much on one question that you are forced to slight others. A help on answering lengthy questions is to jot down a hasty outline of points to include so they will not be overlooked in the process of composition.

After the questions have been answered, take a final critical look at your paper to correct misspelling, grammatical errors, punctuation, and indistinct writing. If time permits, add sketches, examples, or diagrams that may come to mind. Sometimes a period of quiet contemplation, reviewing mentally your notes, will help recall needed additional facts.

If the test has mathematical problems to solve, again read through the questions and budget your time. Plan to answer the easy questions first. Determine the "ground rules" such as whether points will be given for correct procedure regardless of the correctness of the arithmetic. Unless the problem solution is obviously short, plan to work only one problem per page. If a mistake is detected, you can more easily and more quickly line out the mistake than attempt erasure. An answer per page also permits room for computations and makes checking your work easier. Usually it is better to do all the work on that page and avoid scratch paper.

If the test is an open book test, use the reference books only for tabular or formula data that you reasonably could not remember. If you try to look up things you should already know, you will surely run out of time.

Let each problem stand by itself. First, analyze it from the standpoint of a pattern into which it can be fitted. Consider then what steps will need to be used in the solution, and finally determine how these solution steps will be presented. When the analysis is complete, then solve the problem in the framework of the analysis.

Usually it is better to go ahead and work through all problems and then come back and check for arithmetic mistakes and incorrect algebraic signs. This is the place also to take an objective look at the answer and ask whether it seems reasonable. A questioning attitude here may reveal mistakes that can be corrected.

## ANALYSIS OF RESULTS OF TESTS

Finally, when the test is ended and you get an opportunity to see your graded paper, analyze it and yourself critically. Assuming that you knew the material but that your grade did not reflect your knowledge, find out why the grade was not as good as it should have been. Blame only yourself for any deficiencies. Look for clues such as the ones given below that will help you not to make the same mistake again.

If it was an essay test, was your trouble poor handwriting, incorrect grammar, incorrect spelling, or incorrect punctuation? Correction of these faults is a matter of the mechanics of learning the rules and making a conscious effort to improve on your shortcomings.

Was your trouble failure to follow instructions, lack of organization of ideas, or lack of examples? Look for clues such as marks on your paper by graders stating "not clear," "not in sequence," "why?," "explain," "?," "trace," "compare," "contrast," and so forth, which indicate a failure on your part to follow instructions. The remedies are twofold. Look for key words in instructions on tests, and practice before hand the listing, contrasting, or comparing of factual data.

When the grader's marks include words such as "incomplete," "hard to follow," "meaning not clear," or "rambling," these comments indicate that your ideas need to have better organization. A remedy is to consider carefully what is being asked for in the question. Make a brief outline before you start writing. This affords a means of placing ideas in the most effective sequence and also helps to avoid omitting good points.

The grader's marks may be "for example," "explain," "be more specific," or "illustrate." These marks usually indicate a need for illustrations and examples. Your answers may show that you know something about the subject, but they may not convey precise information. Examples will convince the grader that you know the material covered.

For objective tests, evaluate the patterns of the questions missed. Did you misread the questions? Were you tripped up by double negatives in true-false questions? Did you fail to look for key words in multiple choice questions? Did you realize immediately after the examination that you had answered incorrectly? Some aids in improving grades on objective tests follow.

For true-false questions, did you give each question undivided attention, and were you careful not to read something into the question that was not there. If you missed several questions in sequence, you probably were thinking about more than the question at hand. Try rewording questions that have double negatives next time if you show a pattern of missing them.

For multiple choice questions, determine whether you concentrated on each question alone and determined, if possible, what the answer was before looking at the set of multiple choice answers. You should have eliminated as quickly as possible answers that obviously did not fit the question and concentrated on key words that would have provided clues to select from the remainder.

If the test consisted of problems to be solved, check for mistakes in two things: analysis and arithmetic. If your paper shows false starts on a problem, if you worked part-way and could go no further, or if the solution process was incorrect from the beginning, your principal trouble probably is lack of skill in problem analysis. The remedy, of course, is to work more problems illustrating the principles so that the test situations will be more familiar. If you use no scratch paper on tests, and keep all parts of your solution on the page, checking to ascertain your mistakes should be easy.

If the processes are correct but the answers are incorrect, look for careless mistakes: in arithmetic, in employing algebraic signs, in mixing systems of units such as feet and centimeters, in copying the problem or in copying from one step to the next, or in making numbers so indistinct that they are misread. The remedy for these mistakes is to go over the solution carefully checking for these things. If time permits, one independent solution will help. Finally, look at the answer—does it seem reasonable?

The employment of the techniques discussed above should help you to achieve grades based on your knowledge of a subject without a handicap in the skill of presenting the knowledge on an examination. No more should you have to say, "I knew it but I couldn't put it down on paper."

## BIBLIOGRAPHY

MORGAN, CLIFFORD T. and JAMES DEESE, *How to Study*, McGraw-Hill, New York, (1957).

NASON, LESLIE J., *You Can Get Better Grades*, U. of Southern California, (1961).

# Chapter 8

# Spoken and Written Communication

Skills in communication are important for the engineering student and for the engineer in practice. If an engineer cannot express clearly his ideas and the results of his endeavor to others, even though he may have the intellect of a genius and the capability of performing the most creative work, the benefits of his intellect and creative abilities will be of little use to others.

What are the skills that are needed in communications? For the engineer they generally are classed as verbal, graphical, and mathematical. In this respect we shall consider that *verbal* means language communication, either oral or written; that *graphical* constitutes all pictorial language such as engineering drawings, charts, diagrams, graphs, and pictures; and that *mathematical* includes all symbolic language in which concepts and logic processes are presented by use of a system of prearranged symbols.

A question may arise as to whether the use of models and demonstrations constitutes communication. In the truest sense, they do but usually they are inadequate within themselves to convey all concepts. Since usually words, pictures, or symbols are used as a supplement to explain such devices, these methods should not be considered to be a separate means of communication.

## VERBAL COMMUNICATION

We begin practicing our oral communication at an early age. As we progress through school, we add to our vocabulary and pick up experience in presenting ideas in writing. By the time a student is a freshman in college, he is expected to have a working vocabulary of several thousand words, to be able to organize ideas into a coherent pattern, and to present these ideas either orally or in writing. How does the objective of verbal communication for an engineer differ from this objective of other people?

Primarily, the engineer communicates to present ideas and to gain ideas. For some people, talking or writing is purely an entertainment, or an outlet for creative feelings. On the other hand, for the engineer, verbal communication is a part of his professional life. He communicates on a technological level with other engineers and with scientists and technicians and on a layman's level with nontechnically trained people.

For example, suppose you have been working on a device for inclusion in the design of an autopilot control for an airplane. This device includes a potentiometer and a gyroscope. Consider how different your description of the device would be to an engineer and to an accountant. The ability to "speak their language" is an important skill which the engineer should possess in dealing with diverse people.

Not only should the engineer's verbal skill be descriptive, but also it should be persuasive. Frequently, good ideas are considered by the uninformed to be too impractical or too revolutionary. Here, the engineer should have not only an adequate vocabulary, but also skills in presenting his ideas in a way that others will be led to accept them. In situations like this, practice in idea organization, a knowledge of psychology, and training in debate are all helpful.

In college, many opportunities are available for participation in group discussions, for the presentation of concepts both written and oral, and for gaining vocabulary skills. This is the time for the engineering student to learn by trial and

Illustration 8–1. The engineer must be able to explain his ideas to his fellow engineers, and also to the workmen who will fabricate his designs. (Courtesy Alcoa.)

error his best ways to communicate. After graduation, trial and error methods may be economically impractical. A conscious effort while in college to improve one's ability to communicate verbally will make the transition to work as a practicing engineer after graduation much easier.

## GRAPHICAL COMMUNICATION

How often have you heard someone exclaim, after a futile attempt to describe an object to another person, "Here, let me draw you a picture of it!" The old adage of a picture being worth a thousand words is still true. The ability to present ideas by such means as pictures, diagrams, and charts is a valuable asset. In general, the engineer is expected by nontechnical people to be able to sketch and draw better than the average person. Today, most engineering curricula include some work in engineering graphics, and although the engineer may not be considered as a professional draftsman, he should be able to attain and maintain an acceptable level of performance in engineering drawing and lettering.

Since ideas in research and development are frequently somewhat abstract, diagrams and graphs not only help to present ideas to others but also help the engineer to crystalize his own thought processes.

For the design engineer, the ability to present ideas graphically is a necessity. In almost every case, instructions prepared by a design engineer for use by technicians or workmen in building or fabricating articles are transmitted in the form of drawings. In the case of machined parts, for example, usually the workman has only the vaguest idea of the application of the part, so the drawing prepared by the design engineer must tell the complete story to the machinist.

The engineer engaged in sales will need to make frequent use of graphic aids. It usually is easier and faster to project ideas and application by graphic means than by verbal communication alone. Pictures fill the gap between verbal description and actual observance of an operating device. So effective are these techniques that considerable experimentation is now being done in teaching by means of television.

## MATHEMATICAL COMMUNICATION

Mathematics involves the use of symbols to represent concepts and their manipulation in logic processes. It has been stated humorously, but nevertheless somewhat truthfully, that mathematics is a form of shorthand used to describe science and that higher mathematics is shorter shorthand. In his study of mathematics, the engineer learns the meaning of symbols such as $\pi$, $+$, and $\int$, the rules for manipulating mathematical quantities, and the logic processes involved.

The question sometimes arises as to why an engineer needs so much mathematical training. The answer in simple terms is that it is such a valuable and powerful tool, that the engineer cannot afford to ignore its use. By using mathematics, not only is space conserved in the presentation of ideas but also the task of carrying the ideas through logic processes is simplified. Since many engineering science operations follow elementary mathematical laws, it is much easier to transform ideas into symbols, and manipulate the symbols according to prearranged mathematical procedures, and finally to come up with a set of symbols which can be reconverted into ideas.

The engineer's way of thinking is so consistently geared to mathematical processes that it becomes almost impossible for him to think otherwise. For example, if you are asked to find the area of a circle whose radius is known, you may immediately visualize $A = \pi r^2$. Now try to think of finding the area of a circle without using such a mathematical formula—you will probably find such thought to be difficult and unnatural.

Since your mathematical training has given you a skill in communication, as an engineer you should make full use of it. As has been pointed out, the logic processes enable one to predict mathematically the behavior of many engineering science operations. In addition, the mathematical presentation of the ideas, enables others familiar with mathematical rules to envision the practical application of the concepts.

For example, if the effects of gravitational forces, air loads, centrifugal forces, temperatures and humidity are expressed properly in a mathematical formulation, the path of a missile over the earth's surface can be predicted with surprising accuracy. It is not actually necessary then to perform the flight and to measure the trajectory if the parameters involved are accurately known.

Of course, mathematics is not restricted to an application of the known behavior of objects. By mathematical extrapolation, fundamentals of natural laws have been determined even before it has become known that such behavior is possible. For example, the principles of atomic fission were predicted mathematically many years before it was possible to verify them experimentally.

The use of mathematics by engineers permits more time to be given to creative thought, since ideas can be explored symbolically without having to make physical determinations. Of course, the advent of high speed automatic computing machines also has aided both in accelerating exploratory research and in the executing of routine mathematical operations.

## TECHNICAL REPORTING

For the engineer, much of his communication is executed by reports. These reports may be oral presentations in the form of technical talks or they may be written presentations as technical reports. In either case, information must be presented in a form so that the desired meaning can be understood.

Since the objective of a report is to present information, it must be prepared with the reader in mind. Clarity is therefore a prerequisite for a good report. A report that uses rare words or uncommon foreign phrases may serve to point up the brilliance of the author, but it may also discourage readers from attempting to unravel the meaning. A report should be prepared using words and phrases with which the reader will be familiar.

In addition to clarity, a report should state clearly and honestly the results obtained. In the case of reporting on tests, frequently data are taken and the test assembly is dismantled before the test results are available. Therefore, the tests cannot always be rerun, and the data are usually used as recorded. If the results should turn out to be less than desirable, as an engineer, you are obligated to report the facts completely and honestly. Even though reporting the true facts may be distressing to the writer, an honest statement will instill a feeling of confidence in the reader that the results are trustworthy.

In preparing reports, in general, only factual material should be covered. There is often a temptation to include irrelevant subjects, or personal opinions as a part of the factual material. In some cases, it may be desirable to give a personal opinion, but such opinion should be identified clearly as a matter of judgment and not as factual data.

## THE TECHNICAL REPORT

Much of the formal communication between engineers is in the form of written technical reports. There are a number of excellent references that describe in detail the preparation of technical reports, and the student is encouraged to use them when preparing his reports. The following paragraphs outline some of the mechanics of report preparation and are given as a supplement to more complete references in report preparation.

There are a number of ways in which a report can be organized. One sequence which is used by many engineers follows the general procedure of an engineering test. This sequence is:

1. Introduction      4. Results
2. Equipment         5. Discussion
3. Tests             6. Conclusions

Material that is included in each of these sections will be reviewed briefly.

1. *Introduction:* In this section, the background of the problem should be described in sufficient detail to show why the investigation or test was undertaken. After this, outline the general nature of the work that was done, previous investigations of others if applicable, and the extent of the testing proposed. This section is included basically to inform the reader about the test program and to detail reasons for its execution. It is designed to lead the reader into the more detailed parts of the report.

2. *Equipment:* This section describes the apparatus used, how the parts of the test apparatus were employed, and techniques that were used in manipulating the apparatus.

3. *Tests:* This section should outline the test procedure step by step. Such an outline is desirable to help the reader to understand the test apparatus arrangement and its employment to acquire data. In some cases where the apparatus is simple, the sections on Equipment and Tests may be combined into a single section.

4. *Results:* In most test work, it is desirable to present the results as tabular data or as graphs. In cases where data presentation in this form is not feasible, a brief description of results should be given.

5. *Discussion:* In this section, describe the ways in which the data have served to provide answers to the problems. Essentially, this section should answer questions and describe problem areas that were discussed in the introduction part of the report.

**TEXTBOOK**

6. *Conclusions:* In this section, it is customary to gather together the main parts of the problem and its answers and state them in a concise summary. In general, this section should answer the question, "What was the test and what were the results of the test?" If the results were inconclusive or if further testing seems desirable, a brief description of the remaining problem areas should be included with a discussion of the situation and recommendations for future research.

Another sequence frequently employed in industry is as follows:

1. Summary            4. Discussion
2. Introduction       5. Results and Conclusions
3. Apparatus and Tests  6. Tables, Charts, and Figures

In this sequence, the first part of the report gives a short outline of the problem and a summary of the results. For a person who is evaluating a number of reports, the summary will make it possible for him to decide quickly whether a more detailed reading of the report is desirable. The content of each section is substantially the same as for corresponding sections given in the first example. However, in the second example, the first part of the report is brief and general while the remainder is more detailed.

## WRITING THE REPORT

In writing a report, let us consider a few of the major principles of the mechanics of report preparation. One of the first considerations should be the choice of words. As pointed out previously, consider the educational level of the reader. Use words that the reader reasonably could be expected to understand without having to refer to a dictionary.

The next consideration should be the sentence structure of the report. Sentences should not be too long; in general, a sentence should not exceed about thirty-five words. Simple sentences, although they can convey meanings readily, frequently cause abrupt discontinuities in the flow of words. Complex sentences with introductory clauses and phrases usually provide the smoothest reading. A useful device is to tie a sentence or thought into a previous sentence by an opening phrase such as "This conclusion indicates," or "For example," or "Another way in which." This phraseology in effect leads the reader from thought to thought and helps to provide a coherent flow of ideas as the topics develop.

As a final consideration, sentences should be organized into paragraphs. In general, a paragraph should tell a fairly complete story within itself. The opening sentence should give the reader an idea of what is in the body of the paragraph, just as the title of a technical book should give the reader an idea of the nature of its contents. After the opening sentence, the ideas are developed within the paragraph. Here again, the use of opening and transitional words and phrases aids in providing continuity. The last sentence of a paragraph should indicate a relationship to the next paragraph. Like sentences, paragraphs should not be too long. Usually a paragraph should not exceed one fourth to one third of a page. If a single idea appears to require a long paragraph, it is better to break it into subideas for better paragraphing.

## TECHNICAL TALKS

The technical talk, like the written report, should convey information. However, the methods of presenting information differ for these two types of reports. Because of this difference, it is desirable to examine some of the recognized principles of preparing and presenting technical talks.

A primary requirement of a technical talk should be simplicity. In preparing a talk an engineer should remember that his listeners have an opportunity to receive an item of information only once. Someone seeking information can reread parts of a written report, but in listening to a talk he must understand the crucial ideas when they are first expressed. In order to insure that the listener does grasp the ideas, they must be simple and must be expressed in understandable language.

**Illustration 8–2.** The engineer must be able to convey his ideas to others by means of spoken and written communication. (Courtesy Inland Steel Company.)

There are many faults possible in technical talks, but two of the most common are compressing the subject matter unnecessarily and using unfamiliar words. If a talk is scheduled to last twenty minutes and the subject matter is general, a common tendency will be to compress the subject matter into the time allotted by talking rapidly and rushing through each topic. In a few minutes, the listeners are so confused that they will not attempt to follow the thread of the discussion further. At the end of the time, you can say that the subject was presented to the listeners; but probably they would have gained more information had fewer ideas been presented.

The same problem exists if unfamiliar words are used. Although the audience may be amazed at your command of language, they will be using even less of their perceptive powers to follow your thoughts, since the words do not convey ideas to them. In most cases, it is impossible to make the wording of a talk too simple. Inherently, in a technical talk, technical words will be used. However, the meanings of unfamiliar words should be explained, or the ideas should be expressed in two or more different ways so that the real meanings will be evident.

## ORGANIZING A TALK

The organization of a technical talk should follow generally the organization used for a written report. Usually, the introduction outlines the problem, gives reasons for attempting solutions to the problem, and summarizes the work that has been done. A description of the equipment and its use should follow. The presentation of results and a discussion of the significance of the results will usually conclude the talk.

The question of preparing a talk in written form so that it can be read arises frequently. In presentations to technical groups, there is often a requirement that written copies of talks be submitted in advance. With a carefully phrased copy available, the temptation is always present to *read* the material to the audience. It is advisable to resist this temptation! Except in the case of short sections of especially complex subject matter, the material should not be read. You should familiarize yourself enough with the subject so that you can at least give a major portion of the material without reading it. There are few things less appealing in technical education than looking at the top of the head of a person who is droning over his paper in a rapid monotone.

In gathering material for a talk, screen the subject matter carefully. There always is a tendency to present more concepts than can be grasped. A few ideas that have been successfully related in the period allocated for the talk are superior to many ideas that are presented without being very well understood or remembered.

Since the attention span of most people is about twenty-five minutes, it is advisable to arrange talks so they will not exceed this limit. If a talk will be longer than twenty-five minutes, a useful method to maintain attention is to divide the talk essentially into two or more units using such devices as telling a humorous anecdote, providing a demonstration, or changing the style of delivery.

After the talk has been prepared, it is often helpful to rehearse it with a friend who can offer suggestions regarding such things as (1) revisions of subject matter to improve clarity, (2) changing posture or mannerisms to reduce distractions, and (3) improving diction to aid in understanding the subject matter. There is no rigid pattern which all speakers must follow. However, a sympathetic critic can help make your presentation more effective, regardless of the style you use. It is helpful to realize that the audience will listen to your talk because of the worth of its technical content. You need not be a polished speaker, but you should be a clear and understandable one. Remember that your listeners are not interested in judging you but in learning what you have to say.

A question may arise concerning the desirability of using visual aids. In almost all cases, the use of visual aids is recommended. First, they help to illustrate your points because the audience has an opportunity to see as well as hear information relating to the subject. Second, they will assist you in your speaking role by affording you an opportunity for movement to help you relax and speak more naturally. Also they serve as a supplement to notes to help keep the organization of the talk in the proper sequence.

Visual aids that are most useful to supplement a talk are charts, diagrams, graphs, models, slides, and movies. However, in preparing the talk, prepare the visual aids in such manner that they supplement the talk, rather than dominate the presentation. If it becomes necessary to make lengthy explanations of a visual aid, the aid should be simplified or subdivided into simpler parts.

Of course, practice helps in presenting talks, but if you have mastered a definite group of ideas that you have organized properly, lack of experience in making talks is not a great handicap. Actually, your mission in presenting a talk usually will be accomplished successfully if you leave each individual in the audience with a fairly clear impression of your work and its most significant results or contributions.

## PROBLEMS ON SPOKEN AND WRITTEN COMMUNICATION

**8–1.** Write a 250 word paper concerning your career objectives.

**8–2.** Assume that at the end of the semester you are scheduled to graduate from college with a bachelor's degree in engineering. Compose a letter to the Quality Electronics Company, Inc., concerning your desire to secure employment.

**8–3.** Visit a company that manufactures a product. Write a 200 word report concerning improvements that you believe could be made in the manufacturing process.

**8–4.** Prepare a five-minute talk on the topic, "Man's Desire vs. Man's Need for Energy."

**8–5.** Prepare a brief talk concerning the importance of electronic digital computers to our way of life.

## BIBLIOGRAPHY

GLIDDEN, H. K., *Reports, Technical Writing, and Specifications,* McGraw-Hill, New York, (1964).

GRAVES, HAROLD F. and LYNE S. HOFFMAN, *Report Writing,* Prentice-Hall, Englewood Cliffs, N.J., (1965).

HAYS, ROBERT, *Principles of Technical Writing,* Addison-Wesley, Reading, Mass., (1965).

KATZOFF, S., *Clarity in Technical Reporting,* NASA, Washington, D.C., (1964).

MILLER, W. J. and L. E. A. SAIDLA, *Engineers As Writers,* Van Nostrand Inc., New York, (1953).

RATHBONE, ROBERT R. and JAMES B. STONE, *A Writer's Guide for Engineers and Scientists,* Prentice-Hall, Englewood Cliffs, N.J., (1961).

ROSENSTEIN, ALLEN B., ROBERT R. RATHBONE and WILLIAM F. SCHNEERER, *Engineering Communications,* Prentice-Hall, Englewood Cliffs, N.J., (1964).

WILCOX, SIDNEY W., *Technical Communication,* International, Scranton, Pa., (1962).

# PART THREE

## PREPARATION
## FOR PROBLEM SOLVING

The engineer's work is distinguished by clarity of thinking, systematic analysis, and conciseness of presentation. These are trade-marks of his profession. (Courtesy A. M. Byers Company.)

# Chapter 9

# Presentation of
# Engineering Calculations

## FORMAT

In problem solving, both in school and in industry, considerable importance is attached to a proper analysis of the problem, to a logical recording of the problem solution, and to the overall professional appearance of the finished calculations. Neatness and clarity of presentation are distinguishing marks of the engineer's work. Students should strive always to practice professional habits of problem analysis and to make a conscious effort to improve the appearance of each paper, whether it is submitted for grading or is included in a notebook.

The computation paper used for most calculations is 8½ by 11 inches in size, with lines ruled both vertically and horizontally on the sheet. Usually these lines divide the paper into five squares per inch, and the paper is commonly known as cross-section paper or engineering calculation paper. Many schools use paper that has the lines ruled on the reverse side of the paper so that erasures will not remove them. A fundamental principle to be followed is that the problem work shown on the paper should not be crowded, and all steps of the solution should be included.

Engineers use slant or vertical lettering (see Figure 9–1), and either is acceptable as long as there is no mixing of the two forms. The student should not be discouraged if he finds that he cannot letter with great speed and dexterity at first. Skills in making good letters improve with hours of patient practice. Use a well-sharpened H or 2H pencil and follow the sequence of strokes recommended in Figure 9–1.

Several styles of model problem sheets are shown in Figures 9–2 to 9–5. Notice in each sample that an orderly sequence is followed in which the known data are given first. The data are followed by a brief statement of the requirements, and then the engineer's solution.

When the problem solution is finished, the paper may be folded and endorsed on the outside or may be submitted flat in a folder. Items that appear on the endorsement should include the student's name, and the course, section, date, problem numbers, and any other prescribed information. An example of a paper that has been folded and endorsed is shown in Figure 9–6.

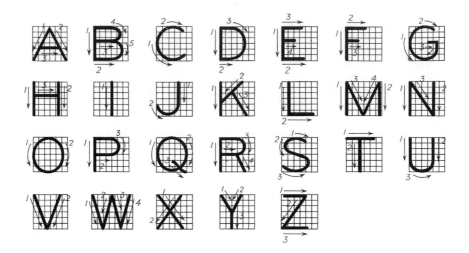

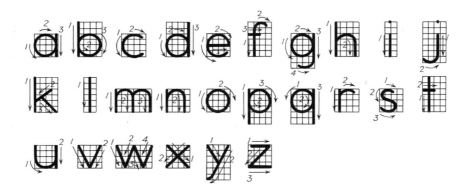

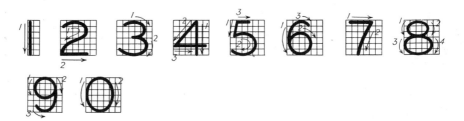

**Figure 9–1.** Vertical lettering.

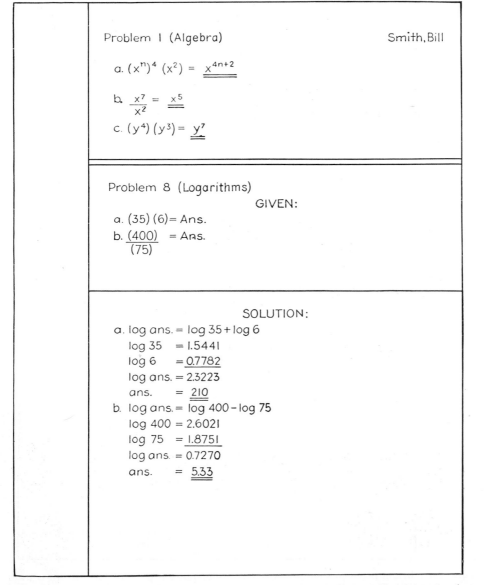

**Figure 9–2.** Model problem sheet, style A. This style shows a method of presenting short, simple exercises.

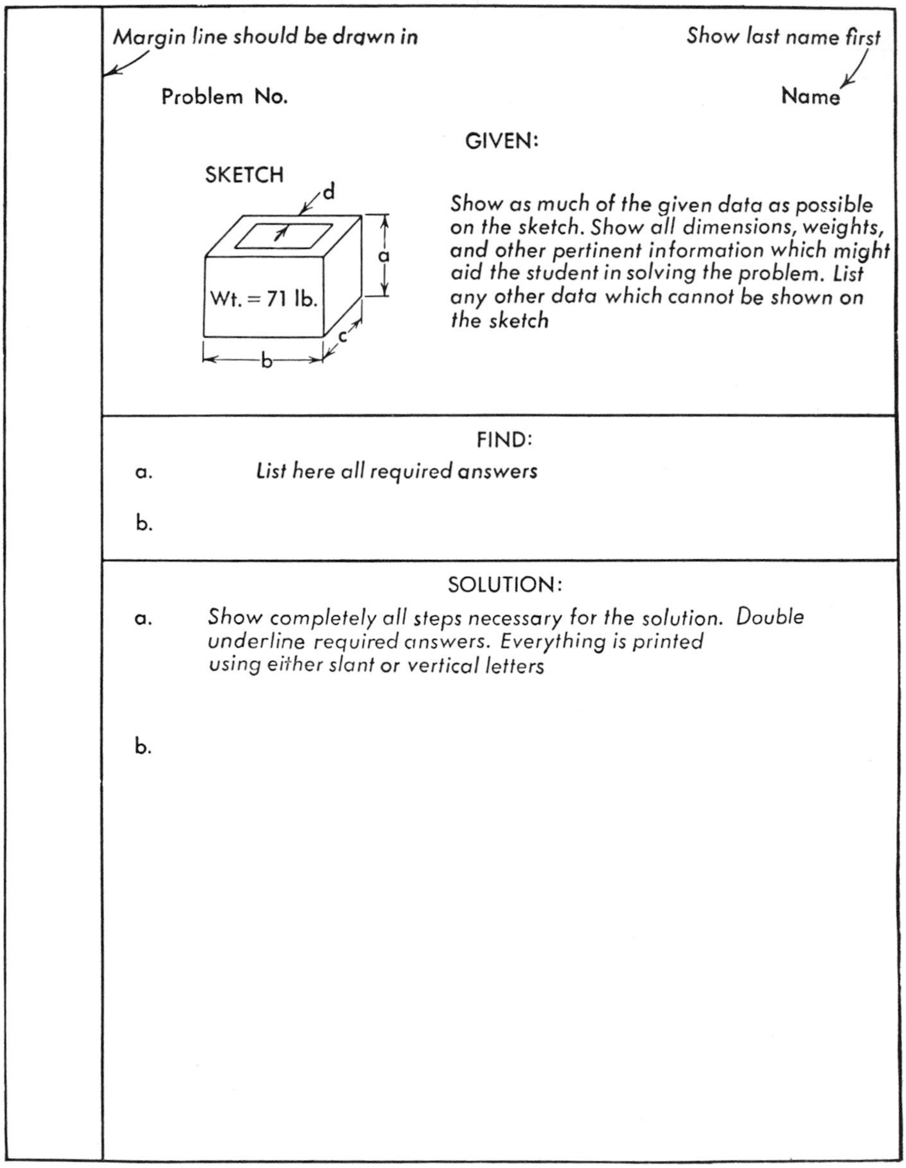

*Margin line should be drawn in*          *Show last name first*

Problem No.                                    Name

GIVEN:

SKETCH

Wt. = 71 lb.

*Show as much of the given data as possible on the sketch. Show all dimensions, weights, and other pertinent information which might aid the student in solving the problem. List any other data which cannot be shown on the sketch*

FIND:

a.          *List here all required answers*

b.

SOLUTION:

a.          *Show completely all steps necessary for the solution. Double underline required answers. Everything is printed using either slant or vertical letters*

b.

**Figure 9–3.** Model problem sheet, style B. This style shows a general form which is useful in presenting the solution of mensuration problems.

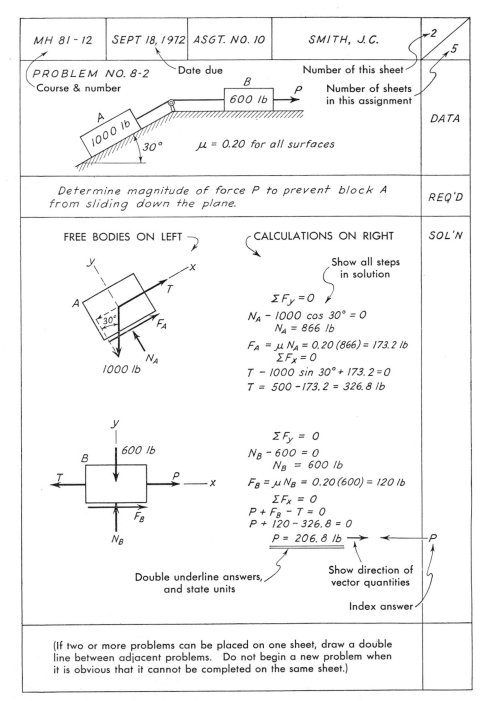

| MH 81-12 | SEPT 18, 1972 | ASGT. NO. 10 | SMITH, J.C. | 2 / 5 |

PROBLEM NO. 8-2
Course & number
Date due
Number of this sheet
Number of sheets in this assignment

*DATA*

B
600 lb P
A
1000 lb
30°
$\mu = 0.20$ for all surfaces

Determine magnitude of force P to prevent block A from sliding down the plane.

*REQ'D*

FREE BODIES ON LEFT
CALCULATIONS ON RIGHT
*SOL'N*

Show all steps in solution

y x
A T
30° $F_A$
$N_A$
1000 lb

$\Sigma F_y = 0$
$N_A - 1000 \cos 30° = 0$
$N_A = 866 \ lb$
$F_A = \mu N_A = 0.20 (866) = 173.2 \ lb$
$\Sigma F_x = 0$
$T - 1000 \sin 30° + 173.2 = 0$
$T = 500 - 173.2 = 326.8 \ lb$

y
600 lb
B
T P x
$F_B$
$N_B$

$\Sigma F_y = 0$
$N_B - 600 = 0$
$N_B = 600 \ lb$
$F_B = \mu N_B = 0.20 (600) = 120 \ lb$
$\Sigma F_x = 0$
$P + F_B - T = 0$
$P + 120 - 326.8 = 0$
$P = 206.8 \ lb$ → ← P

Double underline answers, and state units

Show direction of vector quantities

Index answer

(If two or more problems can be placed on one sheet, draw a double line between adjacent problems. Do not begin a new problem when it is obvious that it cannot be completed on the same sheet.)

**Figure 9-4.** Model problem sheet, style C. This style shows a method of presenting stated problems. Notice that all calculations are shown on the sheet and that no scratch calculations on other sheets are used.

Sheet 1 of 2:

| 11-29-72 | Prob. 1-2; 82 | Jones, J.E. | 1 / 2 |
|---|---|---|---|

*Given:* — Date due / Problem number and page number / Number of this sheet / Number of sheets in this assignment

Sketch: triangle with points A, C, B, D, X, Y; 12.15 mi, 9.167 mi, 42.78 mi, 9.728 mi, 11.26 mi

Show as much of the given data as possible on the sketch

*Required:*
Distance ACDB

Step by step solution in this column — Index answers

Compute CX:
$$CX = CY + ZD$$
$$= 9.167 + 9.728$$
$$= 18.895 \text{ mi} \longrightarrow CX$$

```
  9.167
+ 9.728
 18.895
```
$\frac{0}{1} = -1$

Compute DX:
$$DX = AB - (AY + BZ)$$
$$= 42.78 - (12.15 + 11.26)$$
$$= 42.78 - 23.41$$
$$= 19.37 \text{ mi} \longrightarrow DX$$

```
 12.15    42.78
+11.26   -23.41
 23.41    19.37
```
$\frac{0}{1} = -1$

Necessary arithmetic calculations in this column

Compute ∡A:
$$Tan\ A = \frac{9.167}{12.150}$$
$$= 0.754$$
$$A = 37° \longrightarrow ∡A$$

Compute AC:
$$AC = \frac{9.167}{sin\ 37°}$$
$$= 15.22 \text{ mi} \longrightarrow AC$$
$\frac{0}{-1} = +1$

Sheet 2 of 2:

| 11-29-72 | Prob. 1-2; 82 | Jones, J.E. | 2 / 2 |
|---|---|---|---|

Compute ∡CDX:
$$Tan\ ∡CDX = \frac{18.895}{19.37}$$
$$= 0.975$$
$$∡CDX = 44.25° \longrightarrow ∡CDX$$
$\frac{1}{1+1} = -1$

Compute CD:
$$CD = \frac{18.895}{sin\ 44.25°}$$
$$= 27.04 \text{ mi} \longrightarrow CD$$
$\frac{1}{-1+1} = 1$

Compute ∡B:
$$Tan\ B = \frac{9.728}{11.260}$$
$$= 0.864$$
$$B = 40.8° \longrightarrow ∡B$$
$\frac{0}{1} = -1$

Compute BD:
$$BD = \frac{9.728}{sin\ 40.8°}$$
$$= 14.9 \text{ mi} \longrightarrow BD$$
$\frac{0}{-1} = 1$

Compute Distance ACDB:
$$ACDB = AC + CD + DB$$
$$= 15.22 + 27.04 + 14.9$$
$$= 57.16 \text{ mi} \longrightarrow ACDB$$

```
 15.22
 27.04
 14.90
 57.16
```

**Figure 9-5.** Model problem sheet, style D. This style employs a sheet with heading and margin lines preprinted. Notice that all calculations are shown on the solution sheet.

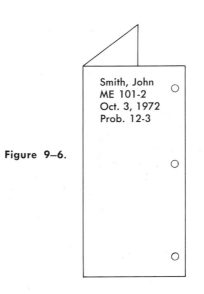

Smith, John
ME 101-2
Oct. 3, 1972
Prob. 12-3

**Figure 9—6.**

## MEASUREMENTS AND THE SCIENTIFIC PRESENTATION OF MEASURED DATA

### The Purpose of Measurement

Measurements are made by the engineer in order to gain quantitative information about processes within the vast complex of physical systems. Not only do measurements enable the engineer to understand more about objects and their behavior but measurements also help him to communicate ideas about his physical surroundings to others.

The ability to make measurements and to employ measurements is a basic requirement of engineering design. Both in science and engineering the ability to organize and evaluate measurements is an essential part of any interpretation of the behavior of physical bodies. In addition, measurements are necessary in order that scientific discoveries can be employed in the design of new devices. For example, every new type of aircraft is tested rigorously, and measurements are made on it to see whether its performance agrees with earlier design predictions. Since some of the original design concepts may have been hypothetical, measured results of tests serve to verify the hypothesis and to provide a sound basis for any extensions of the design to other situations.

Engineering is essentially a science of measurements. The engineer finds that the quantities which he can measure most easily and accurately are the quantities that he employs most confidently in the design, operation, and use of devices. Actually, much of the significant progress in science and engineering is made when effective measuring techniques are devised to support a new discovery. From the time of the Babylonians, when measurements of length were first used in earth work, to modern times, when man has desired to measure interatomic distances and intergalactal space, the limits of his knowledge have been generally the limits of his ability to make accurate measurements.

In the words of the famous scientist, Lord Kelvin, ". . . . when you cannot express it in numbers, your knowledge is of a meager and unsatisfactory kind."

When measurements are made and data are being secured, it is necessary to understand how accuracy is affected when various measuring devices are used and to know how measured quantities can be used in computations. It is also necessary to understand that every measurement will disturb to some degree the state or process on which the measurement is being made.

### Measured Quantities

"Measured quantities" are not the same as "counted quantities." We can get an exact count of the number of pennies in a sack, and this always should be the same number each time the pennies are counted, regardless of who counts them. This is an example of a counted quantity. However, if the sack of pennies is weighed several times by different persons, using different scales, it is unlikely that each of the measured weights would be exactly the same. This is an example of a measured quantity. The true value of any measured quantity is seldom known.

Measurements generally imply that a quantity is compared with a standard value of some sort. Most countries maintain standards of length, mass or weight, and time to which secondary standards periodically are compared. In addition, legal definitions of such quantities as temperature, electric current, and land area are made for use in industry and trade.

For measurements of length or weight (mass), direct comparison with a standard is a common method of determination. Frequently, however, other measurements are made through indirect comparison with a standard. A thermometer, for example, permits a measurement of temperature by converting a volumetric thermal expansion of a fluid into a lineal dimension change. In a similar manner, a spring balance, a pressure gage, or a voltmeter give indications that indirectly are measurements of basic quantities. In many cases complex but much faster indirect methods have supplanted cumbersome direct methods of measurement.

### Measuring Devices

Instruments of various types are employed to enable an engineer or technician to make measurements of physical quantities. Regardless of the type of device used, consideration must be given to the limitations of the instruments and to the factors that enter into the precision of measurements.

Some of the factors in instrument use that affect the accuracy of measurement are (a) readability, (b) sensitivity, (c) lag and hysteresis, (d) environmental effects, (e) calibration errors, and (f) effect of the measurement on the quantity being measured.

**Readability.** Since many instruments are analog devices, a pointer or cursor serves to indicate the location on a scale at which a reading is to be made. Readability is affected by such things as scale size, shape or length, color and contrast, parallax or position errors, and spacing of graduations. For instance, the physical arrangement of the scale has a considerable effect on the ability of an observer to make accurate readings. Tests have shown that a digital readout can be read without mistakes about 99 per cent of the time but that a vertical scale and pointer arrangement may be read without mistakes only about 70 per cent of the time.

**Sensitivity.** The sensitivity of an instrument is determined principally by its physical configuration. For instance, an electrical voltmeter may have a sensitivity of 0.5 volt, which means that the smallest change in applied voltage that can be detected is 0.5 volt. Usually it is desirable to have the size of the smallest subdivision, or least count, about the same as the change in the input that will give a readable movement.

**Lag and Hysteresis.** There are inherent errors in readout devices due to mechanical, electrical, magnetic, elastic, or thermal effects. The inability of a readout device to return to the same place when approached from two different directions is called hysteresis. It is caused many times by friction, but it can be caused by any delaying action. Closely allied with hysteresis is lag, which is a slowing of the indicator as it nears its rest position. The effects of lag and hysteresis in general is to produce a zone of uncertainty of reading around, for example, the rest position of a pointer on a scale. When hysteresis and lag effects are noticeable, it frequently is desirable to take the average of several readings to obtain an idea of the deviation and to use the mean value of the readings rather than a single reading value.

**Environmental Effects.** Many types of measuring devices are affected by changes in the environment in which the instrumentation is located. The principal effects are produced by changes in temperature, pressure, humidity, vibration, and position. For example, in using electrical measuring devices, temperature effects must be taken into account, since temperature usually strongly affects circuit resistance and the behavior of electronic devices. In other cases, vibration may distort the reading pattern of pointer type instruments. Usually ambient environmental effects can be evaluated by varying the conditions surrounding an instrument while maintaining constant input signals.

**Calibration Errors.** An instrument, such as a pointer type of meter, frequently will need corrections applied to the readings at various scale locations. These corrections may be necessary because of nonlinearity of the movement or nonlinearity of the scale divisions, because of environmental conditions changing the instrument response, or because of aging effects changing the basic response of the device. A calibration of an instrument may show the correction to be applied to any given reading to give a value in accord with an accepted standard, or it may show that the difference between the instrument readings and standard values falls within specified limits.

Standards are maintained, usually in laboratories, to be used in the calibrations of instruments. These standards ordinarily have their calibrations traceable to National Bureau of Standards measuring devices. Usually periodic recalibration of standards is scheduled in a manner similar to scheduling periodic recalibration of working instruments.

**Loading Errors.** Measurement is the transfer of information about a state or process, with accompanying energy transfer. If energy is drawn from the process being observed, the process has been altered. The measurement will have influenced the process and this influence may be more or less severe depending on the selection of the instrument.

### Measurement of Length

The process of measuring lengths, areas, volumes, and angles is called *Mensuration*. A number of devices are available for making these measurements, ranging in accuracy from conventional wooden scales to light interference devices that have accuracies of a few wavelengths of light.

Some of the frequently used devices to measure length or "changes in length" (listed in order of increasing precision) are graduated scales, vernier calipers, dial indicators, measuring microscopes, strain gages, gage blocks, and interferometers.

The usual standard of length found in laboratories and gage rooms is the gage block. These steel blocks have two very smooth parallel surfaces whose dimensions are known accurately. A reasonable value of the precision for gage blocks is that the error or uncertainty in length is in the order of 5 millionths of an inch. The surfaces are so smooth and flat that when two blocks are placed together by a process called "wringing," they will stick together by molecular attraction.

### Measurement of Mass or Weight

Standards of weight have been used for thousands of years and usually have consisted of a standard size object to which the weight of other objects is compared. The difference between mass and weight is discussed on page 205 in Chapter 11.

Two common methods are employed to determine weight. As mentioned above, comparison with a standard, using a beam balance for the measurement permits the measurement of mass, and indirectly weight. Another frequently employed method involves the elastic deformation of a body due to a weight. A spring scale is an example of this type of system in which a pointer moves over a graduated scale. The pointer position indicates the force of attraction between an object being weighed and the earth. This force of attraction is called the weight of the object.

In laboratories standard masses are maintained with which other masses are compared in conducting calibration tests.

### Measurement of Time

Since the time of the Babylonians, from whom we have inherited our "units of 60" system of time measurement, time has been reckoned principally from movements of heavenly bodies. The length of the day, the phases of the moon, and the occurrence of solstices have provided our basic time units for centuries. It is only within comparatively recent times that the engineer has recognized a need for more precise time standards.

Our basic time unit in most laboratory work is the second. It is usually reckoned from the apparent movements of stars or of the sun. Since these apparent movements have some irregularity, several proposals for other time standards have been made based on the frequency of vibration of molecules under standard pressure and temperature conditions.

Since most direct measurements of time are somewhat cumbersome, many indirect methods have been developed. Some of the more common methods involve using escapement drives powered by torsion springs, weights, or electrical solenoids.

### Measurement of Electrical Quantities

Two general methods of measuring quantities in electrical circuits are in use. One method involves direct measurement by deflection of an indicating instrument's pointer. The ordinary voltmeter or ammeter is an example of this sort of device. The other method is a "null" method and involves balancing electrical parameters, one against another, until an indicating device shows no deflection. The first method might be compared to mechanically weighing an object on a spring scale, and the second method to balancing one mass against another in a beam balance.

Portable indicating meters used to measure current or voltage usually have errors of 5 per cent or less. Laboratory meters having mirrors behind the pointers to reduce parallax errors usually have errors of 1 per cent or less. In fact, in making many mechanical measurements, an electrical analog device is employed because the basic error of the system can be made smaller.

Null balance methods of measurements usually involve comparisons with standard values. A Wheatstone bridge network is an example of an unknown resistance being compared in its electrical behavior with a known resistance. Impedance bridges permit the measurements of inductances and capacitances by comparison with standard values.

### Measurements of Mechanical Quantities

Measurements of mechanical quantities such as power, pressure, speed, flow, acceleration, or angle, in general, use the basic concepts of measurements of mass, length, and time. Although the discussion of measurements of each of these parameters is beyond the scope of this book, it may be pointed out that in many cases analog methods of measurement of these quantities is a much faster process than the direct measure of the quantity.

As an example, in measuring the flow of fuel to a rocket engine, a direct measurement of flow would involve a scale to measure mass, a timing device to measure time, and perhaps a force sensing transducer to measure pressure. In practice, a common flow measuring system employing analog methods uses a windmill type of vane, which rotates in the fuel-carrying pipe, at a rate proportional to the volume of flow. A magnetic sensing element detects the passage of each vane as the windmill-like assembly rotates and converts this signal to a pulsating electrical voltage. At the same time, a thermocouple senses the fuel temperature. The voltage pulses and the thermocouple signals are transmitted to a computer circuit that converts the input information into a readout in terms of pounds per second of fuel flow.

### Use of Measurements

A large part of engineering work involves measurements. They may be used in planning, in designing, in testing, or in certifying engineering work. Although the actual measurements may be made by technicians or subprofessionals, their planning and direction is the responsibility of the professional engineer whose understanding of the basic principles involved is a guide for the work.

### Scientific Presentation of Measured Data

Since measured data inherently are not exact, it is necessary that methods of manipulating data be examined so that information derived therefrom can be evaluated properly. It should be obvious that the diameter of a saucepan and the diameter of a diesel engine piston, although each may measure about six inches, usually will be measured with different accuracies. Also a measurement of the area of a large ranch which is valued at $50 per acre would not be made as accurately as a measurement of a piece of commercial property that is valued at $1000 per square foot. In order to describe the accuracy of a single measurement, it can be given in terms of a set of significant figures.

### Significant Figures

A significant figure in a number can be defined as a figure that may be considered reliable as a result of measurements or of mathematical computations. In making measurements, it is customary to read and record all figures from the

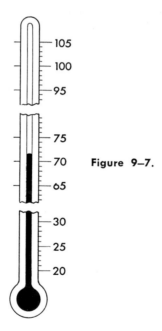

Figure 9–7.

graduations on the measuring device and to include one estimated figure which is a fractional part of the smallest graduation. Any instrument can be assumed to be accurate *only* to one-half of the smallest scale division that has been marked by the manufacturer. All figures read are considered to be significant figures. For example, if we examine the sketch of the thermometer in Figure 9–7, we see that the mercury column, represented in the sketch by a vertical line, lies between 71° and 72°. Since the smallest graduation is 1°, we should record 71° and include an estimated 0.5°. The reading would then be recorded as 71.5° and would contain three significant figures.

As another example, suppose that it is necessary to record the voltmeter reading

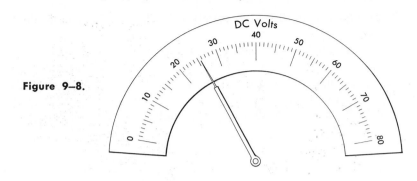

Figure 9–8.

shown in Figure 9–8. The needle obviously rests between the graduations of 20 and 30 volts. A closer inspection shows that its location can be more closely determined as being between 25 and 26 volts. However, this is the extent of the aid which we can get from the individual graduations. Any further refinement must be accomplished by eye.[1] Since the scale of the voltmeter is calibrated to the nearest volt, we can estimate the reading to the nearest half volt—in this case 25.5 volts. An attempt to obtain a more precise reading (such as 25.6 or 25.7) would result only in false accuracy, as discussed below.

The designated digits, together with one doubtful digit, are said to be "significant figures." In reading values previously recorded, assume that only one doubtful digit has been recorded. This usually will be the last digit retained in any recorded measurement.

### False Accuracy

In analysis of engineering problems one must prevent false accuracy from appearing in the calculations. False accuracy occurs when data are manipulated without regard to their degree of precision. For example, it may be desirable to find the sum of three lengths, each having been measured with a different type of instrument. These lengths might have been recorded in tabular form (rows and columns) as:

|  |  | *Columns* |  |
|---|---|---|---|
|  |  | a b c d  e f g |  |
| First Measurement: | Row A . . . . . . . . . . | 1 5 7.3 9 | ±0.02 ft |
| Second Measurement: | Row B . . . . . . . . . . | 1 8.0 2 5 | ±0.001 ft |
| Third Measurement: | Row C . . . . . . . . . . | 8 5 3. | ±2 ft |
|  |  | 1 0 2 8.4 1 5 | (By regular addition) |

Although the sum of the columns would be 1028.415, it would not be proper to use this value in other calculations. Since the last measurement (Row C) could vary from 851 to 855 (maximum variation in Column d), it would be trivial to include the decimal numbers in Rows A and B in the sum. The final answer should

---

[1] In most cases, estimation by eye (beyond the precision obtainable from the graduations) is acceptable. It should be recognized that this final subdivision (by eye) will give doubtful results.

be expressed as $1028 \pm 2$, or merely 1028. In this case the last digit (8) is of doubtful accuracy.

In the tabulation of data (readings from meters, dials, gauges, verniers, scales, etc.), only one doubtful digit may be retained for any measurement. In the preceding example, the doubtful digits are 9 (Row A), 5 (Row B), and 3 (Row C). The example also shows that when numbers are added, the sum should not be written to more digits than the digit under the first column which has a doubtful number.

### Scientific Notation

The decimal point has nothing to do with how many significant figures there are in a number, and therefore it is impossible to tell the number of significant figures if written as 176,000., 96000., or 1000. This doubt can be removed by the following procedure:

1. Move the decimal point to the left or right until a number between 1 and 10 remains. The number resulting from this process should contain *only* significant figures.

2. This remaining number must now be multiplied by a power of ten, $(10)^{\text{number of decimal moves}}$. If the decimal is moved to the left, the power of 10 is positive.

*Example:*   Express the number 1756000 to five significant figures:

$1_x$ 7 5 6 0 0 0 .   (Move the decimal point to the left to get a number be-
        6  5  4  3  2  1         tween 1 and 10.)

ANSWER:   $(1.7560)(10)^6$   (The power of 10 is the number of decimal moves.)

NOTE:   Only the five significant figures remain to be multiplied by the power of 10.

*Example:*   Express the number 0.016900 to three significant figures:

0 . 0 $1_x$ 6 9   (Move the decimal point to the right to get a number between
        1   2         1 and 10.)

ANSWER:   $(1.69)(10)^{-2}$   (The power of 10 is the number of decimal moves and is negative in sign.)

NOTE:   The three significant figures remain to be multiplied by the power of 10.

*Examples of Significant Figures:*

| | |
|---|---|
| 385.1 | 4 significant figures |
| 38.51 | 4 significant figures |
| 0.03851 | 4 significant figures |
| $3.851 \times 10^7$ | 4 significant figures |

| | |
|---|---|
| $7.04 \times 10^{-4}$ | 3 significant figures |
| 25.5 | 3 significant figures |
| 0.051 | 2 significant figures |
| 0.00005 | 1 significant figure |
| 27,855 | 5 significant figures |
| $8.91 \times 10^4$ | 3 significant figures |
| 2200 | May have 2, 3, or 4 significant figures depending on the accuracy of the measurement that obtained the number. Where such doubt may exist, it is better to write the number as $2.2 \times 10^3$ to show 2 significant figures; or as $2.20 \times 10^3$ to show 3 significant figures. |
| 55 | 2 significant figures |
| 55.0 | 3 significant figures. The zero is significant in this case, since it is not otherwise needed to show proper location of the decimal point. |

In engineering computations it is necessary to use standard computed constants, such as $\pi$ (3.14159265 . . .) and $\epsilon$ (2.71828 . . .). It is feasible to simplify these values to fewer significant figures, since most calculations will be done on the slide rule where five, six, and seven significant figures are impossible to read. Usually three or four significant figures are sufficient, but this may vary somewhat with the nature of the problem. Since we do not need a large number of significant figures, let us examine some rules concerning "rounding off" the excess figures which need not be used in a given calculation.

### Retention of Significant Figures

1. In recording measured data, only one doubtful digit is retained, and it is considered to be a significant figure.

2. In dropping figures which are not significant, the last figure retained should be increased by 1 if the first figure dropped is 5 or greater.

3. In addition and subtraction, do not carry the result beyond the first column which contains a doubtful figure.

4. In multiplication and division, carry the result to the same number of significant figures that there are in the quantity entering into the calculation which has the least number of significant figures.

**9–1.** Determine the proper value of $X$ for each problem.

a. $0.785 = 7.85(10^x)$

b. $0.005066 = 5.066(10^x)$

c. $6.45 = 64.5(10^x)$

d. $10.764 = 10764(10^x)$

e. $1973 = 0.01973(10^x)$

f. $0.3937 = 3937000(10^x)$

g. $30.48 = 0.03048(10^x)$

h. $2.54 = 254(10^x)$

i. $1000 = 10(10^x)$

j. $0.001 = 1(10^x)$

k. $44.2 = 0.442(10^x)$

l. $0.737 = 73.7(10^x)$

m. $1.093 = 10930(10^x)$

n. $4961 = 0.4961(10^x)$

o. $1.02 = 0.000102(10^x)$

p. $0.0914(10^{-3}) = 9.14(10^x)$

q. $745.6(10^4) = 7,456,000(10^x)$

r. $7.78(10^0) = 778(10^x)$

s. $14,800,000(10^{-2}) = 14.8(10^x)$

t. $23,700,000(10^6) = 23.7(10^x)$

Preparation for Problem Solving

## Addition of Laboratory Data

**9–2.** Add and then express the answer to the proper number of significant figures.

| | | | | | | | |
|---|---|---|---|---|---|---|---|
| *a.* | 11.565 | *d.* | 757.1 | *g.* | 6282.6 | *j.* | 17.306 |
| | 4.900 | | 54.540 | | 545.81 | | 1.6535 |
| | 226.55 | | 11.5 | | 122.55 | | 0.0762 |
| | 82.824 | | 1.0375 | | 334.75 | | 653.22 |
| | 17.668 | | 378.64 | | 98.88 | | 29.969 |
| | 108.77 | | 4372.1 | | 28.77 | | 0.02202 |
| | | | | | 1.059 | | |

| | | | | | | | |
|---|---|---|---|---|---|---|---|
| *b.* | 858.7 | *e.* | 16.59 | *h.* | 38.808 | *k.* | 61.309 |
| | 404.3 | | 0.0531 | | 11.955 | | 1.9792 |
| | 54.42 | | 11.72 | | 35.306 | | 0.005531 |
| | 19.8 | | 285.5 | | 67.332 | | 122.88 |
| | 8.775 | | 4.41 | | 105.65 | | 52.8 |
| | 12.04 | | 0.0748 | | 575.75 | | 37.075 |

| | | | | | | | |
|---|---|---|---|---|---|---|---|
| *c.* | 1.39395 | *f.* | 0.32 | *i.* | 0.005754 | *l.* | 1.0585 |
| | 8.7755 | | 6171.0 | | 0.006434 | | 18.08 |
| | 10.6050 | | 255.5 | | 0.018466 | | 675.5 |
| | 49.201 | | 80.60 | | 0.085405 | | 70.08 |
| | 88.870 | | 715.55 | | 0.131876 | | 111.0 |
| | 108.887 | | 3707. | | 0.97574 | | 828. |

## Subtraction of Laboratory Data

**9–3.** Subtract and then express the answer to the proper number of significant figures.

| | | | | | |
|---|---|---|---|---|---|
| *a.* | 6508. | *f.* | 10276. | *k.* | −933.0 |
| | 3379. | | 61581. | | 77.12 |
| *b.* | 8.104 | *g.* | 118.72 | *l.* | −156.2 |
| | 7.891 | | 366. | | 0.0663 |
| *c.* | 0.04642 | *h.* | 0.016 | *m.* | −610.01 |
| | 0.0199 | | 0.1513 | | −355.66 |
| *d.* | 731.16 | *i.* | 766. | *n.* | −1.9767 |
| | 189.28 | | −516.16 | | −113.54 |
| *e.* | 7.114 | *j.* | 0.8280 | | |
| | 16.075 | | −0.023 | | |

### Multiplication of Laboratory Data

**9–4.** Multiply and then express the answer to the proper number of significant figures.

| | | | |
|---|---|---|---|
| *a.* 5167.<br>238. | *e.* 1.03975<br>54682. | *i.* 15903.<br>0.00469 | *m.* 17.66<br>0.0307 |
| *b.* 32105.<br>5.28 | *f.* 0.0548<br>0.00376 | *j.* −9757<br>0.05478 | *n.* 558.0<br>80.08 |
| *c.* 535.58<br>0.2759 | *g.* 14.7410<br>0.7868 | *k.* 7.5427<br>−542.16 | *o.* 141.8<br>0.37 |
| *d.* 84.636<br>30869. | *h.* 47.738<br>0.065 | *l.* −0.0989<br>−11.6507 | *p.* 0.0051<br>1.06 |

### Division of Laboratory Data

**9–5.** Divide and then express the answer to the proper number of significant figures:

| | | |
|---|---|---|
| *a.* $\dfrac{3928.}{5636.}$ | *g.* $\dfrac{73.65}{127.1}$ | *m.* $\dfrac{3.58}{100}$ |
| *b.* $\dfrac{216.75}{53.83}$ | *h.* $\dfrac{4.91}{1598.}$ | *n.* $\dfrac{13.550}{120}$ |
| *c.* $\dfrac{7.549}{3.069}$ | *i.* $\dfrac{0.2816}{5383.}$ | *o.* $\dfrac{4.001}{2.5}$ |
| *d.* $\dfrac{539.77}{1.6303}$ | *j.* $\dfrac{-0.005295}{1728.}$ | *p.* $\dfrac{0.0507}{350.1}$ |
| *e.* $\dfrac{0.5322}{0.343}$ | *k.* $\dfrac{0.07737}{-0.1293}$ | *q.* $\dfrac{1.8}{0.006075}$ |
| *f.* $\dfrac{8831.}{128.75}$ | *l.* $\dfrac{-0.3343}{-52.1}$ | |

### Calculation of Error

The word "error" is used in engineering work to express the uncertainty in a measured quantity. When used with a measurement, it shows the probable reliability of the quantity involved. *Error,* as used here, does not mean the same as the word "mistake," and care should be exercised to call operations or results which are mathematically incorrect "mistakes" and not "errors."

Errors are inherent in making any measurement and as such cannot be eradicated by any practical means. Errors can be made smaller by care in making measurements, by employing more precise measuring instruments, and by performing repeated measurements to afford statistical accuracy. Statistical accuracy defines a region in which the true value probably will fall.

Since the reliability of engineering data is of extreme importance, familiarity with methods of computing probable error is essential. As the student has more opportunity to collect his own data, the need for means of expressing the reliability or uncertainty involved in measured quantities will become even more apparent. Although a detailed study of theory of errors is beyond the scope of this book, a general discussion of some of the basic computations of errors is desirable.

### Measurement and Error

Experimentation in the laboratory is necessary to verify the engineer's design analysis and to predict results in processes of manufacture. For certain tests the laboratory technician will attempt to secure data to prove the analytical results as predicted by the engineer. At other times, emphasis will be directed to routine testing of items for acceptance. In any case, the results obtained in the laboratory will only approximate the true values, and the data tabulated will not be exact. Rather, every measurement taken and every gage reading or scale deflection noted will reflect the accuracy with which the individual measuring instruments were designed and manufactured—as well as the human errors that may have appeared in the readings.

For example, it is convenient and many times expedient to estimate distances by eye when under other circumstances an unknown distance could be more accurately measured by using a surveyor's tape or perhaps a graduated scale. In a similar manner we may lift a given object and, from experience, estimate its weight. A more accurate procedure would be to weigh it on some type of balance. In general, the more precise the measuring device, the more accurate the measurement obtained.

As we know from practical experience, length, weight, or time can be measured to various degrees of precision, depending upon the accuracy that has been designed into the measuring instrument being used. The engineer must therefore have some method whereby he can evaluate the degree of accuracy obtained in any given measurement. Where a numerical error of plus or minus ($\pm$) 1 in. would not ordinarily make too much difference in a measured distance of 100 miles, the same numerical error (of 1 in.) would cause considerable concern if it occurred in a measured distance of 2 in. For this reason the engineer will frequently express the maximum error present in a measurement as "per cent error" instead of "numerical error."

By "per cent error" is meant how many parts out of each 100 parts that a number is in error. For example, if a yardstick is too long by 0.02 yd, the numerical error is 0.02 yd, the relative error is 0.02 yd in 1.00 yd, and the "per cent error" is therefore 2 per cent. In other words:

$$\text{per cent error} = \frac{(\text{numerical error})(100 \text{ per cent})}{(\text{measured value})}$$

$$\text{per cent error} = \frac{(1.02 - 1.00)(100 \text{ per cent})}{(1.00)} = 2 \text{ per cent}$$

In any measured quantity, the true value is never known. The measured value is usually expressed to the number of digits corresponding to the precision of measurement followed by a number showing the maximum probable error of the measurement. For example, if we measure the length of a desk to be 5.712 ft and we have estimated the last digit, 2, because of our inability to read our measuring device closely, we would need to know what the probable variation in this last digit could be. Assuming that we can estimate to the nearest 0.001 ft, we could show this measurement with its error as

$$5.712 \pm 0.001 \text{ ft}$$

In order to compute the per cent error of our measurement, we proceed as follows:

$$\text{per cent error} = \frac{\text{numerical error} \times 100 \text{ per cent}}{\text{measured value}}$$

$$\text{per cent error} = \frac{0.001 \times 100 \text{ per cent}}{5.712}$$

$$= 0.02 \text{ per cent}$$

The error in measurement could be less than 0.02 per cent, but this shows the maximum probable error in the measurement.

As another example, a measurement can be shown as a number, and a per cent error as

$$7.64 \text{ lb} \pm 0.2 \text{ per cent}$$

To express this measurement as a number and a numerical error, the procedure is as follows:

$$\text{numerical error} = (\text{measured value}) \frac{(\text{per cent error})}{100 \text{ per cent}}$$

$$\text{numerical error} = (7.64) \frac{(0.2 \text{ per cent})}{100 \text{ per cent}}$$

$$\text{numerical error} = 0.02 \text{ lb}$$

Expressing the measurement as a number,

$$7.64 \pm 0.02 \text{ lb}$$

*Problems*

(Note that the proper number of significant figures may not be given in the reading.)

**9–6.** Compute the Per Cent Error:

    *a.* Reading of $9.306 \mp 0.003$

    *b.* Reading of $19165 \pm 2.$

    *c.* Reading of $756.3 \pm 0.7$

    *d.* Reading of $2.596 \pm 0.006$

    *e.* Reading of $13.750 \pm 0.009$

    *f.* Reading of $0.0036 \pm 0.0006$

    *g.* Reading of $0.7515 \pm 0.02$

    *h.* Reading of $12,835 \pm 20$

    *i.* Reading of $382.5 \pm 5$

    *j.* Reading of $0.03 \pm 0.03$

**9–7.** Compute the Numerical Error:
   a. Reading of 35.219 ± 0.03 per cent
   b. Reading of 651.79 ± 0.01 per cent
   c. Reading of 11.391 ± 0.05 per cent
   d. Reading of 0.00365 ± 2 per cent
   e. Reading of 0.03917 ± 0.6 per cent
   f. Reading of 152 ± 4.0 per cent
   g. Reading of 0.0575 ± 10 per cent
   h. Reading of $7.65(10^7)$ ± 7 per cent
   i. Reading of $3.080(10^{-4})$ ± 2.5 per cent
   j. Reading of $32.5(10^{-2})$ ± 30 per cent

**9–8.** A surveyor measures a property line and records it as being 3207.7 ft long. The distance is probably correct to the nearest 0.3 ft. What is the per cent error in the distance?

**9–9.** The thickness of a spur gear is specified as 0.875 in, with an allowable variation of 0.3 per cent. Several gears that have been received in an inspection room are gaged, and the thickness measurements are as follows: 0.877, 0.881, 0.874, 0.871, 0.880. Which ones should be rejected as not meeting dimensional specifications?

**9–10.** A rectangular aluminum pattern is laid out using a steel scale which is thought to be exactly 3 ft long. The pattern was laid out to be 7.42 ft by 1.88 ft, but it was subsequently found that the scale was incorrect and was actually 3.02 ft long. What were the actual pattern dimensions and by what per cent were they in error?

**9–11.** A resident of a city feels that his bill for water is considerably too high, probably because of a defective water meter. He proposes to check the meter on a do-it-yourself basis by using a gallon milk bottle to measure a volume of water. He believes that the volume of the bottle is substantially correct and that the error of filling should not exceed plus or minus two tablespoons.

   a. What would be the probable maximum error in gallons per 1000 gal of water using this measurement?
   b. Using the milk bottle, he draws ten full bottles of water and observes that the meter indicates a usage of 1.345 ft³ of water. If the average rate for water is $1.05 per 1000 ft³, by how much could his water bill be too high?

# PART FOUR

## ENGINEERING TOOLS
## OF ANALYSIS

The slide rule is a useful instrument at all levels of engineering. (Courtesy Eastman Kodak.)

# Chapter 10

## The Slide Rule

129 - 154

The slide rule is not a modern invention although its extensive use in business and industry has been common only in recent years. Since the slide rule is a mechanical device whereby the logarithms of numbers may be manipulated, the slide rule of today was made possible over three and a half centuries ago with the invention of logarithms by John Napier, Baron of Merchiston in Scotland. Although Napier did not publicly announce his system of logarithms until 1614, he had privately communicated a summary of his results to Tycho Brahe, a Danish astronomer in 1594. Napier set forth his purpose with these words:

> Seeing there is nothing (right well beloved Students of Mathematics) that is so troublesome to mathematical practice, nor doth more molest and hinder calculators, than the multiplications, divisions, square and cubical extractions of great numbers, which besides the tedious expense of time are for the most part subject to many slippery errors, I began therefore to consider in my mind by what certain and ready art I might remove those hindrances.

In 1620 Edmund Gunter, Professor of Astronomy at Gresham College, in London, conceived the idea of using logarithm scales that were constructed with antilogarithm markings for use in simple mathematical operations. William Oughtred, who lived near London, first used "Gunter's logarithm scales" in 1630 in sliding combination, thereby creating the first slide rule. Later he also placed the logarithm scales in circular form for use as a "circular slide rule."

Sir Isaac Newton, John Warner, John Robertson, Peter Roget, and Lieutenant Amédée Mannheim further developed these logarithmic scales until there exist today many types and shapes of rules. Basically all rules of modern manufacture are variations of a general type of construction that utilizes sliding scales and a movable indicator. The principles of operation are the same and they are not difficult to master.

## DESCRIPTION OF THE SLIDE RULE

The slide rule consists of three main parts, the "body," the "slide," and the "indicator" (see Figure 10–1). The "body" of the rule is fixed; the "slide" is the middle sliding portion; and the "indicator," which may slide right or left on the body of the rule, is the transparent runner. A finely etched line on each side of the indicator is used to improve the accuracy in making settings and for locating the answer. This line is referred to as the "hairline."

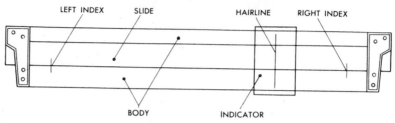

**Figure 10–1.**

The mark opposite the primary number 1 on the C and D scale is referred to as the "index" of the scale. An examination of the C and D scales indicates that each scale has two indexes: one at the left end (called the "left index") and one at the right end (called the "right index").

Regardless of the manufacturer or the specific model of slide rule that may be used, the principles of operation are the same. The nomenclature used here is general although some specific references are made to the Deci-Lon (Keuffel & Esser Co.), the Versalog (Frederick Post Co.), the Maniphase Multiplex (Eugene Dietzgen Co.), and the Model 800 ES (Pickett & Eckel, Inc.) rules. These models are those most frequently used by engineers, scientists, and technicians.

## CARE OF THE SLIDE RULE

The slide rule is a precision instrument and should be afforded reasonable care in order to preserve its accuracy. Modern rules stand up well under normal usage, but dropping the rule or striking objects with it will probably impair its accuracy.

In use, the rule may collect dirt under the glass of the indicator. Inserting a piece of paper under the glass and sliding the indicator across it will frequently dislodge the dirt without necessitating the removal of the indicator glass from the frame. If the glass has to be removed for cleaning, it should be realigned when replaced, using the techniques described below.

The rule should never be washed with abrasive materials, alcohol, or other solvents, since these may remove markings. If the rule needs to be cleaned, it may be wiped carefully with a damp cloth, but the excessive use of water should be avoided because it will cause wooden rules to warp.

The metal-frame rules are not subject to warping due to moisture changes, but they must be protected against blows which would bend them or otherwise throw them out of alignment. A light layer of lubricant of the type specified by the manufacturer of the metal rule will increase the ease with which the working parts move. This is particularly important during the "breaking in" period of the new rule.

## MANIPULATION OF THE RULE

Some techniques in manipulation of the rule have been found to speed up the setting of the slide and indicator. Two of these suggested procedures are described in the following paragraphs.

1. Settings usually can be made more rapidly by using two hands and holding the rule so that the thumbs are on the bottom with the backs of the hands toward the operator.

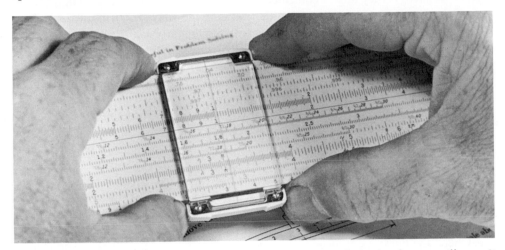

**Illustration 10–1.** In setting the indicator, a rolling motion with the forefingers will permit rapid and precise locations to be made. Keeping the fingers of both hands in contact with the indicator, exert slight forces toward each other with both hands.

2. In moving either the indicator or the slide, the settings are easier to make if the index fingers and thumbs of both hands are used to apply forces toward each other than if only one hand is used to apply force. For example, in setting the indicator, put the forefinger of each hand against the respective edges of the indicator and move it by a combined squeezing and rolling motion of the forefingers. The same general procedure is used in setting the slide, where both hands exert forces toward each other. The student is cautioned in setting the slide not to squeeze the frame of the rule, since this will cause the slide to bind.

**Illustration 10–2.** In moving the slide, use fingers to exert forces toward each other. A rolling motion with the forefinger aids in setting the indexes. Avoid pinching the frame because this will make the slide bind.

## ADJUSTING THE RULE

Regardless of the make, most rules have the same general form of adjustment. The method of adjustment is simple but should not be applied in a hurry. It is desirable to use a magnifying glass, if one if available, to aid in lining up the scales and hairline.

To determine whether or not a rule needs adjustment, line up the indexes of the C and D scales. The indexes of the scales above and below the C and D scales should also be aligned. If they do not coincide, slightly loosen the screws that clamp the top bar of the frame and carefully move the frame to the right or left until the indexes are aligned. Tighten the screws slightly and move the slide to check for proper friction. If the alignment and friction are satisfactory, tighten the frame screws to complete that part of the adjustment.

Next, test the hairline for proper alignment by setting the hairline over the indexes of the C and D scales and checking to see that the hairline also coincides with the other indexes on this side of the rule. If it does not coincide with all the scale indexes, slightly loosen the screws which hold the glass frame to the indicator. Rotate the frame slowly until the hairline coincides with the indexes on this side of the rule. Tighten the screws holding this frame; then, while the hairline is aligned on the indexes of the C and D scales, turn the rule over and check for the alignment of the hairline with the indexes of the scales on the other side of the rule. If the hairline does not coincide with the indexes on this side of the rule, loosen the screws on the indicator and make the necessary adjustment as before.

Check the tightness of all screws when the adjustment is completed. The student is cautioned not to use excessive force in tightening any screws, as the threads may become stripped. With reasonable care, a slide rule will usually require very little adjustment over a considerable period of time.

## ACCURACY OF THE RULE

Most measurements made in scientific work contain from two to four significant figures; that is, digits which are considered to be reliable. Since the mathematical operations of multiplication, division, and processes involving roots and powers will not increase the number of significant figures when the answer is obtained, the slide rule maintains an accuracy of three or four significant figures. The reliability of the digits obtained from the rule depends upon the precision with which the operator makes his settings. It is generally assumed that with a 10-in. slide rule, the error of the answer will not exceed about a tenth of 1 per cent. This is one part in a thousand.

A common tendency is to use more than three or four significant digits in such numbers as $\pi$ (3.14159265 $\cdots$) and $\epsilon$ (2.71828 $\cdots$). The slide rule automatically "rounds off" such numbers to three or four significant figures thus preventing false accuracy (such as can occur in longhand operations) from occurring in the answer.

In slide rule calculations the answer should be read to four significant figures if the first digit in the answer is 1 (10.62, 1.009, 1195., 1,833,000., etc.). In other cases the answer is usually read to three significant figures (2.95, 872., 54,600., etc.). The chance for error is increased as the number of operations in a problem increases. However, for average length operations, such as those required to solve the problems in this text, the fourth significant digit in the slide rule answer should not vary more than ±2 from the correct answer. Where only three significant digits are read from the rule, the third digit should be within ±2 of the correct answer.

*Example:*

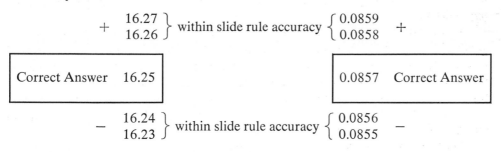

$$+ \begin{array}{l} 16.27 \\ 16.26 \end{array} \Bigg\} \text{ within slide rule accuracy } \begin{cases} 0.0859 \\ 0.0858 \end{cases} +$$

| Correct Answer | 16.25 |

| 0.0857 | Correct Answer |

$$- \begin{array}{l} 16.24 \\ 16.23 \end{array} \Bigg\} \text{ within slide rule accuracy } \begin{cases} 0.0856 \\ 0.0855 \end{cases} -$$

Rules of modern manufacture are designed so that results read from the graduations are as reliable as the naked eye can distinguish. The use of magnifying devices may make the settings easier to locate but usually do not have an appreciable effect on the accuracy of the result.

## INSTRUCTIONS FOR READING SCALE GRADUATIONS

Before studying the scales of the slide rule, let us review the reading of scale graduations in general. First let us examine a common 12-in. ruler (Figure 10–2).

**Figure 10–2.**

12 Inch Ruler

0  1  2  3  4  5  6  7  8  9  10  11  12

*Example:* We see that the total length of 1 ft has been divided into twelve equal parts and that each part is further divided into quarters, eighths, and sixteenths. This subdivision is necessary so that the workman need not estimate fractional parts of an inch.

*Example:* Measure the unknown lengths $L_1$ and $L_2$ as shown in Figure 10–3.

**Figure 10–3.**

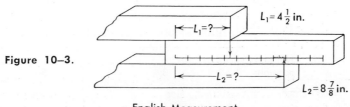

$L_1 = 4\frac{1}{2}$ in.

←$L_1$=?→

←$L_2$=?→

$L_2 = 8\frac{7}{8}$ in.

English Measurement

The English system of measurement as shown in Figure 10–3 is probably familiar to all students. The unit of length in the metric system which corresponds to the yard in the English system is called the *meter*. The meter is 39.37 in. in length.

For convenience, the meter is divided into one hundred equal parts called *centimeters,* and each centimeter is divided into ten equal parts called *millimeters.* Since we can express units and fractional parts of units as tenths or hundredths of the length of a unit, this system of measurement is preferred many times for engineering work.

*Example:*  Measure the unknown lengths $L_1$ and $L_2$ as shown in Figure 10–4.

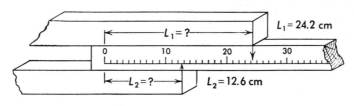

**Metric Measurement**

**Figure 10–4.**

The scales of the slide rule are basically divided as in the metric system in that between each division there are ten subdivisions. However, the student will find that the main divisions are not equal distances apart. Sometimes the divisions will be subdivided by graduations, and at other times the student will need to estimate the subdivisions by eye. Let us examine the D scale of a slide rule (Figure 10–5).

**Figure 10–5.**

Since the graduations are so close together, let us examine the rule in three portions: from left index to 2, from 2 to 4, and from 4 to the right index.

*Example:*  Left index to 2 as shown in Figure 10–6.

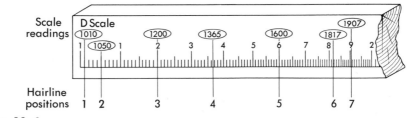

**Figure 10–6.**

The student should refer to his own rule for comparisons as he studies the diagrams in this chapter. In the example using Figure 10–6, we note that from the left index (read as one-zero-zero) to the digit 1 (read as one-one-zero), there are ten graduations. The first is read as *one-zero-one* (101), the second as *one-*

*zero-two* (102), etc. Digit 2 is read as *one-two-zero* (120), digit 3 as *one-three-zero* (130), etc. If need be, the student can subdivide by eye the distance between each of the small, unnumbered graduations. Thus, if the hairline is moved to position 4 (see example above), the reading would be *one-three-six five* or 1365. Position 6 might be read as 1817 and position 7 as 1907. The student is reminded that each small graduation on this portion of the rule has a value of 1.

*Example:*   2 to 4 as shown in Figure 10–7.

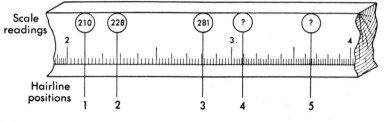

**Figure  10–7.**

Since the distance between 2 and 3 is not as long as the distance from the left index to 2, no numbers are placed over the graduations. However, we can use the same reasoning and subdivide as in the previous examples. Set the hairline in position 1 (see example) and read *two-one-zero,* or 210. We note that the distance between 200 and 210 has been divided into five divisions. Each subdivision would thus have a value of 2. Consequently, if the hairline is in position 2, a reading of 228 would be obtained. Remember that each of the smallest graduations is valued at 2 and not 1. What are the readings at 3, 4, and 5?[1]

*Example:*   4 to the right index as shown in Figure 10–8.

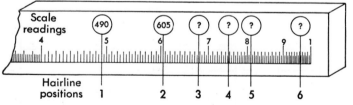

**Figure  10–8.**

The distance between 4 and 5 is still shorter than the distance between 3 and 4, and it becomes increasingly more difficult to print such small subdivisions. For this reason there are ten main divisions between 4 and 5, each of which is subdivided into two parts. With this type of marking it is possible to read two figures and estimate the third, or to get three significant figures on all readings. If the hairline is set as indicated in position 1, the reading would be *four-nine-zero* (490), and position 2 would give *six-zero-five* (605). What are the readings at hairline positions 3, 4, 5, and 6?[2]

[1] Readings at 3, 4, and 5 are respectively 281, 309, and 365.
[2] Readings at 3, 4, 5, and 6 are respectively 678, 746, 810, and 963.

## Problems on Scale Readings

*Read Answer on*

| Set Hairline to | ST Scale | S Scale | LL₃ Scale | CI Scale | K Scale | DF Scale | LL₀₁ Scale | LL₂ Scale | L Scale |
|---|---|---|---|---|---|---|---|---|---|
| 1. 210 on D | | | | | | | | | |
| 2. 398 on D | | | | | | | | | |
| 3. 1056 on D | | | | | | | | | |
| 4. 1004 on D | | | | | | | | | |
| 5. 866 on D | | | | | | | | | |
| 6. 222 on D | | | | | | | | | |
| 7. 1196 on D | | | | | | | | | |
| 8. 439 on D | | | | | | | | | |
| 9. 5775 on D | | | | | | | | | |
| 10. 2325 on D | | | | | | | | | |
| 11. 917 on D | | | | | | | | | |
| 12. 323 on D | | | | | | | | | |
| 13. 1077 on D | | | | | | | | | |
| 14. 1854 on D | | | | | | | | | |
| 15. 268 on D | | | | | | | | | |
| 16. 833 on D | | | | | | | | | |
| 17. 551 on D | | | | | | | | | |
| 18. 667 on D | | | | | | | | | |
| 19. 8125 on D | | | | | | | | | |
| 20. 406 on D | | | | | | | | | |
| 21. 918 on D | | | | | | | | | |
| 22. 5775 on D | | | | | | | | | |
| 23. 1466 on D | | | | | | | | | |
| 24. 288 on D | | | | | | | | | |
| 25. 466 on D | | | | | | | | | |
| 26. 798 on D | | | | | | | | | |
| 27. 1107 on D | | | | | | | | | |
| 28. 396 on D | | | | | | | | | |
| 29. 1999 on D | | | | | | | | | |
| 30. 998 on D | | | | | | | | | |

If the student has followed the reasoning thus far, he should have little trouble in determining how to read an indicated value on any scale of the slide rule. Several of the problems on page 136 should be worked, and the student should thoroughly understand the principle of graduation subdivision before he attempts to delve further into the uses of the slide rule.

It is suggested that one have a good understanding of logarithms before proceeding to learn the operational aspects of the slide rule. Those who may desire to review these principles should refer to Appendix I.

## CONSTRUCTION OF THE SCALES

Let us examine how the main scales (C and D) of the rule are constructed. As a basis for this examination, let us set up a scale of some length with a beginning graduation called a *left index* and an end graduation called a *right index* as in Figure 10–9.

Figure 10–9.

Next let us subdivide this scale into ten equal divisions and then further subdivide each large division into ten smaller divisions as shown in Figure 10–10. We call this the *L scale*.

Figure 10–10.

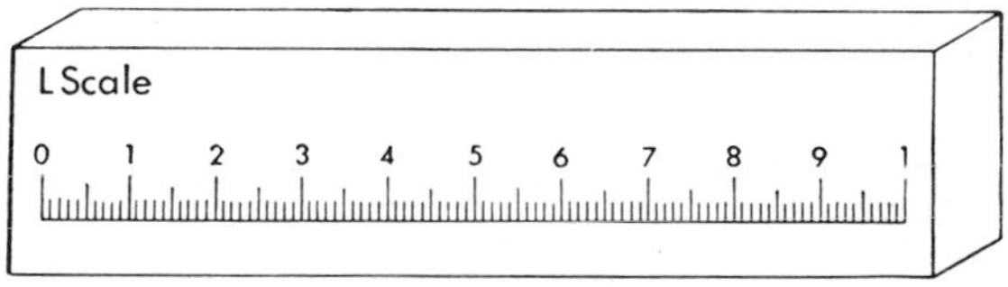

Let us place a blank scale beneath this L scale so that the left index of the L scale will coincide with the left index of the blank scale as shown in Figure 10–11. We shall call the blank scale the *D scale*.

Figure 10–11.

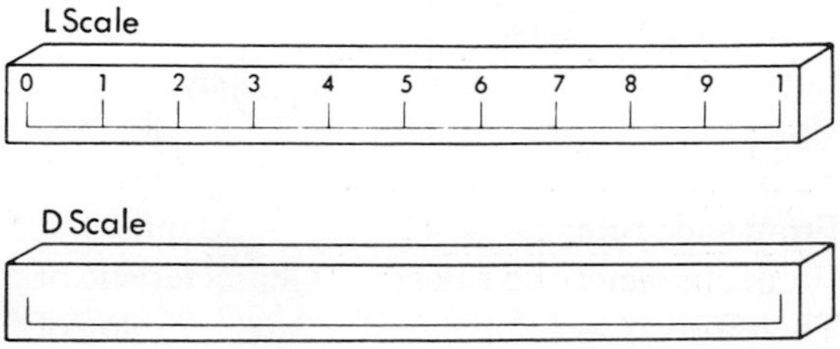

Now let us graduate the D scale in such a way that each division mark is directly beneath the mark on the L scale that represents the mantissa of the logarithm of the number. Before examining the scales closer, we should note that the mantissa of 2 is 0.3010, the mantissa of 3 is 0.4771, the mantissa of 4 is 0.6021, and the mantissa of 5 is 0.6990 as shown in Figure 10–12.

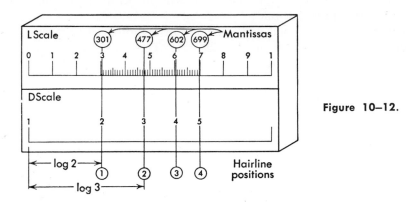

Figure 10–12.

If the student will examine his rule, he will find a C or D scale and an L scale. The C and D scales are identical, so use the D scale since it is printed on the body of the rule. Several problems should be worked, determining the logarithms of numbers by using the slide rule.

Remember to:

1. Set the number on the D scale.
2. Read the mantissa of the number on the L scale.
3. Supply the characteristic, using the *characteristic rules* given in the discussion on logarithms.

*Example:* What is the logarithm of 55.8? Use Figure 10–13.

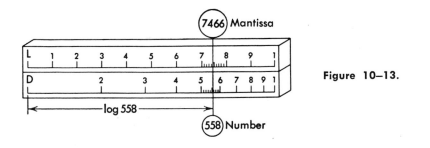

Figure 10–13.

From slide rule:          Mantissa of 55.8 = 0.7466
From characteristic rules:   Characteristic of 55.8 = 1.0000
Therefore                      log of 55.8 = 1.7466

From the preceding example, we can see that the D scale is so constructed that each number lies below the mantissa of its logarithm. Also we note that the distance from the left index of the D scale to any number on the D scale represents (in length) the mantissa of the number as shown in Figure 10–14. Since the characteristic of a logarithm is governed merely by the location of the decimal point, we can delay its determination for the time being.

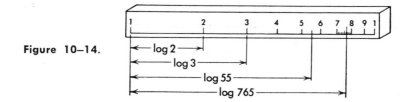

**Figure 10–14.**

## Problems

**10–1.** Use the slide rule and find the logarithms.

| | | |
|---|---|---|
| *a.* 894. | *j.* $5.91 \times 10^7$ | *s.* $33.67 \times 10^{-9}$ |
| *b.* 1.845 | *k.* $9.06 \times 10^{-4}$ | *t.* $4.40 \times 10^3$ |
| *c.* 0.438 | *l.* $66.9 \times 10^8$ | *u.* 98,700 |
| *d.* 81.5 | *m.* $155.8 \times 10^2$ | *v.* $40.3 \times 10^{-9}$ |
| *e.* 604. | *n.* $23.66 \times 10^{-4}$ | *w.* $21.8 \times 10^9$ |
| *f.* 7.41 | *o.* $0.06641 \times 10^8$ | *x.* $1.057 \times 10^{-3}$ |
| *g.* 11.91 | *p.* $9.33 \times 10^{-2}$ | *y.* $719. \times 10^5$ |
| *h.* 215. | *q.* $29.88 \times 10^{-1}$ | *z.* $49.2 \times 10^7$ |
| *i.* 993,000. | *r.* $0.552 \times 10^6$ | |

## MULTIPLICATION

As shown in Figure 10–15, the C and D scales are divided logarithmically with all graduations being marked with their corresponding antilogarithms. These scales can be used for multiplication by adding a given logarithmic length on one of the scales to another logarithmic length which may be found on the other scale.

*Example:*   $(2)(3) = 6$, as shown in Figure 10–15.

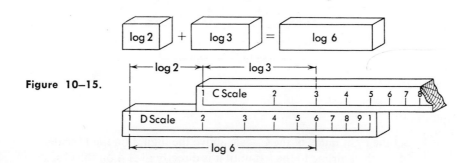

**Figure 10–15.**

PROCEDURE:

1. Set the left index of the C scale above the digit 2 on the D scale.
2. Move the hairline to the right until it is directly over 3 on the C scale.
3. Read the answer (6) directly under the hairline on the D scale.

The A and B scales are also divided logarithmically, but their overall lengths are only one half the lengths of the C and D scales. Therefore, although the A and B scales can also be used for multiplication and division, their shortened lengths will diminish the accuracy of the readings.

Similarly other pairs of scales of the slide rule may be used to perform multiplication if they are graduated logarithmically. A majority of slide rules have at least one set of folded scales that can be used for this purpose. Most frequently they are folded at $\pi$(3.14159 . . .). Special use of these scales will be explained later in this chapter.

In some cases when the logarithm of one number is added to the logarithm of another number, the multiplier extends out into space, and it is impossible to move the indicator to the product (Figure 10–16).

*Example:*    (3)(4) = ?, as shown in Figure 10–16.

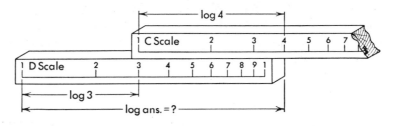

**Figure  10–16.**

In this case it is necessary to relocate the right index of the C scale above the figure 3 on the D scale and move the hairline to 4 on the C scale as shown in Figure 10–17.

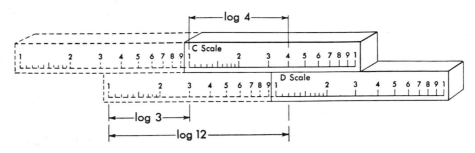

**Figure  10–17.**

PROCEDURE:

    1.  Set the right index of the C scale above the digit 3 on the D scale.
    2.  Move the hairline to the left until it is directly over 4 on the C scale.
    3.  Read answer (12) directly under the hairline on the D scale.

The location of the decimal point in multiplication problems is ascertained either by inspection or by applying one of the several methods explained in the following paragraphs.

## METHODS OF DETERMINING DECIMAL POINT LOCATION

Several methods which may be used are given below. Although these methods by no means include all ways to determine the decimal point location, they will be suitable for instruction of students, particularly those having an elementary mathematical background.

### Inspection Method

This is the simplest method and consists of determining the decimal point location by observing the location of the decimal point in the numbers involved in a slide rule operation and locating the decimal point in the answer by a quick estimation.

*Example:* $\dfrac{(28.1)}{(7.20)} = 390$ (decimal point to be determined)

A quick examination of the numbers involved shows that the answer will be somewhere near the number "4," so the answer evidently will be 3.90. This method will have its widest application where only one or two operations are involved and where the numbers lie between 1 and 100.

*Example:* $(1.22)(58.2) = 70.9$

In the example above, it is seen that the number 58.2 is multiplied by a number which is a little more than 1. Therefore, the answer will be slightly greater than 58.2.

### Approximate Number Method

This method is an extension of the inspection method. It involves the same general procedures except that the numbers used in a problem are "rounded off" and written down and an approximate answer is obtained that will show the decimal point location.

*Example:* $(37.6)(0.188)(5.71)(11.92) = 482$ (decimal point to be located)

Rewrite, using simple numbers that are near in value to the problem numbers.

$$[(40)(0.2)][(6)(10)] = (8)(60) = 480$$

This shows that the answer in the example problem should be expressed as 482.

A problem that is more involved can be solved by this method, as shown by the following example.

*Example:* $\dfrac{(12,560)(0.0387)}{(594,000)} = 819$ (decimal point to be determined)

Using simple numbers near in value to the problem numbers, write the same problem:

$$\frac{(12,000)(0.04)}{(600,000)} = 0.0008$$

By cancellation the numbers can be simplified still further to obtain an approximate answer of 0.0008. One way of doing this would be to divide 12,000 into 600,000, obtaining a value of 50 in the denominator. This value of 50 divided into 0.04 gives 0.0008. Referring to the original problem, the decimal point must be located to give an answer of 0.000819.

### Scientific Notation or Power-of-Ten Method

The power-of-ten or scientific notation method is a variation of the characteristic method discussed later in this book. In this method the numbers in the problem are expressed as a single digit, a decimal point, the remaining digits, and followed by the number "10" that is raised to the appropriate power. This process simplifies the numbers, and the decimal point in the answer can be determined by inspection or by the approximation method. For a review of scientific notation refer to page 120.

*Example:*

$$(15.9)(0.0077)(30500)(4660) = 1741 \text{ (decimal point to be located)}$$

Write the same problem with each number expressed as a digit, decimal point, and the remaining digits followed by the appropriate power of 10.

$$(1.59 \times 10^1)(7.7 \times 10^{-3})(3.05 \times 10^4)(4.66 \times 10^3) = 174.1 \times 10^5$$

Since all the numbers are now expressed as numbers between 1 and 10, followed by 10 to a power, the approximate value of the multiplication can be determined rapidly, by inspection, to be about 170. The power of 10 is obtained by adding algebraically the powers of 10 of each of the rewritten numbers. The answer to the original problem is therefore $174.1 \times 10^5$, or 17,410,000, or $1.741 \times 10^7$.

*Example:* $\dfrac{(28,500)(307)}{(0.552)} = 1585 \text{ (decimal point to be located)}$

Rewrite the problem using powers of 10:

$$\frac{(2.85 \times 10^4)(3.07 \times 10^2)}{(5.52 \times 10^{-1})} = 1.585 \times 10^7$$

By inspection and approximation the product of the numerator will be found to be near 9, and dividing 5.52 into it will give about 1.6. This procedure determines the decimal point location for the digits of the answer. The powers of 10 are added algebraically to give $10^7$, which completes the decimal point location in the answer. The answer may be rewritten as 15,850,000 if desired.

### Digit Method

In this method the numbers of digits in each number are counted and the following rules apply.

**Multiplication.** Add the number of digits to the left of the decimal of each number to be multiplied. This will give the number of digits to the left of the decimal in the answer. If the slide projects to the right, subtract one from the number of digits to be pointed off.

*Example:* $(27,300)(15.1) = 412,000$

There are five digits to be counted in the first number and only two digits in the second number. Since the slide projects to the right, subtract 1. There will be six digits to the left of the decimal point in the answer.

**Division.** Subtract the number of digits to the left of the decimal in the denominator from the number of digits to the left of the decimal in the numerator to obtain the number of digits to the left of the decimal in the answer. If the slide projects to the right in division, add one digit more to be pointed off.

*Example:* $\dfrac{(12.88)}{(466)} = 0.0276$

Subtracting three digits in the denominator from two digits in the numerator gives $(-1)$ digit to be located in the answer. Inspection shows that the answer will be a decimal quantity. In any case where decimal numbers are encountered, the method of counting the digits is to begin at the decimal point and count the number of zeroes between the decimal point and the first digit that is not zero to the right of the decimal. Since the digit difference shown above is $(-1)$, there must be one zero between the decimal point and the first significant figure, which gives an answer of 0.0276. The student will observe that the digit count of decimal numbers is considered as a minus quantity and that the addition and subtraction of the digit count must take into account any minus signs.

Variations and extensions of these methods may readily be set up to solve problems involving roots and powers. Many schools prefer the "characteristic" or "projections method" to determine decimal point location, and this method is given in detail in the discussions which follow.

### Characteristic Method

**Projection Rule for Multiplication.** This method of decimal point location is recommended for students who are inexperienced in slide rule computations:

1. Before attempting to solve the problem, place the characteristic of each quantity above or below it.

2. Solve for the sum of the characteristics by simple addition, and place this number above the space for the answer.

3. Begin the multiplication with the slide rule, and each time the left index of the C scale extends past the left index of the D scale, add a $(+1)$ to the sum of the characteristics previously determined.

4. Add the original sum to the $+1$'s obtained from left extensions. The total number is the characteristic of the answer.

*Example:*

one left extension
↓

CHARACTERISTICS.    $(0) + (0) \rightarrow (0) + 1 = +1 \leftarrow$ characteristic of answer

$(5)\quad(3) = \underline{\underline{15}}\quad$ Answer

---

> ESTIMATION OF ANSWER BY SCIENTIFIC NOTATION:
> $(5)(3) = \underline{\underline{1.5(10)^1}} \leftarrow$ ESTIMATED ANSWER

---

*Example:*

one left extension
↓

CHARACTERISTICS.    $(+2) + (-3) \rightarrow (-1) + 1 = 0$

$(390)\quad(0.0030) = \underline{\underline{1.17}}\quad$ Answer

---

> ESTIMATION OF ANSWER BY SCIENTIFIC NOTATION:
> $(4)(10)^2(3)(10)^{-3} = \underline{\underline{1.2(10)^0}} \leftarrow$ ESTIMATED ANSWER

---

*Example:*

two left
↓ extensions

CHARACTERISTICS.  $(-3) + (+1) + (+2) + (+4) \rightarrow (+4) + 2 = +6$

$(0.001633)\quad(79.1)\quad(144)\quad(96,500) = \underline{\underline{1,800,000}}\quad$ Answer

---

> ESTIMATION OF ANSWER BY SCIENTIFIC NOTATION:
> $(2)(10)^{-3}(8)(10)^1(1)(10)^2(10)^5 = \underline{\underline{1.6(10)^6}} \leftarrow$ ESTIMATED ANSWER

---

*Example:*

three left
↓ extensions

CHARACTERISTICS.

$(+1) + (+3) + (-3) + (-4) \rightarrow (-3) + 3 = 0$

$(73.7)\quad(4460)\quad(0.00704)\quad(0.000853) = \underline{\underline{1.975}}\quad$ Answer

---

> ESTIMATION OF ANSWER BY SCIENTIFIC NOTATION:
> $(7)(10)^1(4)(10)^3(7)(10)^{-3}(9)(10)^{-4} = \underline{\underline{1.8(10)^0}} \leftarrow$ ESTIMATED ANSWER

---

*Example:*

two left extensions
↓

CHARACTERISTICS.    $(+2) + (+2) + (0) \rightarrow (+4) + 1 + 1 = +6$

$(861)\quad(204)\quad(9.0) = 1,580,000$ or $\underline{\underline{(1.58)(10)^6}}\quad$ Answer

---

> ESTIMATION OF ANSWER BY SCIENTIFIC NOTATION:
> $(9)(10)^2(2)(10)^2(9) = \underline{\underline{1.6(10)^6}} \leftarrow$ ESTIMATED ANSWER

### Multiplication Practice Problems

**10–2.** $(23.8)(31.6) = (7.52)(10)^2$
**10–3.** $(105.6)(4.09) = (4.32)(10)^2$
**10–4.** $(286,000)(0.311) = (8.89)(10)^4$
**10–5.** $(0.0886)(196.2) = (1.738)(10)^1$
**10–6.** $(0.769)(47.2) = (3.63)(10)^1$
**10–7.** $(60.7)(17.44) = (1.059)(10)^3$
**10–8.** $(9.16)(115.7) = (1.060)(10)^3$
**10–9.** $(592.)(80.1) = (4.74)(10)^4$
**10–10.** $(7.69 \times 10^3)(0.722 \times 10^{-6}) = (5.55)(10)^{-3}$
**10–11.** $(37.5 \times 10^{-1})(0.0974 \times 10^{-3}) = (3.65)(10)^{-4}$
**10–12.** $(23.9)(0.715)(106.2) = (1.815)(10)^3$
**10–13.** $(60.7)(1059)(237,000) = (1.523)(10)^{10}$
**10–14.** $(988)(8180)(0.206) = (1.665)(10)^6$
**10–15.** $(11.14)(0.0556)(76.3 \times 10^{-6}) = (4.73)(10)^{-5}$
**10–16.** $(72.1)(\pi)(66.1) = (1.497)(10)^4$
**10–17.** $(0.0519)(16.21)(1.085) = (9.13)(10)^{-1}$
**10–18.** $(0.001093)(27.6)(56,700) = (1.710)(10)^3$
**10–19.** $(0.379)(0.00507)(0.414) = (7.96)(10)^{-4}$
**10–20.** $(16.05)(23.9)(0.821) = (3.15)(10)^2$
**10–21.** $(1009)(0.226)(774) = (1.765)(10)^5$
**10–22.** $(316)(825)(67,600) = (1.762)(10)^{10}$
**10–23.** $(21,000)(0.822)(16.92) = (2.92)(10)^5$
**10–24.** $(0.707)(80.6)(0.451) = (2.57)(10)^1$
**10–25.** $(1.555 \times 10^3)(27.9 \times 10^5)(0.902 \times 10^{-7}) = (3.91)(10)^2$
**10–26.** $(0.729)(10)^3(22,500)(33.2) = (5.45)(10)^8$
**10–27.** $(18.97)(0.216)(899)(\pi)(91.2) = (1.055)(10)^6$
**10–28.** $(7160)(0.000333)(26)(19.6)(5.01) = (6.09)(10)^3$
**10–29.** $(1.712)(89,400)(19.5)(10^{-5})(82.1) = (2.45)(10)^3$
**10–30.** $(62.7)(0.537)(0.1137)(0.806)(15.09) = (4.66)(10)^1$
**10–31.** $(10)^6(159.2)(144)(7,920,000)(\pi) = (5.70)(10)^{17}$
**10–32.** $(0.0771)(19.66)(219)(0.993)(7.05) = (2.32)(10)^3$
**10–33.** $(15.06)(\pi)(625)(0.0963)(43.4) = (1.236)(10)^5$
**10–34.** $(2160)(1802)(\pi)(292)(0.0443) = (1.582)(10)^8$
**10–35.** $(437)(1.075)(0.881)(43,300)(17.22) = (3.09)(10)^8$
**10–36.** $(\pi)(91.6)(555)(0.673)(0.00315)(27.7) = (9.38)(10)^3$
**10–37.** $(18.01)(22.3)(1.066)(19.36)(10)^{-5} = (8.29)(10)^{-2}$
**10–38.** $(84.2)(15.62)(921)(0.662)(0.1509) = (1.210)(10)^5$
**10–39.** $(66,000)(25.9)(10.62)(28.4)(77.6) = (4.00)(10)^{10}$
**10–40.** $(55.1)(7.33 \times 10^{-8})(76.3)(10)^5(0.00905) = (2.79)(10)^{-1}$
**10–41.** $(18.91)(0.257)(0.0811)(92,500)(\pi) = (1.145)(10)^5$

### Multiplication Problems

**10–42.** $(46.8)(11.97)$
**10–43.** $(479.)(11.07)$
**10–44.** $(9.35)(77.8)$
**10–45.** $(10.09)(843,000.)$

**10–46.** $(77,900)(0.467)$
**10–47.** $(123.9)(0.00556)$
**10–48.** $(214.9)(66.06)$
**10–49.** $(112.2)(0.953)$

### Multiplication Problems (continued)

**10–50.** $(87.0)(1.006)$
**10–51.** $(1,097,000)(1.984)$
**10–52.** $(43.8)(0.000779)$
**10–53.** $(31.05)(134.9)$
**10–54.** $(117.9)(98.9)$
**10–55.** $(55.6)(68.1)$
**10–56.** $(1.055)(85.3)$
**10–57.** $(33,050.)(16,900.)$
**10–58.** $(6.089)(44.87)$
**10–59.** $(34.8)(89.7)$
**10–60.** $(43,900.)(19.07)$
**10–61.** $(41.3)(87.9)$
**10–62.** $(99.7)(434,000.)$
**10–63.** $(0.0969)(0.1034)(0.1111)(0.1066)$
**10–64.** $(1.084 \times 10^{-5})(0.1758 \times 10^{13})(66.4)(0.901)$
**10–65.** $(234.5)(10)^4(21.21)(0.874)(0.0100)$
**10–66.** $(\pi)(26.88)(0.1682)(0.1463)(45.2)(1.007)$
**10–67.** $(75.8)(0.1044 \times 10^8)(10)^{-2}(54,000)(0.769)$
**10–68.** $(34.5)(31.09)(10)^{-6}(54.7)(0.677)(0.1003)$
**10–69.** $(6.08)(5.77)(46.8)(89.9)(3.02)(0.443)(\pi)$
**10–70.** $(1.055)(6.91)(31.9)(11.21)(\pi)(35.9)(4.09)$
**10–71.** $(10.68)(21.87)$
**10–72.** $(88,900.)(54.7)$
**10–73.** $(113,900.)(48.1)$
**10–74.** $(95,500.)(0.000479)$
**10–75.** $(0.0956)(147.2)(0.0778)$
**10–76.** $(15.47)(82.5)(975,000.)$
**10–77.** $(37.8)(22,490,000.)(0.15)$
**10–78.** $(1.048)(0.753)(0.933)$
**10–79.** $(1.856)(10)^3(21.98)$
**10–80.** $(57.7)(46.8)(3.08)$
**10–81.** $(0.045)(0.512)(115.4)$
**10–82.** $(0.307)(46.3)(7.94)$
**10–83.** $(2.229)(86.05)(16,090.)(\pi)$
**10–84.** $(44,090.)(38.9)(667.)(55.9)$
**10–85.** $(568.)(46.07)(3.41)(67.9)$
**10–86.** $(75.88)(0.0743)(0.1185)(0.429)$
**10–87.** $(10)^{-7}(69.8)(11.03)(0.901)$
**10–88.** $(46.3)(0.865)(10)^{-9}(0.953)(\pi)$
**10–89.** $(665.)(35,090)(0.1196)(0.469)$
**10–90.** $(888.)(35.9)(77.9)(0.652)$
**10–91.** $(43.4)(0.898)(70.09)(0.113)(\pi)$

### DIVISION

Multiplication is merely the process of mechanically adding the logarithms of the quantities involved. From a review of the principles of logarithms, it follows that division is merely the process of mechanically subtracting the logarithm of the divisor from the logarithm of the dividend.

*Example:*  $\dfrac{(8)}{(2)} = 4$

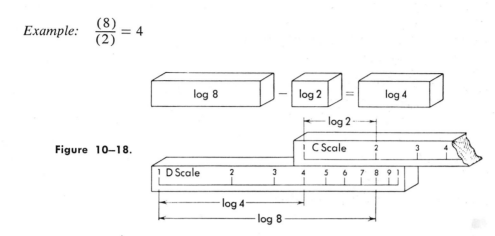

**Figure  10–18.**

PROCEDURE

1. Set the divisor (2) on the C scale directly above the dividend (8), which is located on the D scale.

2. Read the answer (4) on the D scale directly under the left index of the C scale.

For location of the decimal point in division problems the following *Projection Rule* should be observed.

### Projection Rule for Division

1. Locate the characteristic of the dividend above it and the characteristic of the divisor below it.

2. Subtract the characteristic of the divisor from the characteristic of the dividend.

3. For every left extension of the C scale's left index, add a $(-1)$ to the total characteristic already obtained.

4. The sum is the characteristic of the answer.

*Example:*

$$\underset{(0)}{\overset{(+2)}{\underset{(6.05)}{\overset{(575)}{\phantom{\dfrac{}{}}}}}}$$

left extension

characteristic of answer

$$\frac{(+2)}{\underset{(0)}{\frac{(575)}{(6.05)}}} = \underline{\underline{(9.50)(10)^1}}$$

$(+2) - (0) \rightarrow +2 - 1 = +1$

ESTIMATION  OF  ANSWER  BY  SCIENTIFIC  NOTATION:

$$\frac{6(10)^2}{6} = \underline{\underline{1(10)^2}} \leftarrow \text{ESTIMATED  ANSWER}$$

*Example:*

left extension
characteristic of answer

$$\begin{array}{c} (-1) \\ \dfrac{(0.465)}{(54)} \\ (+1) \end{array} \quad \begin{array}{c} (-1)-(+1) \to -2-1=-3 \end{array} = \underline{\underline{(8.61)(10)^{-3}}}$$

---

ESTIMATION OF ANSWER BY SCIENTIFIC NOTATION:

$$\frac{5(10)^{-1}}{5(10)^{1}} = \underline{\underline{1(10)^{-2}}} \leftarrow \text{ESTIMATED ANSWER}$$

---

## Division Practice Problems

**10–92.** $(29.6) \div (18.02) = 1.641$

**10–93.** $(1.532) \div (72.6) = (2.11)(10)^{-2}$

**10–94.** $(0.1153) \div (70.3) = (1.64)(10)^{-3}$

**10–95.** $(89.3) \div (115.6) = (7.72)(10)^{-1}$

**10–96.** $(0.1052) \div (33.6) = (3.13)(10)^{-3}$

**10–97.** $(40.2) \div (50.8) = (7.91)(10)^{-1}$

**10–98.** $(0.661) \div (70,500) = (9.38)(10)^{-6}$

**10–99.** $(182.9) \div (0.00552) = (3.31)(10)^{4}$

**10–100.** $(0.714) \div (98,200) = (7.27)(10)^{-6}$

**10–101.** $(4.36) \div (80,300) = (5.43)(10)^{-5}$

**10–102.** $(1.339) \div (22.6 \times 10^{4}) = (5.92)(10)^{-6}$

**10–103.** $(17.03) \div (76.3) = (2.23)(10)^{-1}$

**10–104.** $(0.511) \div (0.281) = 1.819$

**10–105.** $(67.7) \div (91,300) = (7.42)(10)^{-4}$

**10–106.** $(5.04) \div (29,800) = (1.691)(10)^{-4}$

**10–107.** $(18.35) \div (0.921) = (1.992)(10)^{1}$

**10–108.** $(29.6 \times 10^{5}) \div (0.905) = (3.27)(10)^{6}$

**10–109.** $(0.1037) \div (92.5 \times 10^{5}) = (1.121)(10)^{-8}$

**10–110.** $(537) \div (15.63 \times 10^{-7}) = (3.44)(10)^{8}$

**10–111.** $(26,300) \div (84.3 \times 10^{5}) = (3.12)(10)^{-3}$

**10–112.** $(6,370) \div (0.733) = (8.69)(10)^{3}$

**10–113.** $(1.066) \div (7.51 \times 10^{3}) = (1.419)(10)^{-4}$

**10–114.** $(29.6 \times 10^{4}) \div (0.973) = (3.04)(10)^{5}$

**10–115.** $(0.912) \div (10.31 \times 10^{-5}) = (8.85)(10)^{3}$

**10–116.** $(17.37 \times 10^{-4}) \div (0.662) = (2.62)(10)^{-3}$

**10–117.** $(0.693 \times 10^{5}) \div (1.008 \times 10^{-6}) = (6.88)(10)^{10}$

**10–118.** $(89.1) \times 10^{3}) \div (189.3 \times 10^{4}) = (4.71)(10)^{-2}$

**10–119.** $(0.617) \div (29,600) = (2.08)(10)^{-5}$

**10–120.** $(18.06 \times 10^{7}) \div (15.29) = (1.181)(10)^{7}$

**10–121.** $(56.8)(10)^{4} \div (29.6)(10)^{-3} = (1.919)(10)^{7}$

**10–122.** $(183,600) \div (76.3 \times 10^{-3}) = (2.41)(10)^{6}$

**10–123.** $(75.9) \div (0.000813) = (9.34)(10)^{4}$

**10–124.** $(43.6) \div (0.0837) = (5.21)(10)^2$
**10–125.** $(156.8 \times 10^3) \div (0.715) = (2.19)(10)^5$
**10–126.** $(216 \times 10^{-3}) \div (1557) = (1.387)(10)^{-4}$
**10–127.** $(88.3 \times 10^{-1}) \div (29.1 \times 10^{-4}) = (3.03)(10)^3$
**10–128.** $(1.034 \times 10^3) \div (0.706 \times 10^{-8}) = (1.465)(10)^{11}$
**10–129.** $(55.2)(10)^3 \div (0.1556 \times 10^3) = (3.55)(10)^2$
**10–130.** $(0.01339) \div (1896 \times 10^5) = (7.06)(10)^{-11}$
**10–131.** $(4,030 \times 10^{-7}) \div (75.3 \times 10^{-9}) = (5.35)(10)^3$

**Problems in Division**

**10–132.** $\dfrac{89.9}{45.}$

**10–133.** $\dfrac{147.}{22.}$

**10–134.** $\dfrac{9.06}{7.1}$

**10–135.** $\dfrac{1,985.}{78.55}$

**10–136.** $\dfrac{19,230.}{64.88}$

**10–137.** $\dfrac{87,600.}{43.8}$

**10–138.** $\dfrac{54.8}{9.10}$

**10–139.** $\dfrac{0.877}{33.07}$

**10–140.** $\dfrac{11.44}{24.9}$

**10–141.** $\dfrac{187,900.}{71.45}$

**10–142.** $\dfrac{0.00882}{87.04}$

**10–143.** $\dfrac{0.675}{54.8}$

**10–144.** $\dfrac{87.9}{45.7}$

**10–145.** $\dfrac{164,800.}{3.88}$

**10–146.** $\dfrac{7.09 \times 10^3}{18.45}$

**10–147.** $\dfrac{(0.001755)}{(6.175)}$

**10–148.** $\dfrac{(0.0000559)}{(0.00659)}$

**10–149.** $\dfrac{(5.065)}{(0.0003375)}$

**10–150.** $\dfrac{(469,000)}{(793)}$

**10–151.** $\dfrac{(5,100,000)}{(933 \times 10^5)}$

**10–152.** $\dfrac{(3765 \times .10^3)}{(760.3)}$

**10–153.** $\dfrac{(4917)}{(0.391)}$

**10–154.** $\dfrac{(5516)}{(1.65)}$

**10–155.** $\dfrac{(0.0916)}{(0.331)}$

**10–156.** $\dfrac{(193.7)}{(5.06)}$

**10–157.** $\dfrac{(113.05)}{(72.35)}$

**10–158.** $\dfrac{(32.33)}{(46.77)}$

**10–159.** $\dfrac{(3.17)}{(3.1416)}$

**10–160.** $\dfrac{(0.221)}{(56.91)}$

**10–161.** $\dfrac{(233.17)}{(5506)}$

**10–162.** $\dfrac{(72.13)}{(52.03)}$

**10–163.** $\dfrac{(6607)}{(1.91 \times 10^5)}$

**10–164.** $\dfrac{(1.993 \times 10^{-8})}{(72.31 \times 10^{-6})}$

**10–165.** $\dfrac{(461 \times 10^3)}{(0.003617)}$

**10–166.** $\dfrac{(9903 \times 10^{-5})}{(47.31 \times 10^3)}$

**10–167.** $\dfrac{0.711}{11,980.}$

**10–168.** $\dfrac{0.01253}{66.8}$

**10–169.** $\dfrac{0.974}{1.058}$

**10–170.** $\dfrac{0.000497}{38.9 \times 10^{-5}}$

**10–171.** $\dfrac{48.6 \times 10^{-9}}{1.977 \times 10^5}$

**10–172.** $\dfrac{69,990. \times 10^{18}}{43.9 \times 10^{-2}}$

**10–173.** $\dfrac{5.06 \times 10^{-7}}{0.001853 \times 10^9}$

**10–174.** $\dfrac{1.097 \times 10^{-6}}{458. \times 10^{-1}}$

**10–175.** $\dfrac{89.99 \times 10^{-3}}{40.7 \times 10^{-6}}$

**10–176.** $\dfrac{659,000}{0.1148 \times 10^{-3}}$

**10–177.** $\dfrac{883.8}{3.89 \times 10^{-11}}$

**10–178.** $\dfrac{15.06 \times 10^{-7}}{33.8 \times 10^{-1}}$

**10–179.** $\dfrac{1.095}{24.66}$

**10–180.** $\dfrac{33.97 \times 10^7}{56.98 \times 10^3}$

**10–181.** $\dfrac{22,900. \times 10^{-6}}{76.4 \times 10^4}$

## Combined Multiplication and Division

Since most scientific calculations involve both multiplication and division, the student should master the technique of combined multiplication and division. The projection rules for both multiplication and division also apply in a combination problem.

*Example:*

$$\frac{(+2) \quad (+4)}{(513) \quad (15,300)} \qquad (+6) \; - (+2) \to +4$$
$$\frac{(513) \quad (15,300)}{(238)} = 32,900, \text{ or } \underline{\underline{3.29 \times 10^4}}$$
$$+2$$

> ESTIMATION OF ANSWER BY SCIENTIFIC NOTATION:
> $$\frac{5(10)^2 \;\; (1.5)(10)^4}{(2.5) \;\; (10)^2} = \underline{\underline{3(10)^4}} \leftarrow \text{ESTIMATED ANSWER}$$

In order to work the problem above, first set 513 divided by 238 on the C and D scales. Now, instead of reading this answer, move the hairline to 15,300 on the C scale (thus multiplying this latter quantity by the quotient of the first setting).

The student should always alternate the division and multiplication settings and should not try to take readings as he progresses with the steps. Only the final result is desired and, since each reading of the rule further magnifies any error, the fewest readings possible should be allowed.

*Example:*

(left extension
from the division)
$$\downarrow$$

$$\frac{(+1) \qquad (-4) \qquad (+2)}{(47.30)(0.000391)(693.5)} \qquad (-1) - (+2) \to -3 - 1 = -4$$
$$\frac{(47.30)(0.000391)(693.5)}{(0.312)(55.1)(773.1)} = \underline{\underline{9.66 \times 10^{-4}}}$$
$$(-1) \quad (+1) \quad (+2)$$

> ESTIMATION OF ANSWER BY SCIENTIFIC NOTATION:
> $$\frac{5(10)^1 \;\; 4(10)^{-4} \;\; 7(10)^2}{3(10)^{-1} \;\; 6(10)^1 \;\; 8(10)^2} = \underline{\underline{1(10)^{-3}}} \leftarrow \text{ESTIMATED ANSWER}$$

Remember that when you want to divide, you move the slide, and when you want to multiply, you move the hairline.

A common error committed by many students is to multiply all the quantities in the dividend and all the quantities in the divisor and then divide these two results. This is a bad habit and such practice should not be followed. There are too many chances for mistakes, in addition to the method's being slower.

## Combined Multiplication and Division Practice Problems

**10–182.** $\dfrac{(29.6)(18.01)}{(937)} = (5.69)(10)^{-1}$

**10–183.** $\dfrac{(625,000)(0.0337)}{(48.2)} = (4.37)(10)^2$

**10–184.** $\dfrac{(0.887)(1,109)}{(5.22)} = (1.884)(10)^2$

**10–185.** $\dfrac{(0.1058)(937,000)}{(0.218)} = (4.55)(10)^5$

**10–186.** $\dfrac{(43,800)(0.0661)}{87.2 \times 10^5)} = (3.32)(10)^{-4}$

**10–187.** $\dfrac{(114.3)(0.567)}{(66,400)} = (9.76)(10)^{-4}$

**10–188.** $\dfrac{(76.5 \times 10^4)}{(0.733)(49.7 \times 10^{-6})} = (2.10)(10)^{10}$

**10–189.** $\dfrac{(11.03)}{(20,100)(8.72 \times 10^3)} = (6.29)(10)^{-8}$

**10–190.** $\dfrac{(0.226)}{(87.3 \times 10^4)(0.717)} = (3.61)(10)^{-7}$

**10–191.** $\dfrac{(43.2)}{(9.09)(0.000652)} = (7.29)(10)^3$

**10–192.** $\dfrac{(94.9 \times 10^{-9})}{(33,800)(0.609)} = (4.61)(10)^{-12}$

**10–193.** $\dfrac{(737,000)}{(0.1556)(61.9 \times 10^3)} = (7.65)(10)^1$

**10–194.** $\dfrac{(17.01)(0.0336)}{(52,600)(0.01061)} = (1.024)(10)^{-3}$

**10–195.** $\dfrac{(66.6)(0.937)}{(7.05 \times 10^2)(184,300)} = (4.80)(10)^{-7}$

**10–196.** $\dfrac{(2.96)(1000)(62.1)}{(0.911)(432,000)} = (4.67)(10)^{-1}$

**10–197.** $\dfrac{(45.8)(10.33)}{(29,200)(0.702)} = (2.31)(10)^{-2}$

**10–198.** $\dfrac{(0.604)(9,270)}{(0.817 \times 10^4)(1.372)} = (4.99)(10)^{-1}$

**10–199.** $\dfrac{(176,300)(42.8 \times 10^3)}{(68.3)(15.01)} = (7.36)(10)^6$

**10–200.** $\dfrac{(39,200)(89.3 \times 10^{-7})}{(20.4 \times 10^{-6})(155.5)} = (1.104)(10)^2$

**10–201.** $\dfrac{(0.763 \times 10^{-4})(0.01004)}{(44.3)(7,150,000)} = (2.42)(10)^{-15}$

**10–202.** $\dfrac{(152,300)(88,100)}{(0.00339)(60.4)} = (6.55)(10)^{10}$

**10–203.** $\dfrac{(90,400)(2.05 \times 10^6)}{(24.3 \times 10^{-2})(0.0227)} = (3.36)(10)^{13}$

## Combined Multiplication and Division Practice Problems (continued)

**10–204.** $\dfrac{(14.36 \times 10^2)(0.907)}{(51.6 \times 10^2)(0.00001118)} = (2.26)(10)^4$

**10–205.** $\dfrac{(991,000)(60.3 \times 10^4)}{(23.3 \times 10^{-1})(0.1996)} = (1.285)(10)^{12}$

**10–206.** $\dfrac{(8.40)(10)^3(29.6 \times 10^{-5})}{(0.369)(10.02 \times 10^9)} = (6.72)(10)^{-10}$

**10–207.** $\dfrac{(54.9)(26.8)(0.331)}{(21.6)(11.03)(54.6)} = (3.74)(10)^{-2}$

**10–208.** $\dfrac{(17,630)(0.1775)(92.3)}{(0.433)(0.0061)(57.3)} = (1.908)(10)^6$

**10–209.** $\dfrac{(0.821)(0.221)(0.811)}{(0.0907)(10.72)(66,300)} = (2.28)(10)^{-6}$

**10–210.** $\dfrac{(0.00552)(89.6)(0.705)}{(19.52 \times 10^3)(18.03)(22.4)} = (4.42)(10)^{-8}$

**10–211.** $\dfrac{(30,600)(29.9)(0.00777)}{(485)(19.32)(62.6)} = (1.212)(10)^{-2}$

**10–212.** $\dfrac{(54.1)(0.393)(16,070)}{(49.3 \times 10^3)(11.21)(61.6)} = (1.00)(10)^{-2}$

**10–213.** $\dfrac{(44.2)(100.7)(62,400)}{(90.3)(75,100)(0.01066)} = (3.84)(10)^3$

**10–214.** $\dfrac{(78.4)(15.59)(0.01669)}{(33.6)(88,100)(0.432)} = (1.594)(10)^{-5}$

**10–215.** $\dfrac{(994,000)(21,300)(0.1761)}{(44.4)(71.2)(32.1 \times 10^4)} = 3.67$

**10–216.** $\dfrac{(16.21)(678,000)(56.6)}{(0.01073)(4,980)(30.3)} = (3.84)(10)^5$

**10–217.** $\dfrac{(61.3 \times 10^3)(0.1718)(0.893)}{(21.6)(0.902)(0.01155)} = (4.18)(10)^4$

**10–218.** $\dfrac{(20,900)(16.22 \times 10^4)(0.1061)}{(877)(20.1 \times 10^{-4})(5.03)} = (4.06)(10)^7$

**10–219.** $\dfrac{(999,000)(17.33)(0.1562)}{(0.802)(0.0443)(29.3 \times 10^{-1})} = (2.60)(10)^7$

**10–220.** $\dfrac{(16.21)(0.0339)(151.6)(0.211)}{(0.00361)(0.785)(93.2)(406)} = (1.640)(10)^{-1}$

**10–221.** $\dfrac{(84.3)(0.916)(0.1133)(21.3)}{(66.2)(0.407)(55.3)(462)} = (2.72)(10)^{-4}$

## Problems

Solve by combined multiplication and division method:

**10–222.** $\dfrac{(0.916)}{(90.5)(13.06)}$

**10–223.** $\dfrac{(0.00908)}{(22.3)(33.2)}$

**10–224.** $\dfrac{(24.5)(43)}{(36)}$

**10–225.** $\dfrac{(82)(9.3)}{(56.5)}$

**10–226.** $\dfrac{(167)(842)}{(0.976)}$

**10–227.** $\dfrac{(5.72)(3690)}{(95.7)}$

**10–228.** $\dfrac{(925)(76.9)}{(37.6)}$

**10–229.** $\dfrac{(9.87)}{(1.76)(89)}$

**10–230.** $\dfrac{(85.4)}{(26.3)(213)}$

**10–231.** $\dfrac{(1525)}{(73.6)(0.007)}$

**10–232.** $\dfrac{(84,500)}{(126)(37.3)}$

**10–233.** $\dfrac{(76)(23.7)}{(13.5)(373)}$

**10–234.** $\dfrac{(6.23)(2.14)}{(0.00531)}$

**10–235.** $\dfrac{(21.3)(370)}{(10.9)(758)}$

**10–236.** $\dfrac{(0.00215)(2520)}{(7.57)(118)}$

**10–237.** $\dfrac{(755)(1.15)}{(51.4)(0.093)}$

**10–238.** $\dfrac{(916)(0.752)}{(5.16)}$

**10–239.** $\dfrac{(23.1)(1.506)}{(6.27)}$

**10–240.** $\dfrac{(42.6)(1.935)}{(750.3)}$

**10–241.** $\dfrac{(77.1)(10.53)}{(331.0)(73)}$

**10–242.** $\dfrac{(56.7)(0.00336)}{(15.06)(8.23)}$

**10–243.** $\dfrac{(14.5)(10)^3(6.22)}{(53.3)(0.00103)}$

**10–244.** $\dfrac{(42)(1000)}{(5.23)(0.00771)}$

**10–245.** $\dfrac{(1.331)}{(916)(506)}$

**10–246.** $\dfrac{(4320)(0.7854)}{(134)(0.9)}$

**10–247.** $\dfrac{(0.00713)(329)}{(0.0105)(1000)}$

**10–248.** $\dfrac{(103.4)(0.028)}{(0.0798)}$

**10–249.** $\dfrac{(1573)(4618)}{(3935)(97)}$

**10–250.** $\dfrac{(47.2)(0.0973)}{(85)(37.6)}$

**10–251.** $\dfrac{(0.0445)(0.0972)}{(0.218)(0.318)}$

**10–252.** $\dfrac{(39.1)(680,000)(3.52)(1.1 \times 10^6)}{(0.0316)(9.6 \times 10^6)(26.3)}$

**10–253.** $\dfrac{(7.69)(76,000)(5.63)(0.00314)}{(0.00365)(10 \times 10^6)}$

**10–254.** $\dfrac{(3.97)(6.71 \times 10^{-3})(0.067)}{(63.1)(3 \times 10^7)(7.61)(80,175)}$

**10–255.** $\dfrac{(697)(0.000713)(68.1)}{(234)(9.68)(5.1 \times 10^4)}$

**10–256.** $\dfrac{(43,400)(9.16)(8.1 \times 10^{-6})}{(0.00613)(67,000)(0.416)}$

**10–257.** $\dfrac{(691.6)(7.191)(3 \times 10^7)}{(410,000)(6.39)(0.0876)}$

**10–258.** $\dfrac{(37.615)(81.4)(9.687)(0.0017)}{(13.13)(0.076)(43)}$

**10–259.** $\dfrac{(51.2 \times 10^{-6})(3.41 \times 10^5)(36.1)}{(96.69)(7 \times 10^{-2})(0.134)}$

**10–260.** $\dfrac{(6.716)(3.2 \times 10^3)(0.0173)(413)}{(0.0000787)(6.6 \times 10^4)}$

**10–261.** $\dfrac{(1.061 \times 10^{-1})(96,000)(3.717)}{(7.34 \times 10^{-6})(3.9 \times 10^4)(13.5)}$

**10–262.** $\dfrac{(361)(482)(5.816)(38.91)(0.00616)}{(0.07181)(3 \times 10^3)(39.36)}$

**Problems (continued)**

**10–263.** $\dfrac{(0.019 \times 10^8)(111.15)(0.0168)}{(7.96)(58.6)(0.0987)(3,000)}$

**10–264.** $\dfrac{(21.4)(0.82)(39.6 \times 10^{-1})}{(10.86)(6.7 \times 10^{-2})(37,613)}$

**10–265.** $\dfrac{(63,761)(43,890)(0.00761)}{(8 \times 10^6)(0.0781)(67.17)}$

**10–266.** $\dfrac{(516.7)(212 \times 10^3)(0.967)(34)}{(76,516)(2 \times 10^{-6})(618)}$

**10–267.** $\dfrac{(5.1 \times 10^8)(370)(8.71)(3,698)}{(0.00176)(36,170)}$

**10–268.** $\dfrac{(59.71 \times 10^{-6})(0.00916)(0.1695)(55.61)}{(17.33 \times 10^5)(0.3165)(10.56)(1.105)}$

**10–269.** $\dfrac{(773.6)(57.17)(0.316)(912.3)}{(56,000)(715,000)(471.3)}$

**10–270.** $\dfrac{(51.33)(461.3)(919)(5.03)}{(66,000)(71.52)(0.3316)(12.39)}$

**10–271.** $\dfrac{(0.6617)(75.391)(0.6577)(91.33)}{(0.3305)(5.69 \times 10)(0.00317 \times 10^{-5})}$

## Proportions and Ratios

A "ratio" of one number to another is the quotient of the first with respect to the second. For example, the ratio of $a$ to $b$ may be written as $a:b$ or $\dfrac{a}{b}$. A "proportion" is a statement that two ratios are equal. Thus, $2:3 = 6:B$ means that $\dfrac{2}{3} = \dfrac{6}{B}$.

The slide rule is quite useful in solving problems involving ratio or proportion because these fractions may be handled on any pair of matching identical scales of the rule. The C and D scales are most commonly used for this purpose.

In the example, $\dfrac{2}{3} = \dfrac{6}{B}$, 2, 3, and 6 are known values and $B$ is unknown. The procedure to solve for $B$ would be as follows:

1. Divide 2 by 3 (using the C and D scales). In this position the value 2 on the D scale would be located immediately beneath 3 on the C scale.

2. The equal ratio of $\dfrac{6}{B}$ would also be found on the C and D scales. The unknown value $B$ may be read on the C scale immediately above the known value 6 on the D scale; $B = 9$.

With this particular location of the slide, every value read on the C scale bears the identical ratio of 2:3 to the number directly below it on the D scale. It is also important to remember that the cross products of a proportion are equal. In the above example, $3 \times 6 = 2 \times B$.

*Examples:*

a. $\dfrac{47}{21} = \dfrac{18}{A}$        *Answer, A = 8.04*

b. $\dfrac{0.721}{1.336} = \dfrac{B}{89.3}$        *Answer, B = 48.2*

c. $\dfrac{15.9}{C} = \dfrac{72.1}{166.7}$        *Answer, C = 36.7*

d. $\dfrac{D}{0.1156} = \dfrac{0.921}{0.473}$        *Answer, D = 0.225*

e. $\dfrac{42,100}{7,060} = \dfrac{E}{0.0321}$        *Answer, E = 0.1912*

**Folded Scales**

The CF and DF scales are called *folded scales*. They are identical with the C and D scales except that their indices are in a different position. On the majority of slide rules, the CF and DF scales begin at the left end with the value $\pi$, which means that their indices will be located near the center of the rule. On some rules the CF and DF scales may be folded at $\epsilon(2.718)$ or at some other number.

Since the CF and DF scales are identical in graduations with the C and D scales, they can be used in multiplication and division just as the C and D scales are. Another important fact may be noticed when the scales are examined; that is, if a number such as 2 on the C scale is set over a number such as 3 on the D scale, then 2 on the CF scale coincides with 3 on the DF scale. This means that operations may be begun or answers obtained on either the C and D scales or on the CF and DF scales.

For example, if we wish to multiply 2 by 6, and we set the left index of the C scale over 2 on the D scale, we observe that the product cannot be read on the D scale because 6 on the C scale projects past the right end of the rule. Ordinarily this would mean that the slide would need to be run to the left so that the right index of the C scale could be used. However, by using the folded scales, we notice that the 6 on the CF scale coincides with 12 on the DF scale, thereby eliminating an extra movement of the slide (See Figure 10–19). In many cases the use of the folded scales will reduce the number of times the slide must be shifted to the left because an answer would fall beyond the right end of the D scale.

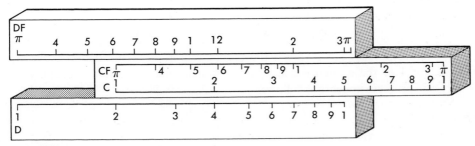

**Figure 10–19.**

There are several methods by which the location of the decimal point in the answer can be determined. The decimal point location can best be found by using the method of scientific notation.

The projection rule can be used if it is always remembered that an answer read on the DF scale to the right of the index (near the center of the rule) corresponds to a left projection. Since in many operations the decimal point location in the answer can be determined by inspection, the decimal point can often be placed without reference to projection rules.

A convenient method of multiplying or dividing by $\pi$ is afforded by the use of the folded scales. For example, to find the product $2\pi$, set the hairline over 2 on the D scale. The product 6.28 is read on the DF scale under the hairline. Of course this same operation may be performed by using either index of the slide.

## Reciprocal Scales

The CI, DI, and CIF scales are known as *reciprocal scales* or *inverted scales*. They are identical with the C, D, and CF scales, respectively, except that they are inverted; that is, the numbers represented by the graduations on these scales increase from right to left. On some slide rules, the inverted scale graduations are printed in red to help distinguish them from the other scale markings.

An important principle to remember when using these scales is that a number on the C scale will have its reciprocal in the same position on the CI scale. Conversely, when the hairline is set to a number on the CI scale, its reciprocal is under the hairline on the C scale.

The inverted scales are useful in problems involving repeated multiplication or division because some movements of the slide may be eliminated.

*Example:* Find the product:

$$(1.71)(8.30)(0.252)(4910)(53.8)$$

In order to perform this operation, using the inverted scales, the following steps are used:

1. Set the hairline to 1.71 on the D scale.
2. Move the slide until 83 on the CI scale is under the hairline.
3. Move the hairline until it is set on 252 on the C scale.
4. Move the slide until 491 on the CI scale is under the hairline.
5. Move the hairline until it is set on 538 on the C scale.
6. Read the product 94600 under the hairline on the D scale.

The actual process has involved the use of reciprocal quantities in division in Steps 2 and 4 of the sequence above. Rewritten as the operation is actually performed, the problem appears as follows:

$$\frac{(1.71)(0.252)(53.8)}{(1/8.30)(1/4910)}$$

ESTIMATION OF ANSWER BY SCIENTIFIC NOTATION:
$$(2)(8)(2)(10)^{-1}(5)(10)^3(5)(10)^1 = \underline{\underline{(8)(10)^5}} \leftarrow \text{ESTIMATED ANSWER}$$

Since the digits read on the slide rule were 946, the actual product would be $9.46(10)^5$. The projection rule should not be used with inverted scales, since the number of left projections are sometimes difficult to determine.

Proper use of the folded and inverted scales will enable one to work each practice problem below with only one setting of the slide.

### Use of Folded and Reciprocal Scales Practice Problems

**10–272.** $(264)(564)(522) = (7.77)(10)^7$
**10–273.** $(387)(7.32)(176) = (4.99)(10)^5$
**10–274.** $(0.461)(4.79)(1140) = (2.52)(10)^3$
**10–275.** $(6.69)(1548)(92,000) = (9.53)(10)^8$
**10–276.** $(561)(3.30)(1.94) = (3.59)(10)^3$
**10–277.** $(1456)(0.351)(0.835) = (4.27)(10)^2$
**10–278.** $(1262)(0.405)(65,100) = (3.33)(10)^7$
**10–279.** $(0.1871)(5.04)(53,000) = (5.00)(10)^4$
**10–280.** $(7.28 \times 10^{-5})(4.16)(14.10) = (4.27)(10)^{-3}$
**10–281.** $(10.70)(19,400)(0.0914) = (1.897)(10)^4$
**10–282.** $(4.56)(47.4)(87.1) = (1.883)(10)^4$
**10–283.** $(0.510)(68.9)(3,370) = (1.184)(10)^5$
**10–284.** $(2,030)(14.72)(129.7) = (3.88)(10)^6$
**10–285.** $(1824)(29.1)(21,800) = (1.157)(10)^9$
**10–286.** $(0.0255)(0.0932)(0.867) = (2.06)(10)^{-3}$
**10–287.** $(93.6)(3.99)(5,680) = (2.12)(10)^6$
**10–288.** $(4.48)(103.5)(0.198) = (9.18)(10)^1$
**10–289.** $(0.580)(43,700)(40.3) = (1.021)(10)^6$
**10–290.** $(7.05)(62.0)(34.9) = (1.525)(10)^4$
**10–291.** $(74.8)(8.)(483,000) = (2.89)(10)^8$
**10–292.** $\dfrac{(208)(90.2)}{(30,600)} = (6.13)(10)^{-1}$
**10–293.** $\dfrac{(0.387)(25,200)}{(0.118)} = (8.26)(10)^4$
**10–294.** $\dfrac{(0.458)(14.05 \times 10^{-15})}{(75.5 \times 10^8)} = (8.52)(10)^{-25}$
**10–295.** $\dfrac{(18,100)(84.4)}{(10.92)} = (1.40)(10)^5$
**10–296.** $\dfrac{(477)(9,720)}{(19,150)} = (2.42)(10)^2$
**10–297.** $\dfrac{(25,600)}{(68,500)(12,080)} = (3.09)(10)^{-5}$
**10–298.** $\dfrac{(3050)(1.00 \times 10^{-20})}{(71.4)(0.946)} = (4.52)(10)^{-19}$
**10–299.** $\dfrac{(1,670)}{(0.000570)(24,700)} = (1.186)(10)^2$
**10–300.** $\dfrac{(51.5)}{(15.14)(0.00194)} = (1.753)(10)^3$
**10–301.** $\dfrac{(917,000)}{(54.3)(119.8 \times 10^{-4})} = (1.41)(10)^6$

### Squares and Square Roots

The A and B scales have been constructed so that their lengths are one-half those of the C and D scales (see Figure 10–20). Similarly some slide rules are so constructed that they have a scale (Sq 1 and Sq 2, or $R_1$ and $R_2$) which is twice as long as the D scale. This means that the logarithm of 3 as represented on the D

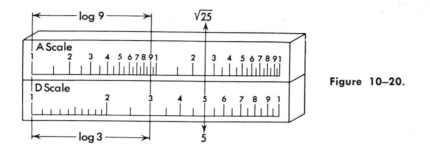

Figure 10–20.

scale would be equivalent in length to the logarithm of 9 on the A scale. Where the Sq 1 and Sq 2 or the $R_1$ and $R_2$ scales are used in conjunction with the D scale, the logarithm of 3 on the Sq 2 ($R_2$) scale would be equivalent in length to the logarithm of 9 on the D scale.

### To Find the Square Root of a Number Using the A and D Scales

1. Get an estimate of the intended answer by placing a bar over every two digits, starting at the decimal point and working outward. There will be a digit in the answer for each bar marked.

2. Set the number on the A scale and read the square root on the D scale under the hairline. Note that the estimated answer will always indicate which A scale to use, since only one of the scales will give a square root near the estimated value.

Greater accuracy can be obtained by using the D scale in conjunction with the Sq 1 and Sq 2 scales ($R_1$ and $R_2$).

*Examples for Finding the Location of Decimal Points:*

*a.* $\sqrt{\overset{9}{\overline{97}}\ \overset{x}{\overline{65}}}$   The estimated answer is somewhere between 90 and 100.

*b.* $\sqrt{.\overset{0}{\overline{00}}\ \overset{5}{\overline{30}}}$   The estimated answer is approximately 0.05.

NOTE: In the last example, since the given value was 0.003, an extra zero would have to be added after the 3 to complete the digits beneath the bar.

*Examples for Finding the Square Root of a Number:*

$$\overset{1 \quad x \quad x}{a. \ \sqrt{1 \ 03 \ 57}} \quad \text{The estimated answer is somewhere between 100 and 200.}$$

$$\sqrt{1 \ 03 \ 57} = 101.8 = \underline{1.018 \times 10^2}$$

$$\overset{0. \ 0 \ 2 \quad x}{b. \ \sqrt{0.00 \ 05 \ 20}} \quad \text{The estimated answer is approximately 0.02.}$$

$$\sqrt{0.00 \ 05 \ 20} = 0.02280 = \underline{2.280 \times 10^{-2}}$$

*Examples for Finding Squares:*

1. Express the number in scientific notation.

   a. $(0.0000956)^2 = (9.56 \times 10^{-5})^2$

2. Square each part of the converted term by setting the number to be squared on the D scale and reading its square on the A scale under the hairline.

   a. $(9.56)^2 \times (10^{-5})^2 = 91.4 \times 10^{-10} = \underline{9.14 \times 10^{-9}}$

   b. $(90100)^2 = (9.01 \times 10^4)^2$
      $(9.01)^2 \times (10^4)^2 = 81 \times 10^8 = \underline{8.1 \times 10^9}$

   c. $(357000000)^2 = (3.57 \times 10^8)^2$
      $(3.57)^2 \times (10^8)^2 = 12.7 \times 10^{16} = \underline{1.27 \times 10^{17}}$

   d. $(0.00000001050)^2 = (1.05 \times 10^{-8})^2$
      $(1.05)^2 \times (10^{-8})^2 = \underline{1.10 \times 10^{-16}}$

### Squares and Square Roots Practice Problems

10-302. $(408)^2 = (1.665)(10)^5$

10-303. $(8.35)^2 = (6.97)(10)^1$

10-304. $(3,980)^2 = (1.584)(10)^7$

10-305. $(0.941)^2 = (8.85)(10)^{-1}$

10-306. $(57.4)^2 = (3.29)(10)^3$

10-307. $(0.207)^2 = (4.28)(10)^{-2}$

10-308. $(784)^2 = (6.15)(10)^5$

10-309. $(296,000)^2 = (8.76)(10)^{10}$

10-310. $(1037)^2 = (1.075)(10)^6$

10-311. $(8.93)^2 = (7.97)(10)^1$

10-312. $(30.9)^2 = (9.55)(10)^2$

10-313. $(43,300)^2 = (1.875)(10)^9$

10-314. $(0.00609)^2 = (3.71)(10)^{-5}$

10-315. $(0.846)^2 = (7.16)(10)^{-1}$

10-316. $(55.2 \times 10^3)^2 = (3.05)(10)^9$

10-317. $(0.0707)^2 = (5.00)(10)^{-3}$

10-318. $(11.92 \times 10^{-4})^2 = (1.421)(10)^{-6}$

10-319. $(0.291 \times 10^{-5})^2 = (8.47)(10)^{-12}$

10-320. $(449,000)^2 = (2.02)(10)^{11}$

10-321. $(0.000977)^2 = (9.55)(10)^{-7}$

10-322. $(33.5 \times 10^{-6})^2 = (1.122)(10)^{-9}$

10-323. $(8,810)^2 = (7.76)(10)^7$

**10–324.** $(50.9 \times 10^6)^2 = (2.59)(10)^{15}$
**10–325.** $(99,300)^2 = (9.86)(10)^9$
**10–326.** $(0.0714 \times 10^{-6})^2 = (5.10)(10)^{-15}$
**10–327.** $\sqrt{96,100} = (3.10)(10)^2$
**10–328.** $\sqrt{0.912} = (9.55)(10)^{-1}$
**10–329.** $\sqrt{24.9} = 4.99$
**10–330.** $\sqrt{0.01124} = (1.06)(10)^{-1}$
**10–331.** $\sqrt{5,256} = (7.25)(10)^1$
**10–332.** $\sqrt{0.3764} = (6.14)(10)^{-1}$
**10–333.** $\sqrt{43,800,000} = (6.62)(10)^3$
**10–334.** $\sqrt{0.01369} = (1.17)(10)^{-1}$
**10–335.** $\sqrt{73.6} = 8.58$
**10–336.** $\sqrt{1.1025} = 1.05$
**10–337.** $\sqrt{487,000} = (6.98)(10)^2$
**10–338.** $\sqrt{580.8} = (2.41)(10)^1$
**10–339.** $\sqrt{0.00002767} = (5.26)(10)^{-3}$
**10–340.** $\sqrt{0.1399} = (3.74)(10)^{-1}$
**10–341.** $\sqrt{6,368} = (7.98)(10)^1$
**10–342.** $\sqrt{1.142 \times 10^{-3}} = (3.38)(10)^{-2}$
**10–343.** $\sqrt{6.496 \times 10^1} = 8.06$
**10–344.** $\sqrt{190,970} = (4.37)(10)^2$
**10–345.** $\sqrt{3,204,000} = (1.79)(10)^3$
**10–346.** $\sqrt{0.003807} = (6.17)(10)^{-2}$
**10–347.** $\sqrt{0.08352} = (2.89)(10)^{-1}$
**10–348.** $\sqrt{3069} = (5.54)(10)^1$
**10–349.** $\sqrt{61.78 \times 10^{-4}} = (7.86)(10)^{-2}$
**10–350.** $\sqrt{3.648 \times 10^{-8}} = (1.91)(10)^{-4}$
**10–351.** $\sqrt{9.92 \times 10^5} = (9.96)(10)^2$

## Problems

Solve by method of squares and square roots.

**10–352.** $(1468.)^2$
**10–353.** $(0.886)^2$
**10–354.** $(67.4)^2$
**10–355.** $(11.96)^2$
**10–356.** $(0.00448)^2$
**10–357.** $(0.000551)^2$
**10–358.** $(9.22)^2$
**10–359.** $(64,800.)^2$

**10–360.** $(0.0668)^2$
**10–361.** $(16.85)^2$
**10–362.** $(1.802 \times 10^9)^2$
**10–363.** $(0.00358)^2$
**10–364.** $(5089)^2$
**10–365.** $(44,900.)^2$
**10–366.** $(64.88)^2$
**10–367.** $\sqrt{11.81}$

**10–368.** $\sqrt{4567.}$
**10–369.** $\sqrt{0.01844}$
**10–370.** $\sqrt{0.9953}$
**10–371.** $\sqrt{1395.}$
**10–372.** $\sqrt{0.0001288}$
**10–373.** $\sqrt{1.082 \times 10^2}$
**10–374.** $\sqrt{75.9}$
**10–375.** $\sqrt{\pi}$

**10–376.** $\sqrt{73,800.}$

**10–377.** $\sqrt{13.38}$

**10–378.** $\sqrt{93.07}$

**10–379.** $\sqrt{0.1148}$

**10–380.** $\sqrt{0.2776}$

**10–381.** $\sqrt{9.31}$

**10–382.** $(0.774)^2(11.47)^{1/2}$

**10–383.** $(0.1442)^{1/2}(33.89)^{1/2}$

**10–384.** $(54.23)^2(88,900)^{1/2}$

**10–385.** $\sqrt{234.5}\ \sqrt{55,900.}$

**10–386.** $\sqrt{16.38}\ \sqrt{45.6}\ \sqrt{0.9}$

**10–387.** $\sqrt{415.}\ \sqrt{\pi}\ \sqrt{86.4}$

**10–388.** $\sqrt{15.66}\ \sqrt{0.1904}\ \sqrt{\pi}$

**10–389.** $(34.77)^2(54.8)^2(0.772)^{1/2}$

**10–390.** $\sqrt{7.90}\ \sqrt{7.02}\ \sqrt{11.54}$

**10–391.** $\sqrt{31.19}\ \sqrt{56.7}\ \sqrt{54.8}$

### Cubes and Cube Roots

The D and K scales are used to find the cube or cube root of a number as shown in Figure 10–21. The same general procedure is used as that followed for squaring

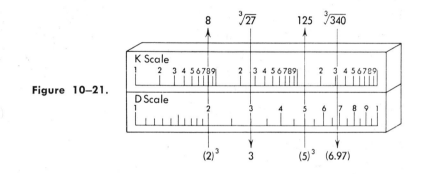

Figure 10–21.

numbers and taking the square root of a number. The K scale is divided into scales $K_1$, $K_2$, and $K_3$, which are each one-third the length of the D scale. Thus, if a number is located on the D scale, the cube of the number will be indicated on the K scale. It follows that if a number is located on one of the K scales, the root of the number would appear on the D scale.

### To Find the Cube Root of a Number

1. Get an estimate of the intended answer by placing a bar over every three digits, starting at the decimal point and working outward. There will be a digit in the answer for each bar marked.

2. Set the number on the K scale and read the cube root on the D scale under the hairline. (Some slide rules, such as those made by Pickett, have three cube root scales instead of the conventional K scale. These cube root scales are used with the D scale to determine cubes and cube roots of numbers. When they are used, however, the number should be set on the D scale and the cube root read on the appropriate cube root scale.)

*Examples for Finding the Location of Decimal Points:*

$$a. \quad \overset{3 \quad \quad x.}{\sqrt[3]{44, \ 800.}} \quad \text{The estimated answer is somewhere between 30 and 40.}$$

$$b. \quad \overset{0. \quad \ 0 \quad \ 2}{\sqrt[3]{0. \ 000 \ 011}} \quad \text{The estimated answer is approximately 0.02.}$$

NOTE: In estimating the answer by marking bars over the digit groupings, be sure that the bars cover three digits instead of two, as was the case in square roots.

Since an estimated answer [see Example *a.* above] has been obtained, it is easy to pick the proper K scale ($K_1$, $K_2$, or $K_3$) to use. Remember that only one of these will give an answer between 30 and 40 [see Example *a.*].

*Examples for Finding the Cube Roots of a Number:*

$$a. \quad \overset{1 \quad \ x \quad \ x}{\sqrt[3]{1 \ 490 \ 000.}} \quad \text{The estimated answer is somewhere between 100 and 200.}$$

$$\sqrt[3]{1 \ 490 \ 000.} = 114.1 = \underline{(1.141)(10)^2}.$$

$$b. \quad \overset{0. \quad \ 0 \quad \ 6}{\sqrt[3]{0. \ 000 \ 156 \ 9}} \quad \text{The estimated answer is approximately 0.06.}$$

$$\sqrt[3]{0. \ 000 \ 156 \ 9} = 0.0537 = \underline{(5.37)(10)^{-2}}.$$

*Examples for Finding Cubes:*

1. Convert the number to a number between 1 and 10 (scientific notation) that must be multiplied by 10 raised to some power.

$$a. \quad (0.00641)^3 = (6.41 \times 10^{-3})^3$$

2. Cube each part of the converted term by setting the number to be cubed on the D scale and reading its cube on the K scale under the hairline.

$$a. \quad (6.41 \times 10^{-3})^3 = (264)(10)^{-9} = \underline{2.63 \times 10^{-7}}$$

$$b. \quad (93.88)^3 = (9.388 \times 10^1)^3$$
$$(9.388)^3(10^1)^3 = 830 \times 10^3 = \underline{8.27 \times 10^5}$$

$$c. \quad (2,618,000.)^3 = (2.618 \times 10^6)^3$$
$$(2.618)^3(10^6)^3 = (17.95 \times 10)^{18} = \underline{1.794 \times 10^{19}}$$

$$d. \quad (0.000001194)^3 = (1.194 \times 10^{-6})^3$$
$$(1.194)^3(10^{-6})^3 = \underline{1.701 \times 10^{-18}}$$

## Cubes and Cube Roots Practice Problems

**10–392.** $(206)^3 = (8.74)(10)^6$
**10–393.** $(7.68)^3 = (4.53)(10)^2$
**10–394.** $(0.00519)^3 = (1.398)(10)^{-7}$
**10–395.** $(33.5)^3 = (3.76)(10)^4$
**10–396.** $(0.229)^3 = (1.201)(10)^{-2}$
**10–397.** $(1090)^3 = (1.295)(10)^9$
**10–398.** $(0.0579)^3 = (1.94)(10)^{-4}$
**10–399.** $(9.89)^3 = (9.67)(10)^2$
**10–400.** $(419)^3 = (7.36)(10)^7$
**10–401.** $(52.4)^3 = (1.439)(10)^5$
**10–402.** $(0.0249)^3 = (1.544)(10)^{-5}$

**10–403.** $(14.9)^3 = (3.31)(10)^3$
**10–404.** $(2.96)^3 = (2.59)(10)^1$
**10–405.** $(397)^3 = (6.26)(10)^7$
**10–406.** $(63.4)^3 = (2.55)(10)^5$
**10–407.** $(9040)^3 = (7.39)(10)^{11}$
**10–408.** $(0.0783)^3 = (4.80)(10)^{-4}$
**10–409.** $(0.844)^3 = (6.01)(10)^{-1}$
**10–410.** $(5.41)^3 = (1.583)(10)^2$
**10–411.** $(35.5)^3 = (4.47)(10)^4$
**10–412.** $(0.1270)^3 = (2.05)(10)^{-3}$
**10–413.** $(20.7)^3 = (8.87)(10)^3$

**10–414.** $(691)^3 = (3.30)(10)^8$
**10–415.** $(0.719)^3 = (3.72)(10)^{-1}$
**10–416.** $(4.34)^3 = (8.17)(10)^1$
**10–417.** $\sqrt[3]{30,960,000} = (3.14)(10)^2$
**10–418.** $\sqrt[3]{0.001728} = (1.20)(10)^{-1}$
**10–419.** $\sqrt[3]{491} = 7.89$
**10–420.** $\sqrt[3]{9.91 \times 10^{11}} = (9.97)(10)^3$
**10–421.** $\sqrt[3]{0.272} = (6.48)(10)^{-1}$
**10–422.** $\sqrt[3]{118,400} = (4.91)(10)^1$
**10–423.** $\sqrt[3]{22.91} = 2.84$
**10–424.** $\sqrt[3]{527,500} = (8.08)(10)^1$
**10–425.** $\sqrt[3]{1.295} = 1.09$
**10–426.** $\sqrt[3]{0.0001804} = (5.65)(10)^{-2}$
**10–427.** $\sqrt[3]{460,100,000} = (7.72)(10)^2$
**10–428.** $\sqrt[3]{261,000} = (6.39)(10)^1$
**10–429.** $\sqrt[3]{0.11620} = (4.88)(10)^{-1}$
**10–430.** $\sqrt[3]{0.0030486} = (1.45)(10)^{-1}$
**10–431.** $\sqrt[3]{0.03096} = (3.14)(10)^{-1}$
**10–432.** $\sqrt[3]{504.4} = 7.96$
**10–433.** $\sqrt[3]{8,869,000} = (2.07)(10)^2$
**10–434.** $\sqrt[3]{174,700,000} = (5.59)(10)^2$
**10–435.** $\sqrt[3]{5.886 \times 10^{10}} = (3.89)(10)^3$
**10–436.** $\sqrt[3]{5.885 \times 10^{-1}} = (8.38)(10)^{-1}$
**10–437.** $\sqrt[3]{76.105 \times 10^{-5}} = (9.13)(10)^{-2}$
**10–438.** $\sqrt[3]{327.1} = 6.89$
**10–439.** $\sqrt[3]{0.02567} = (2.95)(10)^{-1}$
**10–440.** $\sqrt[3]{0.0004118} = (7.44)(10)^{-2}$
**10–441.** $\sqrt[3]{68,420} = (4.09)(10)^1$

## Problems

Solve by Method of Cubes and Cube Roots.

**10–442.** $(86)^3$

**10–443.** $(148)^3$

**10–444.** $(395,000)^3$

**10–445.** $(47.6)^3$

**10–446.** $(1.074)^3$

**10–447.** $(76.9)^3$

**10–448.** $(220.8)^3$

**10–449.** $(9.72)^3$

**10–450.** $(110.7)^3$

**10–451.** $(91.3)^3$

**10–452.** $(1.757 \times 10^4)^3$

**10–453.** $(3.06 \times 10^{-7})^3$

**10–454.** $(44.8 \times 10^{-1})^3$

**10–455.** $(0.933 \times 10^{-2})^3$

**10–456.** $(0.1184 \times 10^8)^3$

**10–457.** $(51.5 \times 10^2)^3$

**10–458.** $\sqrt[3]{118}$

**10–459.** $\sqrt[3]{2,197}$

**10–460.** $\sqrt[3]{9}$

**10–461.** $\sqrt[3]{0.0689}$

**10–462.** $\sqrt[3]{0.001338}$

**10–463.** $\sqrt[3]{0.1794}$

**10–464.** $\sqrt[3]{0.0891}$

**10–465.** $\sqrt[3]{34,690.}$

**10–466.** $\sqrt[3]{0.3329}$

**10–467.** $\sqrt[3]{1,258,000}$

**10–468.** $\sqrt[3]{0.1853}$

**10–469.** $\sqrt[3]{12.88}$

**10–470.** $\sqrt[3]{4.98 \times 10^7}$

**10–471.** $\sqrt[3]{1.844 \times 10^{-5}}$

**10–472.** $\sqrt[3]{3.86 \times 10^{-1}}$

**10–473.** $(9.94)(0.886)^{1/3}$

**10–474.** $(248.)(11.98)^{1/3}$

**10–475.** $(0.117)(0.0964)^{1/3}$

**10–476.** $(\pi)^3(44.89)^3$

**10–477.** $(6.88)^3(0.00799)^3$

**10–478.** $(0.915)^{1/3}(0.366)^{1/3}\sqrt[3]{11,250}(36.12)^{1/3}$

**10–479.** $(2.34)^3(3.34)^3(4.56)^3(5.67)^3$

**10–480.** $(8.26)^{1/3}(8.26)^3(1000)^{1/3}(10)^3$

**10–481.** $\sqrt[3]{2670} \quad \sqrt[3]{3165} \quad \sqrt[3]{1065} \quad \sqrt[3]{7776}$

**10–482.** $\sqrt[3]{206} \quad \sqrt[3]{0.791}(12.35)^3(26.3)^3$

## Trigonometric Functions

Finding trigonometric functions on a log-log rule is a rather simple process. The angle may be read on the S (sine), ST (sine and tangent of small angles), or T (tangent) scales. The functions may be read under the hairline on the C, D, or DI scales without any movement of the slide.

**Sine 0° to 0.574°.** It is not often that the student needs to know the function of extremely small angles, but if he does need them, it is possible to get approximate values for these functions without consulting tables.

**Method 1:** (Based upon the relation that the sine of small angles is approximately equal to the size of the angle expressed in radians)

1. This method is more accurate than the following Method 2, and is preferable.
2. Express the angle in question in degrees.
3. Change the degrees to radians by dividing by 57.3.

NOTE: $57.3° = 1$ radian (approximately)

4. The value obtained is the approximate answer.

*Example:*

$$\sin 6' = ?$$
$$6' = \frac{6}{60} = 0.10°$$
$$\sin 6' = \frac{0.10}{57.3}$$
$$\sin 6' = 0.00174 \text{ approximately}$$

**Method 2:**

1. Keep in mind the following values:

$$\sin 1'' = 0.000005 \text{ (five zeros-five) approximately}$$
$$\sin 1' = 0.0003 \text{ (three zeros-three) approximately}$$

2. For small angles, multiply the value of 1' or 1", as the case may be, by the number of minutes or seconds in question.

*Example:*

$$\sin 6' = ?$$
$$\sin 6' = (6)(\sin 1')$$
$$\sin 6' = (6)(0.0003)$$
$$\sin 6' = 0.0018 \text{ approximately}$$

**Sine 0.574° to 5.74°.** To find the sine of an angle between 0.574° and 5.74°, the ST and D scales are used as shown in Figure 10–22.

*Example:* $\sin 1.5° = ?$

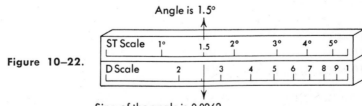

**Figure 10–22.**

Angle is 1.5°

Sine of the angle is 0.0262

INSTRUCTIONS

1. Be certain that the left index of the D scale is directly under the left index of the ST scale.
2. Set the hairline to the angle on the ST scale.
3. Read the answer on the D scale. The answer will be a decimal number and will have one zero preceding the digits read from the rule.

**Sine 5.74° to 90°.** To find the sine of an angle between 5.74° and 90°, the S and D scales are used as shown in Figure 10–23.

*Example:* $\sin 45° = ?$

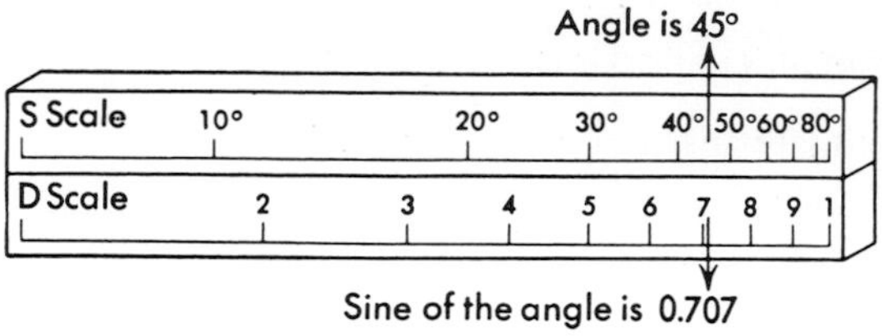

Angle is 45°

| S Scale | 10° | 20° | 30° | 40° 50°60°80° |
| D Scale | 2 | 3 | 4 | 5 6 7 8 9 1 |

**Figure 10–23.**

Sine of the angle is 0.707

INSTRUCTIONS:

1. Be certain that the left index of the D scale is directly under the left index of the S scale.

2. Set the hairline to the angle on the S scale. If the rule has more than one set of figures on the S scale, the angles for sine functions are usually shown to the right of the longer graduations.

3. Read the answer on the D scale. Place the decimal preceding the first digit read from the rule.

**Sines Practice Problems**

**10–483.** Sin 26° = 0.438

**10–484.** Sin 81° = 0.988

**10–485.** Sin 16° = 0.276

**10–486.** Sin 15.5° = 0.267

**10–487.** Sin 42.6° = 0.677

**10–488.** Sin 3.33° = 0.0581

**10–489.** Sin 10.17° = 0.1765

**10–490.** Sin 63.2° = 0.893

**10–491.** Sin 70.83° = 0.945

**10–492.** Sin 26.67° = 0.449

**10–493.** Sin 7.33° = 0.1276

**10–494.** Sin 2.83° = 0.0494

**10–495.** Sin 51.5° = 0.783

**10–496.** Sin 5.17° = 0.0901

**10–497.** Sin 33.8° = 0.556

**10–498.** Sin 20.3° = 0.348

**10–499.** Sin 68.2° = 0.928

**10–500.** Arc Sin 0.557 = 33.8°

**10–501.** $\text{Sin}^{-1}\,0.032 = 1.83°$

**10–502.** $\text{Sin}^{-1}\,0.242 = 14.0°$

**10–503.** Arc Sin 0.709 = 45.15°

**10–504.** $\text{Sin}^{-1}\,0.581 = 35.5°$

**10–505.** Arc Sin 0.999 = 87.5°

**10–506.** $\text{Sin}^{-1}\,0.569 = 34.68°$

**10–507.** $\text{Sin}^{-1}\,0.401 = 23.6°$

**Cosine 0° to 84.26°.** To find the cosine of an angle between 0° and 84.26°, the markings to the left of the long graduations on the S scale are used in conjunction with the D scale. Note that the markings begin with 0° at the right end of the scale and progress to 84.26° at the left end of the scale as shown in Figure 10–24.

*Example:* $\cos 74.1° = ?$

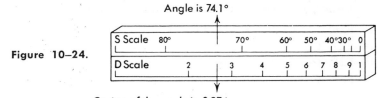

Figure 10–24.

Cosine of the angle is 0.274

**Cosine 84.26° to 89.4°.** To find the cosine of an angle between 84.26° and 89.4°, the complement of the angle on the ST scale is used in conjunction with the D scale.

*Example:*
$$\cos 88.5° = ?$$
$$\text{complement of } 88.5° = 1.5°$$
$$\sin 1.5° = 0.0262$$
$$\cos 88.5° = 0.0262$$

**Cosine 89.4° to 90°.** To find the cosine of an angle between 89.4° and 90°, determine the complement of the angle and find the value of the sine of this angle as previously discussed.

*Example:*
$$\cos 89.94° = ?$$
$$\text{complement of } 89.94° = 0.06°$$
$$\sin 0.06° = \frac{0.06}{57.3} = 0.001048$$
$$\cos 89.94° = 0.001048$$

NOTE: In finding the cosine of any angle, it is sometimes more convenient to look up the sine of the complement of the angle.

*Example:*
$$\cos 60° = ?$$
$$\text{complement of } 60° = 30°$$
$$\sin 30° = 0.500$$
Therefore,
$$\cos 60° = 0.500$$

**Cosines Practice Problems**

**10–508.** Cos 18.8° = 0.947

**10–509.** Cos 33.17° = 0.837

**10–510.** Cos 71.5° = 0.317

**10–511.** Cos 45° = 0.707

**10–512.** Cos 68.3° = 0.370

**10–513.** Cos 26.9° = 0.892

**10–514.** Cos 55.7° = 0.564

**10–515.** Cos 5.5° = 0.995

**10–516.** Cos 81.3° = 0.151

**10–517.** Cos 8.9° = 0.988

**10–518.** Cos 77.6° = 0.215

**10–519.** Cos 39.1° = 0.776

**10–520.** Cos 50.7° = 0.633

**10–521.** Cos 11.5° = 0.980

**10–522.** Cos 49.2° = 0.653

**10–523.** Arc Cos 0.901 = 25.7°

**10–524.** Cos⁻¹ 0.727 = 43.4°

**10–525.** Cos⁻¹ 0.0814 = 85.3°

**Cosines Practice Problems (continued)**

**10–526.** Arc Cos $0.284 = 73.5°$        **10–530.** Arc Cos $0.303 = 72.4°$
**10–527.** $\text{Cos}^{-1} 0.585 = 54.2°$        **10–531.** $\text{Cos}^{-1} 0.505 = 59.7°$
**10–528.** $\text{Cos}^{-1} 0.658 = 48.8°$        **10–532.** $\text{Cos}^{-1} 0.693 = 46.1°$
**10–529.** $\text{Cos}^{-1} 0.1190 = 83.1°$

**Tangent 0° to 5.74°.** For small angles (0° to 5.74°) the tangent of the angle may be considered to be the same value as the sine of that angle.

**Tangent 5.74° to 45°.** To find the tangent of an angle between 5.74° and 45°, the T scale is used in conjunction with the D scale, as shown in Figure 10–25.

*Example:* Find tan 30°.

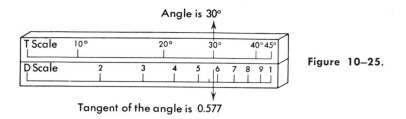

Figure 10–25.

INSTRUCTIONS

1. Be certain that the left index of the D scale is directly under the left index of the T scale.

2. Set the hairline to the angle on the T scale. If the T scale has more than one set of markings, be certain that the correct markings are used.

3. Read the answer on the D scale. Place the decimal preceding the first digit read from the rule.

**Tangent 45° to 84.26°.** To find the tangent of an angle between 45° and 84.26°, the markings to the left of the longer graduations on the T scale are used in conjunction with the CI or DI scales, as shown in Figure 10–26.

*Example:*                         tan 70° = ?

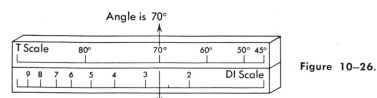

Figure 10–26.

INSTRUCTIONS

1. Be certain that the left index of the DI or CI scale is aligned with the left index of the T scale.

2. Set the hairline to the angle on the T scale.

3. Read the answer on the CI or DI scale. Note that these scales read from right to left. Place the decimal after the first digit read from the rule.

**Tangent 84.26° to 89.426°.** To find the tangent of an angle between 84.26° and 89.426°, the complement of the angle on the ST scale is used in conjunction with the CI or DI scales, as shown in Figure 10–27.

*Example:* $\quad\quad\quad\quad\quad$ tan 88° = ?

**Figure 10–27.**

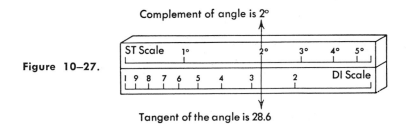

Complement of angle is 2°

Tangent of the angle is 28.6

INSTRUCTIONS

1. Be certain that the left index of the DI or CI scale is aligned with the left index of the ST scale.

2. Complement of 88° = 2°.

3. Read the answer on the DI or CI scale. Note that these scales read from right to left.

4. Place the decimal point after the first two digits read from the rule.

Frequently the value of the function of an angle is known and it is desired to find the value of the angle.

*Example:* $\quad\quad\quad\quad\quad$ $\sin \theta = 0.53;$
$$\theta = ?$$

This may be written in the inverse form in either of two ways:

$$\text{Arc sin } 0.53 = \theta$$

or $\quad\quad\quad\quad\quad\quad\quad\quad$ $\text{Sin}^{-1} 0.53 = \theta$

then $\quad\quad\quad\quad\quad\quad\quad\quad\quad$ $\theta = 32°$

The forms arc sin, arc cos, and arc tan are usually preferred in modern practice.

## Tangents Practice Problems

**10–533.** Tan 29.6° = 0.568
**10–534.** Tan 48.2° = 1.118
**10–535.** Tan 11.5° = 0.203
**10–536.** Tan 71.9° = 3.06
**10–537.** Tan 5.7° = 0.0993
**10–538.** Tan 61.4° = 1.834
**10–539.** Tan 33.3° = 0.657
**10–540.** Tan 69.2° = 2.63
**10–541.** Tan 40.6° = 0.857
**10–542.** Tan 8.7° = 0.1530
**10–543.** Tan 17.5° = 0.315
**10–544.** Tan 85.1° = 11.66
**10–545.** Tan 58.6° = 1.638

**10–546.** Tan 39.3° = 0.818
**10–547.** Tan 20.9° = 0.382
**10–548.** Tan 42.1° = 0.904
**10–549.** Arc tan 0.362 = 19.9°
**10–550.** Arc tan 0.841 = 40.1°
**10–551.** $\text{Tan}^{-1}$ 0.119 = 6.78°
**10–552.** $\text{Tan}^{-1}$ 0.0721 = 4.13°
**10–553.** $\text{Tan}^{-1}$ 1.732 = 60°
**10–554.** Arc tan 21.6 = 87.3°
**10–555.** $\text{Tan}^{-1}$ 0.776 = 37.8°
**10–556** Arc tan 89.3 = 89.36°
**10–557.** $\text{Tan}^{-1}$ 0.661 = 33.5°

The following tables have been prepared for reference purposes. The student should check all the examples with his rule as he proceeds.

| | ANGLE | READ ANGLE ON | READ FUNCTION ON | DECIMAL | EXAMPLES |
|---|---|---|---|---|---|
| sine or tangent | 0°–0.574° Convert the angle to radians (1 radian = 57.3°), and this value is assumed to be equal to the sine or tangent of the angle. | | | | |
| sine or tangent | 0.574°–5.74° | ST | D | 0.0xxx | tan 2° = 0.0349 sin 3° = 0.0523 |
| sine | 5.74°–90° | S (right markings) | D | 0.xxxx | sin 29° = 0.485 |
| cosine | 0°–84.26° | S (left markings) | D | 0.xxxx | cos 43° = 0.7314 |
| tangent | 5.74°–45° | T (right markings) | D | 0.xxxx | tan 13° = 0.231 |
| tangent | 45°–84.26° | T (left markings) | DI | x.xxx | tan 78° = 4.70 |
| tangent | 84.26°–89.426 | Set complement on ST | DI | xx.xxx | tan 89° = 57.3 |
| cosecant | 5.74°–90° | S (right markings) | DI | x.xxx | csc 63° = 1.122 |
| secant | 0°–84.26° | S (left markings) | DI | x.xxx | sec 48° = 1.494 |
| cotangent | 0.574°–5.74° | ST | DI | xx.xx | cot 3.5° = 16.35 |
| cotangent | 5.74°–45° | T (right markings) | DI | x.xxx | cot 23° = 2.36 |
| cotangent | 45°–84.26° | T (left markings) | D | 0.xxxx | cot 68° = 0.404 |

### Trigonometric Functions: Problems

Solve, using the slide rule.

**10–558.** sin 35°
**10–559.** sin 14°
**10–560.** sin 78°
**10–561.** sin 3.7°
**10–562.** sin 88.3°
**10–563.** sin 55.3°
**10–564.** cos 35°
**10–565.** cos 66°
**10–566.** cos 21.3°
**10–567.** cos 11.1°
**10–568.** cos 7.9°
**10–569.** cos 43.8°
**10–570.** tan 33.8°
**10–571.** tan 9.4°
**10–572.** tan 37.7°
**10–573.** tan 22.5°
**10–574.** tan 86.1°
**10–575.** tan 54.4°
**10–576.** tan 70.3°
**10–577.** tan 29.7°
**10–578.** tan 36.5°
**10–579.** tan 13.3°
**10–580.** tan 45.8°
**10–581.** cot 14.7°
**10–582.** cot 81.8°
**10–583.** cot 36.9°
**10–584.** cot 61.2°
**10–585.** cot 54.3°

**10–586.** cot 18.7°
**10–587.** cot 3.77°
**10–588.** cot 66.4°
**10–589.** csc 38.1°
**10–590.** csc 75.2°
**10–591.** csc 88.3°
**10–592.** csc 12.8°
**10–593.** csc 46.4°
**10–594.** csc 81.1°
**10–595.** csc 32.6°
**10–596.** csc 9.03°
**10–597.** sec 6.14°
**10–598.** sec 59.2°
**10–599.** sec 79.4°
**10–600.** sec 19.5°
**10–601.** sec 2.77°
**10–602.** sec 45.9°
**10–603.** arc-sin 0.771
**10–604.** arc cos 0.119
**10–605.** arc tan 34.8
**10–606.** arc sec 7.18
**10–607.** arc csc 1.05
**10–608.** cos 33.4°
**10–609.** cos 3.6°
**10–610.** arc cos 0.992
**10–611.** cos 24.67°
**10–612.** cos$^{-1}$ 0.496
**10–613.** cos 36°6′

**10–614.** arc cos 0.238
**10–615.** cos 0.75°
**10–616.** cos 36.6°
**10–617.** tan 32.6°
**10–618.** tan 16.34°
**10–619.** tan 88°30′
**10–620.** arc tan 0.62
**10–621.** tan$^{-1}$ 0.75
**10–622.** arc tan 0.392
**10–623.** tan$^{-1}$ 1.53
**10–624.** tan 37°24′
**10–625.** arc tan 0.567
**10–626.** tan$^{-1}$ 0.0321
**10–627.** cot 19°33′
**10–628.** sec 46°46′
**10–629.** csc 32°12′
**10–630.** sin 37°
**10–631.** sin 51°50′
**10–632.** sin 68°37′
**10–633.** sin 75°10′
**10–634.** arc sin 0.622
**10–635.** sin 13.6°
**10–636.** sin$^{-1}$ 0.068
**10–637.** sin 14.6°
**10–638.** arc sin 0.169
**10–639.** sin 34.67°
**10–640.** cos 26.26°
**10–641.** csc 20°20′

**10–642.** $(\csc 20°)(\sin 46°)$
**10–643.** $(\cos 32°)(\tan 43°)$
**10–644.** $\dfrac{(\sin 13.9°)}{(\cot 13.9°)}$
**10–645.** $\dfrac{\cot 33°22'}{\sec 4°53'}$
**10–646.** $\dfrac{(\cos 33°15')}{(\cot 46°19')}$
**10–647.** $\dfrac{(\sec 10°)(\cot 10°)}{(\sin 10°)(\csc 10°)}$
**10–648.** $\dfrac{(\sin 35°)(\tan 22°)}{(\sqrt[3]{\sin 5.96°})}$

**10–649.** $\dfrac{(\sec 11°)(\tan 4°)}{(\cot 49°)}$
**10–650.** $\dfrac{(\sin 8°)(\tan 9°)}{(\cot 82°)}$
**10–651.** $\dfrac{(\sin 1.36°)(\cot 26°)}{(\sqrt[3]{0.00916})}$
**10–652.** $\dfrac{\cot \sin^{-1} 0.916}{(1.32)(5.061)}$
**10–653.** $\dfrac{(77.19)(\sec 46°)}{(\tan 3.91°)}$

### Trigonometric Functions: Problems (continued)

**10–654.** $\dfrac{(\sqrt[3]{\tan 25.9°})(\sin \cos^{-1} 0.5)}{(\sin 5.16°)(\tan 22°)}$

**10–656.** $\dfrac{(1.916)(\sqrt[3]{1.916})(\sqrt[3]{\sin 20°})}{(\sqrt[3]{\sec 40°})(\tan 10°22')}$

**10–655.** $\dfrac{(0.0311)(\sec 69°)\sqrt[3]{9.0}}{(\sin 9°)(\cos 9°)}$

**10–657.** $\dfrac{(6.17)(\tan 6.17°)(\sqrt[3]{6.17})}{(6.17)^2(\sin 61.7°)(\cos 6.17°)}$

### Right Triangle Solution (Log-Log Rule)

In the study of truss design, moments, and free body diagrams, the right triangle plays an important role. Since the Pythagorean theorem is sometimes awkward to use, and mistakes in arithmetic are likely to occur, it is suggested that the following method be used to solve right triangles.

Given: Right triangle with sides $a$, $b$, and $c$ and angles $A$, $B$, and $C$ ($90°$), as shown in Figure 10–28.

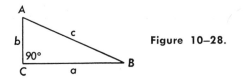

Figure 10–28.

If the smaller side ($b$) is divided by the longer side ($a$) and the quotient is greater than 0.100, use *Solution 1*. If the quotient is between 0.100 and 0.0100, use *Solution 2*. If the quotient is less than 0.0100, assume that the hypotenuse ($c$) is equal in length to the longest side ($a$) and that angle $B \cong 0°$.

### Solution 1

1. Set the index of the T scale above the larger side ($a$) on the D scale.
2. Move the hairline to the smaller side ($b$) on the D scale.
3. Read the two angles of the right triangle on the T scale. The larger angle is always opposite the larger side.
4. Move the slide until the smaller of the two angles just read is under the hairline on the sine scale.
5. Read the hypotenuse ($c$) on the D scale as indicated by the index of the sine scale.

*Example:*  $a = 4$   $A = ?$
 $b = 3$   $B = ?$
 $c = ?$

*a.* Set right index of T to 4 on the D scale.
*b.* Move the hairline to 3 on the D scale.
*c.* Read $B = 36.9°$, $A = 53.1°$ on the T scale. (Note that the smaller angle is opposite the smaller side.)
*d.* Move the slide so that $36.9°$ on the S scale is under the hairline.
*e.* Read side $c = 5$ at the right index of the S scale on the D scale.

**Solution 2**

1. Set the index of the T scale above the largest side ($a$) on the D scale.
2. Move the hairline to the smaller side ($b$) on the D scale.
3. Read the smaller angle ($B$) on the ST scale. The other angle ($A$) is the complement of $B$.
4. The hypotenuse is assumed to be equal in length to the largest side.

**Solution 3:**   This solution is used where the hypotenuse and one side are given.

*Example:*
$$a = 5.26 \quad A = ?$$
$$b = ? \quad B = ?$$
$$c = 8.75$$

*a.* Set index over 8.75 on D scale.
*b.* Move hairline to 5.26 on D scale.
*c.* Read $A = 37.0°$; $B = 53.0°$ on the S scale. (Note that the angle read on the sine scale is opposite the given side.)
*d.* Set hairline to 37° on the cosine scale.
*e.* Read $b = 7.0$ on the D scale.

**Problems**

Solve by right triangle method.

| | | | | | |
|---|---|---|---|---|---|
| **10–658.** | $a = 53$ $b = 4$ | $B = ?$ $c = ?$ | **10–668.** | $a = 11.33$ $B = 26.1°$ | $b = ?$ $c = ?$ |
| **10–659.** | $a = 69.3$ $c = 95$ | $b = ?$ $A = ?$ | **10–669.** | $a = 0.00197$ $A = 11.36°$ | $b = ?$ $c = ?$ |
| **10–660.** | $a = 37$ $c = 40.3$ | $b = ?$ $B = ?$ | **10–670.** | $c = 1904$ $A = 18.33°$ | $a = ?$ $b = ?$ |
| **10–661.** | $a = 1.97$ $c = 2.33$ | $B = ?$ $b = ?$ | **10–671.** | $c = 4.0059$ $B = 86.3°$ | $a = ?$ $b = ?$ |
| **10–662.** | $a = 29.3$ $c = 55.3$ | $b = ?$ $A = ?$ | **10–672.** | $c = 4.266$ $B = 31.06°$ | $a = ?$ $b = ?$ |
| **10–663.** | $a = 49.3$ $b = 29.6$ | $c = ?$ $A = ?$ | **10–673.** | $a = 0.00397$ $c = 0.00512$ | $b = ?$ $A = ?$ |
| **10–664.** | $a = 57.3$ $b = 42.1$ | $c = ?$ $A = ?$ | **10–674.** | $a = 1069$ $A = 85.3°$ | $b = ?$ $c = ?$ |
| **10–665.** | $a = 3.95$ $b = 1.06$ | $c = ?$ $B = ?$ | **10–675.** | $b = 42.1$ $B = 3.56°$ | $a = ?$ $c = ?$ |
| **10–666.** | $a = 333$ $b = 20$ | $A = ?$ $c = ?$ | **10–676.** | $a = 0.0317$ $c = 0.0444$ | $b = ?$ $B = ?$ |
| **10–667.** | $a = 591$ $b = 25$ | $c = ?$ $B = ?$ | **10–677.** | $a = 21.67$ $b = 20.06$ | $c = ?$ $B = ?$ |

### The Log-log (Lon) Scales

There are two groups of log-log scales (also called "Lon" scales) on the slide rule. Scales within the two groups are arranged in matched sets. Some slide rules have four matched sets, whereas others have three. These scales are used to obtain the roots, powers, and logarithms of numbers. The matched sets are arranged as follows:

**Matched Sets of Log-Log Scales**

| FOUR SETS | | THREE SETS | |
|---|---|---|---|
| For Numbers Larger Than One (called "Lon" scales) | For Numbers Smaller Than One (called "Lon-minus" scales) | (called LL scales) | (called $LL_0$ scales) |
| Ln0 . . . . . . . . . . . . . . . . . . . . Ln–0 | | | |
| Ln1 . . . . . . . . . . . . . . . . . . . . Ln–1 | | $LL_1$ . . . . . . . . . . . $LL_{01}$ | |
| Ln2 . . . . . . . . . . . . . . . . . . . Ln–2 | | $LL_2$ . . . . . . . . . . . $LL_{02}$ | |
| Ln3 . . . . . . . . . . . . . . . . . . . Ln–3 | | $LL_3$ . . . . . . . . . . . $LL_{03}$ | |

The C and D scales are used in conjunction with these matched sets of log-log scales. In former years other rules were manufactured with only two $LL_0$ scales, and these are marked $LL_0$ and $LL_{00}$. The A and B scales were used with $LL_0$ and $LL_{00}$ scales on this type of rule. The general principles discussed below apply to all of the various types of log-log scales.

### Scale Construction

If the Lon scales Ln0, Ln1, Ln2, and Ln3 were placed end to end, they would form a continuous scale, as shown in Figure 10–29. Similarly, if the Lon-minus scales Ln-0, Ln-1, Ln-2, Ln-3 were placed end to end, they would form a continuous scale. The Lon-minus scales are graduated from approximately 0.999 to 0.00003 (representing the values of $\epsilon^{-0.001}$ to $\epsilon^{-10}$). The Lon scales are graduated from ap-

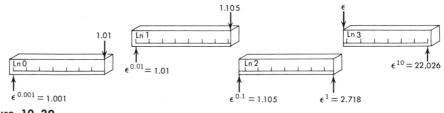

**Figure 10–29.**

proximately 1.001 to 22,026 (representing the values of $\epsilon^{0.001}$ to $\epsilon^{10}$). Since $\epsilon^0 = 1$, values on both the Lon and Lon-minus scales approach the value 1.0000.

Each division on the Lon and Lon-minus scales represents a single unique number. Thus the decimal point is already marked on these scales for all of the numbers located on the scales. For example, there is only one place on the Lon scales that the number 125.0 may be found. The number 125.0 is found on the Ln3 ($LL_3$) scale, whereas the number 1.25 is found on the Ln2 ($LL_2$) scale. Since the manner in which settings are read on the log-log scales is distinctly different from the method of reading the scales previously studied, the student should be very careful in making his slide rule settings.

### Reciprocal Values

The only case where the Lon and Lon-minus (LL and $LL_0$) scales may be used together is in the finding of reciprocals of numbers. The reciprocal of any number on the Lon (LL) scales can be read on the corresponding Lon-minus ($LL_0$) scale.

*Examples:*

1. Find 1.25 on the Ln2 ($LL_2$) scale. On the Ln-2 ($LL_{02}$) scale its reciprocal can be read as 0.80.
2. Find 236 on the Ln3 ($LL_3$) scale. On the Ln-3 ($LL_{03}$) scale its reciprocal can be read as 0.00424.

### Raising a Number to a Power

If such problems as $(5.3)^3 = ?$ were worked entirely by logarithms, the following procedure would be required:

1. $(5.3)^3 = ?$
2. log ans. $= 3(\log 5.3)$
3. $\log [\log ans.] = \log 3 + \log (\log 5.3)$
4. Answer $= (1.488)(10)^2$

Step 3 is rather involved in many instances. It is for this reason that the log-log scales have been added to the slide rule. Since log-log values of numbers are recorded on the Lon (LL) scales and the log values of numbers have been recorded on the C and D scales, it is quite convenient to perform Step 3 in the preceding example.

The Lon (LL) and Lon–minus ($LL_0$) scales are also used in conjunction with the C and D scales to find powers, roots, and logarithms to the base $\epsilon$ of numbers.

In order to raise any number greater than 1.01 to any power:

$$(X)^n = A$$

1. Set the index of the C scale over the value $X$ found on the appropriate Lon (LL) scale (Ln0, Ln1, Ln2, or Ln3).
2. Move the hairline to the value $n$ on the C scale.
3. Read the answer $A$ on the appropriate Lon (LL) scale.

*Example:*
$$(1.02)^{2.5} = ?$$
$$\log [\log \text{ans.}] = \log 2.5 + \log (\log 1.02)$$
$$\text{Answer} = 1.0507$$

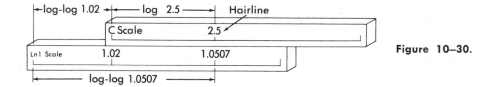

**Figure 10–30.**

SOLUTION:

1. Set the index of the C scale over the value 1.02 on the Ln1 ($LL_1$) scale.
2. Move the hairline to the value 2.5 on the C scale.
3. Read the answer 1.0507 on the Ln1 ($LL_1$) scale.

These scales are arranged so that a number on the Ln3 ($LL_3$) scale is the tenth power of the number directly below it on the Ln2 ($LL_2$) scale, and the Ln2 ($LL_2$) scale gives the tenth power of a number in the corresponding position on the Ln1 ($LL_1$) scale. Therefore the Ln3 ($LL_3$) scale would give the one-hundredth power of a number in the corresponding position on the Ln1 ($LL_1$) scale.

*Example:*
$$(1.034)^{0.23} = 1.00773 \text{ ans. on the Ln0}$$
$$(1.034)^{2.3} = 1.0799 \text{ ans. on the Ln1 } (LL_1)$$
$$(1.034)^{23.} = 2.156 \text{ ans. on the Ln2 } (LL_2)$$
$$(1.034)^{230.} = 2160 \text{ ans. on the Ln3 } (LL_3)$$

In order to raise any number less than 0.99 to any power:

$$(X)^n = A$$

1. Set the index of the C scale over the value $X$ found on the appropriate Lon–minus ($LL_0$) scale Ln-0, Ln-1, Ln-2, or Ln-3 ($LL_{01}$, $LL_{02}$, or $LL_{03}$).
2. Move the hairline to the value $n$ on the C scale.
3. Read the answer $A$ on the appropriate Ln–0 ($LL_0$) scale.

*Example:*  $(0.855)^{4.8} = A$, as shown in Figure 10–31.

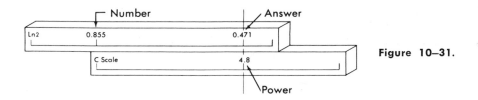

**Figure 10–31.**

**Method of Scale Selection—Powers of Numbers**

To use this method, we must consider three factors: (1) the particular log log scale upon which the *number* is located, (2) the power of ten of the exponent when it is expressed in scientific notation, and (3) the particular index of the C scale that is used in the calculation.

1. Each log log scale is given a positive value as follows:

$$Ln0 = 0 \qquad\qquad Ln\text{-}0 = 0$$
$$Ln1 = +1 \text{ (Also } LL_1) \qquad Ln\text{-}1 = +1 \text{ (Also } LL_{01})$$
$$Ln2 = +2 \text{ (Also } LL_2) \qquad Ln\text{-}2 = +2 \text{ (Also } LL_{02})$$
$$Ln3 = +3 \text{ (Also } LL_3) \qquad Ln\text{-}3 = +3 \text{ (Also } LL_{03})$$

2. The exponent should be expressed in scientific notation and the power of ten indicated.

3. Assume that the *left* index of the C scale has a value of zero (0) and that the *right* index has a value of plus one (+1).

**Rule for Scale Selection of Powers of Numbers**

The number of the scale upon which the answer will be read is the algebraic sum of (1) the value of the scale on which the number to be raised is found plus (2) the C scale index value plus (3) the power of ten of the exponent.

*Example:* $\qquad (1.015)^{56} = ?$

Rewrite as $\qquad (1.015)^{5.6(10)^1} = ?$

| Factor | Description of Factor | Value | |
|---|---|---|---|
| 1.015 | 1.015 is found on $LL_1$ scale | +1 | |
| Left Index | Use left index of C scale | 0 | |
| 56 | Power of ten of exponent = 1 | +1 | |
| ? | Sum = Scale location of answer | +2 | ← Answer on Ln2 ($LL_2$) |

Therefore, the answer will be read under the hairline on the Ln2 ($LL_2$) scale.

$$(1.015)^{56} = \underline{\underline{2.30}} \qquad \text{Answer}$$

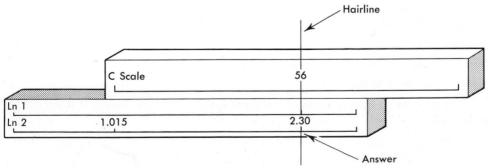

**Figure 10–32.**

Engineering Tools of Analysis

### Negative Exponents

In solving problems which involve raising numbers to a negative power, either of two methods may be employed.

**Method 1.** Set the number and its exponent on the proper scales in the usual manner. Instead of reading the answer on the usual log-log scale, read it on the corresponding scale of the other group.

*Example:* $(9.2)^{-3.5} = ?$

Instead of reading the answer as 2355 on the Ln3 ($LL_3$) scale, read its reciprocal value on the Ln-3 ($LL_{03}$) as 0.000425; therefore

$$(9.2)^{-3.5} = \underline{\underline{4.25 \times 10^{-4}}} \quad \text{(Answer)}$$

**Method 2.** Set the numbers on the rule in the usual manner, ignoring the negative exponent. When the answer by this operation has been obtained, determine its reciprocal, using the CI scale.

On the slide rules that have only the $LL_0$ and $LL_{00}$ scales, Method 2 is the only method that can be used.

### Powers of Numbers: Practice Problems

**10–678.** $(53.2)^{0.84} = 28.2$

**10–679.** $(4.65)^{3.68} = 285.$

**10–680.** $(0.836)^{0.47} = 0.919$

**10–681.** $(1.0042)^{217} = 2.48$

**10–682.** $(0.427)^4 = 0.0360$

**10–683.** $(0.3156)^4 = 0.00988$

**10–684.** $(0.159)^{0.67} = 0.292$

**10–685.** $(1.0565)^{49.5} = 15.2$

**10–686.** $(32.5)^{0.065} = 1.254$

**10–687.** $(3.45)^{4.65} = 318.$

**10–688.** $(0.759)^5 = 0.252$

**10–689.** $(2.127)^4 = 20.5$

**10–690.** $(2.03)^{-5} = 0.0290$

**10–691.** $(4.00)^{0.0157} = 1.022$

**10–692.** $(0.0818)^{-0.777} = 7.00$

**10–693.** $(1.382)^{21.3} = 980.$

**10–694.** $(0.071)^{-0.46} = 3.38$

**10–695.** $(0.232)^{0.0904} = 0.876$

**10–696.** $(2.718)^{0.405} = 1.50$

**10–697.** $(0.916)^{0.724} = 0.9384$

**10–698.** $(1.1106)^{1.72} = 1.197$

**10–699.** $(59.2)^{-0.43} = 0.1727$

**10–700.** $(883)^{0.964} = 688.$

**10–701.** $(7676)^{0.001102} = 1.0099$

**10–702.** $(4.30)^{0.521} = 2.14$

### Finding Roots of Numbers

The process of finding roots of numbers is easier to understand if it is remembered that

$$\sqrt[2.1]{576} = X$$

may be written as $(X)^{2.1} = 576$

Therefore we can "work backward" and apply the principles learned in raising a number to a power. Proceed as follows:

*Example:*

$$\sqrt[n]{A} = X$$

1. Locate the root $n$ on the C scale to coincide with the value $A$ found on the appropriate log-log scale.
2. Move the hairline to the particular index of the C scale which is located within the body of the rule.
3. Read the answer on the appropriate log log scale.

*Example:*     $\sqrt[3.2]{120} = 4.46$ ans. on Ln3 (LL$_3$), as shown in Figure 10–33.

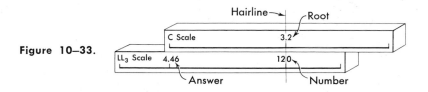

**Figure 10–33.**

Also     $\sqrt[32]{120} = 1.1615$ ans. on Ln2 (LL$_2$)

$\sqrt[320]{120} = 1.0152$ ans. on Ln1 (LL$_1$)

In taking the root of a number, students usually are less certain of the appropriate scale upon which the answer is found. Therefore, a method of scale selection similar to that employed for powers of numbers should be used.

### Method of Scale Selection for Roots of Numbers

As before there are three factors which must be considered: (1) the particular log-log scale upon which the *number* is located; (2) the power of ten of the exponent when it is expressed in scientific notation, and (3) the particular index of the C scale which is used in the calculation.

1. Each log-log scale is given a negative value as follows:

| | |
|---|---|
| Ln0 = 0 | Ln-0 = 0 |
| Ln1 = −1 (Also LL$_1$) | Ln-1 = −1 (Also LL$_{01}$) |
| Ln2 = −2 (Also LL$_2$) | Ln-2 = −2 (Also LL$_{02}$) |
| Ln3 = −3 (Also LL$_3$) | Ln-3 = −3 (Also LL$_{03}$) |

2. The root should be expressed in scientific notation and the power of ten indicated.
3. Assume that the *left* index of the C scale has a value of zero (0) and that the *right* index has a value of plus one (+1).

### Rule for Scale Selection for Roots of Numbers

The number of the scale upon which the answer will be read is the algebraic sum of (1) the value of the scale on which the *number whose root is to be determined* is located, plus (2) the C scale index value, plus (3) the power of ten of the root.

*Example:*

$$\sqrt[4.37]{0.0092} = \text{Answer}$$

| FACTOR | DESCRIPTION OF FACTOR | VALUE | |
|---|---|---|---|
| 0.0092 | 0.0092 is found on Ln-3 ($LL_{03}$) Scale | $-3$ | |
| Left Index | Use left index of C scale | 0 | |
| 4.37 | Power of ten of root = 0 | 0 | |
| ? | Sum = Scale location of Answer | $-3$ | ← Answer on Ln-3 ($LL_{03}$) |

Therefore, the answer will be read on the Ln-3 ($LL_{03}$) scale as 0.342.

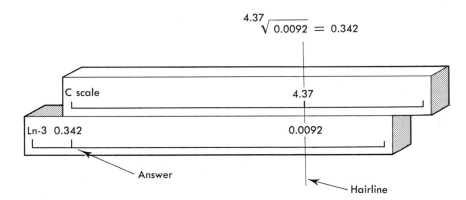

**Figure 10–34.**

### Roots of Numbers Practice Problems

**10–703.** $\sqrt[7.81]{5.85} = 1.254$

**10–704.** $\sqrt[6]{0.0835} = 0.661$

**10–705.** $\sqrt[5]{0.0763} = 0.598$

**10–706.** $\sqrt[194]{460.} = 1.0321$

**10–707.** $\sqrt[6]{0.0001} = 0.215$

**10–708.** $\sqrt[1.65]{8.26} = 3.60$

**10–709.** $\sqrt[0.34]{0.862} = 0.646$

**10–710.** $\sqrt[2.3]{85.9} = 6.92$

**10–711.** $\sqrt[60]{45.} = 1.0655$

**10–712.** $\sqrt[21.5]{1.606} = 1.0223$

**10–713.** $\sqrt[1.91]{92.5} = 10.7$

**10–714.** $\sqrt[50]{0.05} = 0.9418$

**10–715.** $\sqrt[7]{0.0108} = 0.524$

**10–716.** $\sqrt[0.006]{0.9762} = 0.018$

**10–717.** $\sqrt[5.21]{2000} = 4.30$

**10–718.** $\sqrt[0.04]{0.9792} = 0.592$

**10–719.** $\sqrt[2.7]{81} = 5.09$

**10–720.** $\sqrt[2.81]{1.218} = 1.0726$

**10–721.** $\sqrt[2.15]{52.5} = 6.31$

**10–722.** $\sqrt[400]{100} = 1.0116$

**10–723.**  $\sqrt[0.75]{2.37} = 3.16$        **10–726.**  $\sqrt[5.6]{0.0018} = 0.323$

**10–724.**  $\sqrt[0.073]{1.060} = 2.22$       **10–727.**  $\sqrt[0.67]{0.954} = 0.932$

**10–725.**  $\sqrt[1.51]{6.50} = 3.45$

### General Guides for Decimal Location

The student should be able to estimate the approximate answer and thereby know on which scale the answer will be found.

The following suggestions are presented so that the student can more easily decide whether the answer is to be larger or smaller than the original quantity.

$$(\text{Number})^{\text{Exponent}} = \text{Answer}$$

1. If the number is larger than 1.00 and the exponent is larger than 1.00, the answer will be greater than the number.

2. If the number is less than 1.00 and the exponent is less than 1.00, the answer will be greater than the number.

3. If the number is less than 1.00 and the exponent is greater than 1.00, the answer will be less than the number.

4. If the number is greater than 1.00 and the exponent is less than 1.00, the answer will be less than the number.

### Results That Do Not Fall Within the Limits of the Scales

In many computations the final answer may be larger than 22,026 and hence cannot be read within the limits of the scales. In such cases the original expression must be factored before attempting to use the log–log scales. Several such methods of factoring are explained below.

These methods are for use in finding the powers of numbers. For problems involving roots of numbers convert the problem to one involving the power of a number and then apply the appropriate method.

*Example:*
$$\sqrt{5} = (5)^{\frac{1}{2}} = (5)^{0.5}$$
$$\sqrt[4]{5} = (5)^{\frac{1}{4}} = (5)^{0.25}$$
$$\sqrt[0.5]{5} = (5)^{\frac{1}{0.5}} = (5)^2$$

**Method 1.**  Express the number in scientific notation and raise each part to the given power.

*Example:*
$$(35.3)^4 = ?$$
$$(35.3)^4 = (3.53 \times 10)^4$$
$$= (3.53)^4 \times (10)^4$$

Now, using the Lon (LL) scales, and since $(3.53)^4 = 155$, we obtain

$$(35.3)^4 = 155. \times 10^4$$
$$= 1.55 \times 10^6 \quad (\text{Answer})$$

**Method 2.** Factor the number which is to be raised to a power and then treat each part separately, as in Method 1.

*Example:*

$$(15)^5 = ?$$
$$(15)^5 = (3 \times 5)^5$$
$$= (3)^5 \times (5)^5$$
$$= (243)(3125)$$
$$= 7.59 \times 10^5 \text{ (Answer)}$$

**Method 3.** Divide the exponent into two or more smaller parts and, using the log-log scales, compute each part separately. A final computation is made using the C and D scales as in Method 1 and Method 2.

*Example:*

$$(2.36)^{15} = ?$$
$$(2.36)^{15} = (2.36)^5 \times (2.36)^5 \times (2.36)^5$$
$$= (73.2)(73.2)(73.2)$$
$$= 3.93 \times 10^5 \text{ (Answer)}$$

or

$$(2.36)^{15} = (2.36)^8 \times (2.36)^7$$
$$= (960)(410)$$
$$= 3.93 \times 10^5 \text{ (Answer)}$$

$$(2.36)^{15} = (2.36)^{7.5} \times (2.36)^{7.5}$$
$$= (620)^2$$
$$= 3.93 \times 10^5 \text{ (Answer)}$$

*Example:*

$$(0.000025)^{1.3} = ?$$
$$(0.000025)^{1.3} = (2.5 \times 10^{-5})^{1.3}$$
$$= (2.5)^{1.3} \times (10^{-5})^{1.3}$$
$$= 3.29 \times (10)^{-6.5}$$
$$= (3.29)(10)^{-6}(10)^{-0.5}$$
$$= (3.29)(10)^{-6} \left(\frac{1}{3.16}\right)$$
$$= (3.29)(10)^{-6}(0.316)$$
$$= 1.041 \times 10^{-6} \text{ (Answer)}$$

**Method 4.** Express the number in scientific notation and then express the power of 10 in logarithmic form.

*Example:*

$$(250)^{3.2} = ?$$
$$(250)^{3.2} = (2.50 \times 10^2)^{3.2} = (2.50)^{3.2}(10)^{6.4}$$

where $(10)^{6.4} = x$ may be expressed as $\log_{10} x = 6.4$ or $x = (2.51)(10)^6$

Then
$$(2.50)^{3.2}(10)^{6.4} = (1.87 \times 10^1)(2.51 \times 10^6)$$
and
$$(1.87 \times 10^1)(2.51 \times 10^6) = \underline{\underline{4.71 \times 10^7}}$$

**Method 5.** This method is more suitable for those numbers which have 5, 6, 7, 8, or 9 as the first digit.

*Example:*
$$(645)^{13} = ?$$
$$(645)^{13} = (0.645)^{13}(10^3)^{13}$$
$$= (0.00335)(10)^{39}$$
$$= \underline{\underline{3.35(10)^{36}}} \ \text{(Answer)}$$

**Method 6.** Factor the exponent such that one part is equivalent to an exact power of ten.

*Example:*
$$(2)^{52} = ?$$

First raise the base (2) to a power such that the answer is an exact power of ten.
$$(2)^k = 10,000 = (10)^4$$
$$k = 13.29$$

Also:
$$(2)^{52} = (2)^{13.29 + 13.29 + 13.29 + 12.13}$$
$$= (10^4)(10)^4(10)^4(2)^{12.13}$$
$$= (10^4)^3(2)^{12.13}$$
$$= (10)^{12}(4500)$$
$$= \underline{\underline{(4.5)(10)^{15}}} \ \text{(Answer)}$$

*Example:*
$$(1.324)(10)^{-9} = (0.815)^m$$

First choose a factor such that an exact power of ten is obtained.
$$(0.815)^{45} = 0.0001 = (10)^{-4}$$

Then:
$$(1.324)(10)^{-9} = (0.815)^{45+45+t}$$
$$= (0.815)^{45}(0.815)^{45}(0.815)^t$$
$$= (10)^{-4}(10)^{-4}(0.815)^t$$
$$\frac{(1.324)(10)^{-9}}{(10)^{-8}} = (0.815)^t$$
$$1.324(10)^{-1} = (0.815)^t$$
$$t = 9.87$$

Therefore:
$$(1.324)(10)^{-9} = (0.815)^{45+45+9.87}$$
$$(1.324)(10)^{-9} = (0.815)^{99.87}$$

and:
$$m = \underline{\underline{99.9}} \ \text{(Answer)}$$

Methods 1 and 6 are generally preferred over the other methods because they usually make greater accuracy possible in the final answer.

### Finding the Natural Logarithm of a Number

The natural base for logarithms is $\epsilon(2.71828\text{---})$. The logarithm of any number (to the base $\epsilon$) may be found as follows:

For Numbers Greater than 1.00
$$\log_\epsilon X = A$$

1. Locate the number $X$ on the Ln0, Ln1 ($LL_1$), Ln2 ($LL_2$), or Ln3 ($LL_3$) scale.
2. Read the logarithm of the number under the hairline on the D scale.

Location of Decimal Point

| If the number $X$ is on | Decimal point in the answer |
|---|---|
| Ln3 or $LL_3$ | x.xxx |
| Ln2 or $LL_2$ | 0.xxx |
| Ln1 or $LL_1$ | 0.0xxx |
| Ln0 | 0.00xx |

*Examples:*
$$\log_\epsilon 62 \quad = 4.13$$
$$\log_\epsilon 1.271 = 0.240$$
$$\log_\epsilon 1.026 = 0.0257$$

For numbers Less than 1.00

$$\log_\epsilon X = A$$

1. Locate the number $X$ on the Ln–0, Ln–1 ($LL_{01}$), Ln–2 ($LL_{02}$), or Ln–3 ($LL_{03}$) scales.
2. Read the logarithm (to the base $\epsilon$) of the number $A$ directly above $X$ on the D scale.

Location of Decimal Point

| If the number $X$ is on | Decimal point in the answer |
|---|---|
| Ln-3 or $LL_{03}$ | –x.xxx |
| Ln-2 or $LL_{02}$ | –0.xxx |
| Ln-1 or $LL_{01}$ | –0.0xxx |
| Ln-0 | –0.00xx |

3. The logarithm (to the base $\epsilon$) of all numbers less than 1.000 is a negative number.

*Examples:*
$$\log_\epsilon 0.0045 = -5.40$$
$$\log_\epsilon 0.745 \ = -0.294$$
$$\log_\epsilon 0.954 \ = -0.0471$$

## Problems

Solve, using the log–log scales.

**10–728.** $(2.89)^6$

**10–729.** $(4.11)^{5.2}$

**10–730.** $(19.01)^{1.6}$

**10–731.** $(1.185)^{2.7}$

**10–732.** $(1.033)^{5.8}$

**10–733.** $(1.0134)^{25}$

**10–734.** $(3.95)^{0.65}$

**10–735.** $(8.46)^{0.134}$

**10–736.** $(81.2)^{0.118}$

**10–737.** $(7850.)^{0.0775}$

**10–738.** $(1.399)^{0.883}$

**10–739.** $(10.06)^{0.0621}$

**10–740.** $(0.569)^4$

**10–741.** $(0.157)^8$

**10–742.** $(0.985)^{1.568}$

**10–743.** $(0.318)^{4.65}$

**10–744.** $(0.078)^{0.458}$

**10–745.** $(17.91)^{0.012}$

**10–746.** $(4780.)^{0.913}$

**10–747.** $(253.)^{0.269}$

**10–748.** $(0.428)^{0.559}$

**10–749.** $(4.08)^{24}$

**10–750.** $(3.91)^{20}$

**10–751.** $(8.45)^{16}$

**10–752.** $(7.77)^{42}$

**10–753.** $(16.89)^{1.402}$

**10–754.** $(87.8)^8$

**10–755.** $(0.1164)^{0.33}$

**10–756.** $(0.779)^{0.43}$

**10–757.** $(867.)^6$

**10–758.** $(91.05)^{14}$

**10–759.** $(0.775)^{0.0259}$

**10–760.** $\sqrt[6]{8.69}$

**10–761.** $\sqrt[5]{1.094}$

**10–762.** $\sqrt[1.3]{8.74}$

**10–763.** $\sqrt[0.6]{19.77}$

**10–764.** $\sqrt[18]{54.8}$

**10–765.** $\sqrt[7]{1.004}$

**10–766.** $\sqrt[1.95]{0.642}$

**10–767.** $\sqrt[14]{0.1438}$

**10–768.** $\sqrt[3.6]{0.952}$

**10–769.** $\sqrt[2.4]{0.469}$

**10–770.** $\sqrt[1.7]{0.1975}$

**10–771.** $\sqrt[0.55]{0.2218}$

**10–772.** $\sqrt[0.46]{16,430.}$

**10–773.** $\sqrt[0.133]{507.}$

**10–774.** $\sqrt[0.57]{0.964}$

**10–775.** $\sqrt[5.09]{6.49}$

**10–776.** $\sqrt[13.6]{0.1574}$

**10–777.** $\sqrt[2.09]{0.1268}$

Solve for $X$

**10–778.** $X = (43.8)^{6.4}$

**10–779.** $X = (1.853)^{0.447}$

**10–780.** $(31.77)^x = 1.164$

**10–781.** $(2.388)^{3x} = 3.066$

**10–782.** $(1.064)^{0.2x} = 4.99$

**10–783.** $(X)^{5.8} = 8.57$

**10–784.** $(4.92)^{0.66x} = 24.1$

**10–785.** $(0.899)^{4.7x} = (1.552)(10)^{-8}$

**10–786.** $(0.1135)^{0.77x} = 0.775$

**10–787.** $(11.774)^{8.31x} = 12.88$

**10–788.** $(18.73)^{6.4x} = 8688.$

**10–789.** $(34.86)^{1.117x} = 9.44$

**10–790.** $(0.631)^{0.64x} = 0.318$

**10–791.** $(0.1299)^{0.68x} = 0.443$

**10–792.** $(15.84)^x = 4.87$

**10–793.** $(0.679)^x = 0.337$

**10–794.** $(1.461)^{19.66x} = 9.07$

**10–795.** $(0.766)^{5.8x} = 0.239$

**10–796.** $(X)^{7.99} = 0.775$

**10–797.** $(X)^{0.175} = 8.53$

**10–798.** $(X)^{3.33} = 1.055$

**10–799.** $(X)^{0.871} = 0.1557$

**10–800.** $(X)^{4.77} = 1.088$

**10–801.** $(X)^{0.771} = 0.0521$

**10–802.** $(4.51)^{0.199} = \dfrac{X}{3}$

Solve for the natural logarithms of the following numbers:

**10–803.** 15.77

**10–804.** 19,850.

**10–805.** 0.7789

**10–806.** 0.1845

**10–807.** 1.896

**10–808.** 56.87

**10–809.** 13.09

**10–810.** 33.4

**10–811.** 8.09

**10–812.** 1.571

**10–813.** 0.1345

**10–814.** 0.915

**10–815.** 0.001233

**10–816.** 13,890.

**10–817.** 2.066

**10–818.** 1.3157

**10–819.** 1.0047

**10–820.** 89.78

**10–821.** 0.664

**10–822.** 0.459

**10–823.** 0.1175

**10–824.** 1.9974

**10–825.** 0.9974

**10–826.** 0.2378

**10–827.** 0.01663

## Review Problems

Solve by general slide rule methods.

**10–828.** $(51)(9)$

**10–829.** $(426)(51)$

**10–830.** $(6.03)(5.16)$

**10–831.** $(561)(4956)$

**10–832.** $(43.2)(0.617)$

**10–833.** $(6617)(0.00155)$

**10–834.** $(99.043)(3.091)$

**10–835.** $(0.0617)(0.4417)$

**10–836.** $(1.035)(2.31 \times 10^5)$

**10–837.** $(79.81 \times 10^{-4})(0.617)$

**10–838.** $(516 \times 10^{-8})(0.391 \times 10^{-2})$

**10–839.** $(51)(97)(32)$

**10–840.** $(52.3)(759.3)$

**10–841.** $(716.5)(0.03166)$

**10–842.** $(11.65)(-0.9213)$

**10–843.** $(76.2)(-31.45)$

**10–844.** $(-0.6175)(-12,391)$

**10–845.** $\dfrac{(-759.6)}{(0.6175)}$

**10–846.** $\dfrac{(-19.96)}{(3346)}$

**10–847.** $\dfrac{(-1.0366)}{(29.31)}$

**10–848.** $\dfrac{(7575)}{(695.2)}$

**10–849.** $\dfrac{(-516.6)}{(0.06052)}$

**10–850.** $(116.5)(4619)(0.317)$

**10–851.** $(210.9)(151.3)(7716)$

**10–852.** $(706.5)(1.695 \times 10^{-6})(0.006695)$

**10–853.** $(1033)(7.339 \times 10^{-6})(0.0317 \times 10^{-3})$

**10–854.** $(4.017 \times 10^{-8})(0.0991)(0.1756)$

**10–855.** $(5.576)(0.0917)(1.669 \times 10^4)$

**10–856.** $(6.991)(0.75)(0.993)(4.217)$

**10–857.** $(56.88)(0.971 \times 10^{-5})$

**10–858.** $(59.17)(0.3617)(0.5916)(0.00552)$

**10–859.** $(5.691)(0.3316)(0.991)(0.00554)(0.1712)$

**10–860.** $(6.523)(71.22)(4.091)(591)(600)(0.1332)$

**10–861.** $(43.06)(0.2361)(0.905 \times 10^{-4})(3.617 \times 10^{-3})$

**10–862.** $(1917)^{2.16}$

**10–863.** $(4.216)^{1.517}$

**10–864.** $(2.571)^{2.91}$

**10–865.** $(0.3177)^{2.06}$

**10–866.** $\sqrt[5]{26.31}$

**10–867.** $\sqrt[3]{0.03175}$

**10–868.** $\sqrt{116.75}$

**10–869.** $\sqrt[3]{0.6177}$

**10–870.** $\sqrt{3167}$

**10–871.** $(179 \times 10^3)(0.3165)$

**10–872.** $(5033 \times 10^{-4})(0.9116)$

**10–873.** $(0.06105)(77.165)$

**10–874.** $(\sqrt{216})(34)(\pi)^2$

**10–875.** $(\sqrt{819})(107)(\sqrt{\pi})$

**10–876.** $\dfrac{(\sqrt{616})(6.767)}{(\sqrt{39.6})}$

**10–877.** $\dfrac{(1045)}{(X)} = \dfrac{(0.0278)}{(0.0798)}$

**10–878.** $\dfrac{(1.486)}{(33)} = \dfrac{(0.37)(X)}{467}$

**10–879.** $(816) = \dfrac{(244)(2\pi)}{(0.049)(X)}$

**10–880.** $(0.0036)(\sin 49.8°)$

**10–881.** $\dfrac{(20.5)^2(7.49)(\sin 49°)}{(30.5)(0.0987)}$

**10–882.** $\sqrt{\dfrac{(38)^2(6.71)^2}{\pi}}$

**10–883.** $(7.61)(\sqrt[3]{7.61})(\pi)$

**10–884.** $\dfrac{(13.1)(\sin 3.12°)}{(\tan 41.9°)}$

**10–885.** $\dfrac{2}{3} = \dfrac{(X)(\pi)}{8.37}$

**10–886.** $\dfrac{(9616)}{X} = \dfrac{(3.1416)}{(0.0142)}$

**10–887.** $(\sqrt[3]{64.9})(2.1 \times 10^3)$

**10–888.** $(4 \times 10^6)(0.007) = (X)(10{,}980)$

**10–889.** $Y = \left(\dfrac{1}{4}\right)\left(\dfrac{16}{6}\right)\left(\dfrac{1}{17}\right)$

**10–890.** $\dfrac{X}{\pi} = \dfrac{(\sqrt{46.2})(3.14)^2}{(\sin 3.7°)}$

**10–891.** $\dfrac{(3.98)(X)}{(1.07)(38)} = \dfrac{(3 \times 10^6)}{(17{,}680)}$

**10–892.** $\dfrac{(\sqrt[3]{986})}{X} = \dfrac{(14)}{(1/116)}$

**10–893.** $\dfrac{(X)^2}{(9.2)} = \dfrac{(18.17)(3.4)}{(166)}$

**10–894.** $\dfrac{(3.6)}{(X)^2} = \dfrac{(9.6 \times 10^2)}{(67.4)} \dfrac{(Y)^{\frac{1}{2}}}{(64)}$

**10–895.** $\dfrac{(X)^{\frac{1}{2}}}{(31.1)} = \dfrac{(\sqrt{196})(189.1)}{4/76}$

**10–896.** $\dfrac{(96.5)}{(3.9)} = \dfrac{X}{(\sin 46.6°)} = \dfrac{(Y)^2}{(3.14 \times 10^{-2})}$

**10–897.** $\dfrac{(X)^2}{Y} = \dfrac{(67.3)^2(Y)}{(96.61)} = \dfrac{(497.1)}{\tan 75°}$

**10–898.** $\dfrac{(3.7)(4.9)}{X} = \dfrac{(46.7)}{564}$

Engineering Tools of Analysis

**Review Problems (continued)**

Solve by general slide rule methods:

**10–899.** $\dfrac{Y}{(28)} = \dfrac{(3.2)}{(4/118)}$

**10–900.** $\dfrac{Y}{42} = \dfrac{39.1}{(1/45)}$

**10–901.** $(37.3)(X)(46.6) = (175)(\pi)$

**10–902.** $(\sqrt{256})(3) = (X)(197.6)$

**10–903.** $\dfrac{(54.6)(\tan 10.6°)}{(\sqrt{0.0967})(8.1 \times 10^3)}$

**10–904.** $\dfrac{\sqrt[3]{(15.1)^2(31.4)^2}}{(\sin \arccos 0.617)}$

**10–905.** $\dfrac{(0.954)(0.06 \times 10^3)}{(\tan 59°)^{1/2}(6.5)^2}$

**10–906.** $\dfrac{\sqrt[3]{(15.6)^2(0.9618)}}{(0.08173)(61,508)(2\pi)}$

**10–907.** $\dfrac{(68)(765)(391)(0.0093 \times 10^3)}{(571)^2(\sqrt[3]{(64)})}$

**10–908.** $\dfrac{(\cos 11.5°)(\sqrt{6.87})}{(0.00081)(7.7 \times 10^4)}$

**10–909.** $\dfrac{\sqrt[4]{(1.71)^5(6.87)}}{(\tan 53°)(5.1)^2}$

**10–910.** $\dfrac{(0.000817)(\tan 81°)}{(0.00763)(\tan 81°)}$

**10–911.** $(273)^{\frac{1}{2}}(46.9)(\cos 61°)(\pi^3)$

**10–912.** $\dfrac{(\sin \arctan 3.17)(71.7)}{(\sqrt{89.6})(\sqrt[4]{(76.5)^2})}$

**10–913.** $\dfrac{(\sqrt{(16)^3})(\log_{10} 100)}{(6.71 \times 10^{-1})(3.71)^3}$

**10–914.** $\dfrac{(6.93)(\sin \cos^{-1} 0.98)}{(0.937)^2(39.6)}$

**10–915.** $\dfrac{(\sqrt{91.68})(\sqrt[3]{65.9})}{(\tan 68.7°)(0.671)^2}$

**10–916.** $\dfrac{(4.5)^4(\sqrt{(98.71)})(\sin 56.4°)}{(0.09 \times 10)(38.6)^{3/2}}$

**10–917.** $\dfrac{(\sqrt{285})(\cos 36.6°)(1.64)^2}{(67.1 \times 10^{-1})(5780)}$

**10–918.** $\dfrac{(\tan \sin^{-1} 0.87)(61.7)}{(5.64)^{0.98}(3.65)^2}$

**10–919.** $\dfrac{(3174)(\tan 64°)}{(81.6)^2(\sqrt[3]{18})}$

**10–920.** $\dfrac{(44.6)(0.09 \times 10^3)(\sin 80.9°)}{(\sqrt[3]{96.7})(51.6)^2}$

**10–921.** $\dfrac{(\tan 50.6°)(3.4)^2}{(\sqrt{9681})(171)}$

**10–922.** $\dfrac{(296)(0.197 \times 10^5)}{\sqrt[4]{(76.1)}(\sin 49.6°)}$

**10–923.** $\dfrac{(\sin 22.6°)(9.918)}{(\tan 31.6°)(98.71)}$

**10–924.** $\dfrac{(68.7 \times 10^2)(\tan 56.1°)}{(96.7)^{0.86}(18{,}614)}$

**10–925.** $\dfrac{(0.0098)(\sin 17.6°)\sqrt{(0.186)}}{(41.6)^2(689.0)}$

**10–926.** $\dfrac{(\tan 19.8°)^2(6.71 \times 10^3)}{(1{,}876)(\sqrt[4]{59})}$

**10–927.** $\dfrac{(\sqrt{\sin 40°})(17)^2(4\pi^2)}{(0.643)(\tan 60°)}$

### Hyperbolic Functions on the Slide Rule

Hyperbolic functions are useful in several mathematical applications such as the variation of electrical current and voltage with distance in the calculation of transmission of electrical power. Several manufacturers of slide rules make special scales from which hyperbolic functions can be read directly. However, it is possible to obtain numerical values for hyperbolic functions using conventional scales by making use of the relations:

$$\frac{\epsilon^x - \epsilon^{-x}}{2} = \text{hyperbolic sine } x \ (\sinh x)$$

$$\frac{\epsilon^x + \epsilon^{-x}}{2} = \text{hyperbolic cosine } x \ (\cosh x)$$

$$\frac{\epsilon^{2x} - 1}{\epsilon^{2x} + 1} = \text{hyperbolic tangent } x \ (\tanh x)$$

### Reading Hyperbolic Scales

Most slide rules that have hyperbolic scales have the scales marked as Sh and Th. Slide rules manufactured by Pickett identify the hyperbolic sine scales as *upper* and *lower* and the values of sinh $x$ are read on the C scale. Keuffel & Esser identify the hyperbolic sine scales as Sh 1 and Sh 2 and values of sinh $x$ are read on the D scale. Except for these minor differences, reading hyperbolic functions on slide rules made by either company is essentially the same.

**Hyperbolic Sines.** In order to read hyperbolic sine functions on the slide rule, set the value sinh $x$ on one of the Sh scales and read the value of the function on either the C scale or the D scale under the hairline.

*Example:* Find sinh 0.38

SOLUTION: Locate 0.38 on the upper Sh scale or on the Sh 1 scale and read 0.389 on the C or D scale.

*Example:*   Find sinh 1.88

SOLUTION:   Using the method above read sinh $1.88 = 3.20$. Note that the value 1.88 is located on the lower Sh scale (Sh 2 scale) and 3.20 is read on the C scale (D scale).

The decimal point can be determined readily by noting that numbers corresponding to function values on the upper Sh (Sh 1) scale lie between 0.1 and 1.0, and numbers corresponding to function values on the lower Sh (Sh 2) scale lie between 1.0 and 10.0.

**Hyperbolic Tangents.**   Hyperbolic tangents can be read by locating the value of the tangent function on the Th scale and reading the number on the C or D scale under the hairline.

*Example:*   $\tanh 0.206 = 0.1990$

*Example:*   $\tanh 1.33 = 0.870$

**Hyperbolic Cosines.**   Most slide rules do not have a hyperbolic cosine scale. Values for the hyperbolic cosine can be determined by use of the relation:

$$\cosh x = \frac{\sinh x}{\tanh x}$$

In finding values for $\cosh x$ using the Pickett rule, first set the slide so the indexes coincide. Locate the hairline over the value of $x$ on the appropriate Sh scale. Move the slide until the value of $x$ on the Th scale is under the hairline and $\cosh x$ can be read on the D scale at the C index.

*Example:*   $\cosh 0.482 = 1.118$

*Example:*   $\cosh 1.08 = 1.642$

For the Keuffel & Esser Vector slide rule, this procedure can be followed. Set an index of the slide on the value of $x$ on the Th scale. Set the hairline on the value of $x$ on either Sh 1 or Sh 2, depending on its amount. Read the value of $\cosh x$ on the C scale.

*Example:*   $\cosh 0.305 = 1.046$

*Example:*   $\cosh 1.81 = 2.31$

When the value of $\cosh x$ is given and it is desired to find $x$, use can be made of the relation

$$\cosh^2 x - \sinh^2 x = 1$$

*Example:*   Find the value of $x$ when $\cosh x = 2.1$

SOLUTION:
$$\sinh x = \sqrt{\cosh^2 x - 1}$$

Substituting:
$$\sinh x = \sqrt{(2.1)^2 - 1}$$
$$\sinh x = \sqrt{3.41}$$

and
$$\sinh x = 1.85$$

Set 1.85 on the C (D) scale and read the value of $x$ on the lower Sh (Sh 2) scale. The lower scale is used because $\sinh x$ is greater than 1.

Then
$$x = 1.372$$

### Approximations for Large and Small Values of $x$

When the value of $x$ is more than 3, it can be shown that the value of $\sinh x$ and $\cosh x$ is approximately the same as $\dfrac{\epsilon^x}{2}$.

*Example:*
$$\sinh 4.2 = ?$$
$$\frac{\epsilon^{4.2}}{2} = 33.5$$
$$\sinh 4.2 \cong 33.5$$

Also for large values of $x$, $\tanh x$ is approximately 1.0.

*Example:*
$$\tanh 3.7 = ?$$

SOLUTION:
$$\tanh 3.7 = \frac{\epsilon^{(2)(3.7)} - 1}{\epsilon^{(2)(3.7)} + 1}$$
$$= \frac{1650 - 1}{1650 + 1}$$
$$\tanh 3.7 \cong 1.0$$

When $x$ has values below 0.1, it can be shown that $\sinh x$ and $\tanh x$ are approximately the same as $x$, and $\cosh x$ is approximately 1.0.

*Example:*
$$\sinh 0.052 \cong 0.052$$
$$\tanh 0.037 \cong 0.037$$
$$\cosh 0.028 \cong 1.00$$

**Other Hyperbolic Functions.**   While not often needed, other hyperbolic functions can be obtained by using the following defining expressions:

$$\coth x = \frac{1}{\tanh x}$$
$$\operatorname{sech} x = \frac{1}{\cosh x}$$
$$\operatorname{csch} x = \frac{1}{\sinh x}$$

### Problems on Hyperbolic Functions

**10–928.** Find the values of sinh $x$ for the following values of $x$:  (*a*) 0.12, (*b*) 1.07, (*c*) 1.91, (*d*) 2.30, (*e*) 3.11, (*f*) 4.26, (*g*) 5.00

**10–929.** Find the values of $x$ for the following values of sinh $x$:  (*a*) 0.1304, (*b*) 0.956, (*c*) 1.62, (*d*) 4.10, (*e*) 8.70, (*f*) 19.42, (*g*) 41.96

**10–930.** Find the values of cosh $x$ for the following values of $x$:  (*a*) 0.28, (*b*) 1.03, (*c*) 1.98, (*d*) 2.37, (*e*) 3.56, (*f*) 4.04, (*g*) 5.00

**10–931.** Find the values of $x$ for the following values of cosh $x$:  (*a*) 1.024, (*b*) 1.374, (*c*) 2.31, (*d*) 5.29, (*e*) 8.50, (*f*) 21.7, (*g*) 52.3

**10–932.** Find the values of tanh $x$ for the following values of $x$:  (*a*) 0.16, (*b*) 0.55, (*c*) 1.14, (*d*) 1.94, (*e*) 2.34, (*f*) 2.74, (*g*) 5.00

**10–933.** Find the values of $x$ corresponding to the following values of tanh $x$: (*a*) 0.1781, (*b*) 0.354, (*c*) 0.585, (*d*) 0.811, (*e*) 0.881, (*f*) 0.980, (*g*) 0.990

### Slide Rule Solution of Complex Numbers

A complex number, which consists of a real part and an imaginary part, is often used to describe a vector quantity. By definition, a vector quantity, frequently referred to as a *phasor* in electrical engineering, has both magnitude and direction. For example, the expression $3 + j4$ will describe a vector which is $\sqrt{3^2 + 4^2}$ units long and makes an angle arc tan $\frac{4}{3}$ with an $x$-axis. For a more complete discussion on complex number theory, refer to a text on basic algebra.

The symbol $i$ or the symbol $j$ is customarily used to represent the quantity $\sqrt{-1}$. In the discussion in this section the symbol $j = \sqrt{-1}$ will be used.

If we let the scalar length of a vector be designated as $R$, as shown in Figure 10–35, then we can write $R\epsilon^{j\theta} = x + jy$ in polar form as $R/\theta$. This expression $R/\theta$ is a shortened form of $R\epsilon^{j\theta}$ which is obtained from the identity

$$R\epsilon^{j\theta} = R \cos \theta + jR \sin \theta.$$

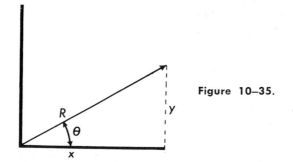

**Figure 10–35.**

**Complex Numbers on the Slide Rule.** From trigonometric relations for a right triangle, we can show that tan $\theta = \dfrac{y}{x}$; $R = \dfrac{y}{\sin \theta}$; and $R = \dfrac{x}{\cos \theta}$. We can use these relations to solve complex number problems on the slide rule. Take, for example, the complex number $3 + j4$ and let it be required to find $R\underline{/\theta}$.

The following method will give the solution to this problem on most types of slide rules:

1. Locate the larger of the two numbers on the D scale and set an index of the C scale at this number. Locate the smaller of the two numbers on the D scale using the hairline, and read the angle $\theta$ on the T scale under the hairline. If $y$ is smaller than $x$, $\theta$ is less than 45°, and if $y$ is larger than $x$, $\theta$ is larger than 45°.

2. Next move the slide until the angle $\theta$ on the S scale is in line with the smaller of the two numbers. Read $R$ on the D scale at the index of the C scale.

*Example:* Express $3 + j4$ in polar form

SOLUTION: Set the right index of the C scale at 4 on the D scale.

Move the hairline to 3 on the D scale and read $\theta = 53.1°$ on the T scale. Note that the $y$ value is larger than the $x$ value; thus the angle is larger than 45°.

Without moving the hairline, move the slide until 53.1° on the S scale (reading angles to the left) is under the hairline.

Read 5 at the right index of the C scale.

The solution is $3 + j4 = 5\underline{/53.1°}$

This method can be performed on most types of rules, requiring the minimum number of manipulations of the rule. It also can be applied readily to the solution of most problems involving right triangles.

When any of the complex numbers have a minus sign, the slide rule operation to solve the problem is the same as though the sign of the numbers were positive. The angles usually are determined by inspection using trigonometric relations. The following general rules apply:

If the expression has the form $+x + jy$, $\theta$ is in the first quadrant.

For $-x + jy$, $\theta$ is in the second quadrant
For $-x - jy$, $\theta$ is in the third quadrant
For $+x - jy$, $\theta$ is in the fourth quadrant

*Example:* Express $-7.1 + j3.8$ in polar form.

SOLUTION: Set the right index of the C scale at 7.1 on the D scale, and read on the T scale $\theta = 28.3°$ at 3.8 on the D scale.

Move the slide so that 28.3° on the S scale is over 3.8 and read $R = 8.03$ at the C index.

By inspection, the angle is in the second quadrant and the total angle is $180° - 28.3° = 151.7°$.

Therefore, the polar form is $8.03\underline{/151.7°}$.

*Example:* Express $4 - j3$ in polar form.

SOLUTION: The angle is read as $36.9°$ and is in the fourth quadrant. The total angle is $360° - 36.9° = 323.1°$.

The polar form is $5\underline{/323.1°}$.

If the polar form is given, the rectangular form can be obtained by multiplying the value of $R$ by the appropriate sine and cosine value. A rapid method of finding the quantities is to use the previously described slide rule manipulation in reverse.

*Example:* Express $3.3\underline{/28°}$ in rectangular form.

SOLUTION: Set the right index of the C scale at 3.3 on the D scale and read 1.55 on D under $28°$ on the sine scale.

Move the slide until $28°$ on the T scale is over 1.55 on the D scale.

Read 2.915 on the D scale at the right index. Since the angle is less than $45°$, the imaginary part of the complex number is the smaller of the two. Therefore,

$$3.3\underline{/28°} = 2.915 + j1.55$$

If the polar angle is larger than $45°$, angles on the T scale and S scale are read to the left, and the real part of the complex number is read first. The real part of the number will be the smaller of the two parts.

*Example:*
$$179\underline{/66°} = 72.9 + j163.5$$

For angles not in the first quadrant, obtain the angle of the vector with respect to the x-axis and treat the solution as outlined above. By inspection, affix the proper signs to the real and imaginary parts after obtaining their values. A sketch will help greatly in this process.

**Conversion for Small Angles.** If the ratio of the $x$ value and $y$ value in the complex number is greater than 10, the angle can be found on the ST scale. The real value is approximately equal to the value of $R$.

*Example:*
$$35 + j1.5 = R\underline{/\theta}$$

SOLUTION: Set the C index at 35 on the D scale and read $\theta = 2.45°$ on the ST scale.

Then $R\underline{/\theta} \cong 35\underline{/2.45°}$.

*Example:*
$$0.075\underline{/4.1°} = x + jy$$

SOLUTION: Set the C index at 0.075 on the D scale. Read 0.00536 on D under $4.1°$ on ST.

Then $x + jy \cong 0.075 + j0.00536$.

**Conversion for Angles Near 90°.** For angles between 84.27° and 90°, the ratio of $x$ to $y$ will be 10 or greater and the imaginary part of the complex number is approximately equal to the value of $R$. The angle can be read on the ST scale after subtracting it from 90°.

*Example:* $$18/\underline{88°} = x + jy$$

SOLUTION: Set the left index of C at 18 on the D scale. Read 0.6 on D under 2° on the ST scale.

Then $x + jy \cong 0.6 + j18$.

Remember that for very large and very small angles, the ratio of $x$ and $y$ will be 10 or greater, and either the real part or the imaginary part of the complex number will be approximately equal to the value of $R$.

**Applications of Complex Numbers.** In solving problems involving complex numbers, addition and subtraction of complex numbers are more easily performed if the numbers are expressed in rectangular form. In this form, the respective real parts and imaginary parts can be added or subtracted directly. However, to multiply or divide complex numbers, it is more convenient to express them in polar form and solve by multiplying or dividing the vector magnitude, and adding or subtracting the angular magnitude.

*Examples:*

$$(a + jb) + (c + jd) = (a + c) + j(b + d) \text{ (Addition)}$$
$$(a + jb) - (c + jd) = (a - c) + j(b - d) \text{ (Subtraction)}$$
$$(a/\underline{\theta_1})(b/\underline{\theta_2}) = (a)(b)/\underline{\theta_1 + \theta_2} \quad \text{(Multiplication)}$$

$$\frac{a/\underline{\theta_1}}{b/\underline{\theta_2}} = \frac{a}{b} /\underline{\theta_1 - \theta_2} \qquad \text{(Division)}$$

From the examples above, we can see that the ability to perform rapid conversions from polar form to rectangular form or vice versa will be helpful in solving problems involving complex numbers.

**Problems on Complex Numbers**

**10–934.** Express in polar form: (*a*) $8 + j3$, (*b*) $2 + j6$, (*c*) $1 + j4$, (*d*) $5 + j5$

**10–935.** Express in rectangular form:(*a*) $6.2/\underline{39°}$, (*b*) $3.6/\underline{48°}$, (*c*) $9.2/\underline{21.4°}$, (*d*) $2.7/\underline{71°}$

**10–936.** Express in polar form: (*a*) $-8.9 + j4.2$, (*b*) $-16.8 + j9.3$, (*c*) $-5.3 + j2.1$, (*d*) $-18.4 + j3.3$

**10–937.** Express in rectangular form: (*a*) $9.7/\underline{118°}$, (*b*) $115/\underline{137°}$, (*c*) $2.09/\underline{160°}$, (*d*) $5.72/\underline{110°}$

**10–938.** Express in polar form: (*a*) $-7.3 - j6.1$, (*b*) $-4.4 - j8.2$, (*c*) $-8.8 - j2.5$, (*d*) $-1.053 - j5.13$

**10–939.** Express in rectangular form: (*a*) $81.3/\underline{200°}$, (*b*) $62.1/\underline{253°}$, (*c*) $1059/\underline{197°}$, (*d*) $0.912/\underline{231°}$

**Problems on Complex Numbers (continued)**

**10–940.** Express in polar form: (*a*) $160.5 - j147$, (*b*) $89.3 - j46.2$, (*c*) $0.0062 - j0.0051$, (*d*) $3.07 - j1.954$

**10–941.** Express in rectangular form: (*a*) $557\underline{/297°}$, (*b*) $6.03\underline{/327°}$, (*c*) $0.9772\underline{/344°}$, (*d*) $19,750\underline{/300°}$

**10–942.** Express in polar form: (*a*) $15.61 + j7.09$, (*b*) $-14.9 - j61.7$, (*c*) $0.617 - j0.992$, (*d*) $-41.2 + j75.3$

**10–943.** Express in rectangular form: (*a*) $1.075\underline{/29.1°}$, (*b*) $10.75\underline{/136°}$, (*c*) $107.5\underline{/253°}$, (*d*) $1075\underline{/322°}$

# Chapter 11

# Unit Systems and Dimensional Analysis

Engineering and scientific calculations make use of measurements of all types. Some measurements are made with precise instruments, while others are the result of crude approximations. Regardless of the accuracy of the measurements or of the particular type of measuring instrument used, the measurements are themselves merely representative of certain comparisons previously agreed upon.

The length of a metal cylinder, for example, can be determined by laying it alongside a calibrated scale or ruler. The 12-inch ruler is known to represent a third of a yard, and a yard is recognized as being equivalent to 36.00/39.37 of a meter—which used to be the distance between two marks on a platinum-iridium bar that is kept in a vault in Troyes, France, but is now defined in terms of the wave length of a particularly uniform monochromatic light. All these methods of measurements are comparisons. Other similar standards exist for the measurement of temperature, time, and force.

Physical quantities to be measured may be of two types: those concerned with *fundamental dimensions* of length $(L)$, time $(T)$, force $(F)$, mass $(M)$, or temperature $(\theta)$; and those concerned with *derived dimensions* of area, volume, pressure, or density. *Fundamental dimensions* may be subdivided into various sized parts, called *units*. The dimension *time* $(T)$, for example, can be expressed in the units of seconds, hours, days, and so forth, depending upon the application to be made or the magnitude of the measurement. *Derived dimensions* are the result of combining *fundamental dimensions*. Area, therefore, is expressed dimensionally as length squared $(L^2)$; pressure, as force per unit area $(F/L^2,$ or $FL^{-2})$; acceleration as length per time squared $(L/T^2,$ or $LT^{-2})$, etc.

Most measured quantities must be expressed in both magnitude and units. To state that an area was 146 would have no meaning. For example an area could be tabulated as 146 sq miles or 146 cm²; a pressure could be recorded as 0.0015 dyne per square centimeter or 0.0015 lb$_f$ per in.²; an acceleration could be indicated as 159 in./sec² or 159 ft/sec², etc. However, some values used in engineering computations are dimensionless (without dimensions). These should be ignored in the unit balancing of an equation. *Radians, $\pi$, coefficient of friction, ratios,* and *per cent error* are examples of dimensionless quantities.

Equations involving measured quantities must be balanced dimensionally as well as numerically. Both dimensions and units can be multiplied and divided or raised to powers just like ordinary algebraic quantities. When all of the dimensions (or units) in an equation balance, the equation is said to be dimensionally homogeneous.

*Example:* An alloy has a specific weight of $400 \frac{lb_f}{ft^3}$. What is the weight of 2 ft³ of the alloy? Show the numerical and dimensional solutions to the problem.

$$W = Vp$$

or

(Weight of metal) = (volume of metal)(specific weight of metal)

Fundamental Dimensions: $F = (L^3)\left(\frac{F}{L^3}\right)$      (Dimensional solution)

Units: $F = (2 \text{ ft}^3)\left(400 \frac{lb_f}{ft^3}\right) = 800 \text{ lb}_f$      (Numerical solution)

*Check:* $lb_f = lb_f$

Frequently it will be necessary to change unit systems, i.e., feet to inches, hours to seconds, pounds to grams, etc. This process can be accomplished by the use of unity conversion factors that are multiplied by the expression to be changed. Refer to pages 522 to 524 for a listing of commonly used conversion factors.

*Example:* Change a speed of 3000 miles per hour (miles/hr) to feet per second (ft/sec).

Fundamental dimensions:      $\dfrac{L}{T} = \dfrac{L}{T}$

Units:      $V = \left(3000 \dfrac{\text{miles}}{\text{hr}}\right)\left(\dfrac{5280 \text{ ft}}{1 \text{ mile}}\right)\left(\dfrac{1 \text{ hr}}{3600 \text{ sec}}\right) = \left(4400 \dfrac{\text{ft}}{\text{sec}}\right)$

The two conversion factors, (5280 ft/1 mile) and (1 hr/3600 sec), are each equivalent to unity, since the numerator of each fraction is equal to its denominator (5280 ft = 1 mile, and 1 hr = 3600 sec).

Note that the word *per* means *divided by.* To avoid misunderstandings in computations, the units should be expressed in fractional form.

*Example:*

a. $(X$ per $Y)$ per $Z = (X \div Y) \div Z = [(X/Y)/Z] = \dfrac{(X/Y)}{Z} = \dfrac{X}{YZ}$

b. Acceleration $= 156$ ft per sec per min $= 156$ ft/sec/min

$$= 156 \frac{\text{ft}}{(\text{sec})(\text{min})}$$

c. Pressure $= 14.7$ lb$_f$ per square inch $= 14.7 \dfrac{lb_f}{in.^2}$

*Example:* Solve for the conversion factor $k$.

a.
$$\frac{c^2b^3d}{a^4} = (k)\left(\frac{c^5ba^2}{e^2}\right)$$

Solving for $k$:
$$k = \frac{b^2de^2}{a^6c^3}$$

and
$$\left(\frac{c^2b^3d}{a^4}\right) = \left(\frac{b^2de^2}{a^6c^3}\right)\left(\frac{c^5ba^2}{e^2}\right)$$

Check:
$$\frac{c^2b^3d}{a^4} = \frac{c^2b^3d}{a^4} = c^2b^3da^{-4}$$

b.
$$\left(\frac{XR^3d^3e}{(f/T)(h^5)}\right)(k) = \left(\frac{Rd}{X^5hT^2}\right)$$

$$(k) = \left(\frac{fh^4}{X^6eR^2d^2T^3}\right)$$

Check: $\left[\dfrac{XR^3d^3e}{(f/T)(h^5)}\right]\left[\dfrac{fh^4}{X^6eR^2d^2T^3}\right] = \dfrac{Rd}{X^5hT^2}$    or    $RdX^{-5}h^{-1}T^{-2}$

*Example:* Solve for the fundamental dimensions of $Q$ and $P$ in the following dimensionally homogeneous equation if $C$ is a velocity and $B$ is an area.

$$Q = C(B - P)$$

Fundamental Dimensions: $Q = \dfrac{L}{T}(L^2 - P)$

Since the equation is dimensionally homogeneous, $P$ must also be length squared ($L^2$) in order that the subtraction can be carried out. If this is true, the units of $Q$ are

$$Q = \frac{L}{T}(L^2 - L^2)* = \frac{L}{T}(L^2) = \frac{L^3}{T}$$

## Problems

Solve for the conversion factor $k$.

**11-1.** $k\left(\dfrac{c^3dxe^5}{hR}\right) = \dfrac{R^3d^5e}{c^2}$

**11-2.** $\dfrac{ABC^2}{DM^3} = k\,\dfrac{D^5M}{B^2}$

**11-3.** $k\left(\dfrac{HRM}{BA^2}\right) = \sqrt{C^4EHR^8}$

**11-4.** $D^2\sqrt{CX^5} = k\left(\dfrac{AB^2}{X^3}\right)$

**11-5.** $k(GJ^2NT^{-2}R^{-3}) = R^5TJG^{-3}$

**11-6.** $D^2EH^{-5}B^{-2} = k\sqrt{DH^2E}$

**11-7.** $\sqrt{TS^3F^{-2}B} = k\sqrt{SF^3B^6}$

**11-8.** $k\,\dfrac{\sqrt{B^3E}}{C^2F^{-2}} = R^3BCF^2$

**11-9.** $k(A^2B\sqrt{CX^{-2}}) = X^{-3}B^{-2}$

**11-10.** $YC^3R^{-1}M^{-3} = k\sqrt{C^2R^{-1}}$

---

* Remember that the terms $L^2$ represent a particular length squared in each instance. Thus the remainder (depending on the numerical magnitude of each term) will also be length squared or will be zero for the special case of the original lengths being equal.

**Problems (continued)**

**11–11.** Is the equation $a = (2S/t^2) - (2V_1/t)$ dimensionally homogeneous if $a$ is an acceleration, $V_1$ is a velocity, $t$ is a time, and $S$ is a distance? Prove your answer by writing the equation with fundamental dimensions.

**11–12.** Is the equation $V_2^2 = V_1^2 + 2as$ dimensionally correct if $V_1$ and $V_2$ are velocities and $S$ is a distance? Prove your answer by rewriting the equation in fundamental dimensions.

**11–13.** In the homogeneous equation $R = B + \frac{1}{2}CX$, what are the fundamental dimensions of $R$ and $B$ if $C$ is an acceleration and $X$ is a time?

**11–14.** Determine the fundamental dimensions of the expression $B/g \sqrt{D - m^2}$, where $B$ is a force, $m$ is a length, $D$ is an area, and $g$ is the acceleration of gravity at a particular location.

**11–15.** The relationship $M = \sigma I/c$ pertains to the bending moment for a beam under compressive stress. $\sigma$ is a stress in $F/L^2$, $C$ is a length $L$, and $I$ is a moment of inertia $L^4$. What are the fundamental dimensions of $M$?

**11–16.** The expression $V/K = (B - 7/3A)A^{\frac{2}{3}}$ is dimensionally homogeneous. $A$ is a length and $V$ is a volume of flow per unit of time. Solve for the fundamental dimensions of $K$ and $B$.

**11–17.** Is the expression $S = 0.031V^2/fB$ dimensionally homogeneous if $S$ is a distance, $V$ is a velocity, $f$ is the coefficient of friction, and $B$ is a ratio of two weights? Is it possible that the numerical value 0.031 has fundamental dimensions? Prove your solution.

**11–18.** If the following heat-transfer equation is dimensionally homogeneous, what are the units of $k$?

$$Q = \frac{-kA(T_1 - T_2)}{L}$$

$A$ is a cross-sectional area in square feet, $L$ is a length in feet, $T_1$ and $T_2$ are temperatures ($^\circ$F), and $Q$ is the amount of heat (energy) conducted in Btu per unit of time.

**11–19.** In the dimensionally homogeneous equation

$$F = \frac{4Ey}{(1 - \mu^2)(Md^2)}\left[(h - y)\left(h - \frac{y}{2}\right)t - t^3\right]$$

$F$ is a force, $E$ is a force per (length)$^2$, $y$, $d$, and $h$ are lengths, $\mu$ is Poisson's ratio, and $M$ is a ratio of diameters. What are the fundamental dimensions of $t$?

**11–20.** In the equation

$$F = \frac{12WV^2}{gr}\left(\cos \alpha + \frac{r}{l}\cos 2\alpha\right)$$

$F$ represents a force, $W$ is a weight, $V$ is a crank velocity, $g$ is the acceleration of gravity at the place of experimentation, $\alpha$ is an angle, and $l$ is a connecting rod length. What must be the fundamental dimensions of $r$ if the equation is to be dimensionally homogeneous?

Solve the following:

**11–21.** Change 5030 $\frac{\text{miles}}{\text{hr}}$ to $\frac{\text{ft}}{\text{sec}}$.

**11–22.** Change 762 in. per sec to miles per day.

**11–23.** Change $(26)(10)^5$ gal of gasoline per sec to ft³ of gasoline per hr.

**11–24.** Change 0.0972 cm³ of water per sec to ton of water per hr.

**11–25.** Change $1.59 \times 10^8$ board-feet to ft³.

**11–26.** Change 6,910,000 $\frac{\text{dynes}}{\text{cm}^3}$ to tons per ft³.

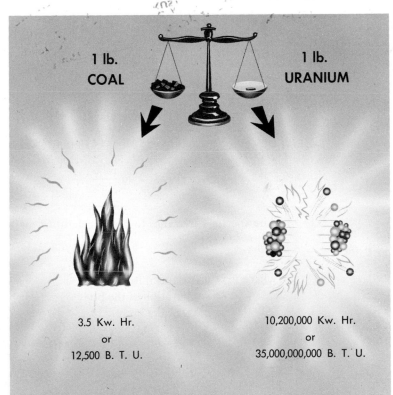

Illustration 11–1. The contrast of energy sources is depicted in this picture, which shows the relative energy conversion from coal and nuclear fuels. In working with such energy sources, the engineer must be able to convert from one unit system to another. (Courtesy Westinghouse Electric Corporation)

**11–27.** Change 2770 acres to cm².

**11–28.** Change 0.0033 $\frac{\text{miles}}{\text{sec}}$ per day to ft per sec².

**11–29.** Change $(0.0139 \times 10^{-7})$ knots per sec to $\frac{\text{miles}}{(\text{hr})(\text{day})}$.

**11–30.** It takes the earth 365 days, 5 hr, 46 min, and 46 sec to make one complete trip around the sun. The orbit is approximately $(5.84)(10)^8$ miles. Find the speed of the earth in (a) miles per hour, (b) feet per second, (c) meters per second, and (d) kilometers per minute.

**11–31.** The kinetic energy of a moving body in space can be expressed as follows:

$$KE = \frac{MV^2}{2} \qquad \frac{2(KE)}{M} = U^2$$

where $KE$ = kinetic energy of the moving body
$M$ = mass of the moving body
$V$ = velocity of the moving body

a. Given: $M = 539 \dfrac{\text{lb}_f \sec^2}{\text{ft}}$; $V = 2900 \dfrac{\text{ft}}{\sec}$

Find: $KE$ in (ft) (lb$_f$)

b. Given: $M = 42.6 \dfrac{\text{lb}_f \sec^2}{\text{ft}}$; $KE = 1.20(10^{11})\,(\text{ft})\,(\text{lb}_f)$

Find: $V$ in $\dfrac{\text{ft}}{\sec}$

c. Given: $KE = 16,900$ (in.) (lb); $V = 3960 \dfrac{\text{in.}}{\text{min}}$

Find: $M$ in slugs.

d. Given: $M = 143$ grams; $KE = 2690$ (in.) (lb)

Find: $V$ in $\dfrac{\text{mile}}{\text{hr}}$

**11–32.** The inertia force due to the acceleration of a rocket can be expressed as follows:

$$F = Ma$$

where $F$ = unbalanced force
$a$ = acceleration of the body
$M$ = mass of the body

a. Given: $a = 439 \dfrac{\text{ft}}{\sec^2}$; $M = 89.6 \dfrac{\text{lb}_f \sec^2}{\text{ft}}$

Find: $F$ in lb$_f$

b. Given: $F = 1500$ lb$_f$; $M = 26.4 \dfrac{\text{lb}_f \sec^2}{\text{ft}}$

Find: $a$ in $\dfrac{\text{ft}}{\sec^2}$

c. Given: $F = (49.3)(10)^5$ lb$_f$; $a = 32.2 \dfrac{\text{ft}}{\sec^2}$

Find: $M$ in $\dfrac{\text{lb}_f \sec^2}{\text{ft}}$

d. Given: $M = 9650 \dfrac{\text{lb}_f \sec^2}{\text{ft}}$; $a = 980 \dfrac{\text{cm}}{\sec^2}$

Find: $F$ in lb$_f$

**11–33.** The force required to assemble a force-fit joint on a particular piece of machinery may be expressed by the following equation:

$$F = \frac{\pi dlfP}{2000}$$

where $d$ = shaft diameter, in.

$l$ = hub length, in.

$f$ = coefficient of friction

$P$ = radial pressure, psi

$F$ = force of press required, tons

    *a.* Given: $d = 9.05$ in.; $l = 15.1$ in.; $f = 0.10$; $P = 10,250$ psi. Find: $F$ in lb$_f$.

    *b.* Given: $F = 4.21 \times 10^5$ lb$_f$; $f = 0.162$; $P = 8.32(10^8)$ psf; $l = 1.62$ ft. Find: $d$ in ft.

    *c.* Given: $d = 25$ cm; $l = 30.2$ cm; $f = 0.08$; $P = 9260$ psi. Find: $F$ in tons.

    *d.* Given: $F = 206$ tons; $d = 6.23$ in.; $l = 20.4$ in.; $f = 0.153$. Find: $P$ in lb$_f$/ft$^2$.

**11–34.** The dynamic stress in the rim of a certain flywheel has been expressed by the following equation:

$$\sigma = 0.0000284\rho r^2 n^2$$

where $\sigma$ = tensile stress, $\dfrac{\text{lb}_f}{\text{in.}^2}$

$\rho$ = specific weight of material, $\dfrac{\text{lb}_f}{\text{in.}^3}$

$r$ = radius of curvature, in.

$n$ = number of rpm

    *a.* Given: $\sigma = 200$ psi; $\rho = 0.282 \dfrac{\text{lb}_f}{\text{in.}^3}$; $r = 9$ in.

    Find: $n$ in rpm.

    *b.* Given: $\rho = 0.332 \dfrac{\text{lb}_f}{\text{in.}^3}$; $r = 23.1$ cm; $n = 200$ rpm.

    Find: $\sigma$ in psi.

    *c.* Given: $\rho = 540 \dfrac{\text{lb}_f}{\text{ft}^3}$; $n = 186$ rpm; $\sigma = (31.2)(10)^3$ psf.

    Find: $r$ in ft.

    *d.* Given: $\rho = 326 \dfrac{\text{lb}_f}{\text{ft}^3}$; $n = 250$ rpm; $r = 0.632$ ft.

    Find: $\sigma$ in psf.

**Problems (continued)**

Solve the following:

**11–35.** The stress in a certain column may be calculated by the following relationship:

$$\sigma = \frac{F}{A}\left[1 + \left(\frac{l}{k}\right)^2 \frac{R}{\pi^2 nE}\right]$$

where $\sigma$ = induced stress, psi

$F$ = applied force, $lb_f$

$A$ = cross-sectional area of member, in.$^2$

$l$ = length of bar, in.

$k$ = radius of gyration, in.

$R$ = elastic limit, $lb_f/in.^2$

$E$ = modulus of elasticity, $lb_f/in.^2$

$n$ = coefficient for different end conditions

  *a.* Given: $n = 1$; $E = (3)(10)^7$ psi; $R = (4.2)(10)^4$ psi; $k = 0.29$ in.; $l = 20.3$ in.; $A = 17.5$ in.$^2$; $F = 12,000\ lb_f$. Find: $\sigma$ in psi.

  *b.* Given: $\sigma = 11,500$ psi; $F = 6.3$ tons; $l = 2.11$ ft; $k = 0.41$ in.; $R = 40,000$ psi; $E = (3.16)(10)^7$ psi; $n = 2$ Find: $A$ in ft$^2$.

  *c.* Given: $n = \frac{1}{4}$; $E = (2.65)(10)^7$ psi; $R = (3.21)(10)^4$ psi; $k = 0.026$ ft; $A = 102$ cm$^2$; $F = 5.9$ tons; $\sigma = 10,000$ psi. Find: $l$ in ft.

  *d.* Given: $\sigma = (1.72)(10)^6$ psf; $F = (1.33)(10)^4\ lb_f$; $l = 1.67$ ft; $k = 0.331$ in.; $E = (7.87)(10)^7$ psi; $n = 4$; $A = 14.2$ in.$^2$ Find: $R$ in psi.

## UNIT SYSTEMS

One serious barrier between scientists and engineers is the fact that the two groups use entirely different systems of units to describe the same things. In addition, the electrical engineers use different units than the other engineers. This situation still exists in all countries except those that have adopted the MKS system of units. At the present time there are seven such countries, including USSR.

Additional handicaps to the engineers are that they use different units for thermal energy, mechanical energy (work) and electrical energy; they use both absolute and gravitational units for mass, and forces are based on the pull of gravity. These handicaps are shared by all engineers outside of the countries that have adopted the MKS system. However, even in these countries a serious burden is imposed on both engineers and scientists by the fact that their units for time and angular measure are unbelievably cumbersome, and they must use both absolute and ordinary temperature scales. These handicaps are shared by all engineers and scientists in the world today.

In the English speaking countries an additional staggering burden is placed on the engineers by the fact that a multitude of units are used for each of the quantities length, mass and force, and none of the units used for the same quantity is derivable from another by a simple shifting of the decimal point. These countries, therefore, have the most to gain by a change in units. In addition, the adoption of the MKS system on a worldwide basis will greatly facilitate the exchange of scientific and technical information.

However, the MKS system still has these disadvantages: The units of time are not decimally related, and neither are the units of angular measure. This requires much needless conversion with the resulting sources of mistakes. The civil engineers must multiply all their masses by 9.807 $m/\sec^2$ to obtain forces that they can use in strength calculations. The mechanical engineers must multiply their pressures in bars by 1.013 to obtain atmospheres in a great many problems involving the pressure of the atmosphere.

There are a number of systems of units that have been used in scientific and engineering calculations. Variations in the preference of unit systems may depend not only upon the language spoken by a particular researcher but also upon whether or not he has been educated as an engineer or as a scientist.

The need for unit systems was first evident when it became necessary to explain the fundamental relationships between force, mass, and acceleration. Sir Isaac Newton (1642–1727) expressed several basic laws that he believed to govern the motion of particles. Only recently has it become evident that in studying the motion of atoms and certain planets, Einstein's theory of relativity must supplant Newton's previous concepts. However, Newton's "second law" still serves as a basis for much of today's engineering mechanics. Briefly this law may be stated as follows:

*When an external unbalanced force F acts on a rigid particle of mass, the motion of the particle will be changed. The particle will be accelerated. Its rate of change in motion will be in the direction of the unbalanced force and will be proportional to it.*

Stated mathematically: $\dfrac{F_1}{a_1} = \dfrac{F_2}{a_2} = \dfrac{F_3}{a_3} = \dfrac{F_n}{a_n} =$ a constant,

where $F_1$, $F_2$, $F_3$, etc., are external unbalanced forces acting on a particle, and $a_1$, $a_2$, $a_3$, etc., are consequential accelerations of the particle.

The quotient of $(F/a)$ is a quantity which is invariant. The units of this term depend upon the units arbitrarily chosen to define $F$ and $a$. This constant has been called the *mass* of the particle under consideration. It is properly designated by the symbol $M$, or in some cases by the product of the two symbols, $km$. In this latter case, $k$ could be a value of 1, or it could be some other dimensional expression of unity. The mass $M$ of a particular body is independent of the location of the body in the universe.

Thus $\qquad\qquad\qquad F = Ma$

or $\qquad\qquad\qquad F = kma$

## The American Engineering System of Units

Early in the development of engineering analysis a system of units was developed that defined both the units of mass and the units of force. It is perhaps unfortunate that the same word, pounds, was chosen to represent both quantities, since they are physically different. In order to help differentiate the quantities, the pound-mass may be designated as $lb_{mass}$ (or $lb_m$) and the pound-force as $lb_{force}$ (or $lb_f$).

For many engineering applications the numerical values of $lb_m$ and $lb_f$ are very nearly the same. However, in expressions such as $F = Ma$, it is necessary that the difference between $lb_m$ and $lb_f$ be maintained. By definition, a mass of 1 $lb_m$ will be attracted to the earth by a force of 1 $lb_f$ at a place where the acceleration of gravity is 32.17 ft/sec². If the acceleration of gravity changes to some other value, the force must change in proportion, since mass is invariant.

Although the pound subscripts, *force* and *mass,* are frequently omitted in engineering and scientific literature, it is nevertheless true that $lb_f$ is not the same as $lb_m$. Their numerical values are equal, however, in the case of sea level, 45° latitude calculations. However, their values may be widely different, as would be the case in an analysis involving satellite design and space travel.

In Newton's equation, $F = Ma$, dimensional homogeneity must be maintained. If length, force, and time are taken as fundamental dimensions, the dimensions of mass must be derived. This can be accomplished as follows:

$$F = Ma$$

Then

$$M = \frac{F}{a}$$

$$M = \frac{(F)}{(L/T^2)} = FL^{-1}T^2$$

and

$$M = lb\ ft^{-1}\ sec^2$$

For convenience, this derived unit of mass (1 lb sec²)/ft is called a *slug*. Thus, a force of 1 lb will cause a mass of 1 slug to have an acceleration of 1 ft/sec².

The relationship between 1 $lb_m$ and 1 slug is given by considering that whereas 1 $lb_f$ will accelerate a 1 $lb_m$ with an acceleration of $g = 32.2$ ft/sec², it will accelerate 1 slug with an acceleration of only 1 ft/sec². Thus:

$$1\ lb_f = (1\ lb_m)(32.2\ ft/sec^2) = (1\ slug)(1\ ft/sec^2)$$

or

$$1\ slug = 32.2\ lb_m$$

It should be noted that, with the FPS system, a unity conversion factor must be used if a mass unit other than the slug is used. Since the acceleration of gravity varies with both latitude and altitude, the use of a gravitational system is sometimes inconvenient. A 100,000-lb rocket on the earth, for example, would not weight 100,000 $lb_f$ on the moon, where gravitational forces are smaller. The mass of the rocket, on the other hand, is a fixed quantity and will be a constant amount, regardless of its location in space.

For a freely falling body at sea level and 45° latitude, the acceleration $g$[1] of the body is 32.174 (approximately 32.2) ft/sec². As the mass is attracted to the earth, the only force then acting on it is its own weight.

then

$$F = Ma$$

If

$$W = Mg$$

and

$$M = \frac{W}{g}$$

where

$$a = g \quad \text{and} \quad F = W$$

[1] The value of the acceleration of gravity, $g$, at any latitude $\theta$ on the earth may be approximated from the following relationship: $g = 32.09(1 + 0.0053\ sin^2\ \theta)$ ft/sec².

In this particular system of units, then, the mass of a body in slugs may be calculated by dividing the weight of the body in pounds by the local acceleration of gravity in ft/sec².

The engineer frequently works in several systems of units in the same calculation. In this case, it is only necessary that the force, mass, and acceleration dimensions all be expressed in any valid set of units from any unit system. Numerical equality and unit homogeneity may be determined in any case by applying unity conversion factors to the individual terms of the expression.

*Example:* Solve for the $lb_m$ which is being accelerated at 3.07 ft/sec² by a force of 392 $lb_f$.

SOLUTION:
$$F = Ma \quad \text{or} \quad M = \frac{F}{a}$$

$$M = \frac{392 \ lb_f}{3.07 \ ft/sec^2} = 127.8 \ \frac{lb_f \ sec^2}{ft}$$

The direct substitution has given mass in the units of slugs instead of $lb_m$ units. This is a perfectly proper set of units for mass, although not in $lb_m$ units as desired. Consequently the final equation must be altered by applying the unity conversion factor $\left(\frac{32.2 \ lb_m}{1 \ lb_f \ sec^2 \ ft^{-1}}\right)$. The object, of course, is to cancel units until the desired units appear in the answer. Thus

$$M = \left(\frac{127.8 \ lb_f \ sec^2}{ft}\right)\left(\frac{32.2 \ lb_m \ ft}{1 \ lb_f \ sec^2}\right) = (4.11)(10)^3 \ lb_m$$

*Example:* Solve for the mass in slugs being accelerated at 13.6 meters/sec by a force of 1782 $lb_f$.

SOLUTION:
$$F = Ma$$

$$M = \frac{F}{a} = \frac{(1782 \ lb_f)}{(13.6 \ meters/sec^2)} = \left(\frac{1782 \ lb_f \ sec^2}{13.6 \ meters}\right)\left(\frac{1}{3.28} \ \frac{meter}{ft}\right)$$

$$M = 40 \ \frac{lb_f \ sec^2}{ft} = 40 \ slugs$$

It is recommended that in writing a mathematical expression to represent some physical phenomena, the engineer should avoid using stereotyped conversion symbols such as $g$, $g_c$, $k$, or $J$ in the equation. If one of these, or any other conversion factor, is needed in an equation to achieve unit balance, it can *then* be added. Since many different unit systems may be used from time to time, it is best to add unity conversion factors *only* as they are needed. Unfortunately, in much engineering literature, the equations used in a particular instance have been written to include one or more unity conversion factors. Considerable care must be exercised, therefore, in using these expressions since they represent a "special case" rather than a "general condition." The engineer should form a habit of always checking the unit balance of all equations.

Remember that:

$$1 \ slug = 1 \ \frac{lb_f \ sec^2}{ft} = 32.2 \ lb_m$$

### Table 11–1.  Unit Systems

| | GRAVITATIONAL | | | ABSOLUTE | | |
|---|---|---|---|---|---|---|
| FUNDAMENTAL DIMENSIONS | (1) FPS | (2) MKS | (3) AMERICAN ENGINEERING | (4) FPS | (5) MKS | (6) CGS |
| Force ($F$) | $lb_f$ | kg | $lb_f$ | $\cdots$ | $\cdots$ | $\cdots$ |
| Length ($L$) | ft | meter | ft or in. | ft | meter | cm |
| Time ($T$) | sec | sec | sec | sec | sec | sec |
| Mass ($M$) | $\cdots$ | $\cdots$ | $lb_m$ | $lb_m$ | kg | gram |
| **DERIVED DIMENSIONS** | | | | | | |
| Force ($F$) | $\cdots$ | $\cdots$ | $\cdots$ | $lb_m$ ft sec$^{-2}$ (called a *poundal*) | kg meter sec$^{-2}$ (called a *newton**) | gram cm sec$^{-2}$ (called a *dyne*) |
| Mass ($M$) | $lb_f$ sec$^2$ ft$^{-1}$ (called a *slug*) | kg sec$^2$ meter$^{-1}$ | $\cdots$ | $\cdots$ | $\cdots$ | $\cdots$ |
| Energy ($LF$) | ft-$lb_f$ | meter-kg | ft-$lb_f$ | ft-poundal | meter-newton | cm-dyne (called an *erg*) |
| Power ($\frac{LF}{T}$) | $\frac{\text{ft-}lb_f}{\text{sec}}$ | $\frac{\text{meter-kg}}{\text{sec}}$ | $\frac{\text{ft-}lb_f}{\text{sec}}$ | $\frac{\text{ft-poundal}}{\text{sec}}$ | $\frac{\text{meter-newton}}{\text{sec}}$ | $\frac{\text{erg}}{\text{sec}}$ |
| Velocity ($\frac{L}{T}$) | $\frac{\text{ft}}{\text{sec}}$ | $\frac{\text{meter}}{\text{sec}}$ | $\frac{\text{ft}}{\text{sec}}$ | $\frac{\text{ft}}{\text{sec}}$ | $\frac{\text{meter}}{\text{sec}}$ | $\frac{\text{cm}}{\text{sec}}$ |
| Acceleration ($\frac{L}{T^2}$) | $\frac{\text{ft}}{\text{sec}^2}$ | $\frac{\text{meter}}{\text{sec}^2}$ | $\frac{\text{ft}}{\text{sec}^2}$ | $\frac{\text{ft}}{\text{sec}^2}$ | $\frac{\text{meter}}{\text{sec}^2}$ | $\frac{\text{cm}}{\text{sec}^2}$ |
| Area ($L^2$) | ft$^2$ | meter$^2$ | ft$^2$ | ft$^2$ | meter$^2$ | cm$^2$ |
| Volume ($L^3$) | ft$^3$ | meter$^3$ | ft$^3$ | ft$^3$ | meter$^3$ | cm$^3$ |

* A newton is the force required to accelerate a 1-kg mass at 1 meter/sec². The acceleration of gravity at sea level and 45° latitude has the measured value of 9.807 meters/sec². A force of 1 kg equals 9.807 newtons of force.

The foregoing discussion has shown that:

1. If mass units in slugs are used in the expression $F = Ma$, the force units will come out in the usual units of pounds ($lb_f$).

2. If mass units in pounds ($lb_m$) are used in the expression $F = Ma$, force units will come out in an absolute system unit called the *poundal* (see Table 11–1).

In engineering calculations the inch is used just as often as the foot to represent the unit of length, and this necessitates the introduction of an additional unit of mass. Consider Newton's law, $F = Ma$, where $F = 1\ lb_f$ and $a = 1\ in./sec^2$. Then

$$M = 1\ lb_f\ sec^2/in.$$

where lb now is $lb_{force}$.

*Example:* A body weighs $W\ lb_f$ at a place where $g = 386\ in./sec^2$. Find the mass of the body in units of $lb_f\ sec^2/in.$

SOLUTION: The relationship between weight and mass is given by

$$W = Mg$$

and if $W$ is given in $lb_f$ and $g$ in $in./sec^2$, this gives

$$M = \frac{W}{g} = \frac{W}{386}\ lb_f\ sec^2/in.$$

The most commonly used units in engineering calculations are the following:

**Units of Time.** The mean solar day is the standard unit of time in all systems of units used at present. The hour (hr), the minute (min), and the second (sec) are all derived from the mean solar day, but not decimally. Since all four of these units are used, sometimes even in the same problem, it is easy to see how mistakes can be made and considerable extra work required. This is also the case with the International System of Units (SI), which system has the same units of time as the American engineering system. The most common unit used in engineering calculations is the second, defined as

$$1\ sec = \frac{1\ mean\ solar\ day}{86,400}$$

Then, 1 min = 60 sec and 1 hr = 3600 sec.

**Units of Length.** The world standard of length is the meter (m), defined now in terms of the wave length of a particularly uniform monochromatic light. It is quite close to being equal to the distance from the earth's equator to the North Pole divided by ten million, which was its original definition. This unit of length is used by American electrical engineers and engineers working in the field of space mechanics.

The most common units of length that are used in engineering calculations are the inch (in.), the foot (ft), and the mile (mi). Less common are the yard and the nautical mile. They are defined as

$$1 \text{ in.} = 2.54 \, (10)^{-2} \text{ m (exactly by definition)}$$
$$1 \text{ ft} = 12 \text{ in.}$$
$$1 \text{ yard} = 3 \text{ ft}$$
$$1 \text{ mile} = 5280 \text{ ft}$$
$$1 \text{ nautical mile} = 6080.27 \text{ ft approximately}$$

Often feet and inches or feet and miles are used in the same problem. The foot is sometimes decimalized and sometimes the last fractional foot is given in inches and fractions of an inch. Sometimes the inch is decimalized and sometimes it is fractionalized; sometimes it is both decimalized and fractionalized in the same problem.

**Units of Mass.** The world standard of mass is the kilogram (kg), defined originally as being one thousandth of one cubic meter of water at a temperature of 4° Celcius and standard atmospheric pressure, but now defined as the mass of a block of platinum kept at the French Bureau of Standards. This unit is used by American electrical and space engineers.

The pound mass ($lb_m$) is the unit that the average American engineer thinks he is using most of the time. In most instances this is incorrect. Generally the pound that he uses is the pound force ($lb_f$), from which he derives units of mass by means of Newton's law $F = Ma$. Thus,

$$1 \, lb_m = 0.4535924277 \text{ kg (by definition)}$$

$$1 \, \frac{lb_f \, \sec^2}{ft} \text{ (also called a slug)} = 32.174 \, lb_m$$

$$1 \, \frac{lb_f \, \sec^2}{in.} = 386.088 \, lb_m$$

**Units of Force.** The newton (N) is derived from the kilogram by means of Newton's law $F = Ma$. Thus,

$$1 \, N = 1 \text{ kg m/sec}^2,$$

and it is the force required to accelerate a kg mass one m/sec². This unit of force is used by American electrical and space engineers, but the most common unit of force that is used by American engineers is the pound ($lb_f$). This is the force required to accelerate a pound mass with the mean acceleration of gravity, or $g = 32.174 \text{ ft/sec}^2$. Its value is

$$1 \, lb_f = 4.448 \text{ N}$$

**Units of Area and Volume.** Units of area and volume are derived from the units of length for the most part. However, the gallon is a commonly used measure of volume that is in no way related to units of length.

**Units of Velocity and Acceleration.** These units are all derived from the units of length and time.

**Units of Work and Energy.** Several different units are used. For example, ft–lb, in.–lb and horsepowerhours are all used for work and mechanical energy; both the joule and the kilowatthour are used for electrical energy; and both the calorie (two types) and the British Thermal Unit (BTU) are used for heat energy. In some problems all of these units occur, which frequently makes the task of unit conversion the most formidable part of the solution.

**Units of Power.** Since power units are derived units, they also involve the various work and energy units described above. In addition, the ton of refrigeration (3517 watts) has been added.

**Units of Pressure.** In general, the units of pressure have been derived from conventional units of force and area. However, other measures are also used. For example, the standard atmospheric pressure is commonly used as a unit, and for fractional atmospheres the millimeter of mercury, the inch of mercury, and the inch of water are used.

**Units of Density.** These units frequently create confusion in the minds of engineers. The units most commonly used are $lb/ft^3$ and $lb/in.^3$ where the lb is usually a unit of force, $lb_f$. Therefore these quantities do not truly represent density. They represent the attraction, in lb, of the earth on either one cubic foot or one cubic inch of the material. To convert to density for use in a gravitational system, one must divide these quantities by the acceleration of gravity, $g$. If one divides the first unit by $g = 32.174$ ft/sec², he obtains the unit of density $lb_f$ sec²/ft⁴, or slugs/ft³; and, if one divides the second unit by $g = 386.088$ in./sec², he obtains the unity of density $lb_f$ sec²/in⁴.

**Units of Temperature.** Temperature is an arbitrary measure which is proportional to the average kinetic energy of the molecules of an ideal gas. Four temperature scales are used by American engineers. The degree Celcius (°C), formerly called centigrade, reads zero at the freezing point of water and 100°C at the boiling point of water under standard conditions of pressure. It is the world standard of temperature. The temperature in degrees Kelvin (°K) is derived from the Celcius scale by the following equation:

Temperature in °K = Temperature in °C + 273.16

The degree Fahrenheit (°F), reads 32°F at the freezing point of water and 212°F at the boiling point of water under standard conditions of pressure. The degree Rankine (°R) is derived from the Fahrenheit scale by the equation:

Temperature in °R = Temperature in °F + 459.69

When a temperature is measured in either °K or in °R, it is said to be the *absolute* temperature, because these scales read zero for the condition where the kinetic energy of the molecules of an ideal gas is zero.

## Absolute Unit Systems

Scientists the world over have chosen to use dimensional or unit systems that are *absolute*. That is, the fundamental units chosen do not depend upon gravitational effects on the earth or other planets. In absolute systems the dimensions of force are derived in terms of the fundamental units of time, length, and mass. There are three absolute systems.[2] Two of these are used extensively in scientific work today. These are the MKS (meter, kilogram, second) absolute system, and the CGS (centimeter, gram, second) absolute system. The other absolute system, the FPS Absolute System, is used primarily in engineering computations.

The first one of these, which is also called the International System of Units, or SI units, from the French "Systéme International d'Unités", is now rapidly replacing both the CGS system and the old engineering systems in all parts of the world. The reason for this is that SI units are equally convenient for both engineers and scientists, which is a great advantage now that the two groups must cooperate closely for the purpose of making rapid technological progress. It is particularly convenient in calculations involving energy, since only one unit is used for all types of energy, whether atomic, electric, chemical, heat, or mechanical. This unit of energy is the joule, which previously was used only by electrical engineers, and the corresponding unit of power is the watt, which is one joule per second.

The following is a complete list of SI units and their dimensions:

Fundamental Units:
  Length = 1 m
  Mass = 1 kg
  Time = 1 sec
  Current = 1 ampere (amp); Electrical Charge = 1 coulomb = 1 amp sec
  Temperature = $1°K$ or $1°C$
  Light Source = 1 candela (International candle)

Derived Units:
  area = $1 m^2$
  volume = $1 m^3$
  velocity = $1 m/sec$
  acceleration = $1 m/sec^2$
  force = 1 newton (N) = $1 kg\, m/sec^2$
  work and energy = 1 joule (j) = $1 kg\, m^2/sec^2$
  moment and torque = $1 N\, m$
  power, 1 watt (w) = $1 kg\, m^2/sec^3$
  pressure, $1 N/m^2 = 1 kg/sec^2 m$ $(1 bar = 10^5 N/m^2)$
  thermal conductivity = $1 w/m°C = 1 kg\, m/sec^3 °C$
  heat transfer coefficient = $1 w/m^2 °C = 1 kg/sec^3 °C$
  dynamic viscosity = $1 N\, sec/m^2 = 1 kg/m\, sec = 1$ decapoise
  kinematic viscosity = $1 m^2/sec = 1$ myriastoke
  density = $1 kg/m^3$
  heat coefficient = $1 j/kg°C = 1 m^2/sec^2 °C$
  enthalpy, heat content and internal energy = $1 j/kg = 1 m^2/sec^2$
  potential = 1 volt (v) = $1 w/amp = 1 kg\, m^2/sec^3\, amp$
  resistance = 1 ohm (Ω) = $1 w/amp^2 = 1 kg\, m^2/sec^3\, amp^2$

[2] See page 208.

Derived Units (continued):

capacitance = 1 farad (f) = 1 coulomb/v = 1 amp$^2$ sec/w
= 1 amp$^2$sec$^4$/kg m$^2$
inductance = 1 henry (h) = 1 v sec/amp = 1 j/amp$^2$ = 1 kg m$^2$/sec$^2$ amp$^2$

capacity or permittivity $\epsilon_0 = \dfrac{10^7}{4\pi c^2} = 8.854 \times 10^{-12}$f/m

magnetic permeability $\mu_0 = 4\pi(10)^{-7} = 1.2566(10)^{-6}$h/m

## Problems on Unit Systems

**11–36.** In the FPS gravitational system, what mass in slugs is necessary to produce 15.6 lb$_f$ at standard conditions?

**11–37.** In the engineering gravitational system, what mass in lb$_m$ is necessary to produce a 195.3 lb$_f$ at standard conditions?

**11–38.** Using the FPS gravitational system, calculate the fundamental dimensions of $E$ in Einstein's equation,

$$E = mc^2 \left[ \frac{1}{\sqrt{1 - (V^2/c^2)}} - 1 \right]$$

if $m$ is a mass, $V$ is a velocity, and $c$ is the speed of light. What would be the fundamental dimensions of $E$ in the CGS absolute system of units?

**11–39.** Using the relationship for $g$ on page 206 and the FPS gravitational system of units, determine the weight, at the latitude 0°, of a stainless steel sphere whose mass is defined as 150 lb$_f$ sec$^2$/ft.

**11–40.** The mass of solid propellant in a certain container is 5 kg. What is the weight of this material in newtons at a location in Greenland, where the acceleration of gravity is 9.83 m/sec$^2$? What is the weight in kg?

**11–41.** Change 100 newtons of force to lb$_f$.

**11–42.** If a gold sphere has a mass of 89.3 lb$_m$ on earth, what would be its weight in lb$_f$ on the moon, where the acceleration of gravity is 5.31 fps$^2$?

**11–43.** Assuming that the acceleration due to gravitation is 5.31 fps$^2$ on the moon, what is the mass in slug units of a 100 lb$_m$ located on the moon?

**11–44.** A silver bar weighs 382 lb$_f$ at a point on the earth where the acceleration of gravity is measured to be 32.1 fps$^2$. Calculate the mass of the bar in lb$_m$ and slug units.

**11–45.** The acceleration of gravity can be approximated by the following relationship:

$$g = 980.6 - (3.086)(10)^{-6}A$$

where $g$ is expressed in cm/sec$^2$, and $A$ is an altitude in cm. If a rocket weighs 10,370 lb$_f$ at sea level and standard conditions, what will be its weight in dynes at 50,000 ft elevation?

**11–46.** At a certain point on the moon the acceleration due to gravitation is 5.35 fps$^2$. A rocket resting on the moon's surface at this point weighs 23,500 lb$_f$. What is its mass in slugs? In lb$_m$?

**11–47.** If a 10-lb weight on the moon (where $g = 5.33$ fps$^2$) is returned to the earth and deposited at a latitude of 90° (see page 206), how much would it weigh in the new location?

### Problems on Unit Systems (continued)

**11–48.** A 4.37-slug mass is taken from the earth to the moon and located at a point where $g = 5.33$ fps². What is the magnitude of its mass in the new location?

**11–49.** Is the equation $F = WV^2/2g$ a homogenous expression if $W$ is a weight, $V$ is a velocity, $F$ is a force, and $g$ is the linear acceleration of gravity? Prove your answer, using the FPS absolute system of units.

**11–50.** Sir Isaac Newton expressed the belief that all particles in space, regardless of their mass, are each attracted to every other particle in space by a specific force of attraction. For spherical bodies, whose separation is very large compared with the physical dimensions of either particle, the force of attraction may be calculated from the relationship $F = Gm_1m_2/d^2$, where $F$ is the existing gravitational force, $d$ is the distance separating the two masses $m_1$ and $m_2$, and $G$ is a gravitational constant, whose magnitude depends upon the unit system being used. Using the CGS absolute system of units [$G = 6.67 \times 10^{-8}$ (cm³/gm sec²)], calculate the mass of the earth if it attracts a mass of 1 gram with a force of 980 dynes. Assume that the distance from the center of the earth to the gram mass is 6370 km.

**11–51.** Referring to Problem 11–50, calculate the mass of the sun if the earth ($6 \times 10^{24}$ kg mass) has an orbital diameter of $1.49 \times 10^7$ kms and the force of attraction between the two celestial bodies is $(1.44)(10)^{25}$ newtons.

**11–52.** From Problem 11–50 calculate the acceleration of gravity on the earth in CGS absolute units.

**11–53.** An interstellar explorer is accelerating uniformly at 58.6 fps² in a spherical space ship which has a total mass of 100,000 slugs. What is the force acting on the ship?

**11–54.** At a certain instant in time a space vehicle is being acted on by a vertically upward thrust of 497,000 lb$_f$. The mass of the space vehicle is 400,000 lb$_m$, and the acceleration of gravity is 32.1 fps². Is the vehicle rising or descending? What is its acceleration? (Assume "up" means radially outward from the center of the earth.)

**11–55.** Some interstellar adventurers land their space craft on a certain celestial body. Explain how they could calculate the acceleration of gravity at the point where they landed.

**11–56.** A volt is defined as the electric potential existing between two points when one joule of work is required to carry one coulomb of charge from one point to the other. An ampere is defined as a flow of one coulomb of charge per second in a conducting medium. From these definitions, derive an expression for power in watts in an electrical circuit.

**11–57.** An electric light bulb requires 100 w of power while burning. At what rate is heat being produced? What will be the horsepower corresponding to 100 w?

**11–58.** A 440 v electric motor which is 83 per cent efficient is delivering 4.20 horsepower to a hoist which is 76 per cent efficient. At what rate can a mass of 1155 kg be lifted?

**11–59.** How many kilograms of silver will be transferred in an electroplating tank by a passage of 560 amp for one hour? (Hint: 96,500 coulombs will deposit a gram-equivalent of an element in a plating solution.)

**11–60.** A window mount type of air conditioning unit is rated at ¾ tons capacity for cooling. If the overall efficiency of the motor and compressor unit is 26 per cent, what electric current will be necessary to operate the unit continuously when connected to a 120 v alternating current power line?

**11–61.** A large capacitor is rated at 10,000 microfarads. If it is connected to a 6.3 v battery, how many coulombs will be required to charge it?

**11–62.** A capacitor used in transistor circuits is rated at 5 picofarads. How many coulombs will be required to charge it if it is connected to a 9 v battery?

**11–63.** The reactance in ohms of a coil of wire is given as $X_L = 2 fL$ where $f$ is the frequency of an electric current in cycles per second and $L$ is the coil inductance in henries. Compute the reactance of a small solenoid coil whose inductance is 2.75 millihenries if the coil is conected to a 109 v line whose frequency is 412 hertz.

**11–64.** A galvanometer has a resistance of 612 ohms and gives a deflection of 18.0 cm for a current of 28 ma. What will be its current sensitivity, (amperes per meter), and its voltage sensitivity, (volts per meter)?

**11–65.** A current of 0.63 amp will produce 15.0 cals of heat in a small light bulb in 10.0 sec. What power is expended in the bulb and what is the lamp resistance?

**11–66.** A coil of resistance wire having a resistance of 3.11 ohms is immersed in a beaker containing 1.150 kg of water. At what rate is heat being produced when a current of 47.5 amp is flowing?

**BIBLIOGRAPHY**

IPSEN, D. C., *Units, Dimensions, and Dimensionless Numbers*, McGraw-Hill, New York, (1960).

# Chapter 12

# Statistics and Graphical Analysis

## STATISTICS

Certain statistical operations are commonly encountered in engineering work, particularly when data are acquired and evaluated. We might even say that science is based on statistics and that the scientific "laws" that we use relate not to how nature will certainly behave, but rather to how nature has behaved within limits and to how nature is likely to continue to behave under similar conditions. It is within the realm of statistics to determine what these limits are and to attempt to determine the probability of recurrence of any given set of events based on the frequency and regularity of their occurrence in the past.

If we consider some natural phenomena, such as the sun's rising in the east rather than in the west, we cannot say with certainty that the same thing will happen tomorrow. We can say, however, that as far as any records show, the sun has always risen in the east, and so far as we know, no changes in conditions have occurred to alter the probability of its rising in the east, so we conclude that it is highly probable that tomorrow's sunrise will be in the east.

In a like manner, we can make a general statement that at some given city in the United States, it will be colder on New Year's Day than it will be on the first day of July. Statistically, we can show that for many years it has always been colder on New Year's Day than on the first of July, but it is within the realm of possibility, knowing how local weather conditions can vary, that a set of weather circumstances can occur that could make, for a certain year, a colder July 1st than New Year's Day.

The probability of such an occurrence is slight but it definitely is greater than that of the sun's sudden appearance in the morning on the western horizon. Thus, we see that there not only is an uncertainty even in well ordered natural phenomena, but also there is a degree of uncertainty of future happenings which is based on the variability in the past of certain occurrences.

Statistics then is the science of making decisions based on observation, collection, analysis, and interpretation of data that are affected by chance causes.[1] The importance of the use of statistics has been emphasized in recent years by the national effort to place a man on the moon and effect his safe return to earth.

The best statistical methods are useless unless the data obtained have been collected so that the methods are applicable. Accuracy in tabulation, in calculation, and in thought are essential ingredients to all statistical work, since the data used are themselves subject to chance errors. Care and neatness in preparing all calculations are important aids to accuracy. However, it is no less important that the engineer develop a natural skepticism and inquisitive attitude toward all data collected and toward their methods of collection, their analyses, and their interpretation.

### Variables

From a statistical point of view, the chance variations which occur in measured data are a major problem in any evaluation. Fortunately, in the physical sciences and in engineering work, the variables usually are easier to control and are better known than they are in some other fields such as psychology, where animal and human behavior are being studied. For example, if we should desire to determine the relation between current and voltage in an electrical circuit, we can establish a test setup of a power source, a set of conductors, and a power receiver together with appropriate meters to measure the electrical quantities. However, we recognize that variables inherent in the test setup must be controlled, held constant, or evaluated for effects on the meter readings. Of all the possible variables, temperature is most likely to change the circuit resistance and consequently alter the data secured. Fortunately, it usually is fairly easy to maintain constant temperature conditions and then to obtain a relation between a voltage change and the corresponding current change in order to establish a relationship describing their behavior within the limits of error of the experiment. Again, if we should try other circuit conditions of power and resistance, we probably would arrive at substantially the same results; therefore, we can reasonably conclude that the ratio between the voltage change and the corresponding current change in a circuit is a constant.

On the other hand, if a psychological test were to be made to determine the effect of loss of sleep on ability to perform simple arithmetical operations, we would find quite a wide variance between subjects and even between the ability of the same subject at various times. We conclude then that the relationship of loss of sleep to arithmetical accomplishments involves variables of many sorts most of which are hard to control or evaluate.

## NORMAL PROBABILITY LAW

If a large glass jar were filled to the top with marbles and placed in view of a large class of students and each student was asked to write down his estimate of the number of marbles in the jar, it is extremely unlikely that every student would estimate the same number and that this number would be the exact number of

[1] Irving W. Burr, *Engineering Statistics and Quality Control*, McGraw-Hill, New York (1953), p. 3.

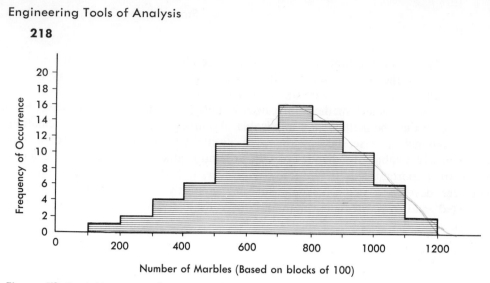

**Figure 12–1.** A histogram of estimates of marbles in a jar.

marbles in the jar. Rather it is likely that if the answers were compiled, a pattern of distribution of estimates would focus upon a certain estimated number of marbles.

If for simplicity in plotting, the estimates are grouped into blocks to the nearest 100 marbles, a graph of this distribution might look like Figure 12–1. This figure is plotted so that the width of a column is equal to the interval, in this case 100 marbles, and the height is equal to the frequency, which is the number of persons making any given block of estimates.

If the number of persons making estimates of the marbles were doubled and the blocks within which the estimates fall were made smaller, the histogram probably would take on an appearance similar to Figure 12–2.

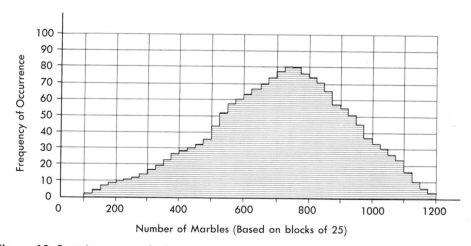

**Figure 12–2.** A histogram of a large number of estimates.

If this process were to be continued, we see that the appearance of the graph would begin to assume the shape of a smooth curve. Although the proof of this statement is beyond the scope of this book, we can show that for a large number of types of observations, the pattern becomes similar to the graph in Figure 12–3.

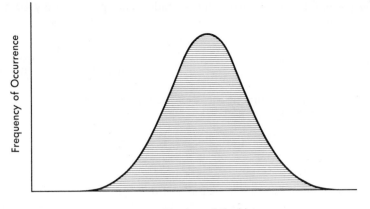

**Figure 12–3.** Normal probability curve.

This graph shows the usual frequency distributions of a large number of observations and is typical of the distribution of any set of chance events. In practice, it can be taller or shorter, fatter or thinner, but it is usually symmetrical and bell-shaped.

If a person should take ten coins and toss them on a table many times and keep a tally of the number of heads that show up each time, he would find that the occurrence of ten heads is extremely rare, that the occurrences of zero heads is extremely rare and that the greatest number of occurrences is for five heads to show up. If the frequencies of occurrences is plotted against the number of heads, we would find that the bell-shaped curve described above will result.

This graph, which pictures the distribution of frequencies of certain chance events, is called the *normal probability curve*. It is of great use in many forms of testing in engineering and science.

The horizontal axis (abscissa) of the graph represents the values of the measurements made ($X_1$, $X_2$, $X_3$,—etc.) and the vertical axis (ordinate) represents the fraction of the total number of observations made corresponding to each value of $X$.

The general mathematical expression for the probability curve is a log function of the form $y = Ce^{Kx^2}$. From an inspection of the probability curve determined either by trial or by derivation, several principles can be observed.

1. Small errors occur more frequently than large ones.
2. Errors of any given size are as likely to be positive as they are to be negative.
3. Very large random errors seldom occur.

### Some Fundamental Statistical Measures

The terms "arithmetic mean," "median," and "mode" are used extensively in statistical work. These terms will be defined here in order that the student can gain a better appreciation of their use.

**Arithmetic Mean.** This term is used to denote the point about which the data tend to cluster. It is often referred to as the *average* or *central tendency*. It is calculated by obtaining the sum of the individual measurements and dividing this quantity by the number of measurements made. This process may be represented mathematically by:

$$\overline{X} = \sum_{i=1}^{i=n} \frac{X_i}{n} = \frac{X_1 + X_2 + X_3 \ldots \ldots X_n}{n}$$

where $\overline{X}$ = arithmetic mean
$X_i$ = individual measurements
$n$ = total number of measurements

*Example:* Find the arithmetic mean of the following data:
7, 4, 9, 5, 6, 8, 3

$$\overline{X} = \frac{7 + 4 + 9 + 5 + 6 + 8 + 3}{7} = \frac{42}{7} = 6$$

**Median.** This term is similar to the mean in that it is also a measure of the tendency of the data to collect about a central point. The median is the midpoint (not average) of a group of data. When the total number of data is odd, the median is the middle number of the set of numbers. If the total number of data is even, the median is the arithmetic mean of the two middlemost numbers in the set.

*Examples:*

a. 4, 6, 9, 10, 11, 12, 15          Median = 10
b. 5, 7, 7, 8, 10, 11, 15, 19      Median = 9
c. 2, 5, 7, 9, 9, 11, 15, 16       Median = 9

**Mode.** As in the other cases, the mode is also a measure of the "central tendency" of the data. The mode is that value which occurs with the greatest frequency in the set of data. It is the most common value, and for this reason it may exist in some sets of data. In other cases there may be more than one mode.

*Examples:*

a. 2, 4, 5, 5, 5, 3, 2, 6          Mode = 5
b. 2, 3, 4, 6, 7, 8                There is no mode.
c. 2, 3, 4, 4, 5, 5, 6, 7          There are two modes—4 and 5.
                                    (This is called bimodal)

### Deviations from the Normal Curve

The most common deviation from the normal probability curve is a condition known as "skewness." In this condition the curve is distorted, and the high part of the curve corresponding to the greatest frequency is nearer to one end, rather than being in the middle. One of the most common causes of this nonnormality is that the distribution may be restricted from going beyond a certain point. This situation would exist, for example, if the measurement has a physical limit of zero. Such a graph could also be formed if the scores on an examination given to students were plotted, and the test had been much too easy or much too difficult. In another case, if the length of a group of parts made by an improperly adjusted machine are measured with a steel scale, the plot of the measurements could be distorted or skewed.

Another abnormal condition is produced when the group being sampled is not homogeneous. The curve produced could have two peaks and would be known as a "bimodal" distribution. Such a plot could be obtained if an examination were given to a group of students some of whom were rather dull and the remainder of whom were very apt and intelligent. As another example, if a box of similar type of resistors is measured to determine the distribution of resistance values, and the box contains resistors from two different machines set to produce slightly different values of resistance, it is likely that a "two-humped" graph would result showing that two somewhat independent groups are present in the test sequence.

If deviations from the normal curve are excessive, accurate results cannot be obtained from the statistical tools described in the following topics. Usually it is necessary to examine the method of measurement to see whether systematic errors are present or to examine the group being measured to determine whether a proper sample is taken, so that results can be made to approximate the normal curve.

### Theory of Errors

As suggested above, the normal curve may be considered to be the frequency distribution of the infinite number of possible measurements of the quantity being observed. When practical, *all possible* measurements in a given situation should be tabulated. When this can be accomplished it is said to be a study of the *total population* or *universe*. In many situations such measurement is not possible. For example, if someone wanted to obtain the heights of all the men in the world, he could not do so. In such cases, it is necessary to examine a small part of the total population, called a *sample*. If the *sample* is representative of the *total population,* certain important conclusions can be drawn about the nature of the *total population*. The size of the *sample* chosen will depend upon how close it is desired to approximate the *total population.*

### Standard Deviation

Since, in any group of measured quantities the true value is never known, it is desirable to have a means of estimating the uncertainty, and consequently the accuracy, of a measurement. In order to do this, we must make use of several statistical tools, one of which is known as the "Standard Deviation." The standard deviation may be calculated for a *total population* (usually designated as $\sigma$)[2] and for the *sample*. For the sample, the standard deviation is given by the equation:

$$s = \sqrt{\frac{\Sigma(X_i - \overline{X})^2}{n - 1}}$$

Where $\sigma$ and $s$ represent the standard deviations for the respective situations, $\Sigma$ is the Greek capital letter *sigma* which represents the sum, $(X_i - \overline{X})$ represents the deviation of a single observation from the mean, and $n$ is the number of observations. For example, if we weigh a block of wood on ten different scales and record the weight from each weighing in a tabular form, the deviations from the mean can be obtained readily by subtracting any single reading from the mean of the values. The standard deviation for the *sample* can then be calculated as shown.

[2] Greek letters are usually used to represent descriptive quantities about the population whereas Arabic letters are used to represent descriptive quantities about a sample.

| TRIAL | WEIGHT IN GRAMS | $X_i - \overline{X}$ | $(X_i - \overline{X})^2$ |
|-------|-----------------|----------------------|--------------------------|
| 1 | 522 | + 10 | 100 |
| 2 | 506 | − 6 | 36 |
| 3 | 513 | + 1 | 1 |
| 4 | 510 | − 2 | 4 |
| 5 | 519 | + 7 | 49 |
| 6 | 508 | − 4 | 16 |
| 7 | 512 | 0 | 0 |
| 8 | 504 | − 8 | 64 |
| 9 | 512 | 0 | 0 |
| 10 | 514 | + 2 | 4 |
| | $\Sigma = 5120$ | $\Sigma = 0$ | $\Sigma = 274$ |

$\overline{X} = \text{Mean} = 5120/10 = 512$

From this table the value of $\Sigma(X_i - \overline{X})^2 = 274$, which, if substituted in the expression for standard deviation, gives:

$$s = \sqrt{\frac{274}{10 - 1}} = \sqrt{\frac{274}{9}} = \sqrt{30.44} = 5.52 \text{ grams}$$

The use of the standard deviation will be discussed more in detail later in this chapter.

### Population Dispersion

If the plot of a series of measurements is made to produce a histogram and the tops of the rectangles are connected by a smooth curve, the bell-shaped curve is a typical probability curve.

After a normal probability curve is obtained from a histogram, if the values of $\sigma$ (assuming a *total* population study) are plotted on the abscissa, it will be found that about 68.27 per cent of the measurements will fall within the $\pm$ one $\sigma$ range of the mean (that is, one standard deviation on either side of the mean). This means that there is a 68.27 per cent chance that the value of any single observation will fall between $+\sigma$ and $-\sigma$ of the mean, $\overline{X}$.

Referring to Figure 12–4, we can show experimentally that 68.27 per cent of the values will be plotted between $-\sigma$ and $+\sigma$. However, this percentage can be shown best where a large number of observations, 100 or more for example, are made.

If an abscissa value of $\pm 2\sigma$ is plotted on a probability curve, it can be shown that about 95.45 per cent of the observations will fall between $-2\sigma$ and $+2\sigma$ of $\overline{X}$, Figure 12–5.

### Use of Probability Curve

A probability curve does not give the true value of a quantity being measured. If we assume that the mean, or arithmetical average, of a number of observations is acceptable as a value to use to present a measured quantity, then the standard deviation gives an indication of the reliability of any single observation.

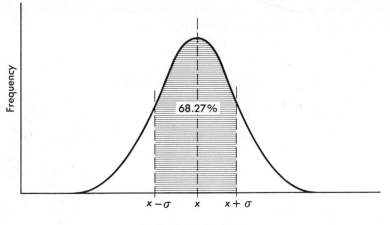

**Figure 12–4.** Normal probability curve.

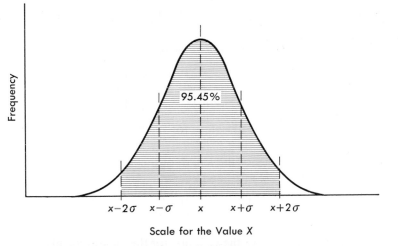

**Figure 12–5.** Sigma error on a normal probability curve.

## Standard Error

It usually is desirable to evaluate the uncertainty of the arithmetic mean. We know that the uncertainty of the mean, $\overline{X}$, is considerably less than the uncertainty of any single observation, $(X_i)$. The uncertainty of the mean can be expressed in the following form:

$$\sigma_m = \frac{\sigma}{\sqrt{n}} \text{ and this is usually approximated by } s_m = \frac{s}{\sqrt{n}}$$

where $\sigma_m$ is the standard error of the mean, $S_m$ is the standard deviation of the mean, $s$ is the standard deviation of a sample, and $n$ is the number of observations in the sample.

Engineering Tools of Analysis

*Example:* The mean of 25 measurements of an angle gives a value of 32° 17.1′, *s* is 1.2′. What is the probable range of the true value?

SOLUTION:

1. The mean of 32° 17.1′ is the most likely true value.

2. $s_m = \dfrac{1.2'}{5} = 0.24' \cong \pm 0.2'$

There is a 68.27 per cent certainty that the true value lies between 32° 16.9′ and 32° 17.3′ ($\pm s_m$).

3. There is a 95.45 per cent certainty that the true value lies between 32° 16.7′ and 32° 17.5′ ($\pm 2s_m$).

Since the true value is never known, an estimate based on mathematical processes can be made as to the confidence that can be placed in the mean as an assumed true value.

## Problems

**12–1.** A series of weighings of a sample of metal powder are made with the following results:

WEIGHT IN GRAMS OF A SAMPLE

| | | | | |
|---|---|---|---|---|
| 2.020 | 2.021 | 2.021 | 2.019 | 2.019 |
| 2.018 | 2.021 | 2.018 | 2.021 | 2.017 |
| 2.017 | 2.020 | 2.016 | 2.019 | 2.020 |

Compute the mean, *s*, and $s_m$ values for the weighings. What is the probable weight of the sample?

**12–2.** A series of measurements of the length of a concrete runway is made using a steel tape. The results are tabulated below:

| | | | | |
|---|---|---|---|---|
| 1,363.7 meters | 1,364.5 | 1,364.0 | 1,363.8 | 1,364.0 |
| 1,364.1 | 1,363.9 | 1,364.1 | 1,363.9 | |

Compute the mean and give the $s_m$ limits for the measurements.

**12–3.** A series of readings was taken, using an electronic interval timer, for one complete swing of a pendulum to occur. The data are tabulated as follows:

| TIME IN SECONDS | NUMBER OF OCCURRENCES | TIME IN SECONDS | NUMBER OF OCCURRENCES |
|---|---|---|---|
| 1.851 | 1 | 1.859 | 18 |
| 1.852 | 3 | 1.860 | 15 |
| 1.853 | 6 | 1.861 | 12 |
| 1.854 | 9 | 1.862 | 10 |
| 1.855 | 12 | 1.863 | 5 |
| 1.856 | 14 | 1.864 | 4 |
| 1.857 | 18 | 1.865 | 2 |
| 1.858 | 19 | 1.866 | 1 |

What is the mean time of a swing, and what would be the standard error of the mean?

**12–4.** The test scores on an intelligence test given to a class of elementary students are tabulated as follows:

| | | | | | |
|----|----|----|----|----|----|
| 35 | 58 | 46 | 67 | 47 | 53 |
| 55 | 38 | 50 | 47 | 50 | 53 |
| 46 | 54 | 45 | 52 | 62 | 48 |
| 45 | 51 | 48 | 42 | 48 | 65 |
| 51 | 55 | 60 | 53 | 55 | |
| 56 | 43 | 47 | 58 | 34 | |
| 42 | 55 | 46 | 59 | 68 | |
| 60 | 52 | 61 | 39 | 31 | |
| 52 | 44 | 42 | 39 | 70 | |

Plot a histogram of the scores and sketch in a probability curve. Compute the mean, median, and mode. Is there any tendency to skewness or bimodality? Does the mean value of the scores have a significance comparable to the mean of, for example, a series of measurements of the length of a steel block?

**12–5.** Take ten coins and toss them at least twenty-five times, keeping count of the number of heads and tails for each toss. Plot a probability curve and determine whether $s$ does represent 68.27 per cent of the total observations.

**12–6.** The distribution of ages of a group of recruits at an Army camp is given as follows:

| Age in Years and Months | Number of Persons | Age in Years and Months | Number of Persons |
|---|---|---|---|
| 18–1 | 1 | 19–7 | 9 |
| 18–2 | 0 | 19–8 | 5 |
| 18–3 | 1 | 19–9 | 3 |
| 18–4 | 3 | 19–10 | 3 |
| 18–5 | 8 | 19–11 | 0 |
| 18–6 | 5 | 19–12 | 2 |
| 18–7 | 8 | 20–1 | 5 |
| 18–8 | 10 | 20–2 | 1 |
| 18–9 | 14 | 20–3 | 0 |
| 18–10 | 7 | 20–4 | 2 |
| 18–11 | 12 | 20–5 | 6 |
| 18–12 | 11 | 20–6 | 0 |
| 19–1 | 11 | 20–7 | 1 |
| 19–2 | 6 | 20–8 | 0 |
| 19–3 | 10 | 20–9 | 2 |
| 19–4 | 8 | 20–10 | 0 |
| 19–5 | 7 | 20–11 | 0 |
| 19–6 | 6 | 20–12 | 0 |

Plot a histogram and sketch a probability curve for the ages. Show the $s$ and $2s$ locations. Does this graph show any unusual departures from a standard probability curve? Compute the mean, median and mode.

**Problems (continued)**

12–7. Measurements were made of the lengths of a number of steel rods which were supposed to be cut to a length of 6.80 inches. The measurements are as follows:

| | | | |
|---|---|---|---|
| 6.81 | 6.80 | 6.79 | 6.80 |
| 6.82 | 6.80 | 6.78 | 6.80 |
| 6.81 | 6.83 | 6.79 | 6.77 |
| 6.82 | 6.80 | 6.78 | 6.80 |
| 6.81 | 6.81 | 6.79 | 6.87 |

What is the average length of the rods, and what maximum tolerance can be set up if 95.45 per cent of the rods are to be acceptable?

## GRAPHICAL ANALYSIS

Graphs are a valuable aid in presenting many types of information where facts must be readily grasped. They aid in the analysis of engineering data and facilitate the presentation of statistical information. Graphs generally can be classified as those used for technical purposes and those used for general presentation of information. To be of greatest value, graphs should be prepared in accord with the best current practice.

A graphical display of information may take any of several forms, depending upon the type of information to be presented and the use to be made of the information. For rapid dissemination of information, pictographs are convenient. Where more exact representation is desired, bar graphs or circle graphs may be employed.

**Illustration 12–1.** Graphs are an important method of displaying data for rapid visualization of the variations of one quantity with respect to another. In this picture engineers are discussing a curve of measured valve positions in an automobile engine as compared with theoretical curves of cam contours to determine appropriate changes that may be necessary in the manufacture of the cams. (Courtesy Oldsmobile Division, General Motors Corporation.)

**Illustration 12–2.** Engineers use principles of graphics in many phases of their work. In this picture, two engineers are investigating methods of detecting satellites by use of a polar chart display. (Courtesy Standard Oil Co. of Ohio.)

Most engineering data are displayed in line graphs. Such information usually is more exact and offers opportunity to interpolate values, to extrapolate values, and to draw conclusions as to the behavior of the variable quantities involved. Examples of several types of graphs are shown in Figures 12–6 to 12–10.

Since line graphs offer the best opportunity to present engineering data, the discussion here will be concerned chiefly with the preparation and use of line graphs. The general form of the graph sheet illustrated by Figure 12–11 is the form used by the majority of engineering schools and is the style widely used in industry.

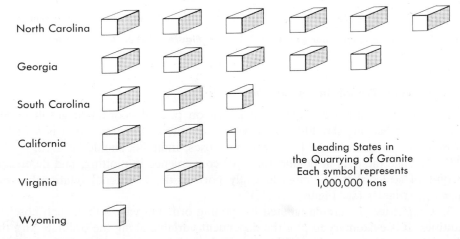

Leading States in
the Quarrying of Granite
Each symbol represents
1,000,000 tons

**Figure 12–6.** A pictograph (data comparative in nature).

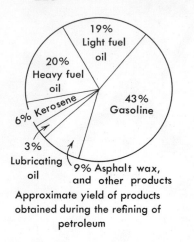

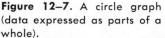

Approximate yield of products
obtained during the refining of
petroleum

**Figure 12–7.** A circle graph (data expressed as parts of a whole).

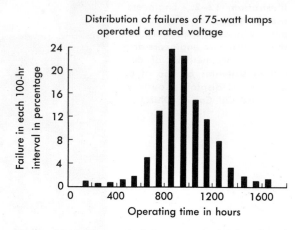

**Figure 12–8.** A vertical bar graph (a family of individual sets of data).

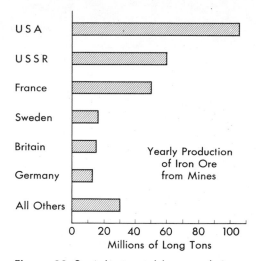

**Figure 12–9.** A horizontal bar graph (numerical data).

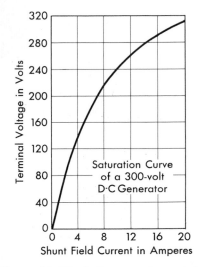

**Figure 12–10.** A line graph used for display purposes.

## Notes on the Preparation of Graphs

1. Graphs usually are prepared in pencil on printed coordinate graph paper. Carbon paper backing should be used where sharpness of reproduction is a factor. For more permanent work or for display purposes, India ink should be used.

2. Arrange the data in tabular form for convenience in plotting, and determine the type of scales that will most logically portray the functional relationship between the variables (see Figure 12–11.)

3. Graphs usually are designated by naming ordinate values first, then abscissa quantities. It is customary to plot the dependent variable along the ordinate and the independent variable along the abscissa.

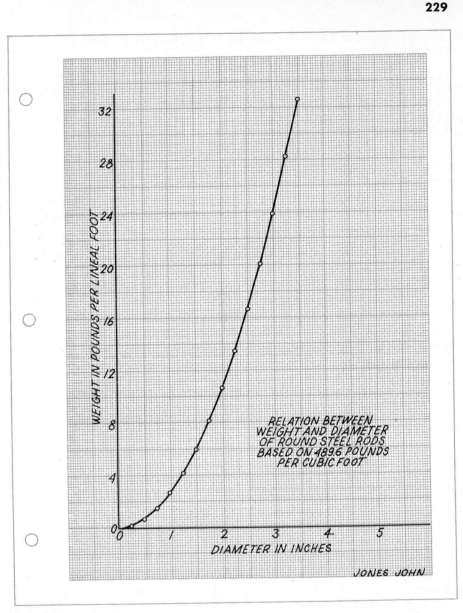

**Figure 12–11.**

4. Make a trial computation to select the scale on each axis.

$$\text{Scale} = \frac{\text{range in the variable}}{\text{scale length available}}$$

5. The scale must be suitable for the paper used. For graph paper having twenty divisions per inch, scale divisions of 1, 2, 5, 10, or a multiple of these numbers are desirable for ease of plotting and reading. Do not use a scale that will require awkward fractions in the smallest calibration on the paper. The scale should be consistent with the precision of the data. If the numbers are very large or very small,

they may be written as a number times ten to a power; for example $(3.22)(10)^{-5}$, or $(7.50)(10)^6$.

6. It is desirable to show zero as the beginning of the ordinate and abscissa quantities unless this would compress the curve unnecessarily. The origin is usually placed in the lower left corner except in cases where both positive and negative values of a function are to be plotted. In such cases the origin should be located so all desired values can be shown.

7. Printed rectangular coordinate paper is not normally available with sufficient margins to accommodate the axes and the description of the quantities plotted. Therefore the axes should be drawn in far enough from the edge of the paper to allow for lettering. The sheet may be turned so that the abscissa is along either the short or long side of the paper. If the graph is prepared for a report, the holes in the paper should be either to the left or at the top of the sheet.

8. Lettering usually is three squares, or approximately 3/20 in. high. Either vertical or slant lettering may be used.

9. The ordinate and abscissa variables together with their respective units of measure should be labeled. For example: WEIGHT IN POUNDS

10. The plotted points are fine, tiny dots in pencil. After the points are located, draw a circle, not more than 1/16 in. in diameter, around each point. Where multiple curves are plotted on one sheet, the points for each curve may be identified by using distinctive identification symbols such as squares, triangles, diamonds, or other simple geometric figures. Distinctive line work such as solid line, dashed line, or long dash-short dash also may be used to aid identification.

11. Graphs may be drawn for theoretical relationships, empirical relationships, or measured relationships. Curves of theoretical relationships will not normally have point designations. Empirical relationships should form smooth curves or straight lines, depending upon the form of the mathematical expression used. Datum points in measured relationships, not supported by mathematical theory or empirical relationships, should be connected by straight lines drawn from point to point. Otherwise, the data obtained from measured relationships will be drawn to average the plotted points. For this reason curves showing measured data do not necessarily go from center to center of the points.

12. Much experimentally determined data when plotted will show a dispersion of the points about an average position due to the many variable factors entering into the measurement. For this condition draw a smooth curve or a straight line, as the data indicate, which as nearly as possible will average the plotted points. A light pencil freehand line will aid in locating the average, but the final line should be mechanically drawn. The example of Figure 12–12 is taken from an actual test to show the dispersion that may occur.

13. In drawing the final curve do not draw the line through the symbols that enclose the plotted points, but rather stop at the perimeter.

14. The title of the graph should include the names of the plotted quantities and should include other descriptive information such as sizes, weights, names of equipment, date that the data were obtained, where data were obtained, serial numbers of apparatus, name of manufacturer of apparatus, and any other information that would help describe the graph.

15. The title should be placed on the sheet where it will not interfere with the

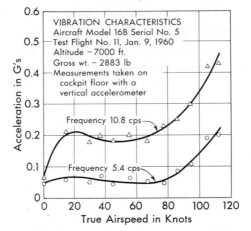

**Figure 12–12.** An example of a graph displaying data which were subject to considerable variation. Obviously the curves can be only approximately located. Such curves are sometimes referred to as "paintbrush" curves.

curve. The title section of display graphs is usually placed across the top of the sheet. Simple graphs that comprise parts of reports frequently have the title in either the lower right quadrant or the upper left quadrant.

16. The name of the person preparing the graph and the date the graph is plotted should be placed in the lower right hand corner of the sheet.

### Problems on Graphs

**12–8.** Plot a graph showing the relation of weight to diameter for round steel rods. Plot values for every quarter-inch to and including 3½ in. in diameter. (See model Figure 12–11).

#### Weight of Round Steel Rods in Pounds Per Lineal Foot
#### (Based on 489.6 lb/ft³)

| SIZE IN. | WEIGHT LB/FT | SIZE IN. | WEIGHT LB/FT |
|---|---|---|---|
| ¼ | 0.167 | 2 | 10.66 |
| ½ | 0.668 | 2¼ | 13.50 |
| ¾ | 1.50 | 2½ | 16.64 |
| 1 | 2.68 | 2¾ | 20.20 |
| 1¼ | 4.17 | 3 | 24.00 |
| 1½ | 6.00 | 3¼ | 28.30 |
| 1¾ | 8.18 | 3½ | 32.70 |

**12–9.** Plot a graph showing the relation of normal barometric pressure of air to altitude. Plot values up to and including 15,000 ft.

| ALTITUDE, FEET ABOVE SEA LEVEL | NORMAL BAROMETRIC PRESSURE, INCHES OF MERCURY | ALTITUDE, FEET ABOVE SEA LEVEL | NORMAL BAROMETRIC PRESSURE, INCHES OF MERCURY |
|---|---|---|---|
| 0 | 29.95 | 5000 | 24.9 |
| 500 | 29.39 | 6000 | 24.0 |
| 1000 | 28.86 | 7000 | 23.1 |
| 1500 | 28.34 | 8000 | 22.2 |
| 2000 | 27.82 | 9000 | 21.4 |
| 2500 | 27.32 | 10000 | 20.6 |
| 3000 | 26.82 | 15000 | 16.9 |
| 4000 | 25.84 | | |

**Problems on Graphs (continued)**

**12–10.** Plot a graph showing the relation between horsepower transmitted by cold drawn steel shafting and diameter for a speed of 72 rpm based on the formula:

$$\text{hp} = \frac{D^3 R}{50}$$

where hp = horsepower
  $D$ = diameter of shaft in inches
  $R$ = revolutions per minute of shaft

Calculate and plot values for every inch diameter up to and including 8 in.

**12–11.** Plot a graph for the following experimental data showing the relation between the period in seconds and the mass of a vibrating spiral spring.

| Period in Seconds | Mass in Grams | Period in Seconds | Mass in Grams |
|---|---|---|---|
| 0.246 | 10 | 0.650 | 70 |
| 0.348 | 20 | 0.740 | 90 |
| 0.430 | 30 | 0.810 | 110 |
| 0.495 | 40 | 0.900 | 130 |
| 0.570 | 50 | 0.950 | 150 |

**12–12.** Using data in Problem 12–11 plot a graph between period squared and mass on a vibrating spring.

**12–13.** Plot a graph of the variation of the boiling point of water with pressure.

| Boiling Point, Degrees Centigrade | Pressure in cm of Mercury | Boiling Point, Degrees Centigrade | Pressure in cm of Mercury |
|---|---|---|---|
| 33 | 3.8 | 98 | 72.9 |
| 44 | 5.3 | 102 | 85.8 |
| 63 | 17.2 | 105 | 93.7 |
| 79 | 34.0 | 107 | 102.2 |
| 87 | 48.1 | 110 | 113.5 |
| 94 | 69.1 | | |

**12–14.** *a.* Plot a graph showing the variation of the following measured values of sliding force with the normal force for a wood block on a horizontal wood surface.

| Sliding Force in Grams | Normal Force in Grams |
|---|---|
| 100 | 359 |
| 130 | 462 |
| 155 | 555 |
| 185 | 659 |
| 210 | 765 |
| 240 | 859 |

*b.* Determine the slope of the line plotted and compare with the average value of the coefficient of sliding friction obtained from individual readings of normal force and sliding force.

Slope = tan $\theta$ (where $\theta$ is the angle that the line makes with the abscissa axis)    $\tan \theta = \dfrac{y_2 - y_1}{x_2 - x_1}$

**12–15.** Plot the variation of pressure with volume, using data as obtained from a Boyle's law apparatus.

| PRESSURE IN CM OF MERCURY | VOLUME IN CM³ | PRESSURE IN CM OF MERCURY | VOLUME IN CM³ |
|---|---|---|---|
| 50.3 | 23.2 | 76.8 | 15.1 |
| 52.5 | 22.4 | 79.7 | 14.7 |
| 54.5 | 21.5 | 82.7 | 14.1 |
| 56.9 | 20.9 | 84.2 | 13.6 |
| 59.4 | 19.6 | 87.9 | 13.2 |
| 63.0 | 18.5 | 90.6 | 12.8 |
| 65.3 | 17.8 | 93.5 | 12.5 |
| 67.2 | 17.3 | 95.7 | 12.3 |
| 72.6 | 16.1 | 101.9 | 11.4 |
| 74.5 | 15.6 | | |

**12–16.** Using data in Problem 12–15, plot a graph of the relation between the pressure and the reciprocal of the volume.

**12–17.** Plot the relation between magnetic flux density in kilolines per square centimeter ($B$) and magnetizing force in gilberts per centimeter ($H$) for a specimen of tool steel. This graph will form what is customarily called a *B-H* curve.

| $B$ KILOLINES PER CM² | $H$ GILBERTS PER CM | $B$ KILOLINES PER CM² | $H$ GILBERTS PER CM |
|---|---|---|---|
| 9.00 | 27.1 | 14.66 | 189.7 |
| 11.80 | 54.2 | 14.86 | 216.8 |
| 13.02 | 81.3 | 14.98 | 243.9 |
| 13.75 | 108.4 | 15.23 | 271.0 |
| 14.09 | 135.5 | 15.35 | 298.1 |
| 14.22 | 162.6 | 15.57 | 325.2 |

**12–18.** The formula for converting temperatures in degrees Fahrenheit to the equivalent reading in degrees Celsius is:

$$C° = \tfrac{5}{9}(F° - 32°)$$

Plot a graph so that by taking any given Fahrenheit reading between 0° and 220° and using the graph, the corresponding Celsius reading can be determined.

**12–19.** Plot a graph showing the relation between drill speed and size of drill for carbon steel drills in brass.

| DIAMETER OF DRILL IN INCHES | DRILL SPEED IN RPM | DIAMETER OF DRILL IN INCHES | DRILL SPEED IN RPM |
|---|---|---|---|
| $\frac{1}{16}$ | 6112 | $\frac{5}{8}$ | 612 |
| $\frac{1}{8}$ | 3056 | $\frac{11}{16}$ | 555 |
| $\frac{3}{16}$ | 2036 | $\frac{3}{4}$ | 508 |
| $\frac{1}{4}$ | 1528 | $\frac{13}{16}$ | 474 |
| $\frac{5}{16}$ | 1222 | $\frac{7}{8}$ | 438 |
| $\frac{3}{8}$ | 1018 | $\frac{15}{16}$ | 407 |
| $\frac{7}{16}$ | 874 | 1 | 382 |
| $\frac{1}{2}$ | 764 | $1\frac{1}{16}$ | 359 |
| $\frac{9}{16}$ | 679 | $1\frac{1}{8}$ | 340 |

### Problems on Graphs (continued)

**12–20.** Plot a graph showing the variation of temperature with electric current through a heating coil, using the following data which were taken in the laboratory.

| CURRENT IN AMP | TEMPERATURE CHANGE IN °C |
|---|---|
| 0.0 | 0.0 |
| 0.46 | 0.5 |
| 1.05 | 1.2 |
| 1.50 | 2.0 |
| 2.06 | 5.1 |
| 2.20 | 7.7 |
| 2.35 | 8.8 |

**12–21.** The following data were taken in the laboratory for a 16-cp, carbon-filament electric light bulb. Plot a resistance-voltage curve.

| VOLTAGE IN VOLTS | RESISTANCE IN OHMS | VOLTAGE IN VOLTS | RESISTANCE IN OHMS |
|---|---|---|---|
| 10 | 169.5 | 70 | 114.5 |
| 20 | 140.0 | 80 | 113.2 |
| 30 | 129.0 | 90 | 112.5 |
| 40 | 121.5 | 100 | 111.8 |
| 50 | 117.0 | 110 | 111.2 |
| 60 | 113.2 | | |

**12–22.** The following data were taken in the laboratory for a 60 w, gas-filled, tungsten-filament light bulb. Plot a resistance-voltage curve.

| VOLTAGE IN VOLTS | RESISTANCE IN OHMS | VOLTAGE IN VOLTS | RESISTANCE IN OHMS |
|---|---|---|---|
| 10 | 47.5 | 70 | 160.2 |
| 20 | 77.5 | 80 | 170.0 |
| 30 | 100.3 | 90 | 178.3 |
| 40 | 119.0 | 100 | 189.0 |
| 50 | 132.6 | 110 | 200.1 |
| 60 | 144.2 | | |

**12–23.** The equation which expresses the variations of electric current with time in an inductive circuit is

$$i = I_0 \epsilon^{(-Rt)/L}$$

where:

$i$ is the current in amperes.

$I_0$ is the original steady-state value of current and is a constant.

$\epsilon$ is the base of the natural system of logarithms and is approximately 2.7183.

$R$ is the resistance in ohms in the circuit and is constant.

$t$ is the time in seconds measured as the current $i$ varies.

$L$ is the inductance in henries and is a constant.

Let

$$I_0 = 0.16 \text{ amp}$$
$$R = 1.2 \text{ ohms}$$
$$L = 0.5 \text{ henry}$$

Calculate and plot values of $i$ as $t$ varies from 0 to 0.5 sec.

**12–24.** Plot the variations of efficiency with load for a 1/4-hp, 110 v, direct-current electric motor, using the following data taken in the laboratory.

| Load Output in Horsepower | Efficiency in Per Cent |
|---|---|
| 0 | 0 |
| 0.019 | 24.0 |
| 0.050 | 42.0 |
| 0.084 | 44.9 |
| 0.135 | 50.7 |
| 0.175 | 56.5 |
| 0.195 | 58.0 |
| 0.248 | 59.1 |
| 0.306 | 58.0 |
| 0.326 | 56.2 |

### Plotting on Semilogarithmic Graph Paper

The preceding discussion has concerned the graphing of data on rectangular coordinate paper. There are cases where the variation of the data is such that it may be desirable to compress the larger values of a variable. To do this, semilogarithmic graph paper may be used. Semilog paper, as it is usually called, is graph paper which has one coordinate ruled in equal increments and the other coordinate ruled in increments which are logarithmically expressed. When plotting on this type of paper, it can be turned so that either the horizontal coordinate or the vertical coordinate will have the logarithmic divisions. Semilog paper is available in either one-cycle, two-cycle, three-cycle, four-cycle, or five-cycle ruling.

A semi-log grid is especially useful in the derivation of relationships where it is difficult to analyze the rate of change or trend as depicted on rectangular coordinate paper. Data that will plot as a curve on rectangular coordinate paper may plot as a straight line on semilog paper. In many instances this is desirable because the trends are more easily detected. Where straight lines do not occur on a semilog grid, the rate of change is varying.

The same rules apply for plotting on semilog paper as were given for rectangular coordinate paper, except that the numbering of the logarithmic divisions cannot begin with zero. Each cycle on the paper represents a multiple of ten in value, and the graduations may begin with any power of ten. When reading from a logarithmic graph, interpolations should be made logarithmically rather than arithmetically. An example of data plotted on semilog paper is shown in Figure 12–13.

**Figure 12–13.**

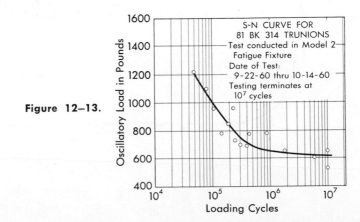

Engineering Tools of Analysis

**236**

### Plotting on Log-Log Graph Paper

Log-log graph paper, as its name indicates, has both coordinate divisions expressed as logarithmic functions. This subdivision of the sheet serves to compress the larger values of the plotted data. In addition, data that plotted as a curve on rectangular coordinate paper may plot as a straight line on log-log paper. For example, the graphs of algebraic equations representing multiplication, division, powers, and roots may be straight lines on log-log paper.

As an example, the plot of the algebraic expression

$$X = Y^2$$

on rectangular coordinate paper is a parabola. However, if its values are plotted on log-log paper, it is equivalent to taking the logarithm of the expression

$$\log X = 2(\log Y)$$

This expression has the form of a linear equation having a slope of 2. Thus, a relationship of variable quantities that may be expressed as $X = Y^2$ when plotted on log-log paper will be a straight line with a slope of 2.

Log-log paper may be secured in 8½ by 11-in. or larger sheets that have one or more cycles for each coordinate direction. The axis lines are drawn on the sheet in a manner similar to the procedure described for plotting on rectangular coordinate paper. However, the beginning values for the axes will never be zero but will always be a power of ten.

An example of data plotted on log-log paper is shown in Figure 12–14.

**Figure 12–14.**

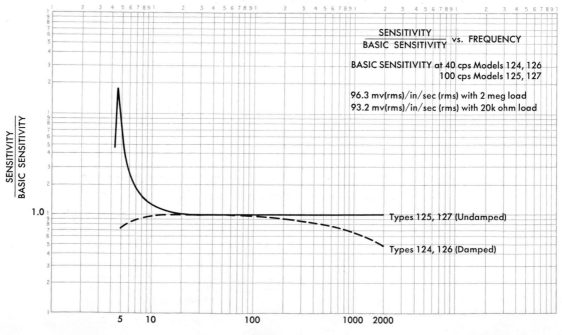

MB MANUFACTURING COMPANY
A Division of Textron Inc.

TYPICAL FREQUENCY RESPONSE — MB VIBRATION PICKUPS
MODELS 124, 125, 126, 127

$$\frac{\text{SENSITIVITY}}{\text{BASIC SENSITIVITY}} \text{ vs. FREQUENCY}$$

BASIC SENSITIVITY at 40 cps Models 124, 126
100 cps Models 125, 127

96.3 mv(rms)/in/sec (rms) with 2 meg load
93.2 mv(rms)/in/sec (rms) with 20k ohm load

Types 125, 127 (Undamped)

Types 124, 126 (Damped)

FREQUENCY IN CPS

T-307A

### Plotting on Polar Graph Paper

Polar graphs are sometimes used where a variable quantity is to be examined with respect to various angular positions. The same general principles of plotting apply as were outlined for rectangular plots except that the outer border is marked off in degrees for the independent variable, and either the horizontal or vertical radial line is marked off for the dependent variable.

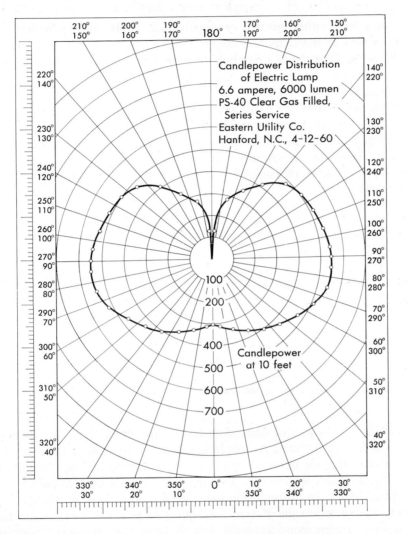

**Figure 12–15.**

Polar graphs frequently are used to display the light output of luminous sources, the response of microphone pickups, and the behavior of rotating objects at various angular positions. An example of a graph plotted on polar coordinate paper is shown in Figure 12–15.

### Determining Empirical Equations from Curves

Experimentally determined data when plotted usually will approximate a straight line or a simple curve. By plotting experimentally determined data, it is frequently possible to obtain a mathematical equation that closely expresses the relations of the variables.

Many equations encountered in engineering work have the form

$$y - k = m(x - h)^n$$

where $n$ may have either positive or negative values. If the exponent $n$ is 1, the equation reduces to the familiar straight-line slope-intercept form. If the value of $n$ is positive, the equation is a parabolic type, but if the value of $n$ is negative, the equation is a hyperbolic type. This expression affords a means of securing empirical equations from experimental data.

If experimental data are to be plotted and an empirical equation is to be determined, it is advisable first to plot the test data on rectangular coordinate paper in order to gain some idea of the shape of the graph. If the locus approximates a straight line, the general equation $y = mx + b$ may be assumed. The $Y$-intercept $b$ and the slope $m$ may be measured by taking a straight line drawn so as to average the plotted points.

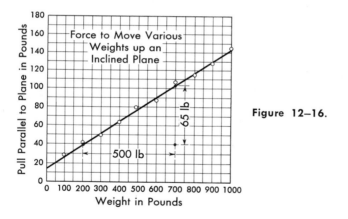

Figure 12–16.

Figure 12–16 is a plot of data taken in the laboratory for a test involving the magnitude of frictional forces. A straight line is drawn to average the plotted points, and the slope of the line is found by taking any two points along the line and determining the $X$-component and the $Y$-component between the two points according to the plotted scales. In this example the slope is approximately 65/500, or 0.13. If the line is projected to the $Y$-axis, corresponding to a value of $x = 0$, the $Y$-intercept is seen to correspond approximately to 14 lb. An approximate equation of these data would be $y = 0.13x + 14$.

If a plot of experimental data on rectangular coordinate paper should appear to be approximately parabolic in shape, an empirical equation may be obtained by plotting the datum points on log-log paper. The slope of the line determines the exponent of the independent variable, and the $Y$-intercept, when $x = 1$, defines the coefficient of the independent variable. For example, a plot of data taken in the laboratory is shown in Figure 12–17.

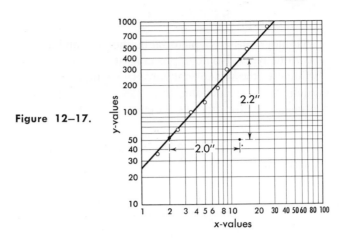

**Figure 12–17.**

A straight line is drawn to average the plotted points. Using a linear scale, measure the $X$-component and $Y$-component values for two points on the plotted line. The slope of the graph in Figure 12–17 is 2.2/2.0, or 1.1, and the $Y$-intercept is 23.3. Substituting these values in the basic equation of a parabola gives $y = 23.3(x^{1.1})$ for the approximate equation.

In case the plotted points on log-log paper curve upward as $x$ increases, the expression may approximate the form $y = ax^n + k$. To straighten the curve, try subtracting a constant from the $y$-values. By trial and error, a value of $k$ may be found that will cause the plot to follow a straight line. If this is done, the approximate equation may be determined.

If log-log paper is not available, it is still possible to use rectangular coordinate paper to plot a curve as a straight line. If the data indicate the equation may be of the form $y = ax^n$, we can take the logarithm of the equation and plot logarithmic values for the datum points. For example, if we express $y = ax^n$ in logarithmic form, it will be $\log y = \log a + n \log x$. Let $v = \log y$; $C = \log a$; and $u = \log x$. The straight line equation will then be

$$v = nu + C$$

Plot the logarithm of the data values on rectangular coordinate paper. Measure the slope and the $Y$-intercept. Assume that the slope is measured to be 1.8, using the scales of the plot, and the $Y$-intercept is 0.755. The straight line equation is

$$v = 1.8u + 0.755$$

or $\qquad\qquad \log y = 1.8 \log x + 0.755$

Since $\qquad\qquad C = \log a = 0.755$

then $\qquad\qquad a = 5.69$

The equation then is $\qquad y = 5.69(x^{1.8})$

There are other methods of determining empirical equations, such as the method of least squares, but a complete discussion of such techniques is beyond the scope of this book. Also, data that plot into curves following harmonic laws or exponential laws are not discussed here.

Engineering Tools of Analysis

240

## Nomographs

Nomographs are a pictorial method of solving problems which involve equations
of various types. Nomographs consist of scales graduated so that distances are proportional to the variables involved. A simple example would be a single line having
graduations corresponding to inches on one side and graduations corresponding to
centimeters on the other (see Figure 12–18).

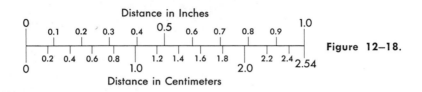

Figure 12–18.

The layout of nomographs is beyond the scope of this book, but since the solution to problems involving repeated readings of process or laboratory data may be
obtained readily by use of nomographs, a brief discussion of the types and uses of
the charts is presented.

Figure 12–18 is an example of a *functional chart*. Charts of this type are frequently used when two variables are related by a constant coefficient.

An *alignment chart* is another example of a nomograph. A simple form consists
of three parallel lines graduated so that a straight line passing through points on
two of the graduated lines will intersect the third graduated line at a point that will
satisfy the relations between the variables (see Figure 12–19).

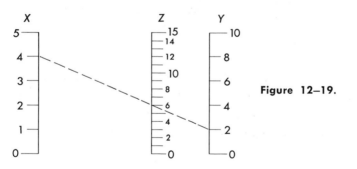

Figure 12–19.

*Example:* Given an alignment chart for the equation $x + y = z$. Solve for
the value of $z$ when $x = 4$ and $y = 2$.

SOLUTION: Lay out a straight line connecting the point on the $x$-scale corresponding
to 4 and the point on the $y$-scale corresponding to 2. The intersection of this line
with the $z$-scale at 6 is a solution to this problem. Repeating this procedure with
other values will enable one to locate the position of the $z$-scale with regard to the
$x$- and $y$-scales.

Another form of alignment chart that is of considerable use is the Z-chart, so
named because the center graduated line runs diagonally. It may be set up to provide
a solution to equations of the form $x = (y)(z)$. Other alignment charts may pro-

vide solutions to problems having three or four variable quantities by employing multiple interior graduated lines.

Alignment charts are all used in the same manner; that is, a straight line connects two points on the graduated lines and intersects another graduated line, thereby providing a solution to a given problem.

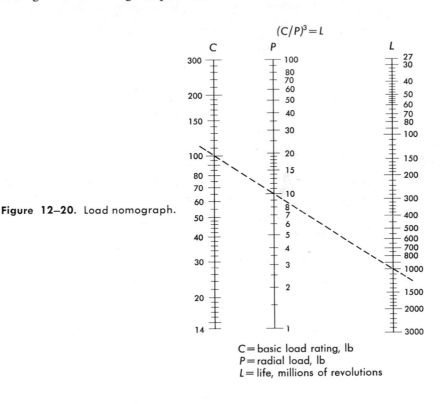

Figure 12–20. Load nomograph.

$$(C/P)^3 = L$$

C = basic load rating, lb
P = radial load, lb
L = life, millions of revolutions

As an example, the nomograph given in Figure 12–20 permits an evaluation of factors concerned with the life of a ball bearing. The straight line drawn across the chart shows that for a basic load rating of 100 lb and a radial load of 10 lb, the expected service life of the ball bearing should be 1000 million revolutions.

### Problems

**12–25.** Plot the values given in Problem 12–8, page 231, on semilog paper.
**12–26.** Plot the values given in Problem 12–11, page 232, on semilog paper.
**12–27.** Plot the values given in Problem 12–15, page 233, on semilog paper.
**12–28.** Plot the values given in Problem 12–23, page 234, on semilog paper.
**12–29.** Plot the values given in Problem 12–8, page 231, on log-log paper.
**12–30.** Plot the values given in Problem 12–10, page 232, on log-log paper.
**12–31.** Plot the values given in Problem 12–15, page 233, on log-log paper.

Determine the slope of the line and give the approximate form of the equation shown by the plot.

**Problems (continued)**

**12–32.** The following data were taken from an acoustical and electrical calibration curve for a Type 1126 microphone. The test was run with an incident sound level of 85 db perpendicular to the face of the microphone.

| Frequency in cps | Relative Response in db |
|---|---|
| 20 | −40 |
| 50 | −29 |
| 100 | −19 |
| 400 | −5 |
| 1,000 | +1 |
| 2,000 | +1 |
| 3,000 | 0 |
| 6,000 | −4 |
| 10,000 | −11 |

Plot a graph on semilog paper showing the decibel response with frequency.

**12–33.** The electrical frequency response of a Type X501 microphone is given below.

| Frequency in cps | Relative Response in db |
|---|---|
| 20 | −40 |
| 40 | −33 |
| 80 | −22 |
| 100 | −18 |
| 200 | −11 |
| 400 | −5 |
| 600 | −2 |
| 1,000 | +1 |
| 2,000 | +2 |
| 4,000 | −1 |
| 6,000 | −4 |
| 10,000 | −10 |

Plot a graph on semilog paper showing the decibel response with frequency.

**12–34.** According to recommendations of the Thrust Bearing Engineers Committee, bearing loads for bearings lubricated with oil having a viscosity range of 115 to 165 Saybolt sec at 100°F should fall between values given in tables below.

| Speed in rps | Bearing Load in lb |
|---|---|
| 10 | 400 |
| 100 | 170 |
| 1,000 | 74 |
| 10,000 | 32 |
| 40,000 | 20 |
| | |
| 10 | 1,700 |
| 100 | 650 |
| 1,000 | 275 |
| 10,000 | 123 |
| 40,000 | 70 |

Plot graphs of bearing loads against speeds to show the range of acceptable operating speeds.

**12–35.** The variation of sensitivity of a Model 932 vibration sensing unit with frequency is given below. The basic sensitivity is taken as 96.3 mv (rms) with a 2-megohm load.

| FREQUENCY IN CPS | RATIO OF SENSITIVITY AT VARIOUS FREQUENCIES TO BASIC SENSITIVITY |
|---|---|
| 4.0 | 4.6 |
| 4.8 | 19.0 |
| 5.0 | 11.0 |
| 6.0 | 2.7 |
| 7.0 | 1.9 |
| 8.0 | 1.6 |
| 10 | 1.3 |
| 20 | 1.05 |
| 40 | 1.00 |
| 80 | 0.98 |
| 100 | 0.97 |
| 300 | 0.85 |
| 600 | 0.76 |
| 1000 | 0.66 |
| 2000 | 0.46 |

Plot sensitivity against frequency on three-cycle log-log paper.

**12–36.** A series of test specimens of a crank arm, part No. 466-1, were tested for the number of cycles needed to produce fatigue failure at various loadings. The results of the tests are tabulated below.

| SPECIMEN NUMBER | OSCILLATORY LOAD IN LB | OPERATING CYCLES TO PRODUCE FAILURE |
|---|---|---|
| 1 | 960 | $1.1 \times 10^5$ |
| 2 | 960 | $2.2 \times 10^5$ |
| 3 | 850 | $1.5 \times 10^5$ |
| 4 | 850 | $2.4 \times 10^5$ |
| 5 | 800 | $4.2 \times 10^5$ |
| 6 | 800 | $6.0 \times 10^5$ |
| 7 | 700 | $2.4 \times 10^5$ |
| 8 | 700 | $3.1 \times 10^5$ |
| 9 | 700 | $5.1 \times 10^5$ |
| 10 | 650 | $1.8 \times 10^6$ |
| 11 | 650 | $2.6 \times 10^6$ |
| 12 | 600 | $7.7 \times 10^6$ |
| 13 | 550 | $1.0 \times 10^7$ |

Plot a graph of load against operating cycles (*S-N* curve) on semilog paper for the tests above.

**12–37.** A Weather Bureau report gives the following data on the temperature over a 24-hr period for October 12.

| | | | |
|---|---|---|---|
| MIDNIGHT | 47° | 2 PM | 73° |
| 2 AM | 46° | 4 PM | 75° |
| 4 AM | 44° | 6 PM | 63° |
| 6 AM | 43° | 8 PM | 58° |
| 8 AM | 49° | 10 PM | 57° |
| 10 AM | 55° | MIDNIGHT | 57° |
| NOON | 68° | | |

Plot the data above.

**Problems (continued)**

**12–38.** A test on an acorn-type street lighting unit shows the mean vertical candle-power distribution to be as given in the table below.

| Midzone Angle Degrees | Candlepower at 10 ft | Midzone Angle Degrees | Candlepower at 10 ft |
|---|---|---|---|
| 180 | 0 | 85 | 156 |
| 175 | 0 | 75 | 1110 |
| 165 | 0 | 65 | 1050 |
| 155 | 1.5 | 55 | 710 |
| 145 | 3.5 | 45 | 575 |
| 135 | 5.5 | 35 | 500 |
| 125 | 8.5 | 25 | 520 |
| 115 | 13.5 | 15 | 470 |
| 105 | 22.0 | 5 | 370 |
| 95 | 40.0 | 0 | 370 |

Plot the data above. (While data for only half the plot are given, the other half of the plot can be made from symmetry of the light pattern.)

**12–39.** The candlepower distribution of a 400 w, Type J-H1 flourescent lamp used for street light service was measured with a photometer, and the following data were obtained:

| Midzone Angle Degrees | Candlepower at 10 ft | Midzone Angle Degrees | Candlepower at 10 ft |
|---|---|---|---|
| 180 | 0 | 75 | 7700 |
| 165 | 0 | 72 | 8600 |
| 145 | 0 | 65 | 7100 |
| 135 | 3 | 55 | 5300 |
| 125 | 20 | 45 | 4300 |
| 115 | 100 | 35 | 3500 |
| 105 | 700 | 25 | 2700 |
| 95 | 1200 | 15 | 2300 |
| 85 | 3000 | 5 | 2100 |
| | | 0 | 2000 |

Plot the data above. (While data for only half the plot are given, the other half of the plot can be made from symmetry of the light pattern.)

**12–40.** From data determined by the student, draw a circle chart (pie graph) to show one of the following.

    *a.* Consumption of sulfur by various industries in the United States.
    *b.* Budget allocation of the tax dollar in your state.
    *c.* Chemical composition of bituminous coal.
    *d.* Production of aluminum ingots by various countries.

**12–41.** Make a bar chart showing the number of men students registered in your school for each of the past ten years.

**12–42.** Plot the following data and determine an empirical equation for the plotted points:

| X: | 100 | 200 | 300 | 400 | 500 | 600 | 700 | 800 | 900 |
|---|---|---|---|---|---|---|---|---|---|
| Y: | 0.25 | 0.38 | 0.53 | 0.66 | 0.79 | 0.90 | 1.06 | 1.17 | 1.30 |

**12–43.** Determine the empirical equation, using the following data which were taken in the laboratory for a test involving accelerated motion:

| t: | 5 | 10 | 20 | 40 | 60 | 80 | 100 |
|---|---|---|---|---|---|---|---|
| s: | 0.93 | 5.6 | 32 | 175 | 490 | 989 | 17,600 |

**12–44.** Laboratory data taken on an adjustable time-delay relay show the following values:

| Dial index settings $D$: | 2 | 4 | 6 | 8 | 10 |
|---|---|---|---|---|---|
| Seconds delay time $T$: | 0.124 | 0.084 | 0.063 | 0.026 | 0.014 |

Find an empirical equation to express the data.

**12–45.** The following data were recorded during a laboratory test of a system of gears. Find an empirical equation to express the data.

| Applied force $F$: | 11.0 | 13.0 | 21.5 | 26.0 | 34.0 | 39.0 | 41.0 | 49.0 | 50.5 |
|---|---|---|---|---|---|---|---|---|---|
| Weight lifted $W$: | 135 | 180 | 210 | 345 | 275 | 310 | 340 | 370 | 400 |

**12–46.** Data taken on a laboratory test involving pressure-volume relations of a gas are as follows:

| $P$: | 14.6 | 17.5 | 20.9 | 25.0 | 29.0 | 33.6 | 39.0 | 45.5 |
|---|---|---|---|---|---|---|---|---|
| $V$: | 26.4 | 22.3 | 19.1 | 16.3 | 14.1 | 12.2 | 10.5 | 9.2 |

Determine an empirical equation for the data.

**12–47.** Determine an empirical equation to express data given in Problem 12–9, page 231.

**12–48.** Determine an empirical equation that will express data given in Problem 12–11, page 232.

**12–49.** Plot a graph on rectangular coordinate paper of $N = (1.296)^x$ for values of $x$ from $-9.0$ to $+9.0$ in 0.5 increments.

**12–50.** Plot a graph on rectangular coordinate paper of the equation $N = (0.813)^x$ for values of $x$ from $-9.0$ to $+9.0$ in 0.5 increments.

**12–51.** Using the nomograph of Figure 12–22, what will be the allowable radial load on a ball bearing if the basic load rating is 22 lb and the expected life of the bearing is to be $1.4(10)^8$ revolutions?

**12–52.** Construct a functional scale about 6 in. long that will relate temperatures in degrees Fahrenheit and degrees Celsius for the range of $-40°C$ to $100°C$.

**12–53.** Construct a functional scale about 10 in. long that will show the relation between the diameter and circumference of a circle for values of diameter from 2 to 9 in.

**12–54.** The graph Figure 12–21 has been plotted as a calibration of air flow in a 1 in. duct used in testing bleed air from a turbine engine. If during a test involving the use of this calibrated duct, the following readings are obtained, compute the pounds per minute of air flowing through the duct. Differential pressure, ($\triangle$P), 6.8 in. of water; Static pressure, $Ps$), 68.0 lb per sq in. gage pressure; Temperature, (T), 421°F; Barometric pressure, ($P_B$), 29.71 in. of mercury.

**12–55.** Using the graph in Figure 12–21, compute five points to plot a graph on log-log paper of differential pressure (ordinate), against pounds of air per minute flow (abscissa) for air at a constant temperature of 200°F.

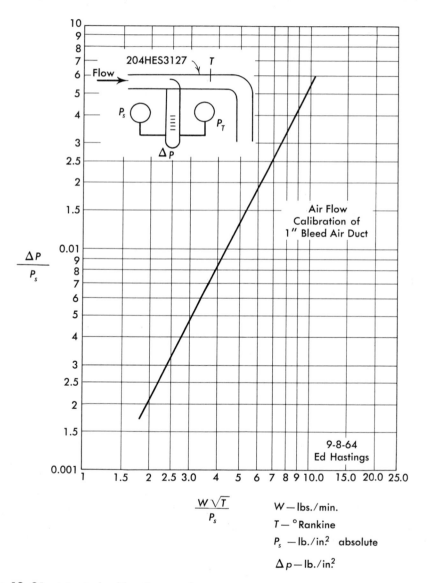

Figure 12–21. A typical calibration graph.

Package Code 8

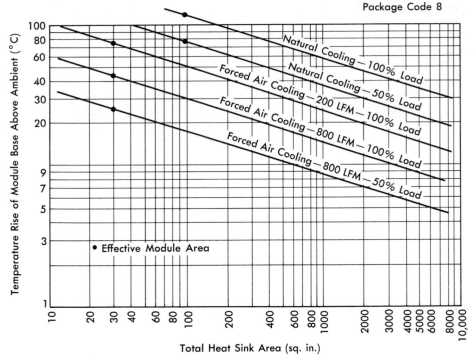

**Total Heat Sink Area (sq. in.)**

**Figure 12–22.** Heat sink requirements for a code 8 power supply module using silicon diodes. (Courtesy Consolidated Avionics.)

**12–56.** A heat sink is needed on certain types of electronic apparatus to dissipate the heat evolved in some of the components. A typical heat sink is made of copper or aluminum and has a large surface of fins to promote heat dissipation. The graph in Figure 12–22 gives the dimensions of a typical heat sink for certain allowable temperature rises for a power supply.

    *a.* If the maximum allowable temperature of a unit mounted on the heat sink is 90°C and the highest ambient temperature expected is 25°C, what area of heat sink will be needed for natural cooling at 100 per cent load?

    *b.* With forced air cooling, the effective area of the module producing the heat is 30 in². If a forced air flow of 200 linear feet per minute (LFM) is available, what area of heat sink will need to be provided for 100 per cent load conditions?

**12–57.** Prepare a line chart that will permit converting readings from grams to ounces up to 64 ounces and a line chart that will convert readings from pounds to kilograms up to 10 lb.

**12–58.** The height of a helicopter is to be determined accurately in order to check its altimeter calibration. It is proposed that the helicopter hover over a fixed point at an altitude of approximately 700 ft and that a surveyor's transit be set up some reasonable distance away on level ground and the vertical angle to the helicopter be measured using the transit. The transit vertical angle can be read to ± 1' of angle, and it is desired that the vertical height of the helicopter be determined within ± 6 in. Discuss the advantages and disadvantages of this method and give an opinion as to its desirability.

## BIBLIOGRAPHY

BARRY, B. AUSTIN, *Engineering Measurements,* Wiley, New York, (1964).

BURR, IRVING W., *Engineering Statistics and Quality Control,* McGraw-Hill, New York, (1953).

FOGEL, CHARLES M., *Introduction to Engineering Computations,* International, Scranton, Pa., (1960).

FRENCH, THOMAS E. and CHARLES J. VIERCK, *Graphic Science,* McGraw-Hill, New York, (1963).

SPIEGEL, MURRAY R., *Theory and Problems of Statistics,* Abelard-Schaum, New York, (1961).

# Chapter 13

# Digital and Analog Computers

## INTRODUCTION

After the close of World War II, a revolution began in industry—a revolution that still is in progress and one which may be as far reaching in its effect as the Industrial Revolution of the eighteenth Century. This second industrial revolution can be called the era of automation. While automatic machines have been used for years, a programmable machine that could count and solve mathematical problems or one that could shape and machine intricate parts, or a machine that could search any number of phone lines to find an unused one to establish a circuit, has been a development within the past two decades.

The engineer, from the beginning, has been closely associated with the development of automatic computing machines. In fact, the engineer originally created much of the demand for a computing machine to aid in solving problems encountered in military applications. As soon as it became possible to obtain solutions to problems heretofore considered impractical to solve because of time, widely varied applications became apparent in all phases of industry. The engineer now has computing machines thousands of times as fast and effective as the mechanical computers used before World War II.

Before beginning a description of types of computers, it is desirable to discuss some of the basic principles of computers. A question can be asked, "What is a computer?" A computer can be described as a person or a machine that is capable of taking information, performing an operation on this information, and obtaining an answer. Since our discussion will relate to machines, let us use an adding machine as a simple example. If we punch keys to put into the machine the two numerals 234 and 567 and then obtain a sum, the answer, 801, is the end of the mathematical operation. This operation just described has been carried out using our symbolic language of numbers and translating it into machine language that the machine is capable of handling. From this we can arrive at some principles of machine computing.

### Fundamental Principles

Some of the fundamental principles involved in a computer operation are as follows:

1. The machine accepts the input data without regard to its meaning unless programmed otherwise.

2. The machine accepts the input data as being true unless programmed otherwise.

3. The machine usually will present an answer without attempting to evaluate it as being factual unless the machine is programmed to make such an evaluation. For a computer to operate, it must accept information, act on it, and present it. Information then may be defined as concepts, symbols, or objects which the computer can accept and manipulate.

In the example of the adding machine, the numerals as symbols were inserted, the machine manipulated the information, and symbols representing the answer were obtained. The machine could not check the validity of the inputs, it could act only on the information furnished and, based on this, it gave a result in its symbolic language.

For example, if we should desire to obtain a series of sums by adding 234 to several numbers, it would be helpful if we could store this numeral 234 for retrieval and automatic reinsertion into the computing mechanism after we obtain each sum. The ability to store and retrieve information is a characteristic of almost all modern electronic computers.

### Definitions

Computing equipment can be divided into two general categories: *analog* and *digital*. The *analog computer* can be described as a device that presents the variables in a situation by proportional physical quantities such as electrical voltages or mechanical positions of parts. For instance, the level of fuel in an automobile gasoline tank can be indicated by an electrical meter suitably marked that is connected electrically to a position transducer attached to a float in the tank. As the fuel level rises and falls, the resistance of an electrical circuit is varied, and a change is indicated on a meter on the dash. The same indication can be obtained, perhaps not as conveniently, by a mechanical linkage connected to the float in the gasoline tank and then to a mechanical arm that shows the float position in the tank. As is shown in this example, a continuous indication and representation of variable quantities is a characteristic of analog devices. Their accuracy is limited by the accuracy of the individual components making up the assembly.

A *digital computer* in essence is a counting machine that can discriminate. It is constructed to work with discrete numbers and to follow rules of mathematical logic. For example, in using an adding machine, a definite number is always put into the computing mechanism. The number may be part of a variable system, but at any instant the quantity to be manipulated is a number represented by a series of fixed digits. In general, the accuracy of a digital computer is determined by the number of significant digits involved in an operation.

A digital computing device usually performs mathematical operations by combinations of additions or subtractions. Multiplication, for example, is performed by successive summations. Also, trigonometric functions can be represented by a converging series. This means that all mathematical operations ordinarily must be reduced to an arithmetical form before the digital computer can handle them.

Devices, usually involving electronic circuits, have been devised to convert analog information to digital coding or to convert a digital code to an analog display. Such devices are called analog-to-digital (A-to-D) or digital-to-analog (D-to-A) converters. A more complete description of these devices can be found in texts on data acquisition and digital process control.

Computers also can be classed generally as to purpose. A computer can be built either as a general purpose machine or as a special purpose machine. A general purpose machine is capable of solving many varied types of problems covering a wide range of situations. An example of this type of machine would be an IBM 360 computer that could be programmed to handle problems varying from presenting flight test data from missiles into engineering units to keeping a running total on inventory of agricultural machinery spare parts. A special purpose machine usually has limited or no programming ability and is built to do one, or at most, a very few types of computation. An example of this type of machine would be a fire control director for artillery firing.

Since analog and digital computers constitute the majority of present day machines, their construction features and uses will be considered in more detail.

## ANALOG COMPUTERS

Early development of the electronic analog computer was fostered principally by the urgent needs for faster computation and presentation of data from machines developed for the armed forces during World War II. The actual development of a general purpose analog computer did not occur until about 1947. By 1949, computer design had developed so rapidly that several companies were designing and building computers. Such extraordinarily rapid growth of the computer industry was due in large part to prior development of reliable electronic amplifiers. With most of the building blocks already available, it was much easier to make the assembly into a completed computer.

Analog computers may be classified into two groups. One group is the direct or physical analog type and the other group is the indirect or mathematical analog type. An example of a direct analog computer is an installation built up with combinations of resistances, inductances, and capacitances in networks to simulate the constants in electrical power distribution systems. By varying the electrical quantities in the computer network, the behavior of a full-size power system can be simulated, and proportional voltages and currents can be read at selected points. This simulation can be extended to mechanical system analysis by using electrical quantities to represent mechanical friction, inertia, and springs.

The indirect or mathematical analog type of computer uses amplifiers in various combinations to perform arithmetic and algebraic operations. A type of problem well adapted to solution on this computer involves systems of simultaneous differential equations. The solution of these equations can be accomplished by setting the variable and constant terms into the computer as simulated electrical quantities and reading out on an $X$-$Y$ plot a graphical picture of the behavior of the variable

**Illustration 13–1.** Engineers may use an analog computer and X-Y plotter to solve mathematical equations. (Courtesy Electronics Associates, Inc.)

quantities. For example, as the frequency of a current is varied, different parts of a network may show nonlinear responses and, under resonance conditions, quite large changes in amplitude of oscillations can occur. This information is of great help to an engineer as it materially shortens the time to perform mathematical solutions, particularly those involving the solution of more than three simultaneous equations.

Let us consider a process of multiplication using an analog computer. One way this can be done is by using a simple mechanical system with gear wheels of different sizes on two shafts, as shown in Figure 13–1. For example, if the ratio of the gear diameter is 1.5 to 1, then one turn of the larger gear will produce 1.5 turns of the smaller. If this motion is shown on a circular scale, the motion provides a multiplication of 1.5 times. The same result can be accomplished by scaling. For instance, if a circular scale, Figure 13–2, shows 10 divisions, an equivalent multiplication by 2 can be accomplished by changing the marking of the scale so that the original 10 divisions have a value of 20. Now, any given reading, such as the 7th division will be read as 14 units. An example of this scaling technique is shown in an automobile speedometer. By using a proper scale, the revolutions of the driveshaft, and indirectly the automobile's speed, can be shown in miles per hour units. However, the same device by using a different scale, and in effect a different multiplying factor, can indicate kilometers per hour.

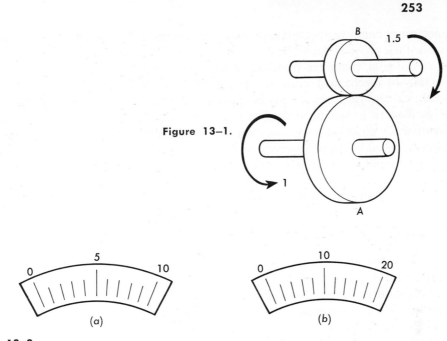

Figure 13–1.

Figure 13–2.

Another way in which multiplying factors can be entered into a machine is by using differential gearing. For example, in certain fire control equipment for artillery it is necessary to enter variables (multipliers) into the machine to compensate for variations in temperature, humidity, and atmospheric pressure in addition to the range settings which are made. Suitable arrangements of gearing can make adjustments automatically in range settings to compensate for environmental variables so that the location of shell impacts will be the same.

It must be noted that in practically all analog machines, the results are read out as digital numbers. This is a convenience in recording analog results, but it does not alter the purpose of an analog machine, which fundamentally is to make a continuous measure of physical variables.

Mathematical operations such as multiplication, division, integration, or differentiation can be accomplished in analog devices by electrical or electronic means. Amplifiers that permit these operations are commonly used in addition to converters that will accept a voltage input and give an output voltage proportional to some function, such as logarithmic, of the input.

## DIGITAL COMPUTERS

Although the basic ideas involved in digital computers are more than a century old, the modern automatic digital computer was not developed until after 1940. The first machine of this generation was named "Harvard Mark I" and was developed by Professor Aiken at Harvard in cooperation with International Business Machines Corporation. So successful was this machine, that almost immediately a large number of individuals and companies started on versions of it. In this spirit of competition, development has been rapid; and with the advent of miniaturized electronic components, the capabilities of computers have increased appreciably while their physical size has remained the same or decreased.

A digital computer performs arithmetical processes, such as multiplication, usually by mechanical means in small machines such as desk-size calculators or by electrical and electronic means in larger size computers. Since the digital computer, regardless of its size or method of operation will accept only discrete and separate symbols or digits, any manipulation of these symbols or digits by the computer is accomplished by a pre-set program which will mechanically or electrically multiply a digital input and exhibit a result as a digital or symbolic answer. The actual construction details of the mechanical and electrical systems that do this is beyond the scope of an introductory discussion.

## STORING INFORMATION

Most digital computing machines must store or "remember" information inserted into them, or they must store information that is developed during their operating sequence and will be used later. As a simple example of "storage," our early ancestors stored information regarding animals for food as pictographs in caves. This information was "retrieved" and "processed" as a help to survival. A modern example of data storage is shown in an ordinary adding machine. In this device, a number such as 231 is set up on a digital keyboard and entered ("written") into machine storage by operating its mechanical linkages either manually by a crank, or electrically by a motor. This number can remain stored indefinitely until needed. However, when another number such as 88 is entered, the "memory" is altered to accept the sum of the numbers. When it is desired to retrieve ("read") the storage, an operation is initiated to display the data as stored so far (subtotal key) or to display and cancel ("erase") the storage (total key).

**Illustration 13–2.** Solid state electronic digital computers are essential tools of the engineer. (Courtesy Universal Oil Products Company.)

In more advanced memory storage systems, a location code for a particular part of the stored data is necessary. This location code is called the "address" and is simply a series of numbers that identify the place where particular information is stored.

Information can be stored in many ways, by marks on a piece of paper, by mechanical linkages, by punched cards, by punched paper tape, and by electromagnetic means to name only a few. Since a digital computer usually relies on storage of information in its data processing, a further discussion of data storage for digital machines will be made.

Modern electronic computers employ several methods of storing data for later retrieval. The data storage ("memory") can be classed either as sequential or as random access. As an example of a sequential system, a stack of 3-inch by 5-inch punched cards having information on them but in no special order would require turning through each card in sequence until the card with the desired data is found. On the other hand, a dictionary would be an example of a random access device, since the word list ("storage") can be entered at any place without reference to the last use of it, and the words are located at predetermined places ("addresses").

Some of the common methods used to provide data storage in digital computers are by magnetized surfaces, magnetized cores, electrostatically charged surfaces, and delay lines. Information can also be stored in other ways, for example, on punched cards or on punched paper tape, but this generally is not considered as data storage for computers.

Information storage on magnetized surfaces is usually accomplished by magnetizing a spot on a thin film of magnetic iron oxide coated on a nonmagnetic base material. Figure 13–3 is a diagram of the essential parts of the magnetizing process. An electric current passing through the wire around the core produces a magnetic field that travels through a small section of the iron oxide layer. This condition

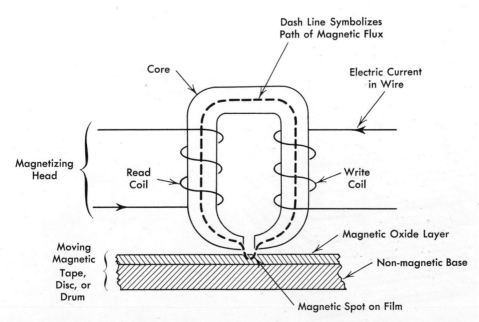

**Figure 13–3.** Simplified diagram of a magnetic head and base as used in computers.

impresses a magnetic pattern that is retained after the current is shut off. When the impressed pattern is to be read, the magnetized surface is passed under the gap in the core. As a magnetic spot passes the core gap, the minute change in the magnetic pattern induces a current in the read coil. This is amplified electrically and is available for machine use as digital information. The presence or absence of these signals is the method of presenting data to the machine.

The magnetized surface storage usually is a tape, a disc, or a drum. Information stored on tapes is arranged in a sequential order, and as a result, access to the data may be somewhat slow. Since a reel of tape can contain as much as 2400 feet, if the needed stored information is near one end of a reel of tape, it is possible that several hundred feet of tape must be run through a reader before reaching a block of data needed. When more rapid access to data is required, magnetic drums or discs are used. Data stored on discs or drums are available more rapidly, since the machine spins the disc or drum at speeds up to 150 revolutions per second and will position a read head quickly to the desired address. Discs and drums therefore are classed as random access memory systems. Reading this information does not destroy the impressed data, and the same information can be read again and again.

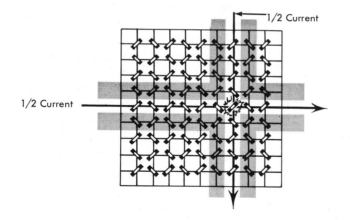

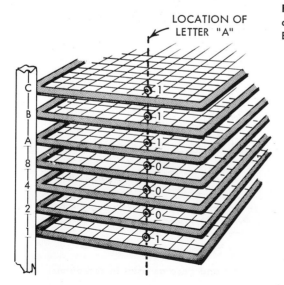

**Figure 13–4.** A storage unit consisting of an array of planes. (Courtesy International Business Machines Corporation.)

However, if stored information is to be changed on a magnetic surface, in the process of writing a new magnetic message, the old pattern automatically is erased.

Magnetized core storage systems consist of a flat array of wires forming a grid with a tiny ring or bead of iron oxide a few hundredths of an inch in diameter strung at the intersection of each wire. These beads can be magnetized easily in a few microseconds and will retain their magnetic state indefinitely.

The polarity of the magnetism in the cores is used to represent 0 or 1 and is the basis of the binary system of storing information. The cores are arranged so that any combination of zeroes or ones representing a character can be written magnetically or can be read back when needed.

The physical structure of the core plane is shown in Figure 13–4 and in Figure 13–5, a small section of a core plane is shown. The process of magnetizing a specific core is as follows:

If we consider that when half the current needed to magnetize a core is run through wire $S$, no core strung on it will be magnetized. If at the same time half the required current is run through wire $E$, no core strung on it will be magnetized except number 499 which has received current from both wires $S$ and $E$. This con-

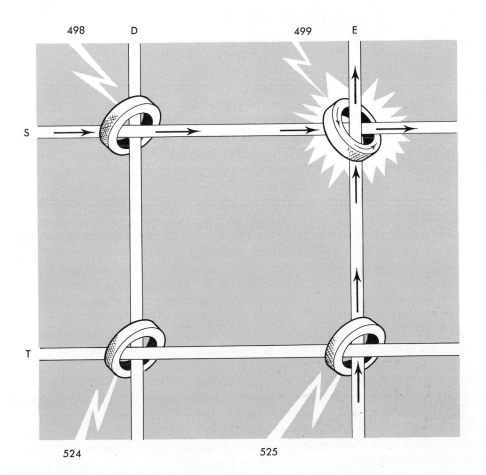

**Figure 13–5.** Part of a magnetic core plane.

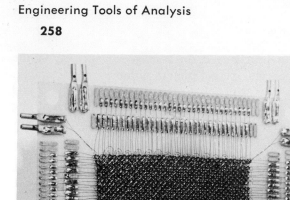

**Illustration 13—3.** A 4096 word, 30 mil ferrite core plane on 30 mil centers used for coincident current applications. (Courtesy Burroughs Corporation.)

sideration provides a unique place in the grid to store a "bit" of information magnetically. The readout is accomplished by a current induced in a third wire running diagonally through all cores. This pulse is caused by an "inquiry" current in a grid wire producing reversal or nonreversal of the magnetic state of the core. Although this "inquiry" is destructive of the magnetic state of the core, a special circuit restores the original grid magnetic pattern after readout.

Core storage is more compact and affords faster random access than does disc or drum storage. For example, a typical core plane is made with 128 cores each way, which gives 16,384 cores per plane. An array of 72 such planes will give a core storage capacity of 1,179,648 bits of information.

The switching speed of the "inquiry" circuits is very rapid and varies from a few microseconds to less than 500 nanoseconds. To give an idea of this time interval, if an orbiting space vehicle is traveling 17,500 miles per hour, it will travel a distance of less than two-tenths of an inch in 500 nanoseconds.

In memory devices employing electrostatic charges, a series of charged spots are placed on a screen of a tube similar to a TV picture tube. By scanning the face of the tube with an "inquiry" electron beam, the presence or absence of a charged spot can be detected. Since the electrons in a charged spot tend to dissipate within a short time, the pattern must be renewed continuously as long as it is needed for reference.

A delay line is a device for storing data for very short periods of time either in electrical circuits or in acoustical circuits. The echo we hear from airborne sounds being reflected from a surface is an example of an acoustical delay in which energy is being transmitted over a closed path in some finite time. In a similar manner, information can be stored in echo circuits for later retrieval. Since the energy in these devices dissipates rapidly, special circuits are provided to reinforce the impressed data continuously so that they will not be lost.

## COMPUTER CODES

It must be noted that practically all memory storage is in a binary code; that is, it represents the presence or absence of a bit of intelligence. This means that the information is stored either as a 1 or 0 in a binary system of notation. Since the majority of our data originally are in a decimal, or ten symbol system, it is necessary to convert from one system to the other for computer use.

### Number Codes

A large number of codes can be used to convert from decimal to binary system, but only one representative system will be discussed here as other systems follow the same general pattern. First, consider some examples of binary indicators, Figure 13–6.

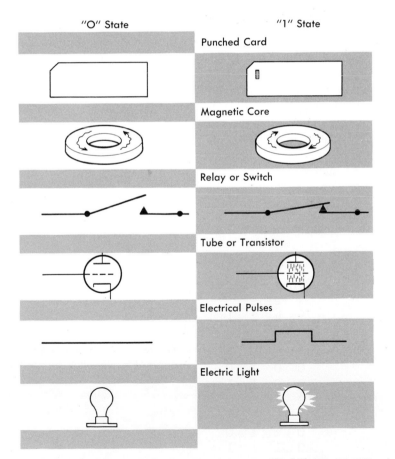

Figure 13–6. Binary state. (Courtesy International Business Machines Corporation.)

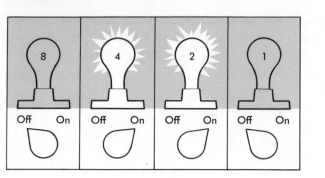

**Figure 13–7.**

In Figure 13–6 examples are shown of the absence or presence of information that can be coded as a binary 0 or 1. In order to convert to our more commonly used decimal system, the example in Figure 13–7 can be used. If we assign an arbitrary value of 8, 4, 2, and 1 to the bulbs and add the numerical values using a binary code to represent decimal data assigned to bulbs that are lighted, we can get all decimal numbers from 0 through 9 with combinations of the four lights. For example, with bulbs 4 and 2 lighted, the number 6 is represented. Using this example, we can prepare a table of conversion for binary to decimal notation.

Thus by combinations of lights, we can represent any decimal digit, and by using the code we can write any number of digits in the same way. For example, the number 1837 in the Binary Coded Decimal (BCD) system can be written as 0001–1000–0011–0111. This example illustrates only one system that is used to symbolize data into a code which can be placed in the computer storage. It is the system that is commonly used for reading information into a computer or for transferring information from a computer to a typewriter or other output device.

The binary coded decimal system of notation should not be confused with the binary number system. This is the system usually used for the arithmetical operations inside the computer itself. The binary number system uses two symbols or digits as does the BCD system, but the binary equivalent of a decimal number is not obtained by transforming one digit at a time as was done with BCD numbers. The

| Decimal Value | Binary Place Value | | | |
|---|---|---|---|---|
| 0 | 8 | 4 | 2 | 1 |
| 0 | 0 | 0 | 0 | 0 |
| 1 | 0 | 0 | 0 | 1 |
| 2 | 0 | 0 | 1 | 0 |
| 3 | 0 | 0 | 1 | 1 |
| 4 | 0 | 1 | 0 | 0 |
| 5 | 0 | 1 | 0 | 1 |
| 6 | 0 | 1 | 1 | 0 |
| 7 | 0 | 1 | 1 | 1 |
| 8 | 1 | 0 | 0 | 0 |
| 9 | 1 | 0 | 0 | 1 |

**Figure 13–8.** Binary representation of decimal values in a Binary Coded Decimal (BCD) system.

decimal number is transformed as a whole from a base 10 number to a base 2 number. The number 1837 would be written 11100101101. Binary number systems are seldom used in communicating with a computer, although the actual storage and processing inside a computer usually is a binary system.

## DIGITAL COMPUTER FUNCTIONAL UNITS

So far, the discussion of computers has been confined to general principles and to a description of some of the component parts. Let us now see how these parts can be fitted together to make up a complete computer system. Figure 13–9 shows a block diagram outlining the functions of the different parts of a typical computer.

### Input Devices

In order to process data, a means must be provided to insert instructions and data into a processing unit. This function is performed by input devices which read or sense data on punched cards, punched paper tape, magnetic tape, magnetic characters and so on, and read this information into the central processing unit.

### Central Processing Unit

The central processing unit is the nerve center of the whole processing system. The central processing unit receives information and instructions, acts in accord with instructions, and either stores or displays a result. Its actual operation is two fold. First, an arithmetic-logic section performs mathematical operations such as adding, subtracting, multiplying, and dividing. Moreover, it usually is set up to test the validity of computations and to take a preprogrammed action if necessary. Second, a control section performs the function of coordinating the operation of the whole system. It provides a planned control over the input units, output units, and storage units.

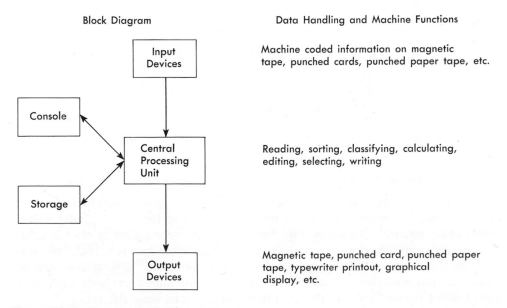

Figure 13–9. Data processing by computer.

As part of the central processing unit, the storage unit provides the important functions of receiving calculated data from the central processing unit and storing them until needed for use later in further calculations and also of accepting and storing instructions from the program input as to what preplanned procedures are to be used in processing data. All data must be placed in storage before they can be processed by the computer. This can be likened to an electrical filing cabinet where instructions are placed for manipulating data and where the data are inserted into specific locations for later recall and processing.

Although not directly a part of the computing section, the console is a useful accessory to the central processing unit. It is probably the most noticeable part of the whole system, as an operator here can communicate directly with the computer. The lights, switches, push buttons, and controls are used to turn on the equipment, monitor operation, and exercise supervision over processing. In addition, in some systems an electrically operated typewriter provides a limited output display capability.

### Output Devices

After data have been manipulated or processed according to instructions fed into the central processing unit, the results must be presented in a manner usable by people. This display usually is provided by printing devices actuated by electrical pulses from the central processing unit.

Another kind of output device is a card punch or a paper tape punch. From processed data sent out by the central processing unit, holes are made in cards or tape for use on other machines, or for storage for later processing. Output data also can be placed on magnetic tape for use in other computer operations or for storage for future use.

Another common way in which output data can be presented is either by print out on a printer or as a graph (or picture) on a plotter or cathode-ray tube. The print out is usually in typed characters, although magnetic ink characters can be printed for special uses. Frequently, the limiting factor in processing data is the time it takes to print it out. Modern high speed printers will print 1200 lines per minute and models are available using light sensitive paper that will print 6000 lines per minute.

In some engineering applications, a plot of data is desirable rather than a tabular data presentation. For this purpose, plotters are available and can be used to plot directly on a sheet of graph paper. These plotters are usually referred to as "incremental plotters," since they plot each data item as a separate point rather than by drawing a continuous line such as an analog machine would plot.

### Inputs to Computer Systems

Information is placed into computers by a code mutually ·acceptable to man and machine. In the case of cards or paper tape, it is in the form of holes whose presence or absence is sensed by tiny fingers or brushes or by photo electric cells. For magnetic tape, the presence or absence of a magnetized spot is sensed. Information can also be placed in by special typewriters that code each alphabet or numerical character into machine notation. There are other specialized methods such as a coded direct readout using characters printed in a special magnetic ink.

Magnetic character readers provide banks with a time saving method of reading and processing large volumes of daily transactions and transcribing these data directly into machine storage. A magnetic character is read by passing it under a read head and ten data channels examine the pattern in a 70 character matrix. The presence or absence of a response from any given area establishes a 0 or 1 in that part of the matrix. The numerals are shown in Figure 13–10 in this matrix pattern. The machine will recognize a symbol such as the numeral 3 by comparing its pattern with stored patterns of all the numerals.

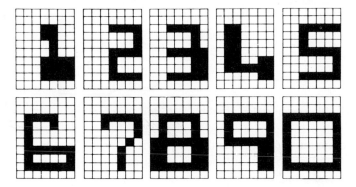

**Figure 13–10.** Matrix pattern of the numerals. (Courtesy International Business Machines Corporation.)

The optical character reader (OCR) is a machine containing a drum that carries a paper past a scanner capable of distinguishing between light and dark patterns. Special upper case characters are used, and the reflected pattern is compared with a stored set of patterns and matched. When character recognition occurs in the matching process, special circuits transfer the information into the computer system for processing.

Other specialized input systems include sheets of paper in which specified areas are marked with graphite pencils, and a reading device employing electrical resistance sensing between closely spaced fingers detects the presence or absence of a mark. This system sometimes is used in grading answer sheets for quizzes. A variation of this method uses photo electric cells to detect the presence or absence of marks at specified locations on a sheet of paper. So far, a successful device has not been made that will read handwriting directly into a machine.

## PROGRAMMING

Like a cooperative but unimaginative and noncreative giant, the computer is ready and willing to perform, but it will not perform on its own initiative. The computer must be instructed what to do, and the instructions must be in detail. A sequence of instructions, orders, or commands placed into a computing machine is called a "program" or "routine." These instructions must be written in a code or machine language acceptable to the computer.

A "programmer" is a person who establishes a sequence of instructions that will solve a problem. A "coder" is a person who converts these instructions into codes

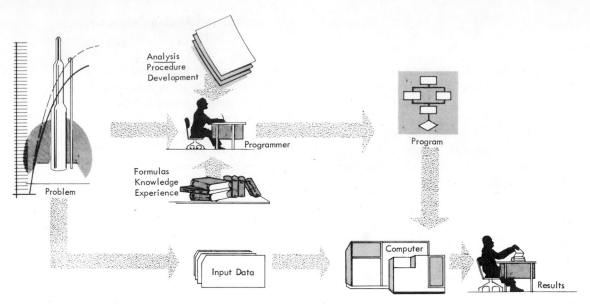

**Figure 13–11.** Direct conversion of problem to machine program.

which the computer can accept and on which it can act. An "operator" is a person who physically places program tapes, punched cards or other prepared material on the computer and punches buttons to operate it.

The place of the programmer in the scheme of the programming system can best be shown by Figure 13–11. As is shown in this picture, the programmer has responsibility for organization and logic features of a program.

### Programming Approach

Before starting to write any program, a good programmer will follow a systematic approach in analyzing the problem and developing its solution. The following steps may appear too obvious to warrant any great attention, but the importance of this logical method cannot be overstressed.

1. *Define the problem.* A hazy understanding of the problem leads to "garbage" for a solution.

2. *Determine the output.* What is the final result of the job expected to look like in both form and content?

3. *Determine the input.* What information will be needed to produce the desired output?

4. *Determine the method of solution* (*algorithm*). What operations must be performed to convert the input into output?

5. *Draw a flow chart.* This is a diagrammatical picture of the calculations and decisions which will be required to achieve the solution.

6. *Write the program.* Convert the flow chart into a "language" that is acceptable to the particular computer that will be used.

7. *"Debug" the program.* Larger programs will almost always include errors when they are first written.

To repeat, though the steps above may seem obvious, many beginning programmers unfortunately try to approach the computer, which has been designed to be completely logical, in a completely illogical and disorganized manner.

## Flow Charts

Flow charting, like writing, is a rather personal matter and, as no two persons will compose an identical paper about the same subject, so will no two programmers be likely to compose identical flow charts to describe the same program. The structure of the flow chart and the specific symbols used in its composition are not nearly as important as that each serves completely the two main purposes of a flow chart. *First,* the flow chart is an indispensable aid in writing a computer program because it requires that the programmer follow a methodical, step-by-step, description of the problem solution. *Second,* the flow chart serves as a means of documentation and communication to others. Frequently it is necessary for a person other than the one who wrote the program to make changes or corrections. In such instances the availability of an accurate and complete flow chart is essential.

Flow charts are divided into two general categories: system or application charts, and program flow charts.

The *first* category, application charts, shows how the system is to operate in its environment, and the emphasis is placed on the documents involved rather than upon the actual machine operations to be performed.

As an example of an application chart, consider the problem of scheduling students in a large school. The desired output consists of two parts: class rosters that show the students who have been scheduled into each class, and student schedules that list the classes scheduled for each student. To produce this output, the system will require as input (1) the courses requested by each student and (2) a master file of all the courses offered. The simplified application chart shown below, Figure 13–12, indicates how such a computer system might operate. The shapes of the symbols used in this example are typical of those used in industry.

The *second* category of flow charts, the program flow chart, is used to describe how the program operates. It shows all of the major steps that the computer will execute to convert the input into output.

Just how detailed a flow chart should be, and what steps it should show, will depend mainly on the complexity of the program. In general, it should show all input and output operations, all major decisions, and all major calculations used in solving the problem.

As an example, a flow chart showing the steps that a computer might follow in calculating the formula $x = a + (e) \left( \dfrac{b - c}{d} \right)$ can be drawn as in Figure 13–13.

However, if this formula were only a small part of a whole program, a flow chart written in this minute detail would be very cumbersome. In such case it would be better to show the above operation as shown in Figure 13–14 as long as the formula for calculating $x$ is given somewhere else in the documentation.

To illustrate how a flow chart is organized, consider the following problem:

A manufacturer of industrial hardware makes many different parts. He keeps his inventory by punching a card for each part made. These cards contain such information as the part number, color, cost, and selling price. The plant manager has asked for a program to count the number of green, right and left handed wozzles now in stock. A possible flow chart for the program is shown below in Figure 13–15.

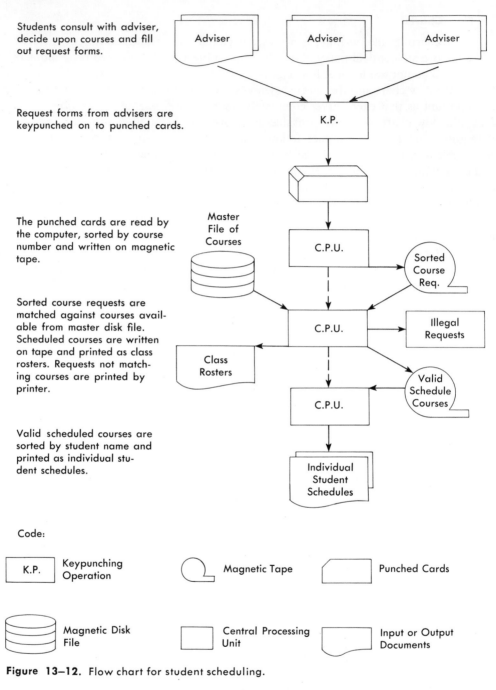

Students consult with adviser, decide upon courses and fill out request forms.

Request forms from advisers are keypunched on to punched cards.

The punched cards are read by the computer, sorted by course number and written on magnetic tape.

Sorted course requests are matched against courses available from master disk file. Scheduled courses are written on tape and printed as class rosters. Requests not matching courses are printed by printer.

Valid scheduled courses are sorted by student name and printed as individual student schedules.

Code:

| | |
|---|---|
| K.P. | Keypunching Operation |
| | Magnetic Tape |
| | Punched Cards |
| | Magnetic Disk File |
| | Central Processing Unit |
| | Input or Output Documents |

**Figure 13–12.** Flow chart for student scheduling.

Start → Subtract *b-c* → Divide by *d* → Mult. by *e* → Add *a* → Store as *x* → End

**Figure 13–13.**

Figure 13–14.

Calculate
*x*

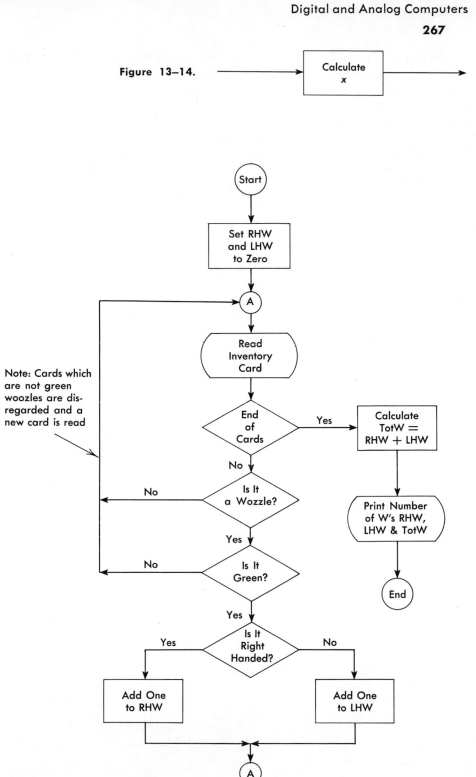

**Figure 13–15.** Flow chart to count wozzles.

Note: Cards which are not green woozles are disregarded and a new card is read

Note that the chart has a definite starting and ending point, that it shows the input (inventory cards), the output (wozzle report), and that it shows the decisions which are required to perform the count. The symbols, RHW, LHW, and TOTW represent the memory locations used to count the right hand, left hand, and total number of wozzles. Observe that these locations have been set to zero at the beginning of the program. This process is called initializing and *must* be done to insure that the locations do not contain numbers which have been left in the computer from a previous program. The small circles with letters inside are called "connectors" and are used to connect widely separated parts of the program.

Flow charts are the key to successful programming efforts and their value cannot be overemphasized.

### Looping

Perhaps the greatest advantages offered by the computer are combined in its ability to make logical decisions and in addition to perform a given set of instructions repetitively—over and over again.

As an example of the value of these two attributes, consider the problem of adding 1000 numbers. The most obvious method is that used by a man with an adding machine as shown in the following flow chart, Figure 13–16.

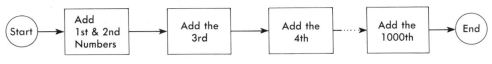

Figure 13–16.

This process will be both time consuming to program and wasteful of computer space since it requires 999 separate "add" instructions to the computer.

There is another way to do the same job, using very few instructions, which takes advantage of the computer's decision-making and repetitive abilities. The flow chart for this method, called "looping," would appear as shown in Figure 13–17.

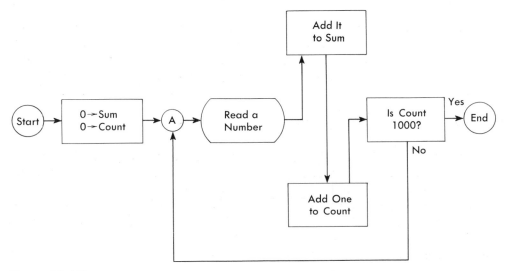

Figure 13–17.

This method uses two locations in memory, "sum" and "count," which are used (1) to accumulate the sum of the numbers and (2) to count how many numbers have been added. After each number has been added and counted, the value of "count" is compared to 1000 (count: 1000 in the decision block) to determine if 1000 numbers have been added. If not, the program returns to Ⓐ to read and add another number; this process is repeated until count = 1000. (Note that if count had been set equal to "one" initially, the program would have had to continue until count was *greater* than 1000).

The advantage of the looping method is that ten numbers or ten million numbers can be added with a single and simple set of computer instructions.

### Problems

**13–1.** Draw a flow chart of the process used to solve for $x$. Assume that the constants $a, b, c$ are in the computer.

$$x = a + b - c$$

**13–2.** Draw a flow chart of the method to evaluate the equation

$$y = 2a + \frac{bc}{d}$$

**13–3.** Draw a detailed flow chart similar to Figure 13–13 for a program to calculate:

$$x = \left(\frac{a + b}{c + d}\right)a^2$$

**13–4.** Draw a flow chart of the method you would use to calculate $e^x$.

$$e^x = 1 + x + \frac{x^2}{2!} + \frac{x^3}{3!} + \ldots \ldots \frac{x^7}{7!}$$

**13–5.** Draw a flow chart for a program that will be used to calculate the miles per gallon used by an automobile. Input data to be read in at each gas stop will be (1) the indicated miles on the odometer, and (2) the number of gallons required to fill the tank. Note that the first stop will *not* give an answer.

**13–6.** Pick a simple process such as changing a tire on an automobile, and draw a flow chart to illustrate how it is done.

**13–7.** Flow chart a program that will read 10 numbers and print out the sum of these numbers.

**13–8.** Draw a flow chart of a program used to calculate the volume of the solid shown in Figure 13–18. Assume that only the dimensions shown are in the computer's memory.

**13–9.** Draw a flow chart to read 100 numbers, to count the number of positive numbers in the list, and to calculate their sum. Print the number of positive numbers and the sum.

**13–10.** Draw a flow chart to read in "$n$" numbers, calculate and print their average. (Hint: first read in a value of "$n$.")

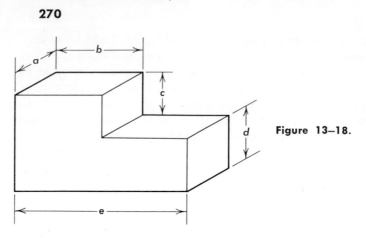

Figure 13–18.

**13–11.** Construct a flow chart that will read the value of $x$ and calculate the value of sine $x$ correct to $\pm 0.0005$. Use the series approximation

$$\text{sine } x = x - \frac{x^3}{3!} + \frac{x^5}{5!} - \frac{x^7}{7!} \cdots$$

You will have to determine how many terms are required for the given accuracy. Assume $x$ will be:

$$0 \le x \le \frac{\pi}{2}$$

**13–12.** A contractor who builds earthfill dams wants a program to calculate the volume of earth required for a given dam. His dams are all the shape shown in Figure 13–19, and only the dimensions shown are subject to change. Draw the flow chart of a program to calculate the volume in ft³ and yd³.

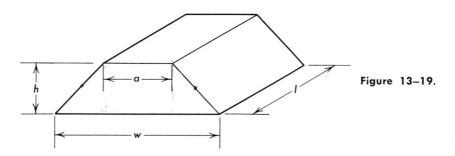

Figure 13–19.

**13–13.** Draw a flow chart to find the roots of the quadratic equation

$$ax^2 + bx + c$$

Assume that the computer has the capability of taking the square root of a *positive* number. (Hint: begin with the quadratic formula.)

**13–14.** The Shade-Tree Rocket Company has been taking hundreds of exhaust temperature readings of their newest engine. The engineers require a program that will give them the average temperature, the number of readings processed, the number of readings below 1000°C, and the number above 2000°C. Draw the flow chart for this program. (Hint: Assume the last piece of data will be followed by a negative number.)

**13–15.** The Better Mousetrap Co. pays a bonus to the employee (of its three employees) who makes the most traps in each year. The bonus is calculated by taking the difference between the total number of traps made by the highest man and the lowest man and multiplying this value by ten.

$$\text{Bonus} = (\text{highest no.} - \text{least no.}) \times \$10$$

Draw the flow chart to read the twelve monthly production figures for each man and to calculate the bonus. The program should indicate which employee (I, II, or III) receives the bonus.

**13–16.** The Outer-Globbonian Dept. of Rocketry and Fireworks has commissioned you to draw the flow chart of a program to plot the flight of their missiles. They will give you the initial velocity ($V_0$), initial angle of inclination ($\alpha$), and a set of time values ($t$), as shown in Figure 13–20.

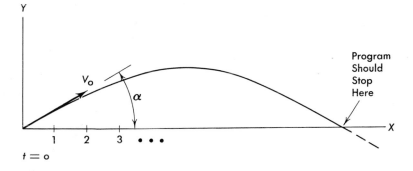

**Figure 13–20.**

The program should calculate and print the values of the height $y$ and the distance from origin $x$ for each value of time $t$. The program should stop when the calculated height is less than zero.

Outer Globbonia is flat and has no air so you may use the formulas:

$$y = (V_0 \, \text{Sin} \, \alpha) \, t - \frac{1}{2} g t^2$$

$$x = (V_0 \, \text{Cos} \, \alpha) \, t$$

Assume that the computer "knows" how to calculate the sine and cosine of $\alpha$. Use 32 ft/sec² as the value of "$g$."

# Chapter 14

# Technical Sketching – A Universal Language for the Engineer

The engineer must be able to communicate his ideas to others without excessive loss of time or accuracy. Although the spoken and written word are very important ingredients for communication and understanding, neither can replace the *technical sketch* as a means of quickly, accurately, and completely describing any object of the engineer's imagination. For this reason the ability to make a freehand drawing or sketch is an essential part of every engineer's reservoir of ability. Sketches are also valuable aids to the engineer in clarifying or developing instructions and in sharpening the accuracy of his observation. In recent years people from all parts of the world have been brought into close contact with each other. Many times problems have arisen because of a lack of understanding. Regardless of any educational or language barriers that may arise, engineers can usually communicate their ideas to others if they are adept at technical sketching.

The engineer will frequently find that he is able to organize his own thoughts more effectively if he can represent his mental impressions in freehand sketches or drawings. Even in school such an ability can be utilized to excellent advantage.

Figures 14–1 and 14–2 are examples of sketches that have been drawn to convey technical ideas. Figure 14–3 is a representation of a survey of a tract of land whose approximate shape has been sketched as shown with basic line lengths and angles included. Figure 14–4 shows a design sketch which has been prepared by an engineer for the use of his detailers or draftsmen. A skilled workman could also take this sketch and make the part directly if requested by the engineer.

Experimental electronic circuits are frequently assembled from an engineer's sketches. These sketches, as part of the instructions given to a technician, outline the procedure and needed materials for fabrication. Figure 14–5 is an example of a sketch such as might be furnished a technician for fabricating an amplifier.

The engineer does not need to be an artist or possess unusual talents in drawing. However, adherence to certain basic principles and procedures will usually produce more desirable results.

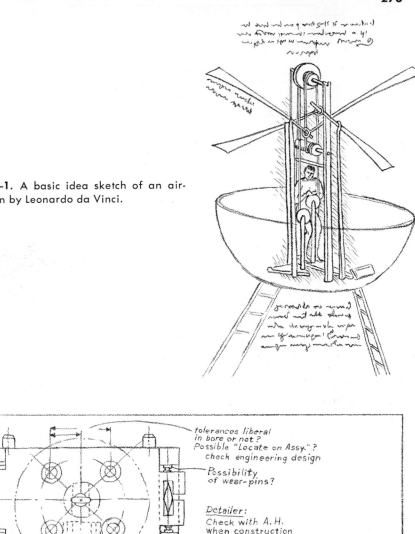

**Figure 14–1.** A basic idea sketch of an aircraft design by Leonardo da Vinci.

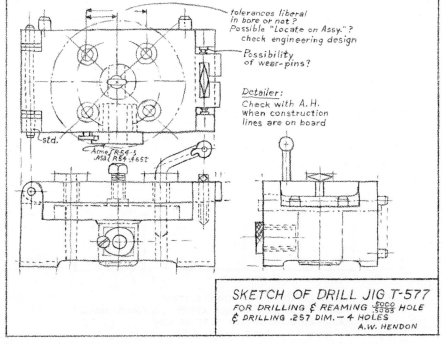

tolerances liberal
in bore or not?
Possible "Locate on Assy."?
check engineering design

Possibility
of wear-pins?

Detailer:
Check with A. H.
when construction
lines are on board

std.

Acme ⌈R54-5
.ASA⌊R54-.465t

SKETCH OF DRILL JIG T-577
FOR DRILLING & REAMING .5000/.5005 HOLE
& DRILLING .257 DIM. — 4 HOLES
A.W. HENDON

**Figure 14–2.** Design sketch of drill jig.

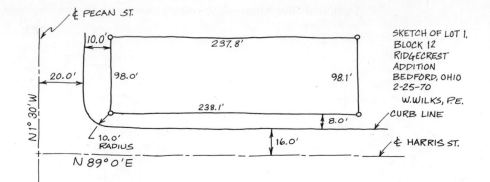

**Figure 14-3.** Sketch of a survey.

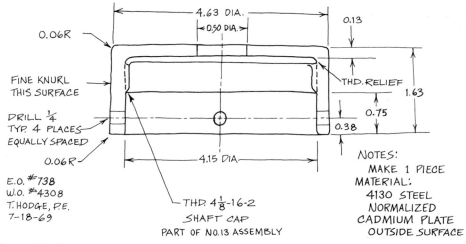

**Figure 14-4.**

0.06R

FINE KNURL
THIS SURFACE

DRILL ¼
TYP. 4 PLACES
EQUALLY SPACED

0.06R

E.O. #738
W.O. #4308
T. HODGE, P.E.
7-18-69

4.63 DIA.

0.50 DIA.

0.13

THD. RELIEF

1.63

0.75

0.38

4.15 DIA

THD. 4⅛-16-2
SHAFT CAP
PART OF NO.13 ASSEMBLY

NOTES:
MAKE 1 PIECE
MATERIAL:
4130 STEEL
NORMALIZED
CADMIUM PLATE
OUTSIDE SURFACE

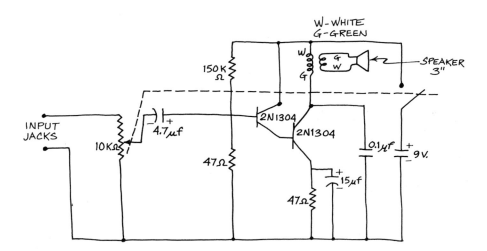

AUDIO AMPLIFIER FOR TAPE SYSTEM
MOUNT IN ALUMINUM BOX APPROX. 6×6×3 INCHES
PAINT OUTSIDE OF BOX FLAT BLACK
3-11-69          D. JERNIGAN, P.E.

**Figure 14-5.**

## MATERIALS

A chief advantage of freehand sketching is that the only essentials are a pencil, paper, and an eraser—items which are usually readily available. A pencil with soft lead, such as F, HB, or H, should be used. The eraser should be soft and pliable for best results. Frequently an art gum eraser is useful also. The paper used may be tracing paper or plain bond but cross-section or coordinate paper is preferable, Figure 14–6. One technique commonly used is to prepare a master cross-section sheet with India ink (horizontal and vertical lines ruled to form squares ⅛″ or ¼″ on a side). Ordinary bond paper or tracing paper can then be superimposed over the master sheet to obtain a working surface. The drawing is done on the top sheet, and the background lines are removed when the sketch is completed.

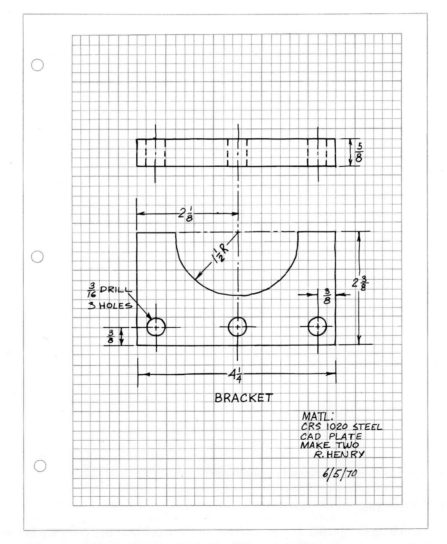

**Figure 14–6.** Cross-section paper is useful for technical sketching.

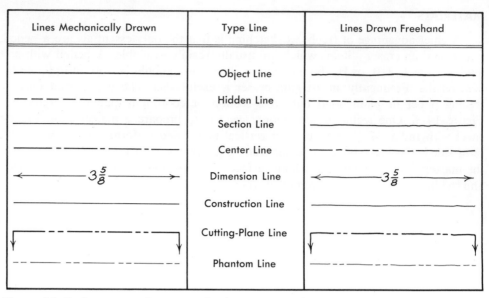

| Lines Mechanically Drawn | Type Line | Lines Drawn Freehand |
|---|---|---|
| | Object Line | |
| | Hidden Line | |
| | Section Line | |
| | Center Line | |
| $3\frac{5}{8}$ | Dimension Line | $3\frac{5}{8}$ |
| | Construction Line | |
| | Cutting-Plane Line | |
| | Phantom Line | |

**Figure 14—7.** Comparison between ruled lines and sketched lines.

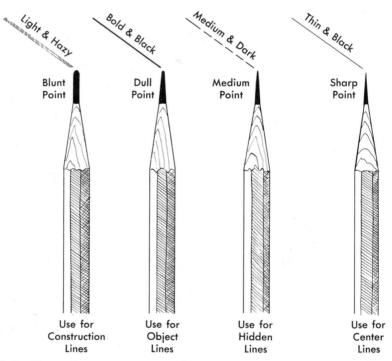

**Figure 14—8.** Choose the appropriate pencil point.

## LINE TECHNIQUE

In sketching the *quality* and *preciseness* of linework will not compare favorably with instrument drawings. Since smoothness and exacting uniformity of linework are not necessary, as in mechanical drawings, the quality of a line drawn freehand

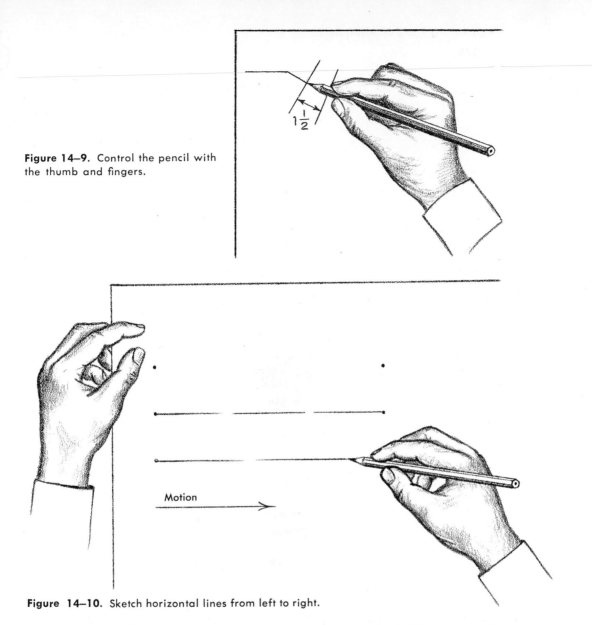

**Figure 14–9.** Control the pencil with the thumb and fingers.

$1\frac{1}{2}$

Motion

**Figure 14–10.** Sketch horizontal lines from left to right.

is judged by its *accuracy of direction* and its *density,* Figure 14–7. The construction line should be a very hazy, thin, light line. The other lines, however, should be crisp and distinct. The ends of all dashes should be accented slightly, but a contrast in the different line weights should be maintained. The visible lines on the drawing, especially those outlining the object, should be drawn with bold lines. Conversely, dimension lines, center lines, and extension lines should be very thin. For general linework, the pencil should be sharpened to a long conical point, not too sharp. A needle-sharp pencil may be used for making thin lines such as center lines or dimension lines, Figure 14–8.

In most engineering drawings there are many straight lines of varying lengths. For this reason the engineer should become proficient in sketching them. The pencil should be held naturally and firmly but with freedom. The thumb and fingers should control the pencil about 1½ inches from its point, Figure 14–9. Horizontal lines should be drawn from left to right, Figure 14–10, with a wrist motion for short lines

277

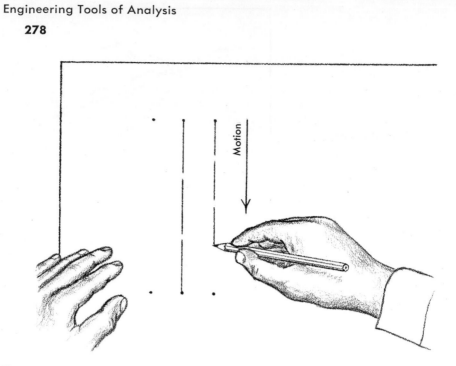

**Figure 14–11.** Sketch vertical lines downward.

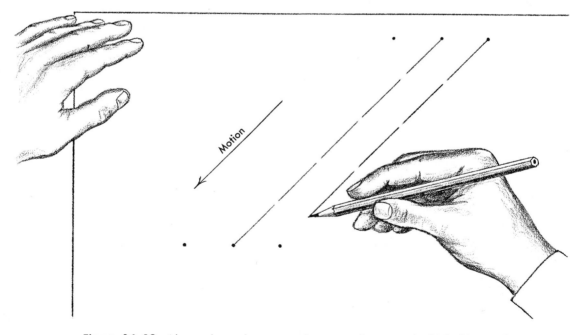

**Figure 14–12.** Always keep the eye on the target dot toward which the pencil is moving.

and a forearm motion for longer ones. Vertical lines are sketched downward with a finger and wrist movement in a series of overlapping strokes, Figure 14–11. Inclined lines running from upper right to lower left should be drawn in a downward direction with the same pencil movement as with vertical lines, Figure 14–12. However, it may be more convenient to rotate the paper to a position where the lines can be treated as horizontal or vertical.

When it is necessary to sketch long lines, mark the ends of the proposed line with tiny dots and then move the pencil with successive strokes between the dots.

*Always keep the eye on the "target" dot toward which the pencil is moving rather than upon the pencil point.* The point of the pencil should just skim lightly across the paper and corrections for accuracy should be made with each successive stroke. When the direction of the light line has been established it can be covered with a heavier object line.

When long lines are desired whose directions are parallel to the sides of the paper, the edge of the pad or clip board may be used as a guide for the fingers to slide against, Figure 14–13.

**Figure 14–13.** Slide fingers along the guiding edge.

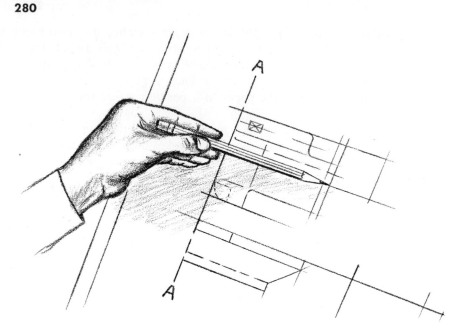

**Figure 14–14.** The sketch pencil may be used to transfer distances.

In some instances it may be expedient to use a bit of paper or card to estimate distances that can be transferred at intervals to the drawing. This may be especially true where a rectangular outline is desired. Finished lines can then be drawn through the reference points marked. Another convenient aid that may be used in measuring or transferring distances is the sketch pencil, which can be used as shown in Figure 14–14.

## CURVES, CIRCLES, AND ARCS

Small circles or arcs may be sketched in progressive steps as shown in Figure 14–15. The circumscribing square should be sketched first using very thin, wispy

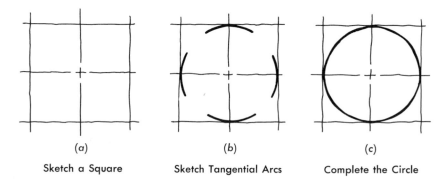

(a)                    (b)                    (c)

Sketch a Square      Sketch Tangential Arcs      Complete the Circle

**Figure 14–15.** Sketching a circle using a circumscribing square.

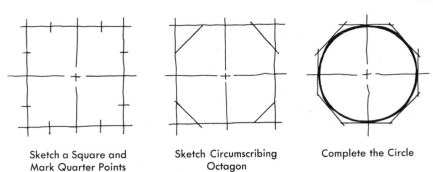

| Sketch a Square and Mark Quarter Points | Sketch Circumscribing Octagon | Complete the Circle |

**Figure 14–16.** Sketching a circle using an octagon as a reference.

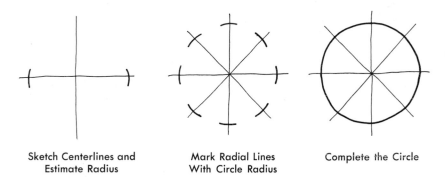

| Sketch Centerlines and Estimate Radius | Mark Radial Lines With Circle Radius | Complete the Circle |

**Figure 14–17.** Sketching a circle using radial lines.

lines. Then, when a center line has been marked through the midpoints of the sides, arcs can be drawn tangent to the sides of the square. An octagon may also be used to circumscribe the circle, Figure 14–16. Another technique, utilizing radial lines that are marked with the estimated circle radius, is shown in Figure 14–17. In each procedure the resulting circle should be retraced to achieve object line intensity, and the construction lines should be partially erased to emphasize the circle definition.

Other techniques such as those shown in Figure 14–18 should be used when

**Figure 14–18.** Sketching large circles using a piece of paper for the circle radius.

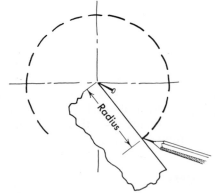

Motion

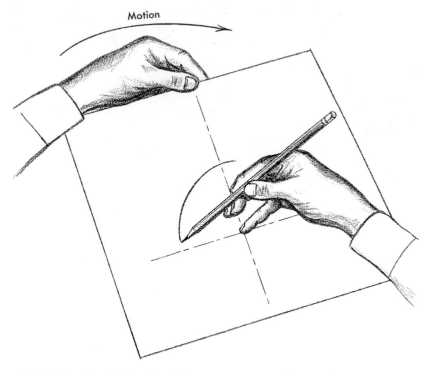

**Figure 14—19.** Use the third or fourth finger as a pivot and rotate the paper.

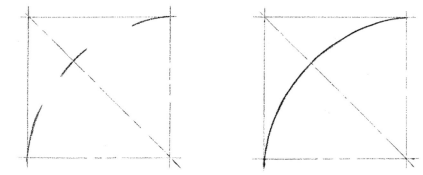

**Figure 14—20.** Sketching an arc using radial lines.

large circles are desired. Figure 14—19 shows how the tip of the little finger may be used as a pivot when the paper is rotated with the other hand. In this case, it will be necessary for the pencil to be held at varying distances from the point in order to achieve the desired circle diameter. Arcs may be drawn using the same technique as described above for the drawing of circles. Reference lines should be used as before, Figure 14—20. In all cases it is important that the points of tangency be carefully observed.

## ELLIPSES

Multiview or projection drawings are most commonly used in sketching, how-ever engineering single-view sketches are frequently made in three dimensions to emphasize the relationships between depth, width, and height. These sketches are pictorial and they are usually classified as either *isometric, oblique,* or *perspective drawings,* Figure 14–21. In these types of sketches, circles that are viewed obliquely appear to the eye as ellipses, Figure 14–22. For this reason the engineer should practice until he is proficient in sketching ellipses. As in the drawing of circles, there are some preferred techniques that should be followed.

First grasp the pencil lightly and move the arm with a free movement generated from the shoulder. Keep your elbow off the desk, as illustrated in Figure 14–23, and allow it to follow the desired circular or elliptical motion, which is transmitted to

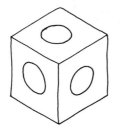
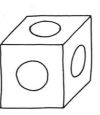
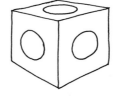

Isometric          Oblique          Perspective

**Figure 14–21.** Pictorial sketches.

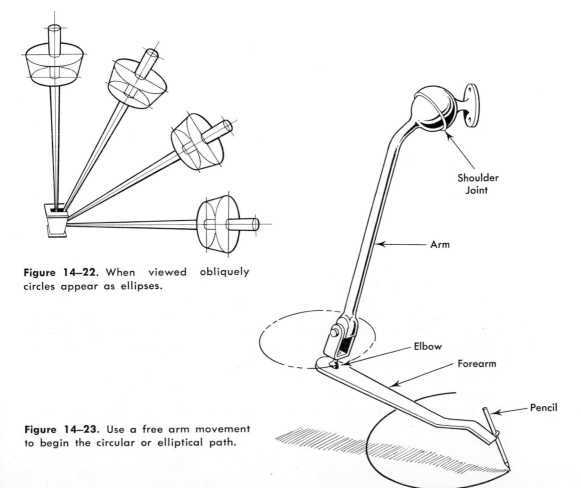

**Figure 14–22.** When viewed obliquely circles appear as ellipses.

**Figure 14–23.** Use a free arm movement to begin the circular or elliptical path.

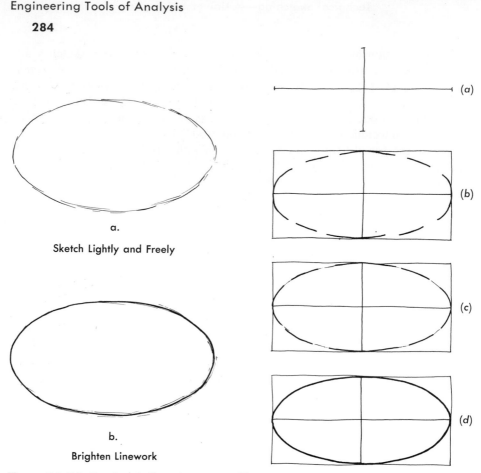

a.

**Sketch Lightly and Freely**

b.

**Brighten Linework**

**Figure 14–24.** Freehand ellipses.　　　**Figure 14–25.** Sketch construction of an ellipse.

the paper via the forearm, hand, and pencil. Finally, lower the pencil to the paper until successive ellipses are lightly drawn. The final path may be carefully traced to form the desired object line, Figure 14–24. As in the case of drawing circles, a circumscribing rectangle can be sketched first for reference purposes, Figure 14–25. The midpoints of the sides should be indicated prior to sketching light tangent arcs.

## SCALES, PROPORTION, AND SYMMETRY

Unlike mechanical drawings, technical sketches are not drawn to an exact scale. It is very important, however, that all width and height relationships *be drawn in proportion to those of the object being sketched.* The overall size of the sketch is optional with the engineer and depends upon its intended use, its complexity, and the size of paper that is available. In general, small objects are usually sketched oversize and large objects to some reduced scale. Where objects are symmetrically formed about some axis or plane, the sketch should also convey this impression.

In sketching an object it is first necessary to establish the relative height and width proportions of the object. As shown in Figure 14–26, a pencil can be used to

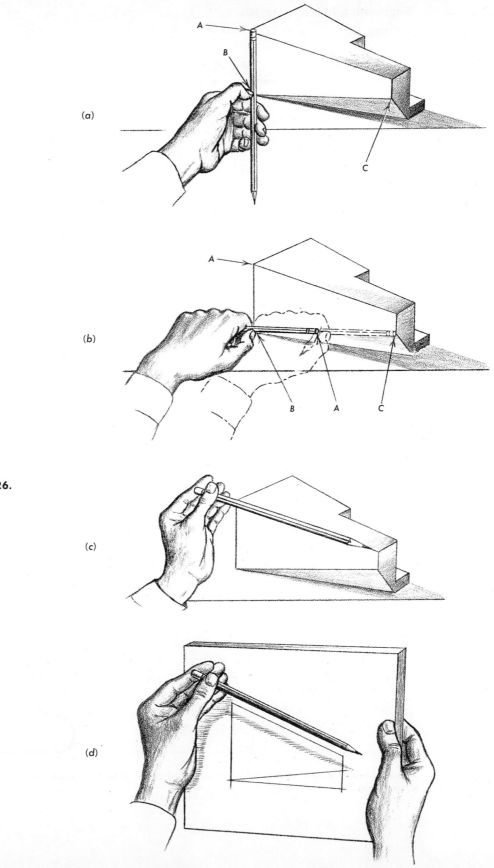

Figure 14–26.

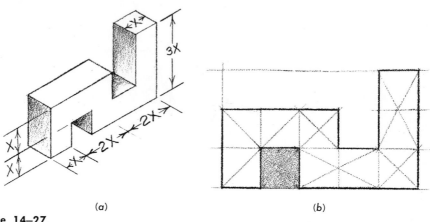

(a)                                              (b)

**Figure 14–27.**

advantage in making these comparisons. Suggested steps to follow in estimating proportionality are:

1. Using light thin lines sketch a rectangle which will contain within its boundaries the overall width and height of the object.

2. By eye subdivide the enclosing rectangle into smaller sections in accordance with the characteristics of the object. Lightly drawn diagonals will usually aid in establishing lines and planes of symmetry, Figure 14–27.

3. Sketch in other pertinent details to impart a good understanding of the composition of the object.

Where irregularly shaped objects must be sketched, the overall width and height should first be estimated so that rectangles can be "blocked in." As before, attention should first be given to the overall proportions, next to the general sizes and direction of sweep of the curved shapes, and finally to the brightened object lines of the completed sketch, Figure 14–28.

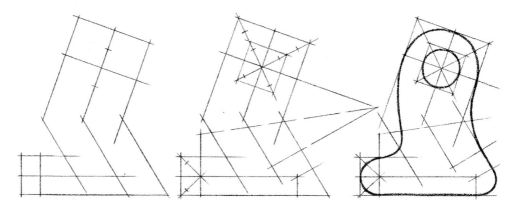

**Figure 14–28.** When sketching irregularly shaped objects, begin by blocking in the proportions.

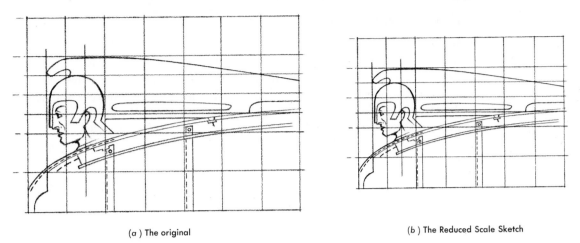

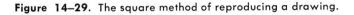

(a) The original          (b) The Reduced Scale Sketch

**Figure 14–29.** The square method of reproducing a drawing.

Frequently it will be desirable to sketch an object from a photograph or drawing that has many odd curves and projections. In such instances, ruling a grid across the original picture is frequently helpful. Then the sketch can be made on grid paper, not necessarily of the same scale but proportional to the original. The final sketch can then be made by drawing within and across the squares of the new grid and estimating by eye the relationships in the original photograph as shown by its grid system. Figure 14–29 shows how this may be accomplished.

When sketching an actual object that is too large to hold in the hand or set on a table, proportionality can be established by holding the pencil, Figure 14–30, and sighting across it. Use the smallest distance (width, height, depth) as a basis for estimating distances. In this way comparison of length, width, and height can be made. Care should be exercised to hold the pencil the same distance from the eye and to maintain a constant body position throughout the estimation phase.

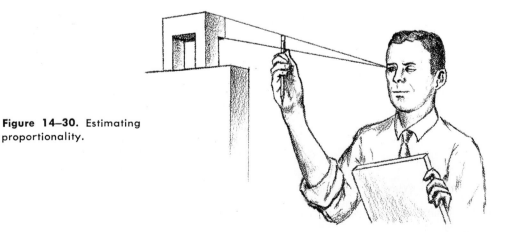

**Figure 14–30.** Estimating proportionality.

## MULTIVIEW DRAWING

Photographs and pictorial drawings serve very well to produce an illusion of depth and volume representation. Another advantage is that they depict the view as it is actually seen by the observer. However, they are limited in that they cannot always show the exactness of detail that would be necessary to make a duplicate of the object, Figure 14–31. This is particularly true where the object is a composite of several components or where surfaces or voids are hidden from view. Therefore, a number of views should be drawn of an object, systematically arranged, so that there can be no misinterpretation of the design specifications. Such a system of views is called *multiview drawing*. Each view is chosen in a direction perpendicular to one

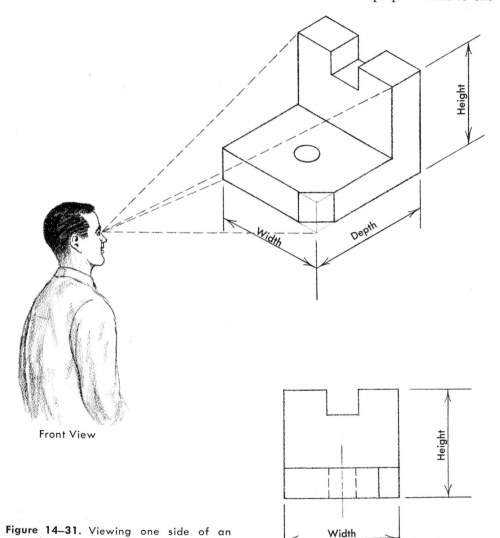

Front View

**Figure 14–31.** Viewing one side of an object does not usually show the detail which would be necessary to make a duplicate.

Front View

of the principal surfaces or one of the sides of the object, as shown in Figure 14–32. Another name commonly used to describe this type of drawing is *orthographic projection*. In this way the observer will see a "true view" of the size and shape of the object, but only from one direction and only if the observer is located at infinite distance from it. As can be seen from Figure 14–32, only two principal dimensions can be shown on any one of these views—in this case the width and height. From this vantage point the viewer cannot judge the depth of the object. For depth to be shown a top, bottom, or side view must be used.

The engineer should learn to select appropriate views of an object so that a minimum of drawing is necessary. For example, in many instances only two views

**Figure 14–32.** Look at the object perpendicularly to one of principal surfaces.

are required, as for a cylindrical shape. Conical and pyramidal shapes also can be described with two views.

Ordinarily the three views used to describe an object are the front, top, and right or left side views. They are called *principal views*. The top and right side views are obtained by revolving the object as shown in Figure 14–33. Notice that the top view is obtained by rotating the top of the object up and forward toward the observer. The right side view is obtained by bringing the right side to the right and toward the observer.

Views of the other sides may be obtained in like manner. From Figure 14–34 we can see that multiview drawings have the advantage over photographs or pictorial drawings in that the location of hidden lines can be clearly shown. The hole that appears as a circle in the top view is shown as hidden lines in the front and right side views.

Customarily, each view is drawn in a standard relationship and in line with the other views. Figure 14–35 shows the arrangement of views which is most common. Instead of rotating the object, it is possible that the observer might wish to walk around the object in order that he can see it from its various sides.

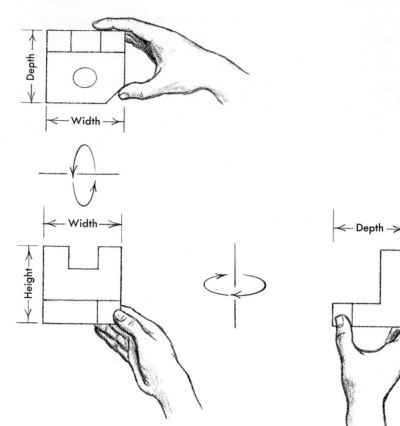

Figure 14–33. The three principal views are the front, top, and right side views.

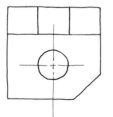

Figure 14–34. The principal views should be systematically arranged.

Top View

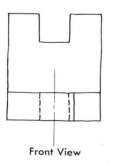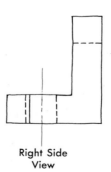

Front View

Right Side
View

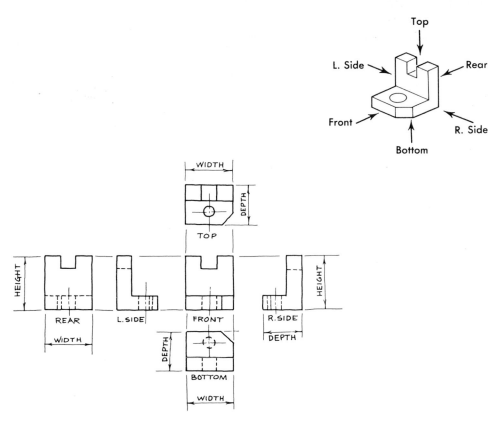

**Figure 14–35.** The six standard views.

### The Selection of Views

Careful study should be given to the silhouette of an object before selecting the views to be sketched. Only those views that are necessary for a clear and complete description should be selected. The most important view is the one that shows the characteristic contour of the object. This is usually selected as the front view. Also the object should be placed such that the least number of hidden lines will result.

The object shown in Figure 14–35 has three distinctive features that should be completely described by the sketch:

1. The square silhouette top and the rectangular slot in the vertical surface, both of which can be seen from the front view.

2. The hole in the horizontal surface, and the beveled front corner, which are described by the top view.

3. The right angle at the rear, which can be seen from the side.

Upon examination we can see that the left side, back, and bottom views are unnecessary.

In many situations less than three views will suffice, for example in the sketching of cylinders, screws, bolts, or bushings. In other cases three views will not be

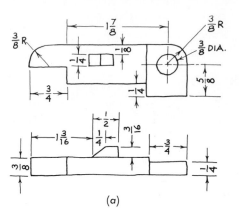

(a)

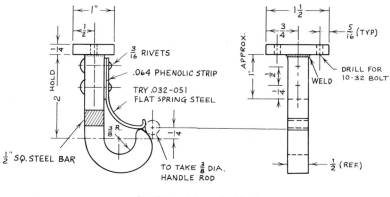

SKETCH — SPRING CATCH
MAKE ONE — NOTIFY ENGINEERING
FOR TEST        *H.H.C c/n/c*

(b)

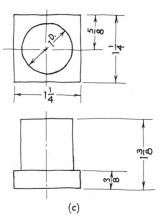

(c)

**Figure 14–36.** Sketch only necessary views.

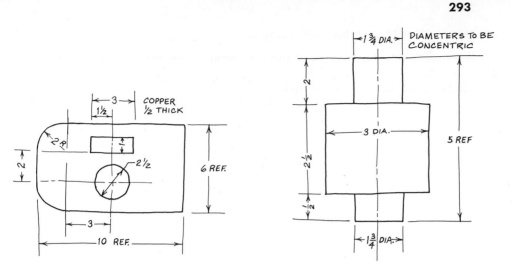

Figure 14–37.

Figure 14–38.

adequate, and they must be supplemented with sectional or auxiliary views. Figure 14–36 shows three examples where two views are sufficient to completely describe the object.

As suggested above some objects can be adequately described with a single view. When one view is used, supplementary descriptive notes should be added adjacent to the view. In Figure 14–37 the view would be incomplete without the note specifying the thickness. In Figure 14–38 the notes are needed to call out the cylindrical shapes of the various portions of the roller.

### Hidden Lines

There are certain conventional practices that should be observed in drawing hidden lines:

1. When a hidden line forms a continuation of a visible line, there must be a clear separation at their intersection.

2. Intersecting hidden lines should form perpendicular corners as in the letters "L" and "T"

3. Where possible, a hidden line should not intersect a visible line.

4. Parallel hidden lines should alternate the spaces between the dashes.

5. When hidden lines join at a point, the dashes should touch, as would be the case at the bottom of a drilled hole.

Although they are not visible, center lines are also very important. They are used to indicate axes of symmetry such as for round objects, centers of holes, or of large arcs. The symbol "₵" is sometimes used with centerlines. For symmetrical views or portions of views the center lines should be among the first lines drawn. As shown in Figure 14–7, the center line is made up of very light, long, and thin lines with alternating short dashes. They always extend slightly beyond the outline of the view, or portion of view, to which the center line applies. The center of a circle should be located by the intersection of short dashes.

### Steps in Sketching Multiview Drawings

When sketching multiview drawings care should be exercised that the space for each view has been properly allocated. Each reserved area should be blocked in with light construction lines. Figure 14–39 shows how this should be done in

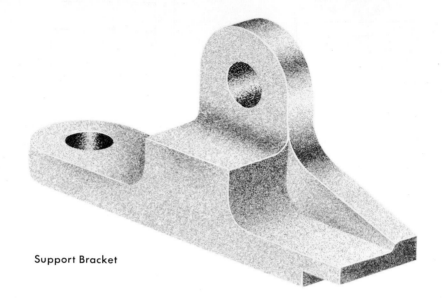

Support Bracket

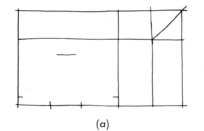

(a)

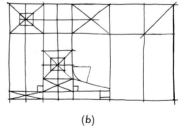

(b)

(c)

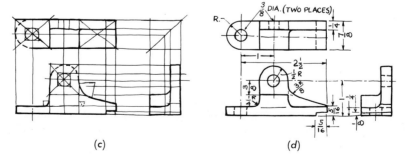

(d)

**Figure 14–39.** Allocate the proper spaces for each view.

successive steps to prepare the multiview sketches of the support bracket. Note that vertical lines are drawn to separate the view locations and to establish the width of the front and top views. As before diagonals can be drawn in lightly to serve as locators for the center of the holes. Be certain that the views presented by the sketches are in proper alignment with each other.

### Precedence and Representation of Lines

Often in a multiview sketch some priority of linework must be established, since two or three lines may appear in identical locations. Since visible lines are necessary to establish the physical features of the object, they take precedence over all other lines. A solid line could cover a hidden line, but not vice versa, (see Figures 14–40 and 14–41).

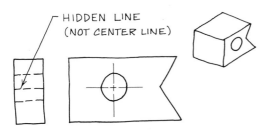

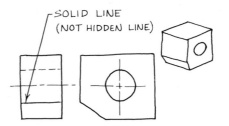

Figure 14–40. A hidden line takes precedence over a center line.

Figure 14–41. A solid line takes precedence over a hidden line.

The following order of preference of lines is recommended:

1. Solid line
2. Hidden line
3. Center line or cutting plane
4. Break lines
5. Dimension and extension lines
6. Crosshatch lines

Visible lines or hidden lines can be used to show (1) the intersection of two surfaces, (2) an edge view of a surface, or (3) a contour view of a curved surface. All views should be examined to discover the true meaning of each line shown, since the complete description is usually not evident in a single view and many times not in two views.

## PICTORIAL SKETCHING

Pictorial sketches are the oldest form of graphical communication known. Even today they are more readily understood by the majority of people than are multiview drawings. The types of pictorial drawing most commonly used by engineers in sketching are *isometric, oblique,* and *perspective.* These types will be discussed briefly here.

## Isometric Sketching

The most common form of pictorial sketching is isometric sketching. To make an isometric sketch of an object hold it as in Figure 14–42 and tilt its top forward slightly. The front corner will appear as a vertical line, but the two receding bottom edges, and those parallel to them, will appear to rise at angles of approximately 30° with the horizontal. The steps in sketching an isometric drawing are:

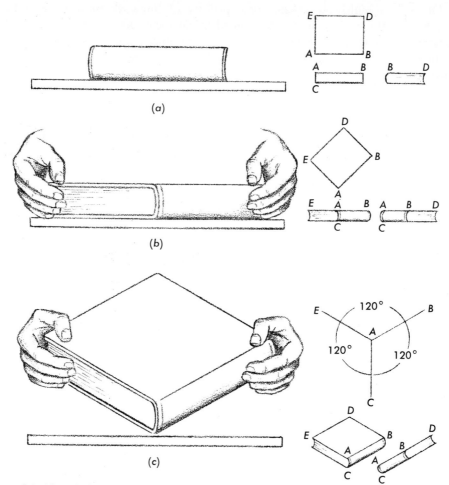

**Figure 14–42.** Tilt the top slightly.

1. Using very light, thin lines sketch a box with its front edge vertical and its sides at 30° angles with the horizontal, as in Figure 14–43a. In this sketch, sides *AB, AC* and *AD* form the *isometric axes*. Their respective lengths are judged by eye to be proportional to the corresponding lines of the object. All other lines that are parallel to one of the sides of the object are parallel to the lines that form the isometric axes.

2. Block in the recessed notch and the semicircular hole.

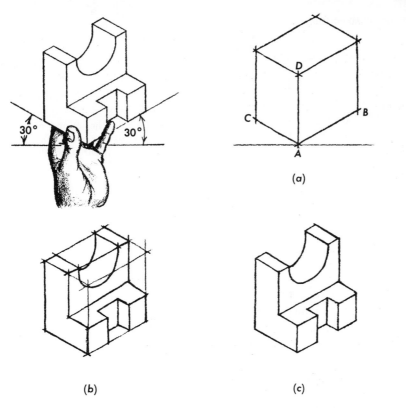

**Figure 14–43.** Isometric sketching.

3. Partially erase the construction lines and brighten the object lines of the finished sketch.

4. Note that hidden lines are normally omitted.

Circles viewed obliquely appear as ellipses. Thus when holes or cylindrical projections are present, they will convey the impression that they are elliptical in shape, Figure 14–44. In sketching an ellipse to represent a circle pictorially, first draw an

**Figure 14–44.** Circles appear as ellipses.

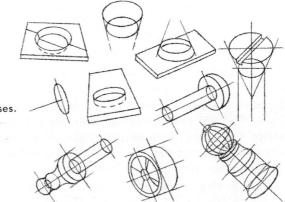

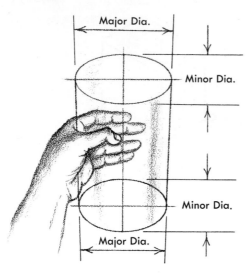

**Figure 14–45.** The minor axis of the ellipse is always at right angles to the major axis and coincident with the center line.

enclosing isometric square (rhombus). The sides of the rhombus are approximately equal in length to the diameter of the true circle. The ellipse is then formed by lightly sketching arcs which are tangent to the midpoints of the sides of the isometric square. Remember that *the major axis of the ellipse should always be at right angles to the center line of the cylinder, and the minor axis is at right angles to the major axis and coincides with the center line,* Figure 14–45.

As an example, let us consider a large rectangular block with a hole through its center, Figure 14–46a. We may proceed as follows, Figure 14–46b,c,d.

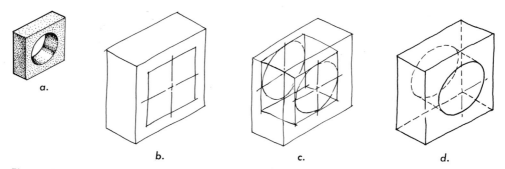

**Figure 14–46.** Sketching the isometric ellipse.

1. Sketch lightly the outlines of the block and also the enclosing isometric squares (rhombus). Each side of the rhombus is equal in length to the diameter of the hole. Locate the center of the hole, and connect the midpoints of the sides, Figure 14–46b. The ellipse that is drawn will be tangent to the sides at these midpoints. The major axis is at right angles to the center line of the hole, and the minor axis coincides with the center line of the hole. Using these points as guides, the elliptical arcs can be drawn.

2. The shorter small-radius arcs are then drawn to complete the ellipse.

3. Block in the rhombus for the back ellipse and complete it in the same manner as the front ellipse, Figure 14–46c.

4. Complete the drawing by adding the hidden lines that are tangent to the two ellipses, if desired for clarity. Brighten the object lines to complete the sketch and dim the remaining construction lines with an eraser to emphasize the features of the object, Figure 14–46d.

Figure 14–47a shows how an isometric sketch is drawn from orthographic views. Remember to first sketch lightly an isometric block large enough to contain the object. Within this "reference volume" the object can be sketched so that correct views are obtained from the front, top, and right side.

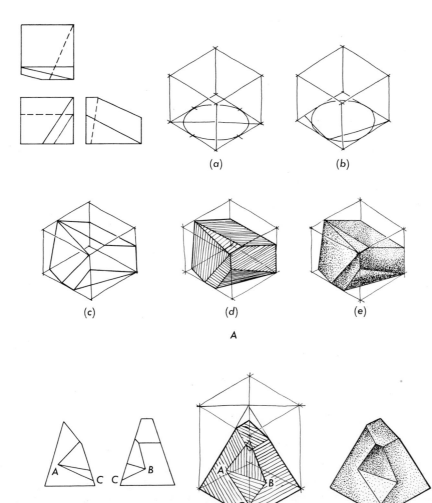

Figure 14–47. Making an isometric sketch from orthographic views.

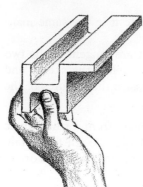

**Figure 14–48.** Channel block.

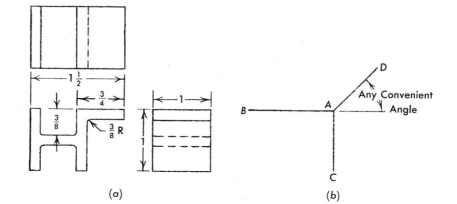

(a)                                              (b)

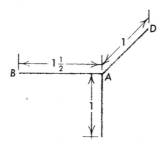

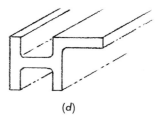

(c)                                              (d)

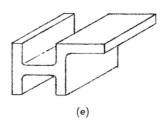

(e)

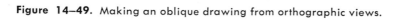

**Figure 14–49.** Making an oblique drawing from orthographic views.

### Oblique Sketching

Another type of pictorial drawing is oblique sketching. A sketch in the oblique has the advantage of showing the front view in its true shape and without distortion. This is especially useful in sketching objects with cylindrical surfaces, since circles can be drawn more easily on the undistorted front view. Oblique sketches are similar to isometric sketches because both have three axes to represent the three mutually perpendicular edges upon which measurements are to be made. Two of the axes are horizontal and vertical. The third axis is usually selected as 30° or 45° with the horizontal, but other angles could also be chosen. Since one view is drawn true shape, oblique sketches are usually easier to draw than isometrics. The procedures to follow in making an oblique sketch are shown in Figures 14–48 and 14–49. Frequently there is less distortion if the depth dimension is foreshortened to a pleasing proportion. Figure 14–50 shows how variations can also be achieved by changing the position of the receding axis.

In making oblique sketches remember to:

1. Position the object to be sketched so that advantage can be taken of the fact that frontal circles appear in their true shape.

2. Position the object so that any irregular outline or contour is parallel to the plane of the paper.

3. Position the object so that the longest dimension is parallel to the plane of the paper.

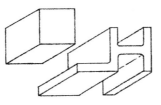

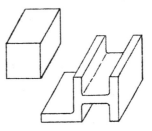

Figure 14–50. Variations of the receding axis.

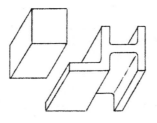

### Perspective Sketching

A sketch drawn in perspective gives a more pleasing and realistic effect than either isometric or oblique drawing. Perspective takes into account the fact that objects appear proportionately smaller as their distance from the eye increases, that parallel lines appear to converge as they recede, and that horizontal lines and planes appear to vanish on the horizon.

The channel block, shown in Figure 14–48, may be sketched in *one-point perspective* (one vanishing point) as follows (Figure 14–51):

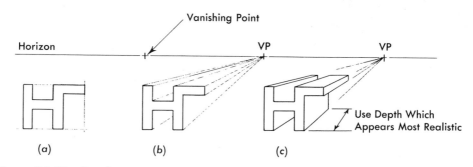

**Figure 14–51.** Sketching in one-point perspective.

1. First lightly sketch in the true shape of the front of the object as in oblique drawing. Select a vanishing point for the receding lines of depth. Usually, when a single vanishing point is used, it is located above and to the right of the object, as illustrated.

2. Lightly sketch "rays of sight" from the front view to the vanishing point.

3. Estimate the depth that appears pleasing to the eye, and sketch in the back portion of the object. Note that curves and arcs at the back will be slightly smaller than their frontal counterparts.

4. Brighten all object lines, and dim the construction lines.

Figures 14–52 and 14–53 illustrate the variations which can be obtained by changing the position of the horizon with respect to the object.

Two point perspective (two vanishing points) sketches give the most realistic results of all pictorial methods. They are, however, somewhat more difficult to make. An example of two-point perspective is shown in the sketch of the block below, Figure 14–54.

Steps in the construction are:

1. Sketch a true-length line, *CD,* to represent the front corner of the block. At eye level locate a *horizon* line and locate left (*VPL*) and right (*VPR*) vanishing points on it. The distance *CM* regulates the eye level of the observer above the block. It is usually recommended that *M–VPL* be one fourth to one half of *M–VPR* for a realistic appearance.

2. Estimate the depth and width relationships and sketch in an enclosing box.

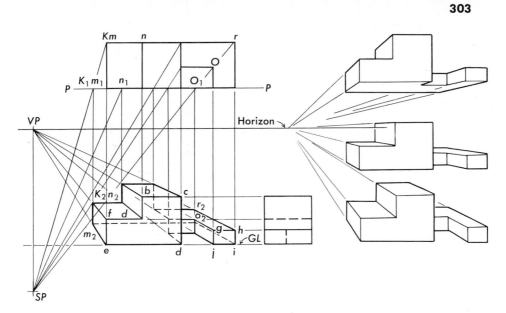

**Figure 14–52.** Construction of a one-point perspective.

**Figure 14–53.** Position of an object relative to the horizon.

3. Block in the remaining details. Note that all parallel lines converge toward the same vanishing point.

4. Brighten the object lines with the darker lines being used for the object outline. Inside lines should be less intense. When the sketch is complete, the construction lines may be erased.

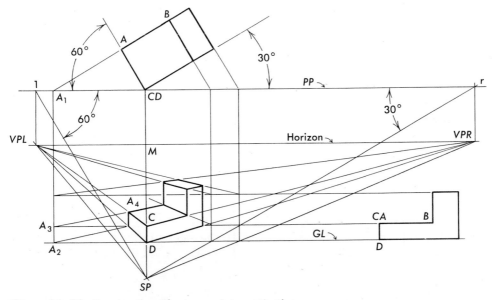

**Figure 14–54.** Construction of a two-point perspective.

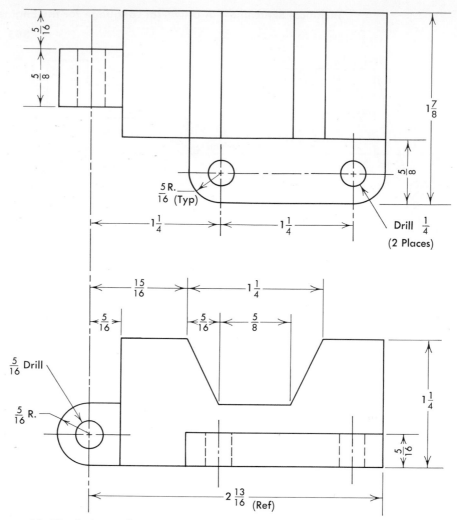

**Figure 14—55.** Orthographic views of a tool support.

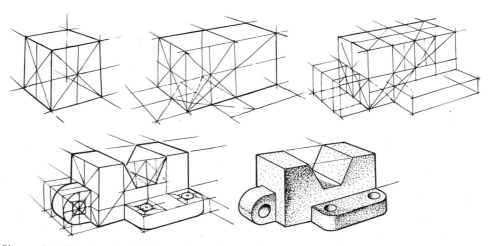

**Figure 14—56.** Steps in sketching the tool support shown in Figure 14—55.

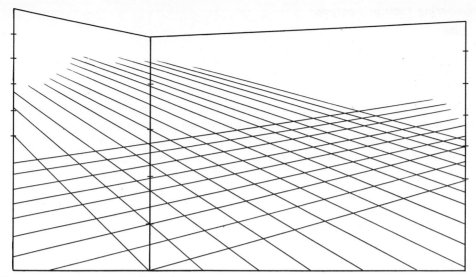

**Figure 14–57.** Mechanically drawn perspective grid.

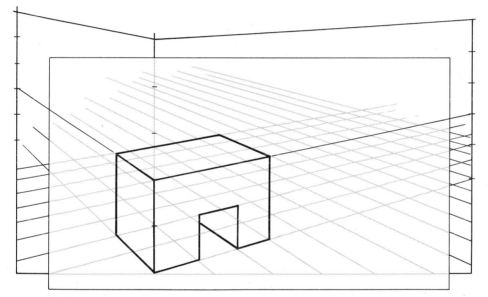

**Figure 14–58.** Use of the perspective grid.

Another example of two-point perspective is given in Figures 14–55 and 14–56.

An excellent aid to use in perspective sketching is the *perspective grid,* Figure 14–57. The grid is arranged for the most commonly selected positions, and it may be used to form a background under ordinary white sketching paper, Figure 14–58.

### Shading

The form of an object is recognized by the eye by the way light falls upon it. For this reason additional clarity and realism can be achieved in the sketching of three-dimensional solids by the addition of shading. Excessive shading is time consuming and the engineer should add only enough to clarify his sketch. A few basic principles of shading will be given here, although students should recognize that proficiency will come only by repeated practice. It is particularly important that the student practice the sketching and shading of simple geometric shapes such as those shown in Figure 14–59.

Light rays travel in straight lines. When an opaque body intercepts incident light rays, a shadow is formed. The shadow will be sharply defined if the source of light is a point source, Figure 14–60. It will consist of two shadow areas, however, if the light comes from a larger source, Figure 14–61. One shadow area will be very dark since it receives none of the light. The other shadow area will be less intense since it receives some of the light. When the source of the light is undetermined it may be assumed to come from a single source at infinity, producing parallel rays generally falling over the left shoulder of the observer at an angle of approximately 45° to the

**Figure 14–59.** Shading applied to the basic geometric shapes.

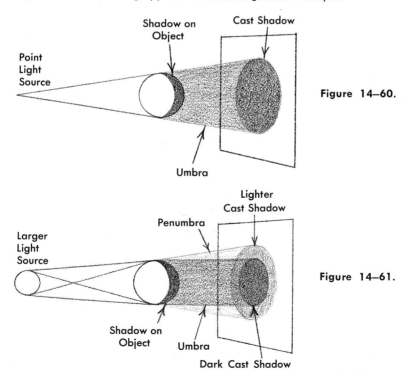

**Figure 14–60.**

**Figure 14–61.**

ground.[1] In general this will mean that the upper, front, and left-hand surfaces of an object will be lighted.

The use of gradation of tone in surface shading will give additional emphasis where it is desired to show depth or curvature. To achieve this impression by shading, darken the surface that is nearest the eye and away from the light. Lighten the surface shading as the surface recedes, but leave a small light area along the length of the back edge to show the presence of reflected light. On the side that is exposed to the light, make the lightest part of the surface nearest to the eye and gradually shade the surface as it recedes into the distance. However, no shadow on the light side should be as intense as the lightest of the shadows on the darkened side.

The surface shading of a cylinder should be most intense at the point where the light rays are tangent to the surface. It should be least intense at the point where the rays strike it directly and are reflected directly to the observer, Figure 14–62.

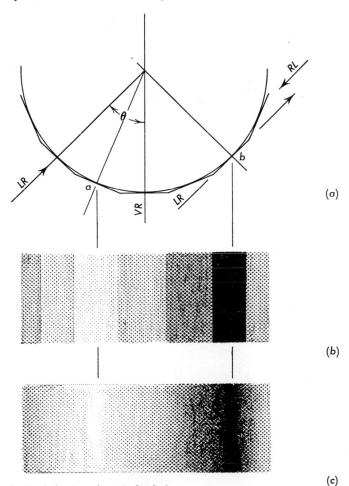

(a)

(b)

(c)

**Figure 14–62.** Analysis of shade values (cylinder).

[1] Hyman H. Katz, *Technical Sketching and Visualization for Engineers,* Macmillan, New York, 1949, p. 121.

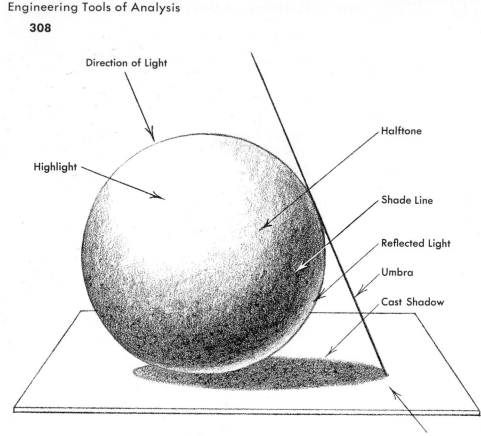

Direction of Light

Highlight

Halftone

Shade Line

Reflected Light

Umbra

Cast Shadow

Base (For Reflection)

**Figure 14–63.** Analysis of shade values (sphere).

The surface shading of a sphere should be most intense where the light rays are tangent to the sphere (along the shade line, Figure 14–63) and lightest at the highlight point.

Figure 14–64 shows how line shading can be used effectively. This simple and effective technique is recommended where speed is a factor or where the sketch is drawn from the imagination.

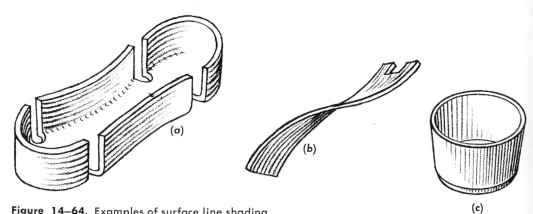

(a)

(b)

(c)

**Figure 14–64.** Examples of surface line shading.

**Illustration 14—1.** Two engineers are checking the quality and accuracy of an experimental drawing created by a man-computer design team. The drawing on the screen is a representation of a mathematical model which is stored in the memory of the electronic digital computer. The computer also can produce tapes that control automatic drafting machines. (Courtesy General Motors Research Laboratories.)

The young engineer should not be discouraged if he lacks natural artistic ability in freehand drawing and sketching. The vast majority of people do not have this talent. However, one's ability to make a clear and accurate technical sketch depends largely upon the mastery of the fundamentals discussed in this chapter, together with repeated practice. The exercises that follow are typical of the types of sketching that are most useful in engineering work.

(e)

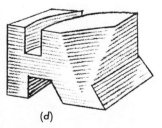

(d)

Sketching Exercises

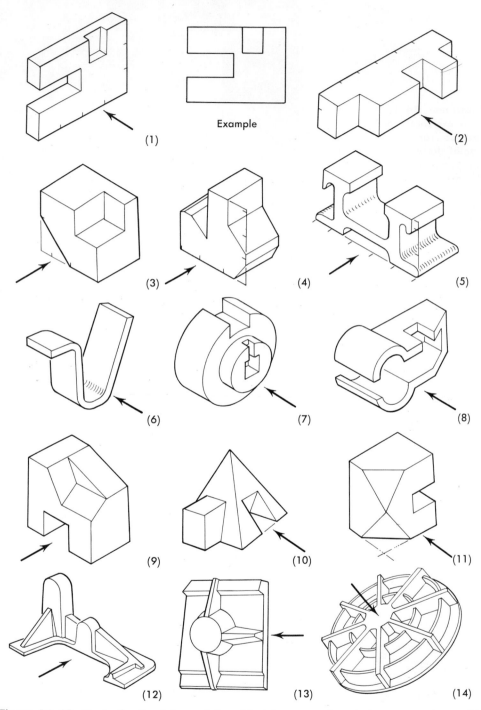

Example

(1)

(2)

(3)

(4)

(5)

(6)

(7)

(8)

(9)

(10)

(11)

(12)

(13)

(14)

**Figure 14–65.** Study the front face of the object (see arrow) and draw an orthographic view of that face.

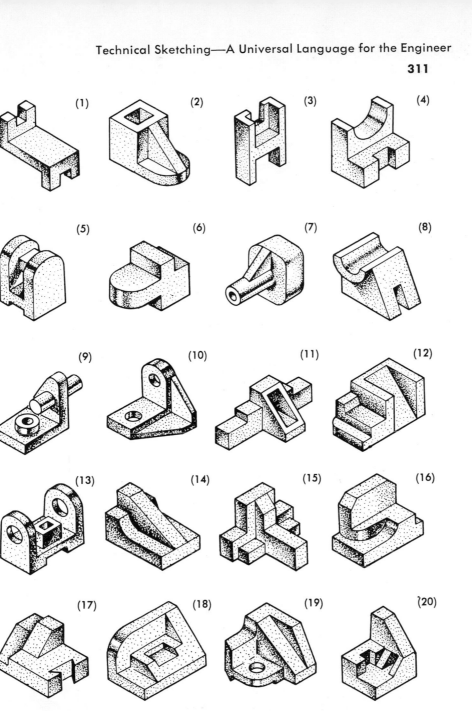

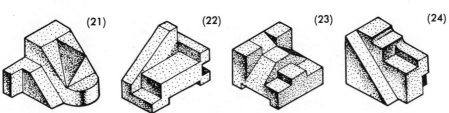

**Figure 14–66.** Sketch the necessary principal orthographic views to describe the object.

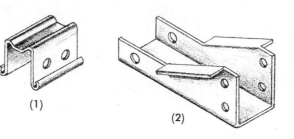

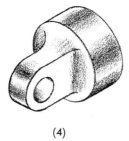

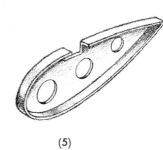

(1)

(2)

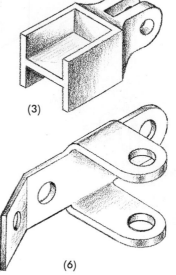

(3)

(4)

(5)

(6)

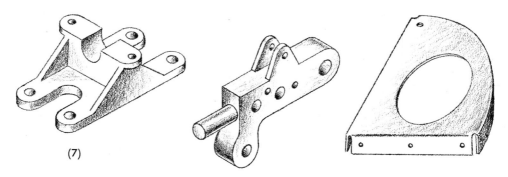

(7)

(8)

(9)

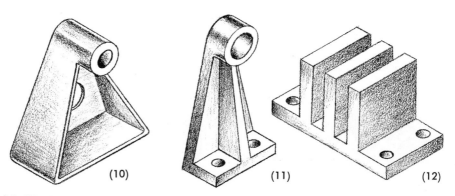

(10)

(11)

(12)

**Figure 14–67.** Sketch the orthographic views necessary to describe the objects.

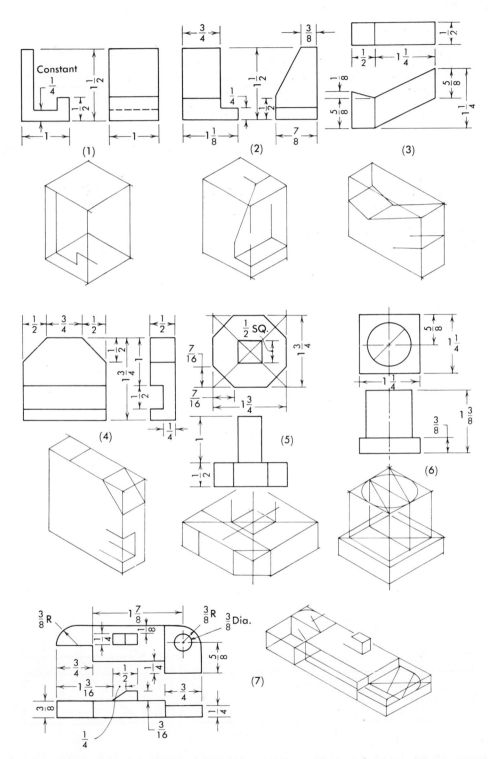

**Figure 14–68.** Make an isometric sketch of each object.

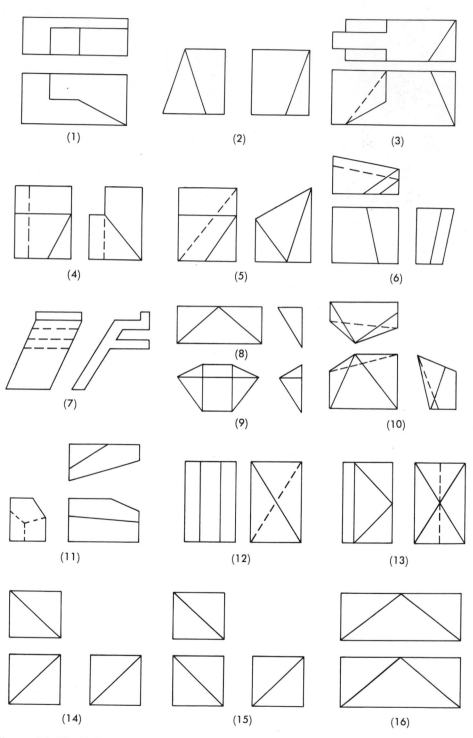

**Figure 14–69.** Make an isometric or oblique sketch of each object.

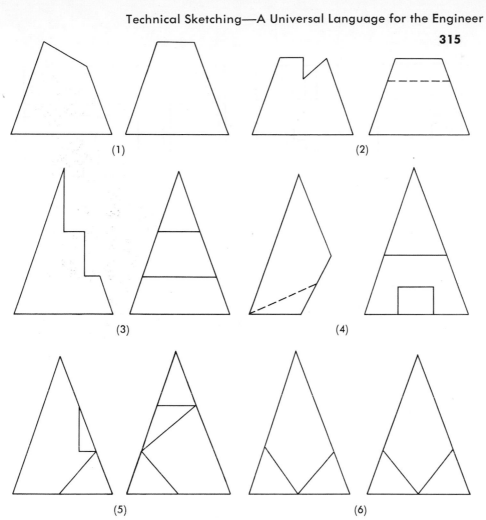

(1)          (2)

(3)          (4)

(5)          (6)

**Figure 14–70.** Make an isometric or oblique sketch of each object.

**Figure 14–71.**

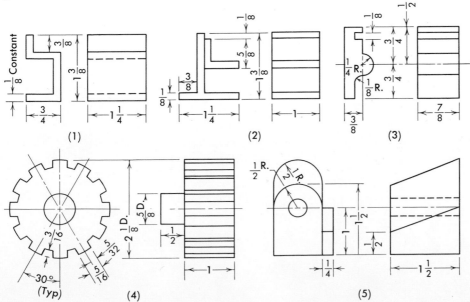

(1)          (2)          (3)

(4)          (5)

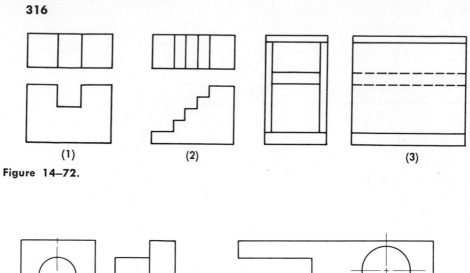

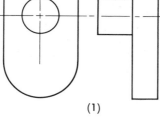

**Figure 14—72.**

(1)        (2)        (3)

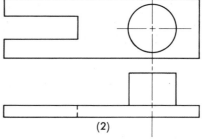

(1)        (2)

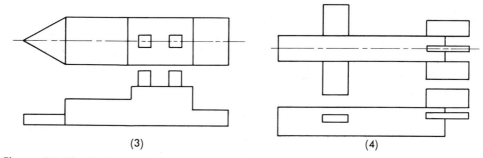

(3)        (4)

**Figure 14—73.** Make a one- or two-point perspective sketch of each object.

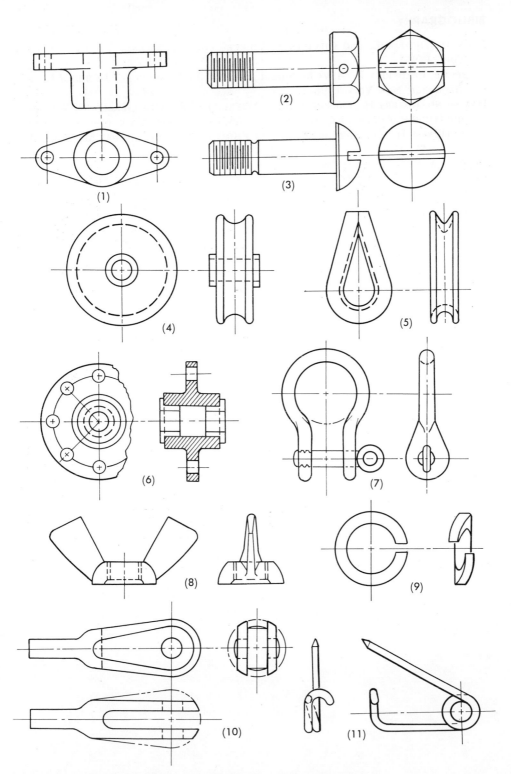

**Figure 14–74.** Make pictorial sketches from the orthographic views.

## BIBLIOGRAPHY

FRENCH, THOMAS E. and CHARLES J. VIERCK, *Graphic Science,* McGraw-Hill, New York, (1963).

GIESECKE, FREDERICK E., ALVA MITCHELL, and HENRY C. SPENCER, *Technical Drawing,* Macmillan, New York, (1967).

HAMMOND, ROBERT H., LARSON P. BUCK, WILLIAM B. ROGERS, GERALD W. WALSH, JR., and HUGH P. ACKERT, *Engineering Graphics,* Ronald, New York, (1964).

KATZ, HYMAN H., *Technical Sketching and Visualization for Engineers,* Macmillan, New York, (1949).

LEVENS, A. S., *Graphics,* Wiley, New York, (1962).

LUZADDER, WARREN J., *Basic Graphics,* Prentice-Hall, Englewood Cliffs, N.J., (1962).

STREET, WILLIAM E. and CARL LARS SVENSEN, *Engineering Graphics,* Van Nostrand, New York, (1962).

# Chapter 15

# The Engineering Method
# of Problem Solving

The engineer is known for his problem solving ability. It is probably this ability more than any other that has enabled many engineers to rise to positions of leadership and top management within their companies. Problem solving may be considered in some degree to be both *art* and *science*. The *art* of problem solving is developed over a period of continuous practice, whereas the *science* of problem solving comes about through a study of the engineering method of problem solving. Both engineers and scientists must be "problem solvers." However, in many instances the end product of the engineer's analysis, which is a working system economically devised, is considerably different from that of the scientist's, which may be a solution without regard to economics or usefulness. Before analyzing the "engineering method," let us consider the two types of thought processes used by the engineer in his problem solving.

## TYPES OF THOUGHT PROCESSES
### Deductive Reasoning

The laws of reasoning by deduction, sometimes called *syllogism,* were defined by Aristotle (384–322 B.C.), a Greek philosopher. This form of reasoning makes use of (1) a statement of a general law (called a *major premise*), (2) a statement assigning a particular zone of interest to the general law (called a *minor premise*), and (3) a statement of *conclusion* which applies the general law to the specific zone of interest.

> *Example: Major Premise.*  The volume of all spheres can be determined by the relationship $V = \pi D^3/6$, where $D$ is the diameter of the sphere.
> *Minor Premise.*  A ball is a sphere.
> *Conclusion.*  The volume of a ball can be found by applying the relationship $V = \pi D^3/6$, where $D$ is the diameter of the ball.

An obvious limitation of this form of reasoning is that the statements of the *major* and *minor premises* may not always be free from error. If an untruth is assumed as a *major* or *minor premise,* for example, the *conclusion* will most likely also be in error. Only by chance could the *conclusion* be a true statement. Thus this form of reasoning is most useful when the *major* and *minor premises* have been proved by experimentation for all possible situations. It also follows that deductive reasoning generally is not useful for the discovering of basic laws, but it may be useful in finding new applications of proven laws.

Undoubtedly complete adherence to the doctrine of deductive reasoning during the Middle Ages was a primary reason for the barrenness of achievement in physical sciences and engineering during this particular period of history. However, mathematics was not so limited because of its basic nature. Mathematics is a process of reasoning based upon fundamental concepts or premises, the parts of which are connected by the process of syllogism, or deductive reasoning.

In using deductive reasoning one must be very careful that the major premise identified is in fact true without exception. The person who accepts someone else's general statement that "there are no poisonous snakes in Henderson County" as being literally true, and then is bitten by one of the few rattlesnakes remaining, is a victim of a faulty premise. A second pitfall concerns the identification of a minor premise that in actuality is not correctly included within the major premise. For example, all $20 Federal Reserve notes are legal tender in the United States. However, a particular $20 note may be refused because it is a counterfeit bill and therefore not covered by the major premise. Although completely honest in his intent, one could violate the law by using the counterfeit money.

### Inductive Reasoning

Methods of inductive reasoning, or *truth by experiment,* have been practiced to some degree since the beginning of man. However, Aristotelian logic was long the accepted authority, and it was not until the thirteenth century that a revolt against deductive logic was successfully launched. Processes of inductive reasoning were first set forth by Roger Bacon (1214–1294) and later amplified by Francis Bacon (1561–1626). This form of reasoning is based upon the premise that if two or more things agree with one another in one or more respects, they will likely agree in still other respects; that things which are true of certain individual items within a class will be true of the entire class; and phenomena which are true at certain times will be true in similar environments at all other times. This is reasoning from a part to a whole, from the particular to the general, and from the individual to the universal.

The aim of inductive reasoning is to arrive at general conclusions sufficiently invariant to be used as major premises in processes of deductive reasoning. Verification and identification of the behavior pattern is achieved by experiment. In many instances too few experiments are performed to give absolute assurance of the truth, and a confidence level of less than 100 per cent is the result. This brings about the use of statistics and probability to determine the most likely performance that can be expected in a particular situation. As with deductive reasoning, there are two pitfalls in using inductive reasoning. First, in an experiment, *"Have the observations been made under true environmental conditions?,"* and second, *"Have*

The Engineering Method of Problem Solving

**321**

*enough observations been made to establish the degree of probability that the circumstances require?"*[1]

It is only by the processes of inductive reasoning that general laws and new scientific truths can be discovered. Consequently it is only in this way that the major premises necessary for deduction can be found.

## REASONING AND PROBLEM SOLVING

Engineers and scientists must master both the inductive or experimental method and the deductive method of logic, since the two processes of reasoning are complementary. Ordinarily a person does not by choice think only by deduction or induction. Rather, he will alternate from one form of logic to the other as he moves through an analysis. It is of considerable value, however, to know which type of reasoning to use in a given situation. Perhaps of even more value is the ability to recognize false premises or improper experimental methods that may have been employed in the processes of analysis.

### Order of Action in the Problem Solving Process

Engineers who have mastered the engineering method of problem solving are considerably more successful in their work than are people who have not been trained in this technique. In the past many engineering problems were of such routine nature that a resort to deductive reasoning would suffice, and premises of deduction could be taken from handbooks. However, many of the engineering problems of today cannot be solved by mere "handbook techniques." Experimentation, research, and development have indeed become significant activities in today's world.

Regardless of the complexity of a problem or the subject area within which the problem might arise, the *method* of solution used by the engineer will probably follow a general pattern similar to that represented by Figure 15–1. Each part of this "cyclic" process will be described in more detail, but first two general characteristics of the process should be recognized:

1. Although the process conventionally moves in a clockwise direction, Figure 15–1, there is continual "feedback" within the cycle.

2. The method of solution is a repetitious process that may be continuously refined through any desired number of cycles.

The concept of *feedback* is not new. For example, *feedback* is used by the human body to evaluate the result of actions that have been taken. The eye sees something bright that appears desirable and the brain sends a command to the hand and fingers to secure it. However, if the bright object is also hot, upon touching the nerves in the fingers "feed back" information to the brain with the message that "contact with this object will be injurious," and pain is registered to emphasize this fact. The brain reacts to this new information and sends another command to the fingers to release contact with the object. Upon completion of the feedback loop the fingers release the object.

---

[1] Edward Hodnett, *The Art of Problem Solving,* Harper, New York, (1955), p. 137.

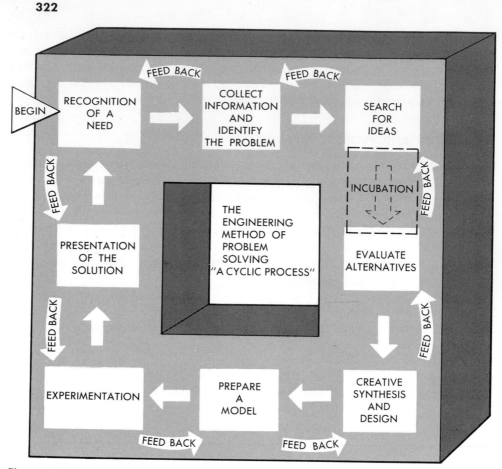

**Figure 15—1.**

As another example a thermostat, as part of a heating or cooling system, is a "feedback" device, since a changing temperature condition produces a response from the thermostat to tend to alter the change.

The speed of movement through the problem solving cycle is a function of many factors, and they change with each problem. Considerable time may be spent at any point within the cycle, and in other situations very little time may be consumed within steps. Thus, the problem solving process is a dynamic and constantly changing process that provides allowance for the individuality and capability of the user.

### Recognition of A Need and Identification of the Problem

The first two steps in the problem solving process are the most important. First, the engineer must be sensitive to the changing condition of his environment, and he must be constantly aware that his immediate surrounding environment is but a small single point of experience which is located within the vast expanse of the universe. The engineer must be able to perceive that a *need* does in fact exist within his own environment. Only then is he ready to give consideration to identification and definition of the particular problem whose solution will satisfy the specific need that he has already recognized. Nothing is more frustrating than for him to solve a problem and then to find that the solution did not satisfy the need and that he had, in fact, been working on the wrong problem all of the time. Figure 15–2 is a diagrammatic representation of these relationships. It should be recognized that the engineer's design is but *one* possible solution to the identified problem. Many other satisfactory designs also probably exist.

The story is told of how a student in a physics class, whom we shall call Henry, was given the assignment of determining the height of his school building by using a small laboratory barometer. Much to the teacher's chagrin, Henry took the barometer, thought a moment, tied a long piece of string to it, and then lowered it to the ground from the roof of the building. He then quickly measured the length of the string and gave the teacher his answer. Unfortunately the teacher was not pleased with Henry's performance and asked him to obtain the solution by "the obvious" method. Henry thought a few moments more and then took the barometer outside in the sunlight. By using a protractor and standing the barometer

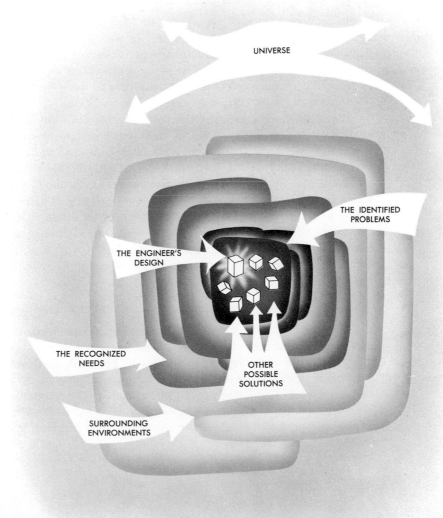

**Figure 15–2.**

vertically and noting the length of its shadow and then comparing it with the length of the building shadow, he once again calculated the height of the building and verified his first solution. The teacher seemed even more irritated with Henry's efforts and tersely instructed him to use a "scientific" method to obtain the solution and "do it quickly." Henry thought and thought. Finally, he asked for a stopwatch and once again he climbed to the roof. He dropped the barometer from the roof into the fountain on the ground below. By carefully timing the free-fall of the instrument and substituting into the equation, $S = V_1 t + \dfrac{at^2}{2}$, he obtained an answer that verified the other two solutions. This time the teacher was very angry with Henry and told him that unless he got the *precise* answer by *the* "correct" method that he would fail the laboratory work. By this time Henry was completely confused and frustrated, and not knowing what the teacher wanted, he decided that he needed some "outside help. Thereupon he took the barometer to the basement, traded it to the building superintendent for a set of architectural and engineering drawings of the building and within a few minutes he gave the teacher the *precise* answer that he had requested. It is said that the teacher collapsed of apoplexy at this point.

In each case the young student had "determined the height of the building by using the small laboratory barometer." In each instance he had obtained a seemingly acceptable solution—although none of them had been found by *the method* that the teacher had in mind. Too many people react as the teacher did and refuse to recognize or use perfectly acceptable designs because they were not the types of solutions that had been preconceived in their minds.

It is also much easier for one to recognize that "he has a problem" than to identify "just what the problem is." The most successful problem solvers are able to see their situation from different vantage points and to bring into focus a definition of "the real problem"—the problem whose solution will bring about the most satisfying result to the identified need. *Successful problem solving does not begin with a search for answers; it begins with the flexibility of your perception, with your ability to ask the right questions.*[2] By asking certain strategic questions, the engineer can collect additional information that he can then evaluate and use in the identification of the problem. In large measure the person who is able to discern the most appropriate questions to ask is the person who will be most successful as a problem solver.

### Search for Ideas, Incubation, and Evaluation of Alternatives

The search for ideas should be deliberate and planned. It is a very important part of the problem solving process. If such a search is not consciously carried out, many desirable and imaginative ideas will be overlooked. Such a search should not be left to chance, since several techniques of idea stimulation are easy to use (see Chapter 17) and are known to be effective. The accumulation of ideas should begin as soon as the problem has been identified *but not before*. All too frequently, when confronted with a difficulty, many people will hurriedly grasp for ideas without

---

[2] *Problem Solving,* Arthur D. Little, Inc., Cambridge, Mass., p. 1.

first having recognized the need or identified the problem. *Such a tendency must be resisted.*

It is also of utmost importance that the search for ideas be a search without evaluation of the worth of the individual ideas. Evaluation is certainly needed later, but such judgment should be brought into play after the passage of a period of time. During this lapse, which has been called the "period of incubation," the subconscious is allowed freedom to wander. The use of the subconscious is also called intuition. Many testify to the fact that after such a period of freedom, insight and inspiration are more likely to emerge. The imagination seems to work best when the mind is unwearied and unrestrained. Of course, insight may occur at any time, and it does not necessarily always follow a period of incubation. However, it is known that insight and illumination do occur most often when one has immersed himself in a problem to the extent that he has become fatigued (and in some cases frustrated) and then has laid the problem to one side for a time.

It is difficult to search for ideas and consciously to defer judgment of those ideas until a later time. However, the value of the "deferment of judgment" principle has been proven many times. By deferring judgment a greater number of imaginative ideas can be collected, and the probability of obtaining an idea of great value is increased.

The practicability and theoretical soundness of each idea generated must now be determined. Previous to this point in the problem solving process the engineer was only concerned with the "quantity and originality" of ideas, but now he must be primarily concerned with the "quality or feasibility" of the ideas. Judgment of their worth will not depend upon the immediate usefulness of the ideas but rather upon where the ideas may lead. Few ideas are practical within themselves. However, a single idea may form the nucleus of a new process or design that the engineer can bring into being by expansion, minification, extension, modification, combination, or by otherwise altering in some way the original thought. Because of the nature of the educational process that engineering students experience, they become considerably more skilled in the evaluation of ideas and alternatives than they do in the birth of creative ideas. Although both abilities are very important to the engineer, neither should obscure the other.

### Creative Synthesis and Design

The heart of the engineering method of problem solving lies in the creative synthesis of ideas and alternatives into an effective design. During this phase of the process the ideas and alternatives that have seemed most profitable to investigate are merged to form a useful solution to the identified problem. The data collected earlier can now be used in this design phase to bring about a specific solution for the specific purpose that has been set forth.

Although novel ideas frequently make their appearance when the conscious mind is not actively seeking them, we should recognize that most of the engineer's inspirational ideas are the result of new combinations and rearrangements of old thoughts which have already been stored within the subconscious. If this were not so, poems in Chinese might be written spontaneously by poets who are unfamiliar with the Chinese language; new mathematical theorems might be revealed in the dreams of Mexican bullfighters; and tomorrow's Chicago newspaper headlines might appear as visions today in the minds of uneducated fishermen in Greece. We recognize that none of these events are likely to happen. Neither is the engineer, regardless of how creative he may be, likely to produce new and useful ideas that lie beyond the realm of his experience. This fact does not, of course, rule out the use of inductive and deductive reasoning by the engineer in extending and applying his knowledge to new situations.

Understanding is necessary for design. It is said that "A man has a certain degree of understanding of an automobile when he can drive one, a higher degree of understanding when he can repair one, and a still higher degree of understanding when he can design one."[3]

The engineer must be skilled in deliberately and creatively refining, combining, and synthesizing his ideas into useful designs. In large measure his success will be proportional to his understanding of man and nature and his skill in obtaining a final design that is both simple and functional.

## SIMPLIFYING ASSUMPTIONS AND PREPARATION OF A MODEL

Generally the engineer will not attempt to find the *perfect* solution to an identified problem, since finding the *perfect* solution would in most instances involve the expenditure of an inordinate sum of money over an extended period of time. Engineering is a profession that deals in realism. As such, it gives recognition to the value of time, money, materials, and human effort. Therefore, the engineer will strive to provide his employer or client with the best possible solution to a given problem within the capability and resources that are available. Some problems might have a great number of solutions. However, the engineer cannot spend several years in investigating, for example, the types of materials and loading conditions for a highway bridge . . . . not to speak of the unlimited number of variations that would exist if a number of sites were considered. Therefore, the engineer will accept certain simplifying assumptions or approximations that limit the scope of the design.

Unlike some other professionals, such as doctors or lawyers, the engineer does not usually work directly with the problem that he has identified. Instead, he will construct an *idealized model* of the real situation, and then he will work with this model to achieve what he believes to be an acceptable solution. Finally he will experiment with his model and test its effectiveness in satisfying the need that he originally found to be present. The *idealized model* is nothing more than an image of the real situation as visualized by the engineer. It is not reality. It may take on the form of a sketch, chart, geometrical diagram, mathematical equation, computer program, scale model, simulation device, or some other type of representation that may be substituted for the real situation for purposes of predicting behavior and simplifying the analysis.

The use of models to represent circumstances and to predict future behavior is

[3] Marshall Walker, *The Nature of Scientific Thought,* Prentice-Hall, Englewood Cliffs, N.J., (1963), p. 1.

not an unusual procedure in other walks of life. For example, each year thousands of school boys who engage in sports study diagrams that are composed of circles, squares, triangles, curved and straight lines, and other similar symbols. These diagrams represent to them actions which are anticipated in some future football or basketball game. Such geometrical models are limited because they are two-dimensional and they do not allow for strengths, weaknesses, and imaginative decisions of the individual athletes. However, their use has been proved to be quite valuable in simulating the outcome of small time-segments of the game and in predicting the eventual outcome of the contest. Other types of models such as the tackling dummy, the blocking sled, the automatic pitcher, and the punching bag have also proved their usefulness in training athletes to cope with circumstances that have been predicted to occur in future athletic events.

An *idealized model* may emphasize the whole of a system and minimize its component parts, or it may be designed to represent only some particular part of the system and ignore the remainder. In selecting an *idealized model* the engineer must recognize that he is merely simplifying or limiting the complexity of the problem in order that he can apply known laws of science in his analysis. *In actuality, the idealization chosen may deviate considerably from the true condition.* Consequently the engineer's solution for the model may or may not be an acceptable solution to the real problem. The engineer must therefore view his answers with respect to the assumptions he made initially in preparing his *idealized model*. If the assumptions were in error, or if their importance was underestimated, then the engineer's analysis will probably not approximate or predict true conditions very closely. Thus, the usefulness of the model to predict future actions must be verified by the engineer. This verification is accomplished by experimentation and testing of the model. Refinement of the model and verification by experimentation are continued until an acceptable representation of the real phenomena is obtained. The design of the model must be the product of creative action by the engineer, but the determination of the behavior or performance of the model will follow a pattern of deductive analysis. In given situations some types of models are more useful to the engineer than other types. A discussion of some of the general types of models that engineers use is given below.

## TYPES OF IDEALIZED MODELS

### The Mathematical Model

A mathematical model can be established for a given situation if the problem has been previously described in words or by use of sketches or diagrams. Mathematics is a means of communication that originated as an abstraction from empirical experience concerning the physical world. Originally the mathematical symbols and operations that were used were concerned with visible objects and processes in nature. Later it was found that the same symbols and operations could also be used in combination to represent hypothetical situations not necessarily descriptive of any physical object. In this way the behavior and characteristics of complex phenomena could be studied.

As an example, Sir Isaac Newton (1642–1727) expressed several basic laws that he believed to govern the motion of particles. His second law was stated as follows:

> *When an external unbalanced force acts on a particle of mass, the motion of the particle will be changed. The particle will be accelerated. Its rate of change in motion will be in the direction of the unbalanced force and will be proportional to it.*

This statement would be very cumbersome and even difficult to use in the printed form shown above. However, if mathematical symbols are used to represent some of the parts of the hypothesis, it becomes much easier to work with.

Stated mathematically:
(for motion in one direction)

$$\frac{F_1}{a_1} = \frac{F_2}{a_2} = \frac{F_3}{a_3} = \frac{F_n}{a_n} = \text{a constant}$$

Where: $F_1$, $F_2$, $F_3$, etc., are the external unbalanced forces acting on a particle; and $a_1$, $a_2$, $a_3$, etc., are the consequential accelerations of the particle.

The relationship is most commonly expressed as $F = Ma$, where $M$ represents the invariant quantity, *mass*.

Another example can be taken from electrical engineering. There is a well known relation of electrical quantities in a circuit which says that *the ratio of the voltage difference across a conductor to the current passing through it is a constant.* This may be expressed as:

$$\frac{\text{Voltage}}{\text{Current}} = \text{a constant called } resistance$$

or

$$\frac{V}{I} = R, \text{ and } V = IR$$

A mathematical model is the most generally applicable and most powerful form of model that the engineer can use. It is also the easiest to understand and manipulate once it has been written.

### The Diagram

A favorite type of model that is used by the engineer is the *diagram.* Typical forms of diagrams are the *block diagram,* the *energy diagram,* the *electrical diagram,* and the *free body diagram.* Some attention should be given to each of these forms.

The *block diagram,* Figure 15–1, is a generalized approach at examining the whole problem and identifying its main components. Such a diagram is particularly useful in indicating the relationships and interdependencies of component parts of the problem. This type of diagram is particularly useful in the early stages of design work and where representation by a mathematical model would be very difficult to accomplish, Illustration 15–1 is an example of a block diagram in which electrical subassemblies are drawn as blocks, and the connecting lines between blocks indicate the flow of information in the whole assembly. This type of presentation is widely used to lay out large or complicated systems—particularly those involving servo-electrical and mechanical devices. No attempt is made on the drawing to detail the inner circuits of any of the subassemblies pictured. This does not, however, provide a substitute for a mathematical model.

The *energy diagram* is particularly useful in the study of thermodynamic systems involving mass and energy flow. Before drawing such a diagram the engineer should set forth simplifying assumptions and selection of boundaries and operating conditions. This type of diagram is a modification of the block diagram. Some examples of the use of an *energy diagram* are given in Figures 15–3 and 15–4.

*Example:* A quantity of high-temperature steam flows into a turbine at high pressure, expands in the turbine while doing work on the turbine rotor, and then is exhausted at low pressure. Draw an *energy diagram* of this situation. The results may be as shown in Figure 15–3.

*Example:* Draw an *energy diagram* showing how nuclear power can be used to operate a submarine. The results may be as shown in Figure 15–4.

The *electrical diagram* is a specialized type of model used in the analysis of electrical problems. This form of *idealized model* represents the existence of particular electrical circuits by utilizing conventional symbols for brevity. These diagrams may be of the most elementary type, or they may be highly complicated and require many hours of engineering time in preparation. In any case, however, they are representations or models in symbolic language of an electrical assembly.

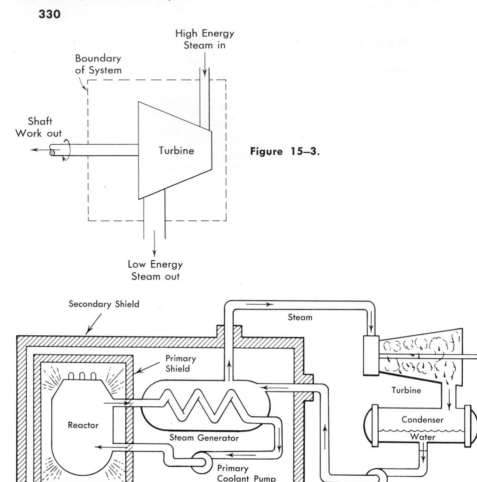

High Energy
Steam in

Boundary
of System

Shaft
Work out

Turbine

**Figure 15–3.**

Low Energy
Steam out

Secondary Shield

Steam

Primary
Shield

Turbine

Reactor

Condenser
Water

Steam Generator

Primary
Coolant Pump

Feed Pump

Courtesy: General Dynamics, Electric Boat Division

**Figure 15–4.** Diagramatic sketch showing how nuclear power can be used to operate a submarine. (Courtesy General Dynamics, Electric Boat Division.)

Figure 15–5 shows an electrical diagram of a photoelectric tube that is arranged to operate a relay. Notice that the diagram details only the essential parts in order to provide for electrical continuity and thus is an idealization that has been selected for purposes of simplification.

The *free-body diagram* is a diagrammatical representation of a physical system which has been removed from all other surrounding bodies or systems for purposes of examination. It may be drawn to represent a complex system or any smaller part of it. This form of *idealized model* is most useful in showing the effect of forces that act upon a system.

The boundaries of a *free-body diagram,* real or imaginary, should be drawn such that they enclose the system under study. All force actions external to the boundaries that act on the "free-body" should be represented by force vectors on the diagram. Force actions internal to the boundaries should be ignored, since the system is usually analyzed as a whole. Extraneous detail of the complex environment

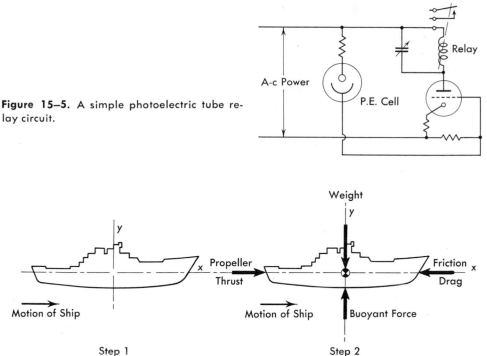

**Figure 15–5.** A simple photoelectric tube relay circuit.

**Figure 15–6.** Step 1. Draw the boundaries of the system. Step 2. Show on the same figure external forces which are acting on the boundaries.

should not appear on the *free-body diagram.* Rather, the diagram should include only the detail that is significant to the problem.

Of course a *free-body diagram* is merely an idealized model of the real situation, and it is imaginary in every sense. Such an idealized condition does not exist in nature, but it is assumed to so exist for purposes of the analysis. The usefulness of the diagram depends upon how well it represents the real situation. The following example problems are typical of some problem types that the student may encounter in the solving of engineering problems.

*Example:* Draw a free-body diagram of a ship which is moving forward in the water.

SOLUTION: It is not necessary that the free-body diagram be drawn to exact scale, since the shape of the *idealized model* is only an imaginary concept. Proceed in two steps as shown in Figure 15–6.

EXPLANATION: In the most general sense, the external forces acting on the *idealized model* are four in number: a forward thrust, which acts at the ship's propeller; a friction drag, which acts in such manner as to retard motion; a buoyant force, which keeps the ship afloat; and the ship's weight, which in simplification may be considered to be acting through the center of gravity of the ship.

NOTE: The symbol ✪ is used to denote the location of the center of gravity of an *idealized model*. Also notice that a coordinate system, as applied to the free-body diagram, is very useful for purposes of orientation. The diagram shown would be an analysis of the relationships between the weight and buoyant force and between the thrust and drag. However, it would not, for example, be useful for determining the loads on the ship's engine mounts. Another model (free body diagram) would now be required.

*Example:* Draw a free-body diagram of a four-wheel drive automobile being driven up an incline, as shown in Figure 15–7.

EXPLANATION: Always show the system under consideration in its true and realistic position in space. For example, it would have been awkward to have shown the automobile as being on a horizontal surface, since it is in actuality moving up an incline.

## GENERAL SUGGESTIONS FOR DRAWING FREE-BODY DIAGRAMS

To aid the student in learning to draw free-body diagrams, the following suggestions are given:

**1. Free Bodies.** Be certain that the body is *free* of all surrounding objects. Draw the body so it is *free*. Do not show a supporting surface but rather show only the force vector which replaces that surface. Do not rotate the body from its original position but rather rotate the axes if necessary. Show all forces and label them. Show all needed dimensions and angles.

**2. Force Components.** Forces are often best shown in their component forms. When replacing a force by its components, select the most convenient directions for the components. Never show both a force and its components by solid-line vectors; use broken-line vectors for one or the other since the force *and* its components do not occur simultaneously.

**3. Weight Vectors.** Show the weight vector as a vertical line with its tail or point at the center of gravity, and place it so that it interferes least with the remainder of the drawing. It should always be drawn vertically.

**4. Refer to the Free-Body Diagram.** Each step of the solution should have a clear cross reference to the free body to which it pertains.

**5. Direction of Vectors.** The free-body diagram should represent the facts as nearly as possible. If a pull on the free body occurs, place the tail of the vector at the actual point of application and let the point of the vector be in the true direction of the pull. Likewise, if a push occurs on the free body, the vector should show the true direction, and the point of the arrow should be placed at the point of application. Force vectors on free-body diagrams are not usually drawn to scale but may be drawn proportionate to their respective magnitudes.

**6. Free-Body Diagram of Whole Structure.** This should habitually be the first free-body examined in the solution of any problem. Many problems cannot be solved without this first consideration. After the free-body of the whole structure or com-

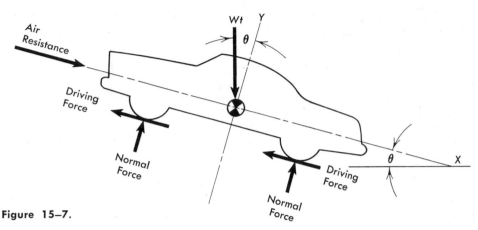

**Figure 15–7.**

plex has been considered, select such members or subassemblies for further free-body diagrams as may lead to a direct solution.

**7. Two Force Members.** When a two-force member is in equilibrium, the forces are equal, opposite, and collinear. If the member is in compression, the vectors should point toward each other; if a member is in tension, they should point away from each other.

**8. Three-Force Members.** When a member is in equilibrium and has only three forces acting on it, the three forces are always concurrent, if they are not parallel. In analyzing a problem involving a three-force member, one should recall that any set of concurrent forces may be replaced by a resultant force. Hence, if a member in equilibrium has forces acting at threepoints, it is a three-force member regardless of the fact that the force applied at one or more points may be replaced by two or more components.

**9. Concurrent Force System.** For a concurrent force system the size, shape, and dimensions of the body are neglected, and the body is considered to be a particle.

*Example:* Draw a free body of point *A*, as shown in Figure 15–8.

**Figure 15–8.**

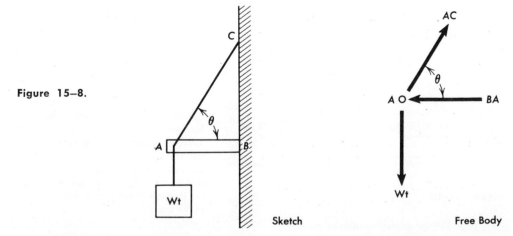

Sketch                                      Free Body

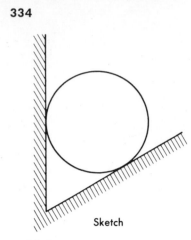

Sketch

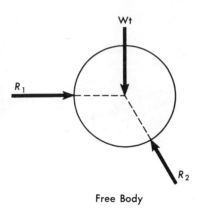

Free Body

**Figure 15–9.**

| Situation | Free-Body | Explanation |
|---|---|---|

A box resting on a plane

$Wt = 10\,lb$

10 lb

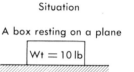

$N$

The normal force always acts at an angle of 90° with the surfaces in contact. This force $N$ usually is considered to act through the center of gravity of the body.

A weight hanging from a ring

$Wt$

$T_2$  $T_1$
30°  30°

$Wt$

Since the ring is of negligible size, it may be considered to be a point. All of the forces would act through this point. The downward force $W$ is balanced by the tensions $T_1$ and $T_2$. The numerical sum of these tensions will be greater than the weight. This is true since $T_1$ is pulling against $T_2$.

A box on a frictionless surface

$Wt = 10$ lb

$P$
30°

10 lb   $P$
30°
$N$

Some surfaces are considered frictionless although in reality, no surface is frictionless. The force $P$ is an unbalanced force and it will produce an acceleration. The symbol ⊕ denotes the location of the center of gravity of the body.

A small box on a rough surface

$Wt = 10$ lb

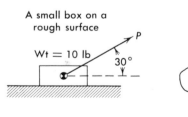

$P$
30°

10 lb   $P$
30°
$F$
$N$

The force of friction will always oppose motion or will oppose the tendency to move. For bodies of small size, the *moment effect*[4] of the friction force may be disregarded and the friction and normal forces may be considered to act through the center of gravity of the body.

**Figure  15–10.**

[4] See page 359 for an explanation of moments.

**10. Pin Joints.** A free-body diagram of the pin itself should be drawn when it lends to simplicity of the solution. Pin connections usually may be considered to be frictionless.

**11. Reaction between Surfaces.** Some problems involve *smooth surfaces* (an imaginary concept) that are considered to offer no frictional resistance to motion. For bodies in equilibrium at rest, this concept is both a useful and practical approximation. Pins and the members they join are in contact on a surface, and the reaction between the surfaces is perpendicular to the common tangent plane at the point of contact. Thus, if a cylinder rests on a plane, the reaction at the point of contact will pass through the center of the cylinder, as shown in Figure 15–9.

Additional examples are given in Figures 15–10 and 15–11 to illustrate situations that the engineer may encounter, together with the resulting free-body diagrams which may be drawn as models to represent the situations.

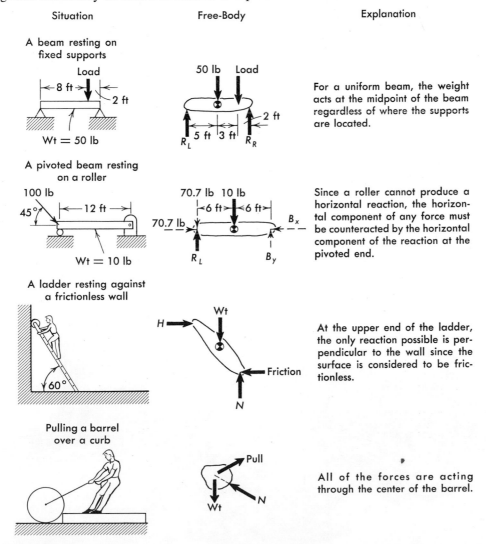

| Situation | Free-Body | Explanation |
|---|---|---|
| A beam resting on fixed supports | | For a uniform beam, the weight acts at the midpoint of the beam regardless of where the supports are located. |
| A pivoted beam resting on a roller | | Since a roller cannot produce a horizontal reaction, the horizontal component of any force must be counteracted by the horizontal component of the reaction at the pivoted end. |
| A ladder resting against a frictionless wall | | At the upper end of the ladder, the only reaction possible is perpendicular to the wall since the surface is considered to be frictionless. |
| Pulling a barrel over a curb | | All of the forces are acting through the center of the barrel. |

**Figure 15–11.**

## The Scale Model

Scale models are used in various problem solving situations, and they are particularly useful where the system under consideration is very large and complex or very small and difficult to observe. They are also used by the engineer in many instances where a mathematical model is either impossible or impractical.

A *scale model* is an idealized replica, usually three-dimensional, of the system, subsystem, or component being studied. The idealization may be constructed to any desired scale and the final *scale model* may be larger in size, the same size, or much smaller in size than the actual design.

Such projects as dam or reservoir construction, highway and freeway interchange design, factory layout, and aerodynamic investigations are particularly adaptable to study by using this type of idealized model. In some cases the scale model is not instrumented, Illustration 15–2; but component parts of the model can be moved about to represent changing conditions within the system. Of considerably more usefulness, however, are those scale models which are instrumented and subjected to environmental and load conditions that closely resemble reality, Illustration 15–3. In such cases the models are tested and experimental data are recorded by the engineer. From an analysis of these data, predictions of the behavior of the real system can be made.

**Illustration 15–2.** Exact scale models are valuable aids to the engineer in acquainting others with design and operating procedures such as this model of an ammonia-nitrogen plant located in Taiwan. (Courtesy Allied Chemical Corporation.)

**Illustration 15–3.** Pictured above is a space craft which is located in a 30-foot diameter space simulation chamber to permit engineers to investigate problems of actual temperature and vacuum conditions which will be encountered in space. The model space craft is altered after each actual space mission to represent more closely the behavior of the vehicle in space. (Courtesy McDonnell Aircraft Corporation.)

**Illustration 15–4.** Centrifuge used to simulate space conditions for training astronauts. (Courtesy Timken Roller Bearing Company.)

By using a scale model the final design can be checked for accuracy prior to actual construction of the design. Although scale models often cost many thousands of dollars, they are of relatively minor expense, considering the total cost of a particular project. Also, a scale model frequently may be constructed and tested in a fraction of the time necessary to build the original system.

### The Simulation Model

A *simulation model* may be used to represent the behavior of environmental conditions, Illustration 15–4. When experimentation is performed on a *scale model,* it is referred to as *simulation.* Such experimentation makes it possible for the engineer to evaluate alternatives and to make adjustments in his design with minimum expense, loss of time, and danger to life. The use of *simulation* devices, as much as any other single factor, is credited with minimizing the fatality rate in the "Manned Space Program," presently being conducted by the United States.

*Computer simulation* has also become very important to the engineer. Analog computers are used in those cases where electrical impulses can be made to behave in a manner analogous to that of the real object or process being simulated. Digital computers are used where the design or process can be broken down into a multitude of small limited-choice decisions. In addition to obtaining a realistic appraisal of the actual design performance, the computer can simulate years of real time in a very few hours because of the exceptionally fast speed with which a digital computer can accomplish a given calculation. Simulation of the passage of time by any other means is very difficult for the engineer to achieve.

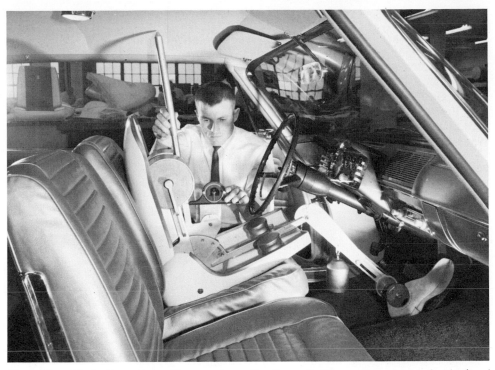

**Illustration 15—5.** Experimentation and verification of the performance of idealized models are important factors to the engineer. Here an engineer is working with a simulation model of the human body which he is using to verify automotive design calculation that he has made. (Courtesy Chrysler Corporation.)

## EXPERIMENTATION, VERIFICATION, AND PRESENTATION OF THE SOLUTION

Much engineering work is concerned with experimentation for the purpose of verifying design calculations. As suggested above a majority of such testing involves a determination of the degree of success or failure of an idealized model to achieve desired standards. Frequently feed-back of the test results will cause the engineer to re-examine his model and to make alterations or adjustments in its design. By repeating this process over and over, an idealized model which closely approximates the real-life situation can be found, Illustration 15–5.

Since the real-life situation cannot be known in advance in many instances, the engineer's model serves also to predict the future. For example, since man had never before experienced the effects of space travel, the engineer could only anticipate such consequences by experimentation involving various types of models that he designed for this purpose. The success of man's first flight into space and his safe return is a tribute to the engineers' abilities in designing and testing models and in simulating man's reactions within a foreign environment.

It has been said that "the proof of the pudding is in the eating." Certainly this is good advice for the engineer to follow. No idealized model or design, regardless of its sophistication or simplicity, is of value to the engineer unless it serves as a satisfactory answer to the need that was recognized originally. This is the final goal of the engineering method of problem solving, and this step serves to complete the cyclic problem solving process.

**BIBLIOGRAPHY**

FISH, JOHN CHARLES LOUNSBURY, *The Engineering Method,* Stanford U. P., Stanford, Calif., (1950).

HODNETT, EDWARD, *The Art of Problem Solving,* Harper, New York, (1955).

KOGAN, ZUCE, *Essentials of Problem Solving,* Arco, New York, (1956).

POLYA, G., *How to Solve It,* Anchor Books, Doubleday, Garden City, (1957).

VER PLANCK, D. W. and B. R. TEARE, JR., *Engineering Analysis,* Wiley, New York, (1954).

WALKER, MARSHALL, *The Nature of Scientific Thought,* Prentice-Hall, Englewood Cliffs, N.J., (1963).

# PART FIVE

## PROBLEM SOLVING

The action of continuous and intermittent forces on a body must be taken into account by the engineer during the design process. In this picture, the actions of "thrustors" as they exert forces on an orbiting vehicle in space to control its attitude and motion are shown as arrows. This vehicle behaves essentially as a true "free-body." (Courtesy McDonnell Aircraft Corporation.)

# Chapter 16

# Applications of the Engineering Method of Problem Solving

In the preceding chapter, methods of reasoning necessary in engineering problem solving were discussed. These methods have been explained in order to provide a positive, logical, and vigorous approach to problem analysis. These techniques should eliminate much of the indecision as to method and the distraction of extraneous detail that complicates any physical situation. It is expected that the student will apply the techniques learned in the preceding chapter to the analysis of problems in this and following chapters.

**General Problems**

16–1. A river has a flow of 3 million gal per 24-hr day. Compute the flow in cubic feet per minute.

16–2. Compute the weight in $lb_f$ of 1982 ft of copper wire ¼ in. in diameter.

16–3. A round iron rod is 0.125 in. in diameter. How long will a piece have to be to weigh 1 $lb_f$?

16–4. A cylindrical tank 2.7 ft high has a volume of 380 ft³. What is its diameter?

16–5. Find the weight of water contained in a cylindrical tank 6 ft in diameter when the water is 8.5 ft deep.

16–6. A piece of flat steel ⅜ in. thick is cut in the shape of a right triangle. The hypotenuse is 4.6 ft long and a side is 2.09 ft long. How much will the piece weigh?

16–7. Find the weight of a lead ball ¾ in. in diameter.

16–8. Find the area of a circular sector with a central angle of 0.805 radian which has been cut from a circle having a diameter of 23.4 in.

16–9. Find the weight of a common brick that is 2.6 in. by 4 in. by 8.75 in.

16–10. An open-top cylindrical tank is 12 ft inside diameter, 16 ft high, and is made of steel plate 3⁄16 in. thick. Water is 3.8 ft deep in the tank. What is the volume of water in the tank in ft³?

**General Problems (continued)**

**16–11.** A white oak beam is 18 ft long and 8 in. by 10 in. in cross section. What is its weight?

**16–12.** What will be the diameter of a tank 22.5 ft high that holds 1620 ft³ of water?

**16–13.** A cylindrical tank is 20.6 ft in diameter, 8 ft high, and contains 15,300 gal of water. What weight of water is contained in the tank?

**16–14.** A cylindrical tank is 20.8 ft in diameter, 8 ft high, and is made of steel ³⁄₁₆ in. thick. What is the area of the side and bottom of the tank? What is the weight of the tank?

**16–15.** A storage vat is 100 yd long, 12 ft deep, and its width is 10 ft at the bottom and 15 ft at the top (trapezoidal cross section). The ends of the vat are vertical. Oil flows into the vat at a rate of 500 gpm. Find the time in hours that is required to fill the vat to a depth of 10 ft.

**16–16.** How many gallons of water will be contained in a horizontal pipe 10 in. in diameter and 15 ft long, if the water is 6 in. deep in the pipe?

**16–17.** Find the cost of 23 pieces of 2-in. by 10-in. yellow pine boards 12 ft long at $100 per 1000 fbm.

**16–18.** A white pine board is 14 ft long and 2 in. by 8 in. in cross section. How much will the board weigh? At $120 per 1000 fbm, what is its value?

**16–19.** A cast iron cone used in a machine shop is 10 in. in diameter at the bottom and 34 in. high. What is the weight of the cone?

**16–20.** How many cubic yards of soil will it take to fill a lot 63 ft wide by 100 ft deep if it is to be raised 3 ft in the rear end and gradually sloped to the front where it is to be 1½ ft deep?

**16–21.** A sphere whose radius is 1.42 in. is cut out of a solid cylinder 8.8 in. high and 7.8 in. in diameter. Find the volume cut away, in cubic inches. If the ball is steel, what does it weigh?

**16–22.** A container is 12 in. high, 10 in. in diameter at the top, and 6 in. in diameter at the bottom. What is the volume of this container in cubic inches? What is the weight of mercury that would fill this pail?

**16–23.** A canal on level land is 19 mi long, 22 ft deep, and has a trapezoidal cross section. The distance across the canal at the top is 36 ft and across the bottom is 15 ft. Find: (a) the number of cubic yards of dirt that were removed to complete the canal; (b) the time in hours required to pump the canal full of water if the pump discharges 600 gpm and gates at either end are closed.

**16–24.** A cylindrical tank 7.50 ft in diameter and 15.9 ft long is lying with its axis horizontal. Compute the weight of kerosene when it is one-third full.

**16–25.** A container that is in the form of a right rectangular pyramid has the following dimensions: base 26 in. by 39 in., height 16 ft. This container has one-half of its volume filled with ice water. Neglect the weight of the container. Find the weight of the contents.

**16–26.** A hemispherical container 3 ft in diameter has half of its volume filled with lubricating oil. Neglecting the weight of the container, how much would the contents weigh if enough kerosene were added to fill the container to the brim?

**16–27.** A concrete water trough is 18 in. deep, 24 in. wide and 8 ft long inside measurements. If the sides and end are 3.5 in. thick and the bottom 4 in. thick, what will the total weight of tank and contents be if ⅔ of its volume is filled with water?

**16–28.** What must be the diameter of a conical tank 16 in. deep that holds 1.25 gal of water?

**16–29.** A certain city lot 50 ft wide by 120 ft deep has a difference in elevation of 1 ft from front to rear. It is to be filled until it is level. How many cubic yards of dirt will be required?

**16–30.** A pipe 7.8 in. inside diameter and 13 ft long is lying horizontally. Water is 5 in. deep in the pipe. How many gallons of water are in the pipe?

**16–31.** An eight-sided wrought iron bar weighs 3.83 $lb_f$ per linear foot. What will be its dimension across diagonally opposite corners?

**16–32.** A solid cylinder of steel has a diameter of 2.4 in. and is 10 in. long. The outside shape of the cylinder is machined, and the cross section is changed from a circle to a hexagon inscribed in the original circle. What is the change in the total outside area of the piece of steel? How much does it weigh after being machined?

**16–33.** A piece of cast iron has a very irregular shape and its volume is to be determined. It is submerged in water in a cylindrical tank having a diameter of 16 in. The water level is raised 3.4 in. above its original level. How many cubic feet are in the piece of cast iron? How much does it weigh?

**16–34.** A 4 in. thick concrete slab for a patio is to be formed in the shape of a right triangle. One angle of the triangle is 66°40′, and the side adjacent this angle is 24 ft 8 in. long. How many cubic yards of concrete will be needed to fill the forms? How many lineal feet of 2 × 4 lumber will be needed to make the forms?

**16–35.** A storage area in a factory is laid out in the shape of a right triangle. One angle is 57°20′, and the side opposite this angle is 84.2 ft. What are the lengths of the hypotenuse and the other side of the triangle?

**16–36.** A sheet of No. 4130 steel, 0.250 in. thick, is cut in the shape of a right triangle with the hypotenuse 7.05 in. long. One of the angles is measured to be 38°45′. What will be the area of the triangular section that has been cut? What will be the weight of the triangular section?

**16–37.** A room is 12 ft wide and 16 ft long. The ceiling is 10 ft from the floor. How long a piece of wire will be needed to reach from one corner at the floor to a diagonally opposite corner at the ceiling?

**16–38.** A wheelbarrow runway, 38 ft long, is to reach from the ground to a point 8 ft above the ground on a building under construction. What is the slope of the runway expressed in percentage? Prepare a simple sketch to be turned over to a workman to show how to support the runway.

**16–39.** A factory is to clear an area in the shape of a right triangle in one corner of a building to install a new testing machine. The area is to be outlined on the floor with a painted stripe. One of the angles in the triangle is 21°21′, and the hypotenuse is 103.3 ft long. What area will be enclosed by the stripe? What length of 3 in. wide adhesive back striping material will be needed?

### General Problems (continued)

**16–40.** Find the area in acres of a tract of land in the shape of a right triangle, one angle being 55°30′, and the shortest side being 1755 ft long. What length of fence will be needed to enclose the tract?

**16–41.** The wall of a masonry building is to have a section in the shape of a right triangle painted as the background for a sign. One of the angles is 73°50′, and the hypotenuse is 18.83 ft long. What will be the lengths of the other two sides and what will be the area to be painted? If the wall is to be brush coated with two coats of masonry paint, how much paint should be provided to do the work?

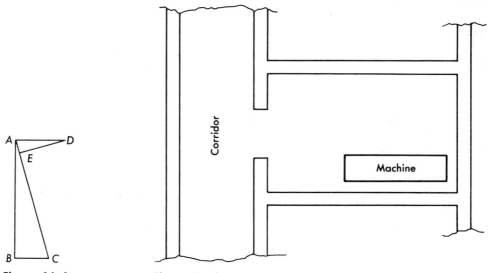

Figure 16–1.　　　　　Figure 16–2.

**16–42.** Two tracts of land adjoin as shown in the sketch in Figure 16–1. $AD = 451$ ft; $AB = 1075$ ft; $BC = 318$ ft. Angles $DAB, ABC,$ and $CED$ are right angles.

　　*a.* How many rods of fence are necessary to enclose each field separately?

　　*b.* How many acres are in each tract of land?

　　*c.* What is the distance $CD$?

**16–43.** A coal hoist track has a slope of 83 per cent. (*a*) What angle does the track make with the vertical? (*b*) What length of track will be needed to raise the coal a vertical distance of 63.4 ft?

**16–44.** An electric light pole is 28.5 ft high and has a guy wire fastened to it one fourth of the distance from the top. The guy wire is fastened on a level with the bottom of the pole at a point 18 ft away from the foot of the pole. If 30 in. on each end of the wire are used for fastening, how long should the wire be? Does 30 in. at each end seem to be enough to allow for fastening?

**16–45.** A machine requiring some half-inch galvanized iron water pipe is to be installed in a room 8½ feet wide, 22½ feet long and having a 10 ft high ceiling. A doorway 2 ft 8 in. wide is centered in the 8½ ft side of the room and opens into a corridor 5 ft 4 in. wide. What is the approximate maximum length of pipe that can be carried into the room? See Figure 16–2.

**16–46.** Points $A$ and $B$ are located on opposite corners of a building and are located so that they can be seen from point $C$. The distance $CA$ is 256 ft and $CB$ is 312 ft. The angle between lines $CA$ and $CB$ is 105°30′. How far apart are points $A$ and $B$?

**16–47.** Find the area of a sheet of titanium 0.063 in. thick having dimensions as shown in Figure 16–3. What will be the approximate weight of the sheet of titanium?

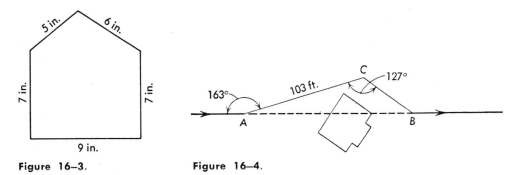

Figure 16–3.                Figure 16–4.

**16–48.** A piece of sheet aluminum in the shape of a triangle has sides of 3.05 in. and 6.11 in., and the angle between these sides is 76°18′. (*a*) What are the other angles? (*b*) What is the area of the piece of metal?

**16–49.** In surveying, the determination of the distance $AB$ is required. The given measurements are shown in Figure 16–4. What is the distance $AB$?

**16–50.** In a survey, an obstacle in the line $AB$ is encountered. To determine the distance $AB$, the measurements shown in Figure 16–5 were made. What is the computed distance $AB$?

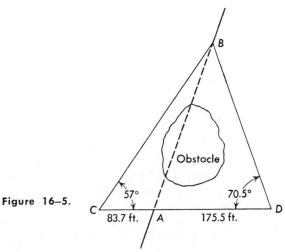

Figure 16–5.

## General Problems (continued)

**16–51.** Convert the following Fahrenheit temperatures to Celsius temperatures. (*a*) 68°, (*b*) 98.6°, (*c*) 156°, (*d*) 359°, (*e*) 711°, (*f*) 2880°, (*g*) 4.7 ($10^4$)°, (*h*) −5°, (*i*) −40°, (*j*) −255°.

**16–52.** Convert the following Celsius temperatures to Fahrenheit temperatures. (*a*) 20°, (*b*) 37°, (*c*) 155°, (*d*) 580°, (*e*) 8800°, (*f*) 1.22 ($10^5$)°, (*g*) −2°, (*h*) −40°, (*i*) −273°.

**16–53.** The temperature of liquid oxygen used as missile fuel is about −183°C. What is its temperature in degrees Fahrenheit?

**16–54.** The temperature of dry ice (solid carbon dioxide), used in shrinking metal parts to fit them together, is −78.5°C. What is the corresponding temperature in degrees Fahrenheit?

**16–55.** An air-storage tank used in windtunnel research has a volume of 138 ft³. How many cubic feet of air at atmospheric pressure will have to be pumped into it to raise the pressure to 185 psig?

**16–56.** A tight-fitting piston 3.77 in. in diameter in a closed cylinder compresses air from an initial pressure of 35 psig to 68 psig. If the final volume of the air is 14.58 in.³, what will be the distance the piston moves?

**16–57.** Natural gas in an underground pipe line 24 in. inside diameter is under a pressure of 375 psig. If this gas is allowed to expand to a pressure of 3.0 psig, what volume would the gas in a mile of high-pressure pipe occupy?

**16–58.** An open-end cylinder with the open end down is lowered into a lake. If the pressure due to water is 0.434 psi for each foot depth of water, how deep would the cylinder be lowered to reduce the volume of trapped air by one fifth its original volume?

**16–59.** The normal pressure of the atmosphere at sea level (14.7 psi) will support a column of mercury 29.92 in. high in a barometer. The atmospheric pressure changes approximately 0.1 in. of mercury for each 90 ft of elevation change at low elevations. What will be the approximate normal atmospheric pressure in psi at an elevation of 3050 ft above sea level?

**16–60.** An automobile tire is inflated to a pressure of 28 psig when the temperature is 51°F. After a period of driving, the temperature of the air in the tire has been raised to 125°F. What will be the gage pressure of the air?

**16–61.** Air that has been confined under a pressure of 5.0 psig in the cylinder of an air compressor is further compressed by a tight fitting piston that decreases the volume from 0.89 ft³ to 0.27 ft³. At the same time the temperature of the air is raised from 43°F to 138°F. What will be the final gage pressure of the confined air?

**16–62.** A balloon used for meteorological research has a volume of 137 ft³. At the time it leaves the ground, the pressure of the gas inside the balloon is 3.0 ounces per in.² gage and the temperature is 88°F. It rises to a height where the temperature is −40°F and the pressure in the balloon is 6.88 psia. If the balloon expands freely, what will be the new volume?

**16–63.** A steel drum of oxygen shows a gage pressure of 2100 psig at a temperature of 95°F. What will be the gage pressure at a temperature of −12°F?

**16–64.** An open end cylinder 10 ft long is lowered into a tank of water with the open end down so that the lower end is at a depth of 9.65 ft. The temperature of the trapped air is 43°F. At what air temperature would the trapped air have expanded until it had displaced all the water which had risen inside the cylinder? The pressure due to water is 0.433 psi per ft of depth.

## PROBLEMS IN STATIC MECHANICS

Mechanics is the physical science that describes and predicts the effects of forces acting on material bodies. The condition under study may be one of rest or one of motion. There are three specialized branches into which the general field of mechanics may be divided for more specific studies. These are:

1. Mechanics of rigid bodies
   a. Statics
   b. Dynamics
2. Mechanics of deformable bodies
3. Mechanics of fluids
   a. Compressible flow
   b. Incompressible flow

Our study here is concerned with an introduction to 1.*a.*, Static Mechanics, as a vehicle for the application of the engineering method of problem solution.

### Fundamental Concepts and Definitions

Concepts used in our study of static mechanics are *force, space,* and *matter.* These concepts are basic and, as a frame of reference, should be accepted on the basis of our general experience. A *force* is the result of the interaction of two or more bodies and in our study here will be considered to be a localized vector quantity. A force may be evolved as the result of physical contact, or it may be developed at some distance—as is the case with magnetic and gravitational forces. *Space* is a region extending in all directions. It is associated with the location or position of a particle or of particles with respect to one another. *Matter* is a substance that occupies space.

A *particle* may be said to be a negligible amount of matter that occupies a single point in space. A *rigid* body is a body that is constructed entirely of particles that do not change their position in space with respect to each other. No real body is rigid. However, in many situations the deformation, or change in position of the particles, is very small and therefore would have a negligible effect upon the analysis. Such is the assumption in this chapter.

A *scalar* quantity is one that can be completely defined by giving its magnitude. Examples of scalar quantities are temperature, work, volume, time, speed, and energy. A *vector* quantity is one that must be described by direction, as well as magnitude, to define it completely. Vectors may be free in space, with no specific line of action, or localized to a unique point of application or fixed position in space. Examples of vector quantities are force, velocity, acceleration, displacement, and momentum. Scalars may be added, subtracted, etc., according to the ordinary laws

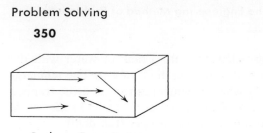

Coplanar Force System
**Figure 16—6.**

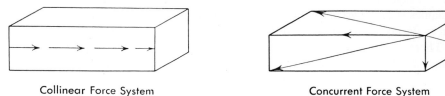

Collinear Force System                           Concurrent Force System
**Figure 16—7.**                                    **Figure 16—8.**

of algebra. Vectors, on the other hand, must be handled according to principles of vector mathematics, which will be discussed later in this chapter. Force systems are said to be:

1. *Coplanar,* when all of the force vectors lie in the same plane (see Figure 16–6).

2. *Collinear,* when all forces act along the same line (see Figure 16–7).

3. *Concurrent,* when all the forces originate or intersect at a single point (see Figure 16–8).

All force vectors should plainly show the sense or direction of force. This can best be done by the use of arrowheads on the point of the force. Space coordinate axes are frequently used to aid in positioning vector systems.

*Example:*   A force of 150 lb$_f$ is pulling upward from a point at an angle of 30° with the horizontal (see Figure 16–9).

The length of the arrow in the above example was scaled (using an engineer's scale) to 1 in. equals 100 lb$_f$ and is 1½ in. long acting upward at an angle of 30° with the horizontal. In graphic work the arrow point should not extend completely to the end of the vector, since it is very easy to "overrun" the exact length of the measured line in the drawing of the arrowhead.

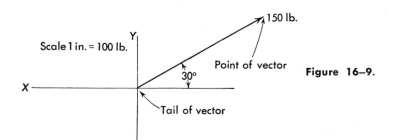

Scale 1 in. = 100 lb.

150 lb.

Point of vector

30°

X

Tail of vector

**Figure 16—9.**

In rigid-body mechanics the external effect of a force on a rigid body is independent of the point of application of the force along its line of action. Thus it would be considered immaterial whether a tractor pushed or pulled a box from a given position. The total effect on the box would be the same in either case. This is called the *Principle of Transmissibility* and will be used extensively in this chapter. This may be illustrated as shown in Figure 16–10.

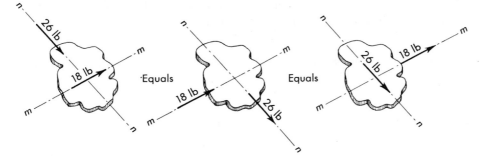

**Figure 16–10.**

*Example:* In each case the body is being acted upon by forces of 26 lb$_f$ and 18 lb$_f$. The total effect on the body is assumed to be the same for each example, since it is the line of action of a force which is significant, rather than its point of application.

### Resolutions of Forces

In this initial study of static mechanics we shall deal mainly with concurrent, coplanar force systems. It is sometimes advantageous to combine two such forces into a single equivalent force, which we shall call a *resultant*. The original forces are called *components*.

*Example:* What single force $R$ pulling at point $O$ will have the same effect as components $F_1$ and $F_2$? (See Figure 16–11.)

There are several methods of combining these two components into a single resultant. Let us examine the *parallelogram method,* the *polygon of forces,* and the *rectangular component method.*

**Figure 16–11.**

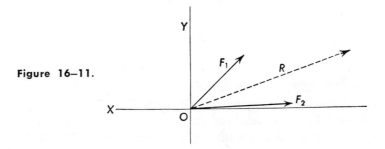

### Parallelogram Method

1. Choose a suitable scale.
2. Lay out the two coplanar components to scale, pointing away from the point of intersection.
3. Using these two components as sides, construct a parallelogram.
4. Draw the diagonal through the point of intersection.
5. Measure the diagonal (which is the resultant of the two components) for magnitude (with engineer's scale) and direction (with protractor).

*Example:* Solve for the resultant of components $F_1$ and $F_2$ if they are separated by angle $\theta$ (see Figure 16–12).

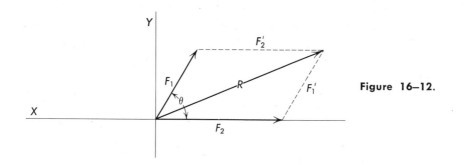

Figure 16–12.

*Example:* Two coplanar forces of 30 lb$_f$ and 40 lb$_f$, respectively, are at right angles to each other. Determine the magnitude of the resultant and the angle between the resultant and the 40-lb$_f$ force (see Figure 16–13). Lay out the two forces to scale as outlined above. The diagonal is measured to be 50 lb$_f$ and is located at an angle of 36.9° with the 40-lb$_f$ force.

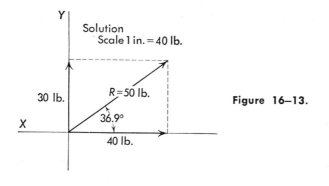

Figure 16–13.

### Problems

Solve, using the parallelogram method.

**16–65.** Find the resultant of two concurrent forces of 1939 lb$_f$ and 1220 lb$_f$, respectively, if the angle between them is 20°; if the angle is 130°.

**16–66.** Find the resultant of two concurrent forces, one 320 lb$_f$ due east and the other 550 lb$_f$ S 30° E.

**16–67.** Force $A$ is 450 lb$_f$. Force $B$ is 325 lb$_f$ and acts at an angle of 54° with $A$. The forces are concurrent. What is the amount of the resultant and what angle does it make with force $A$?

**16–68.** Find the resultant of two concurrent components, one of 1225 lb$_f$ due west and the other of 1450 lb$_f$ S 30° E.

**16–69.** A heavy piece of machinery is being moved along a floor with two cables making an angle of 28°30′ with each other. If the pulls are 45,000 and 25,000 lb$_f$, respectively, by what single force could they be replaced, and at what angle would the force act?

**16–70.** Find the resultant of a velocity of 150 mph due east and a velocity of 280 mph S 70° E. Use a scale of 1 in. equals 20 mph.

**16–71.** Three ropes are attached to a heavy body. If the first is pulled east by a force of 159 lb$_f$, the second by a force of 75 lb$_f$ 30° east of north, and the third north by a force of 108 lb$_f$, what is the resultant pull exerted on the body?

**16–72.** Three lines are connected to a missile. One line, having a tension of 1500 lb$_f$, runs due north; a second line, with a tension of 870 lb$_f$, runs S 75° W; a third line, with a tension of 1240 lb$_f$, runs N 58° E. Find the position and direction of a properly placed guy wire to brace the missile.

**16–73.** A man pulls straight ahead on a test sled with a force of 148 lb$_f$. If this man is replaced by two men, one pulling 36° to his left and the other pulling 20° to his right, what force must each of the new men exert if the sled is to move in the same direction?

**16–74.** A weight is held up by two cables that make angles of 50° and 25°, respectively, with the horizontal. Their resultant is vertical and equal to the weight which is 260 lb$_f$. Find the tension in each cable.

**16–75.** Two men are raising a 100 lb$_f$ container from a reactor by means of two ropes. Find the force each man is exerting on his rope if one rope makes a 15° angle with the vertical and the other makes a 25° angle with the vertical.

### Polygon of Forces

If two or more forces (or components) are concurrent and coplanar, their resultant can be determined by a faster and more convenient method known as the *polygon of forces*. In order to apply this method, proceed as follows:

1. Select a suitable scale.

2. Lay out one of the components with its correct magnitude and direction. At the tip of this component construct very lightly a small space coordinate system.

3. From the origin of this new space coordinate system lay out another component, placing the tail of the second component against the point of the first component.

4. Proceed in like manner until all components are used once (and only once).

5. Draw a vector from the original origin to the tip of the last component. This vector represents the *resultant* of the force system in both magnitude and direction.

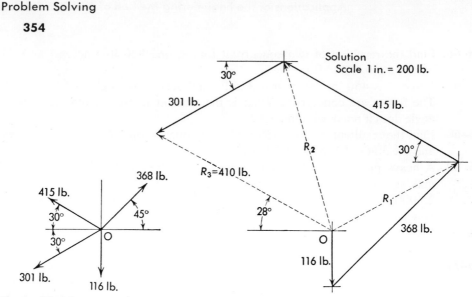

**Figure 16–14.**

*Example:* Solve for the resultant of the vector system shown in Figure 16–14.

Observe that $R_1$ is the resultant of the 116-lb$_f$ component and the 368-lb$_f$ component, $R_2$ is the resultant of $R_1$ and the 415-lb$_f$ component, and $R_3$ is the resultant of $R_2$ and the 301-lb$_f$ component. We see that $R_3$ (410-lb$_f$ at $\theta = 28°$), then, is the resultant of all the components.

It makes no difference in what sequence the components are placed in series. The resultant will be the same in magnitude and direction. In some cases the vectors cross one another, but this, too, is nothing to cause concern.

*Example:* Solve for $R$, and the angle it makes with the $X$-axis.

Note that in solution $A$ in Figure 16–15 we began with the 120-lb$_f$ component

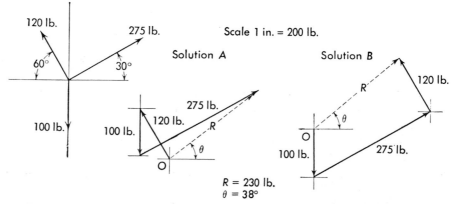

**Figure 16–15.**

and used components in a counterclockwise direction, while in solution $B$ we began with the 100-lb$_f$ component and worked in a counterclockwise direction.

### Problems

Solve, using the polygon of forces. Find the resultant of each of the following force systems and the angle the resultant makes with force $A$.

**16–76.** Forces $A$ and $B$ act 136° apart. $A = 180$ lb$_f$, $B = 325$ lb$_f$.

**16–77.** Forces $A$ and $B$ act 21° apart. $A = 39.3$ lb$_f$, $B = 41.6$ lb$_f$.

**16–78.** Forces $A$, $B$, and $C$ act 49° apart, with $B$ acting between $A$ and $C$. $A = 49.3$ lb$_f$, $B = 66.7$ lb$_f$, $C = 35.8$ lb$_f$.

**16–79.** Find the resultant force which would replace the three forces in Figure 16–16.

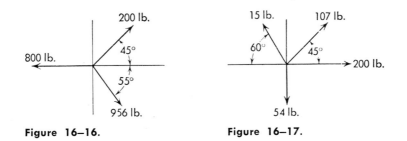

Figure 16–16.                    Figure 16–17.

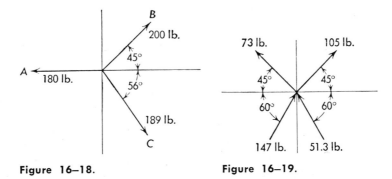

Figure 16–18.                    Figure 16–19.

**16–80.** A man weighing 210 lb$_f$ stands at the middle of a wire supported at points 60 ft apart and depresses it 12 ft below the level of the ends. Solve for the tension in the wire due to the man's weight.

**16–81.** Solve for the magnitude and direction of the resultant of the forces shown in Figure 16–17.

**16–82.** Find the resultant force that would replace the three forces $A$, $B$, and $C$ in Figure 16–18.

**16–83.** Find the resultant of the four forces shown in Figure 16–19.

Problems (continued)

16–84. Solve for the resultant of the force systems shown in Figure 16–20.
16–85. Graphically resolve the force, shown in Figure 16–21 into three components, one of which is 10 lb$_f$ acting vertically upward and another 30 lb$_f$ acting horizontally to the left.
16–86. Find the resultant of the force system shown in Figure 16–22, using a scale of 1 in. equals 10 lb$_f$.
16–87. Find the resultant of the velocity vectors: 33 mph south, 75 fps 20° west of north, and 2530 fpm north.

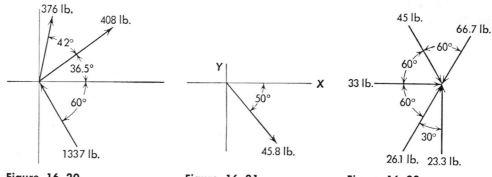

Figure 16–20.          Figure 16–21.          Figure 16–22.

## Rectangular Components

Graphical solutions, such as the *parallelogram method* and the *polygon of forces,* are useful for estimations where time is a factor. However, where exactitude is important, a numerical technique is needed. The method most frequently used by engineers is the *rectangular component method,* which will be discussed here.

As we have seen in the previous methods, vector components can be added together or subtracted—always leaving some resultant value. (This resultant value, of course, may be zero.) Also, any vector or resultant value can be replaced by two or more other vectors that are usually called *components*. If the components are two in number and perpendicular to each other, they are called *rectangular components*. Although it is common practice to use space coordinate axes that are horizontal and vertical, it is by no means necessary to do so. Any orientation of the axes will produce equivalent results.

Figure 16–23 shows a vector quantity $F$ and its rectangular components $F_x$ and

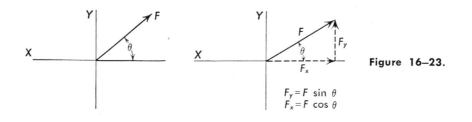

Figure 16–23.

$$F_y = F \sin \theta$$
$$F_x = F \cos \theta$$

$F_y$. Note that the lengths of the components $F_x$ and $F_y$ can be determined numerically by trigonometry. The components $F_x$ and $F_y$ also can be resolved into the force $F$ by the polygon of forces. Hence, they may replace the force $F$ in any computation.

*Example:* Let us examine a concurrent coplanar force system and resolve each force into its rectangular components (see Figure 16–24). By trigonometry, $F_x$ can be found, using $F$ and the cosine of the angle $\theta$, or $F_x = F \cos \theta°$. In the same manner $F_y = F \sin \theta°$.

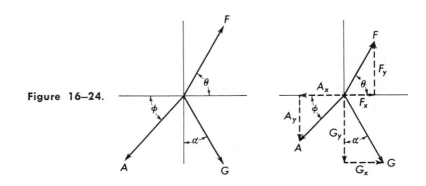

Figure 16–24.

In order to keep the directions of the vectors better in mind, let us assume that horizontal forces acting to the right are positive and those acting to the left are negative. Also, the forces acting upward may be considered positive and those acting downward negative.

In working such force systems by solving for the rectangular components, a table may be used. When the sums of the horizontal and vertical components have been determined, lay off these values on a new pair of axes to prevent confusion. Solve for the resultant in both magnitude and direction, using the method explained on page 172.

*Example:* Solve for $R$ in Figure 16–25, using the method of rectangular components (see Figure 16–26 for the final resolution of the force system).

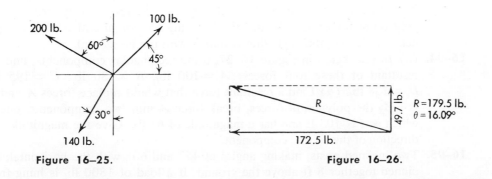

Figure 16–25.

Figure 16–26.

| Forces | Horizontal Component | Horizontal Value | Vertical Component | Vertical Value |
|---|---|---|---|---|
| 100 lb$_f$ | 100 cos 45° = | +70.7 lb$_f$ | 100 sin 45° = | +70.7 lb$_f$ |
| 200 lb$_f$ | 200 sin 60° = | −173.2 lb$_f$ | 200 cos 60° = | +100 lb$_f$ |
| 140 lb$_f$ | 140 sin 30° = | −70.0 lb$_f$ | 140 cos 30° = | −121 lb$_f$ |
| Total value | Positive | +70.7 lb$_f$ | Positive | +170.7 lb$_f$ |
| Total value | Negative | −243.2 lb$_f$ | Negative | −121 lb$_f$ |
| Sum | Horizontal | −172.5 lb$_f$ | Vertical | +49.7 lb$_f$ |

**Problems**

Solve, using rectangular components (analytical method).

**16–88.** Find the resultant, in amount and direction, of the following concurrent coplanar force system: force $A$, 180 lb$_f$ acts S 60° W; and force $B$, 158 lb$_f$, acts S 80° W. Check graphically, using a scale of 1 in. equals 50 lb$_f$.

**16–89.** Find the resultant of the following concurrent coplanar force system: $A$ = 30 lb$_f$ due north; $B$ = 25 lb$_f$ N 30° E; $C$ = 35 lb$_f$ S 45° E; $D$ = 55 lb$_f$ S 30° W.

**16–90.** Four men are pulling a box. $A$ pulls with a force of 115 lb$_f$, N 20°40′ E; $B$ pulls with a force of 95 lb$_f$ S 64°35′ E; $C$ pulls with a force of 140 lb$_f$ N 40°20′ E; and $D$ pulls with a force of 68 lb$_f$ E. In what direction will the box tend to move?

**16–91.** Determine the amount and direction of the resultant of the concurrent coplanar force system as follows: force $A$, 10 lb$_f$, acting N 55° E; force $B$, 16 lb$_f$, acting due east; force $C$, 12 lb$_f$, acting S 22° W; force $D$, 15 lb$_f$, acting due west; force $E$, 17 lb$_f$, acting N 10° W.

**16–92.** Find the resultant and the angle the resultant makes with the vertical, using the following data: 10 lb$_f$, N 18° W; 5 lb$_f$, N 75° E; 3 lb$_f$, S 64° E; 7 lb$_f$, S 0° W; 10 lb$_f$, S 50° W.

**16–93.** Five forces act on an object. The forces are as follows: 130 lb$_f$, 0°; 170 lb$_f$, 90°; 70 lb$_f$, 180°; 20 lb$_f$, 270°; 300 lb$_f$, 150°. The angles are measured counterclockwise with reference to the horizontal through the origin. Determine graphically the amount and direction of the resultant by means of the polygon of forces. Check analytically, using horizontal and vertical components. Calculate the angle that $R$ makes with the horizontal.

**16–94.** (a) In the sketch in Figure 16–27, using rectangular components, find the resultant of these four forces: $A$ = 100 lb$_f$, $B$ = 130 lb$_f$, $C$ = 195 lb$_f$, $D$ = 138 lb$_f$. (b) Find a resultant force that would replace forces $A$ and $B$. (c) By the polygon of forces, break force $A$ into two components, one of which acts N 10° E and has a magnitude of 65 lb$_f$. Give the magnitude and direction of the second component.

**16–95.** Two inclined posts, making angles of 45° and 60° with the horizontal, are pinned together 8 ft above the ground. If a load of 1800 lb$_f$ is hung from the pin, solve for the compression forces in the posts.

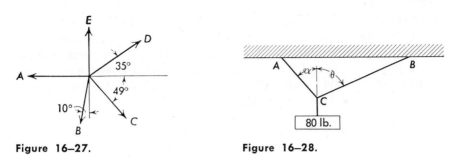

Figure 16–27.                  Figure 16–28.

**16–96.** A weight of 1200 $lb_f$ is hung by a cable 23 ft long. What horizontal pull will be necessary to hold the weight 8 ft from a vertical line through the point of support? What will be the tension in the cable?

**16–97.** A weight of 80 $lb_f$ is suspended by two cords, the tension in $AC$ being 70 $lb_f$ and in $BC$ being 25 $lb_f$, as shown in Figure 16–28. Find the angles $\alpha$ and $\theta$.

## MOMENTS

If a force is applied perpendicular to a pivoted beam at some distance away from the pivot point, there will be a tendency to cause the beam to turn in either a clockwise or counterclockwise direction (see Figure 16–29). The direction of the tendency will depend on the direction of the applied force. This tendency of a force to cause rotation about a given center is called *moment* (see Figure 16–30).

The amount of *moment* will depend upon the magnitude of the applied force as well as upon the length of the moment arm. The moment arm is the perpendicular distance from the point of rotation to the applied force. The magnitude of the moment is calculated by multiplying the force by the moment arm.

The sign convention being used in a given problem analysis should be placed on

Figure 16–29.

Figure 16–30.

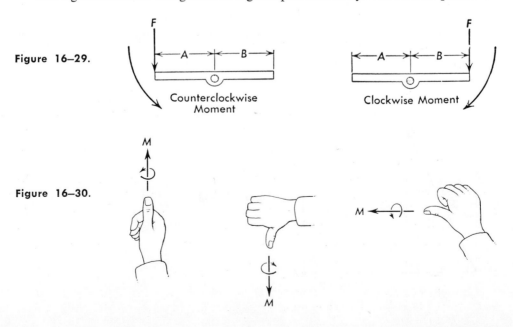

the calculation sheet adjacent to the problem sketch. In this way no confusion will arise in the mind of the reader concerning the sign convention being used. We shall assume that vectors acting to the right have a positive sign, vectors acting upward have a positive sign, and moments directed counterclockwise have a positive sign. To aid in establishing a system of positive senses, the sketch shown in Figure 16–31 will serve as a basis for problem analysis in this text.

*Example:*

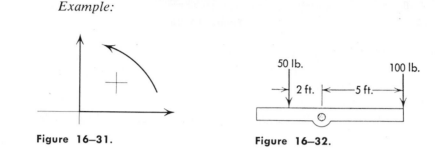

**Figure 16–31.**                    **Figure 16–32.**

*Example:*    Solve for the moments in Figure 16–32 that tend to cause turning of the beam about the axle.

$$\text{Counterclockwise moment} = (\ 50 \text{ lb})(2 \text{ ft}) = +100 \text{ lb-ft}$$
$$\text{Clockwise moment} = (100 \text{ lb})(5 \text{ ft}) = -500 \text{ lb-ft}$$

Since *moment* is the product of a force and a distance, its units will be the product of force and length units. By convention, moments are usually expressed with the force unit being shown first, as $lb_f$-ft, $lb_f$-in., kip-ft (a kip is 1000 $lb_f$), etc. This is done because *work* and *energy* also involve the product of distance and force, and the units ft-$lb_f$, in.-$lb_f$, etc., are commonly used for this purpose.

The moment of a force about some given center is identical to the sum of the moments of the components of the force about the same center. This principle is commonly called *Varignon's theorem*. In problem analysis it is sometimes more convenient to solve for the sum of the moments of the components of a force rather than the moment of the force itself. However, the problem solutions will be identical.

*Example:*    Solve for the total moment of the 1000-$lb_f$ force about point *A* in Figure 16–33.

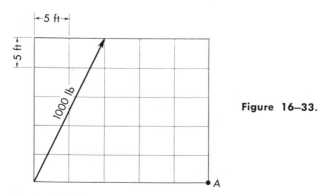

**Figure 16–33.**

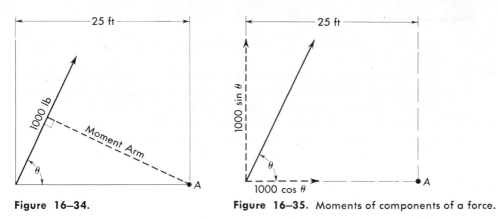

**Figure 16–34.**

**Figure 16–35.** Moments of components of a force.

SOLUTION *A:*    Moment of a force as shown in Figure 16–34.
$$\theta = \text{arc tan } 25/10 = 68.2°$$
$$\text{Moment arm} = 25 \sin 68.2°$$
$$\text{Total moment} = (1000)(25 \sin 68.2°)$$
$$= 23{,}200 \text{ lb}_f\text{-ft}$$

SOLUTION *B:*    Moments of components of a force as shown in Figure 16–35.
$$\text{Vertical component} = 1000 \sin 68.2°$$
and                    $\text{Moment arm} = 25 \text{ ft}$
$$\text{Horizontal component} = 1000 \cos 68.2°$$
and                    $\text{Moment arm} = 0$

(Note that the horizontal component passes through the center *A.*)
$$\text{Total moment} = (1000 \sin 68.2°)(25) = 23{,}200 \text{ lb}_f\text{-ft}$$

### Problems

**16–98.** Solve for the algebraic sum of the moments in pound-feet about *A* when *h* is 20 in. as shown in Figure 16–36.

**16–99.** Solve for the algebraic sum of the moments of forces about *A* in Figure 16–37.

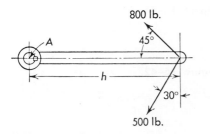

**Figure 16–36.**

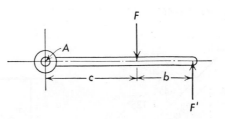

**Figure 16–37.**

**Problems (continued)**

**16–100.** Solve for the algebraic sum of the moments about the center of the axle shown in Figure 16–38.

**16–101.** (*a*) Write an equation for the clockwise moments about the point of application of force *R* in Figure 16–39. (*b*) Write an equation for the counterclockwise moments about the point of application of force *Y*.

**16–102.** (*a*) Solve for the clockwise moments about *A*, *B*, *C*, *D*, and *E* in Figure 16–40. (*b*) Solve for the counterclockwise moments about *A*, *B*, *C*, *D*, and *E*. (*c*) Solve for the algebraic sum of the moments about *A*, *B*, *C*, *D*, and *E*.

**16–103.** Find the summation of the moments of the forces shown around *A* in Figure 16–41. Find the moment sum around *D*.

**16–104.** Find the moment of each of the forces shown about *O* in Figure 16–42.

**16–105.** What pull *P* is required on the handle of a claw hammer to exert a vertical force of 750 lb$_f$ on a nail. Dimensions are shown on Figure 16–43.

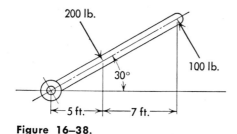

**Figure 16–38.**

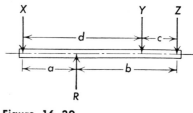

**Figure 16–39.**

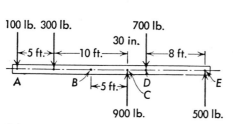

**Figure 16–40.**

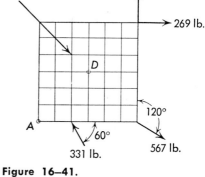

**Figure 16–41.**

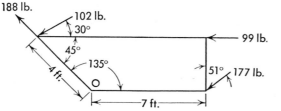

**Figure 16–42.**

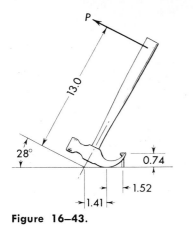

**Figure 16–43.**

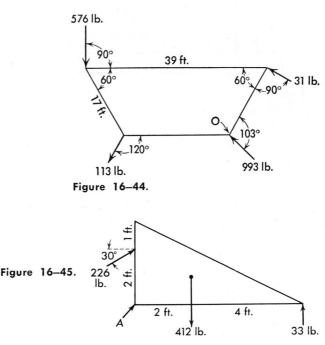

**Figure 16–44.**

**Figure 16–45.**

**16–106.** On the trapezoidal body shown in Figure 16–44 find the moment of each of the forces about point $O$.

**16–107.** Find the moment of each of the forces shown in Figure 16–45 about the point $A$.

## EQUILIBRIUM

The term *equilibrium* is used to describe the condition of any body when the resultant of all forces acting on the body equals zero. For example, the forces acting upward on a body in equilibrium must be balanced by other forces acting downward on the body. Also, the forces acting horizontally to the right are counteracted by equal forces acting horizontally to the left. Since no unbalance in moment or turning effect can be present when a body is in equilibrium, the sum of the moments of all forces acting on the body must also be zero. The moment center may be located at any convenient place on the body or at any place in space. We may sum up these conditions of equilibrium by the following equations:

$\Sigma F_x = 0$ (the sum of all horizontal forces acting on the body equals zero)
$\Sigma F_y = 0$ (the sum of all vertical forces acting on the body equals zero)
$\Sigma M_o = 0$ (the sum of the moments of all forces acting on the body equals zero)

These equilibrium equations may be used to good advantage in working problems involving beams, trusses, and levers.

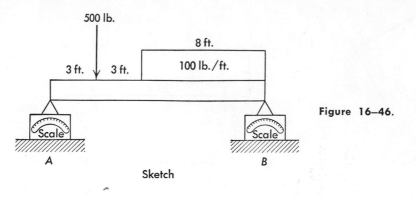

Figure 16–46.

Sketch

*Example:* A beam of negligible weight is supported at each end by a knife-edge. The beam carries a concentrated load of 500 lb$_f$ and one uniformly distributed load weighing 100 lb$_f$ per linear foot, as shown in Figure 16–46. Determine the scale readings under the knife-edges.

SOLUTION: The uniformly distributed load is equivalent to a resultant of 8 ft × 100 lb$_f$/ft = 800 lb$_f$ acting at the center of gravity of the uniform-load diagram. Therefore the entire distribution load can be replaced by a concentrated load of 800 lb$_f$ acting at a distance of 10 ft from the left end as shown in Figure 16–47.

1. Draw a free-body diagram of the beam.
2. Since there are no horizontal forces acting on the free body, $\Sigma F_x = 0$ is satisfied.

3. From $\Sigma F_y = 0$, we know that

$$A + B = 500 \text{ lb}_f + 800 \text{ lb}_f$$
$$A + B = 1300 \text{ lb}_f$$

4. From $\Sigma M_o = 0$, we know that the moments about any point must equal zero. Let us take moments about point $A$.

$$\Sigma M_A = 0$$
$$(B \text{ lb}_f)(14 \text{ ft}) - (500 \text{ lb}_f)(3 \text{ ft}) - (800 \text{ lb}_f)(10 \text{ ft}) = 0$$
$$B \text{ lb}_f = \frac{1500 \text{ lb}_f\text{-ft} + 8000 \text{ lb}_f\text{-ft}}{14 \text{ ft}}$$
$$B \text{ lb}_f = \frac{9500 \text{ lb}_f\text{-ft}}{14 \text{ ft}}$$
$$B = 679 \text{ lb}_f$$

5. From the third step we saw that $A + B = 1300 \text{ lb}_f$. We can now subtract and obtain

$$A = 1300 \text{ lb}_f - 679 \text{ lb}_f = 621 \text{ lb}_f$$

NOTE: The same answer for $A$ could have been obtained by taking moments about $B$ as a moment center.

In this book problems involving trusses, cranes, linkages, bridges, etc., should

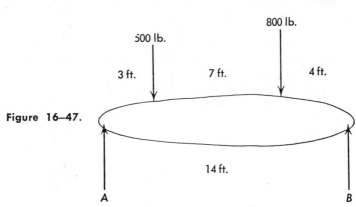

**Figure 16–47.**

be considered to be *pin-connected,* which means that the member is free to rotate about the joint. For simplicity, members also are usually considered to be weightless.

By examining each member of the structure separately, internal forces in the various members may be obtained by the conditions of equilibrium.

*Example:* Solve for the tensions in cables *AF* and *ED* and for the reactions at *C* and *R* in Figure 16–48.

$$\text{Equilibrium Equations}$$

$$\Sigma F_x = 0$$
$$\Sigma F_y = 0$$
$$\Sigma M_o = 0$$

SOLUTION

1. Take moments about point *R* in free body No. 1, (see Figure 16–49).

$$\Sigma M_R = 0$$
$$(12 \text{ ft})(FA) - (100 \text{ lb}_f)(4 \text{ ft}) = 0$$

$$FA = \frac{400 \text{ lb}_f\text{-ft}}{12 \text{ ft}} = 33.3 \text{ lb}_f$$

$$\Sigma F_x = 0$$
$$R_x - FA = 0$$
$$R_x = FA = 33.3 \text{ lb}_f \rightarrow$$

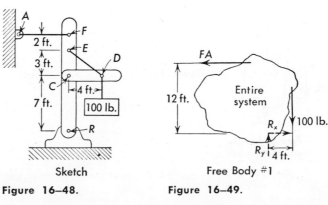

Sketch

**Figure 16–48.**

Free Body #1

**Figure 16–49.**

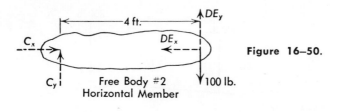

Figure 16–50.

Free Body #2
Horizontal Member

2. Take moments about point $C$ in free body No. 2, (see Figure 16–50).

$$\Sigma M_c = DE_y\,(4) - 100\,(4) = 0$$
$$DE_y = 100\ \text{lb}_f$$

Therefore
$$DE = \frac{100\ \text{lb}_f}{\sin 36.9°} = 166.8\ \text{lb}_f\ \nwarrow$$

And free body No. 2
$$\Sigma F_y = 0$$
$$C_y = 100\ \text{lb}_f - 100\ \text{lb}_f$$
$$C_y = 0$$

Also free body No. 2
$$\Sigma F_x = 0$$
$$C_x = DE_x = \frac{100\ \text{lb}_f}{\tan 36.9°}$$
$$C_x = 133.1\ \text{lb}_f \rightarrow$$

3. Consider $\Sigma F_y = 0$, using the third free body (vertical member) as shown in Figure 16–51. Remember that in two force members, such as cable $DE$, the reactions at each end will be equal in magnitude but opposite in direction; that is, $E_x$ and $E_y$ are equal to $DE_x$ and $DE_y$.

$$\Sigma F_y = 0$$
$$R_y - DE_y = 0$$
$$R_y = 100.0\ \text{lb}_f \uparrow$$

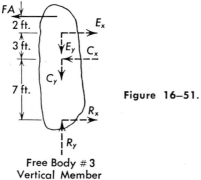

Figure 16–51.

Free Body #3
Vertical Member

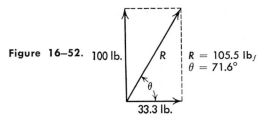

**Figure 16–52.** 100 lb.   R   $R = 105.5$ lb$_f$
$\theta = 71.6°$

33.3 lb.

The resultant is indicated as before and solved by using the slide rule (see Figure 16–52).

### Equilibrium Problems

**16–108.** A horizontal beam 20 ft long weighs 150 lb$_f$. It is supported at the left end and 4 ft from the right end. It has the following concentrated loads: at the left end, 200 lb$_f$; 8 ft from the left end, 300 lb$_f$; at the right end, 400 lb$_f$. Calculate the reactions at the supports.

**16–109.** A horizontal beam 8 ft long and weighing 30 lb$_f$ is supported at the left end and 2 ft from the right end. It has the following loads: at the left end, 18 lb$_f$; 3 ft from the left end, 22 lb$_f$; at the right end, 15 lb$_f$. Compute the reactions at the supports.

**16–110.** A beam 22 ft long weighing 300 lb$_f$ is supporting loads of 700 lb$_f$ 3 ft from the left end and 250 lb$_f$ 7 ft from the right end. One support is at the left end. How far from the right end should the right support be placed so that the reactions at the two supports will be equal?

**16–111.** A beam 18 ft long is supported at the right end and at a point 5 ft from the left end. It is loaded with a concentrated load of 250 lb$_f$ located 2 ft from the right end and a concentrated load of 450 lb$_f$ located 9 ft from the right end. In addition, it has a uniform load of 20 lb$_f$ per linear foot for its entire length. Find the reactions at the supports.

**16–112.** A 12-ft beam which weighs 10 lb$_f$ per foot is resting horizontally. The left end of the beam is pinned to a vertical wall. The right end of the beam is supported by a cable that is attached to the vertical wall 6 ft above the left end of the beam. There is a 200-lb$_f$ concentrated load acting vertically downward 3 ft from the right end of the beam. Determine the tension in the cable and the amount and direction of the reaction at the left end of the beam.

**16–113.** A steel I-beam, weighing 75 lb$_f$ per linear foot and 20 ft long, is supported at its left end and at a point 4 ft from its right end. It carries loads of 10 tons and 6 tons at distances of 5 ft and 17 ft, respectively, from the left end. Find the reactions at the supports.

**16–114.** A horizontal rod 8 ft long and weighing 12 lb$_f$ has a weight of 15 lb$_f$ hung from the right end, and a weight of 4 lb$_f$ hung from the left end. Where should a single support be located so the rod will balance?

**16–115.** A uniform board 22 ft long will balance 4.2 ft from one end when a weight of 61 lb$_f$ is hung from this end. How much does the board weigh?

### Equilibrium Problems (continued)

**16–116.** An iron beam 12.7 ft long weighing 855 lb$_f$ has a load of 229 lb$_f$ at the right end. A support is located 7.2 ft from the load end. (*a*) How much force is required at the opposite end to balance it? (*b*) Disregarding the balancing force, calculate the reactions on the supports if one support is located 7 ft from the left end and the other support is located 4 ft from the right end.

**16–117.** A horizontal rod 8 ft long and weighing 1.2 lb$_f$ per linear foot has a weight of 15 lb$_f$ hung from the right end, and a weight of 4 lb$_f$ hung from the left end. Where should a single support be located so the rod will balance?

**16–118.** A 2-ft diameter sphere weighs 56 lb$_f$, is suspended by a cable, and rests against a vertical wall. If the cable *AB* is 2 ft long, (*a*) calculate the angle the cable will make with the smooth wall, (*b*) solve for the tension in the cable and the reaction at *C* in Figure 16–53. Check results graphically.

**16–119.** What horizontal pull *P* will be necessary just to start the wheel weighing 1400 lb$_f$ over the 4-in. block in Figure 16–54?

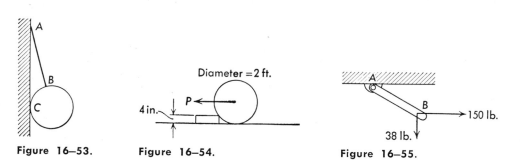

**Figure 16–53.**    **Figure 16–54.**    **Figure 16–55.**

**16–120.** A vertical pole 12 ft long is pinned to the ground at *A* and is stayed by a guy wire running from the top of the pole, *B*, to a point *C*, 8 ft to the left of *A*. If a horizontal force of 1900 lb$_f$ is applied to the pole at *D*, 6 ft above *A*, determine the tension in the guy wire *BC*, and the amount and direction of the pin reaction at *A*.

**16–121.** Find the tension in *AB* and the angle $\theta$ that *AB* makes with the vertical in Figure 16–55.

**16–122.** If the tension in the cable *AB* in Figure 16–56, is 196 lb$_f$, how much does the sphere *B* weigh? How much is the reaction of the inclined plane on the sphere?

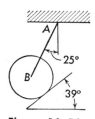

**Figure 16–56.**    **Figure 16–57.**

**16–123.** The wheel $B$ in Figure 16–57 weighs 175 lb$_f$. Solve for the force in member $AB$, the reaction at $C$, and the horizontal and vertical force components at $A$.

**16–124.** A cylinder weighing 206 lb$_f$ is placed in a smooth trough as shown in Figure 16–58. Find the two supporting forces.

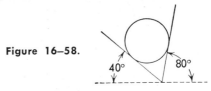

**Figure 16–58.**

**16–125.** A 796-lb$_f$ load is supported as shown in Figure 16–59. $AB$ equals 8 ft, $\theta$ equals 25°. ($a$) Neglecting the weight of the beam $AB$, solve analytically for the tension in the cable and the reaction at $A$. ($b$) If beam $AB$ is uniform and weighs 12 lb$_f$ per foot, solve for the tension in the cable and the reaction at $A$.

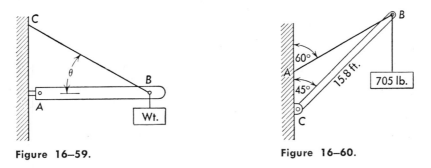

**Figure 16–59.**   **Figure 16–60.**

**16–126.** Find the tension in $AB$ and the compression in $BC$ in Figure 16–60.

**16–127.** A weight of 1355 lb$_f$ is supported by two ropes making angles of 30° and 45° on opposite sides of the vertical. What is the tension in each rope?

**16–128.** Forces are applied on a rigid frame as shown in Figure 16–61. Find the reactions at $A$ and $B$.

**16–129.** ($a$) What is the tension in $BC$ in Figure 16–62? ($b$) What is the amount and direction of the reaction at $A$?

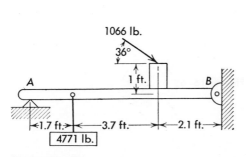

**Figure 16–61.**

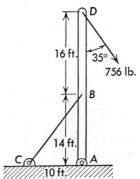

**Figure 16–62.**

## Equilibrium Problems (continued)

**16–130.** (*a*) Find the tension in *AC* in Figure 16–63. (*b*) Find the amount and direction of the reaction at *B*. *BC* = 10 ft, *BD* = 25 ft.

**16–131.** Cylinder No. 1 in Figure 16–64 has a 10-in. diameter and weighs 84 lb$_f$. Cylinder No. 2 has a 6-in. diameter and weighs 27 lb$_f$. Find the reactions at *A*, *B*, and *C*. All surfaces are smooth.

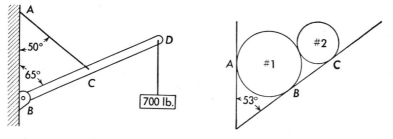

**Figure 16–63.**                          **Figure 16–64.**

**16–132.** (*a*) Find the force in member *AB* in Figure 16–65 and the reaction at point *E*. (*b*) Find the force in member *CG* and the horizontal and vertical components of the reaction at pin *D*.

**16–133.** Solve for the reactions at 1, 2, 3, 4, and 5 in Figure 16–66. Weights: *A* = 150 lb$_f$, *B* = 100 lb$_f$, *C* = 70 lb$_f$, *D* = 35 lb$_f$. Diameters: *A* = 26 in., *B* = 20 in., *C* = 15 in., *D* = 9 in. Angle $\theta$ = 30°.

**16–134.** A 15-ft ladder leans against the side of a smooth building in such a position that it makes an angle of 60° with the ground (horizontal). A man weighing 190 lb$_f$ stands on the ladder three-fourths of the way up the ladder. The bottom of the ladder is prevented from sliding by the ground. Find the horizontal and vertical components of the reaction at the foot of the ladder and the force between the ladder and the wall.

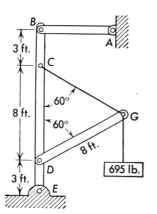

**Figure 16–65.**

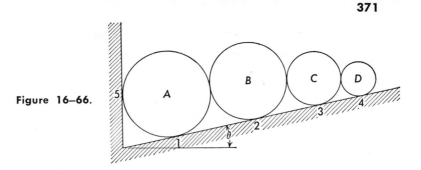

Figure 16–66.

## ELECTRICITY AND ELECTRONICS

The use of electrical machinery and electronic devices has become so much a part of our present day life that practically all engineers will work with electricity in some way in their professional role. The applications of electrical phenomena are so widespread that all engineering students should have some basic knowledge of the principles of electricity.

Although the knowledge of electrostatic and magnetic effects has been available for many centuries, the concept that there was any relation between electric charge effects and magnetic effects was not presented until the last century. An English mathematician, Clerk Maxwell, was the individual principally responsible for providing a mathematical basis for showing a relationship between electricity and magnetism. His mathematical derivations were based on experimental work done previously by such scientists as Ampere, Volta, Faraday, and Coulomb.

Although we can look back and consider with disdain the difficulties of early experimenters in performing what to us are the most elementary demonstrations of electrical and magnetic phenomena, we must remember that in the days of early experimenters, no one knew even the difference between insulators and conductors. The discovery of the insulating properties of certain materials provided a means for isolating charges and directing their flow. This one discovery, which to us is almost an intuitive concept, was to the early experimenters a major breakthrough in their work. Could it be that fifty years from now, engineers will look back at our present difficulties in grasping concepts of solid-state electronic devices and wonder why we made such a task of attempting to understand the behavior of such obviously elementary phenomena?

### The Atom

The basis for explaining the behavior of electricity depends on our concept of the atomic structure of matter. As any student of science knows, within the atom is a system of electrons in orbit surrounding a central nucleus. Some of these electrons in the outer orbit can be transferred to other atoms under the influence of such phenomena as electrical fields, heat, friction, and so on.

Materials differ widely in their tendency to transfer electrons, and all materials can be classified broadly into insulators or conductors as a measure of the ease with which electrons are transferred. For example, if hard rubber is stroked with a woolen cloth, friction will transfer electrons from the cloth to the hard rubber but, since the hard rubber atoms cling tightly to the electrons, little or no movement of the charges can then occur on the surface of the hard rubber.

On the other hand, if a piece of copper is charged, the charges will move readily through the copper by transfer from atom to atom, and, unless insulating structures are provided, the charges usually will dissipate rapidly to other conducting mediums.

The concept of conductors or insulators then deals not with the production of electrical charges but rather with the relative ease with which charges are transferred.

Since the electrons appear to be moving in orbits, each electron will tend to produce a magnetic field due to its own motion. In almost every material, the orientation of the spins is such that the magnetic effects cancel and the resultant field is substantially zero. However, in the case of iron, nickel, and cobalt, together with a few alloys, the magnetic fields due to the electron spins do not cancel and the atom or molecule does have a definite magnetic pattern. In simplified terms, this is the general concept of the relation between electrical and magnetic effects.

In a classical experiment conducted by Professor Millikan early in the century, the numerical value of the charge on an electron was measured. As a result of this measurement, we find that the number of electrons flowing through the filament of an ordinary 100-watt 110-volt electric light bulb is approximately $6 \times 10^{18}$ electrons per second.

Electrostatic generators are used to separate charges in the production of very penetrating x-rays and in research on the acceleration of charged particles. A Van de Graff generator is an example of a static charge generator. With this type of machine, potentials of several million volts can be secured.

Another example of charges being produced by external forces is in the case of piezoelectricity. It has been determined experimentally that certain crystalline substances such as quartz and Rochelle salts will have a separation of charges produced by mechanical deformation of the crystal. Electronic devices can sense this charged condition of certain faces of the crystal and by amplification of the charge effects can convert them to many useful purposes. A microphone, for example, can be made by having sound waves strike a flexible diaphragm that in turn is coupled mechanically to a crystal. The deflections of the crystal will produce in electrical charges corresponding charges that when amplified can be heard in a loudspeaker.

### Electric Currents

If charged particles, usually electrons, move in a conductor, the movement of the charges constitutes what is known as an electric current. Obviously the charges will not move unless there is an excess of charges at one point and a deficiency at another. In the case of a simple electric cell, the tendency of one of the electrode materials to be chemically changed results in an ionization process that will produce a difference in charges on the electrodes. As long as an external path of conducting material exists, the charges flow from one electrode to another in an attempt to equalize the charges. A coulomb is approximately $6.06 \times 10^{18}$ electrons and a flow of 1 coulomb per second past a given point in an electrical circuit is defined as a current of 1 ampere.

Voltage basically is a measure of the amount of work or energy necessary to move a certain number of charges from one place to another against opposition. A voltage can be present even though the charges actually are not moving. For example, in a certain storage battery, a voltage, representing a state of separation of charges within the battery, exists regardless of whether the circuit is completed so that current can flow. This can be compared to having a pile of rocks on a platform. Potential energy due to the rock's elevated position is present even though the rocks are not moving. The usual unit of voltage is the volt—the voltage necessary to move one ampere through an opposition of 1 ohm of resistance.

Resistance of flow of an electric current exists because of the difficulty of moving electrons from one atom to another. All materials have some resistance to current flow except that certain metals at temperatures near absolute zero temperature (approximately −459°F), appear to have negligible resistance. Commonly used materials having quite low resistances at ordinary temperatures are silver, copper, and aluminum. All metals are good conductors; however, the three mentioned are the best conducting materials. Other substances having relatively low resistance are carbon and solutions containing ions. Almost without exception, all other materials are insulators having resistances from thousands to millions of times that of the metals. In some cases, insulators at ordinary temperatures will become fairly good conductors at temperatures of several hundred degrees and upward. Glass and some plastics possess this property of having a markedly lower resistance at elevated temperatures. As mentioned above, the unit of resistance is the ohm and is defined legally as the resistance of a column of mercury 1 sq mm in cross section and 106.3 cm long held at a temperature of 0°C.

### Laws and Principles

A well known relation of electrical quantities in a circuit is called Ohm's Law. Stated briefly, it says that in a circuit, the ratio of the voltage to the current is a constant. Of course, like many laws, it must have limiting conditions, the major one being that the temperature of the conductor must remain constant. In symbol form:

$$\frac{V \text{ (voltage)}}{I \text{ (current)}} = R \text{ (resistance)}$$

This means that in a circuit of fixed resistance, if the voltage of the circuit is doubled, the current (flow) will also double.

There are two basic ways in which circuit elements can be connected. These are series and parallel connections. Examples are given in Figure 16–67.

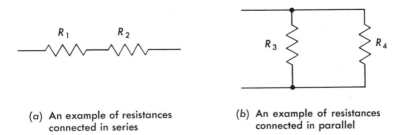

(a) An example of resistances connected in series

(b) An example of resistances connected in parallel

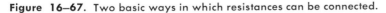

**Figure 16–67.** Two basic ways in which resistances can be connected.

### Series Circuit

As an example of an application of Ohm's Law, if a simple series circuit is sketched showing a cell and a resistance with a cell voltage of 28.3 v and a resistance of 2.10 ohms, the current can be computed readily:

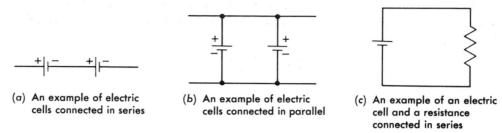

(a) An example of electric cells connected in series

(b) An example of electric cells connected in parallel

(c) An example of an electric cell and a resistance connected in series

**Figure 16–68.** Series and parallel arrangements of circuit elements.

*Example:* First, draw a simple sketch using conventional symbols and label the known quantities. Second, solve for the unknown quantities.

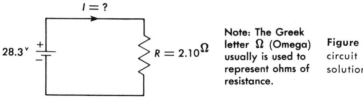

Note: The Greek letter $\Omega$ (Omega) usually is used to represent ohms of resistance.

**Figure 16–69.** A simple series circuit using Ohm's Law for solution to obtain unknowns.

### Applying Ohm's Law

$$\frac{V}{I} = R$$

$$I = \frac{V \text{ (volts)}}{R \text{ (ohms)}}$$

$$I = \frac{28.3}{2.10} = 13.48 \text{ amp}$$

Since this is a closed circuit with no branches, the same current (13.48 amp) is flowing in all parts of the circuit, since it would be unlikely that charges would

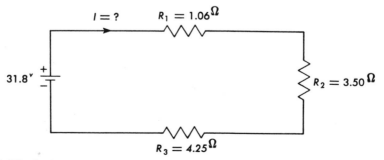

**Figure 16–70.** Resistances in series.

stack up at some given point. Also, the voltage produced by the cell is assumed to be all used in forcing the current through the resistance. This assumes that the resistance of the cell and of the connecting wires is negligible.

For another example, let us take a circuit where several resistances are connected in series as shown in Figure 16–70.

For this type of circuit, first add all the resistances to get a sum which is the equivalent of all the resistances together. This sum is 8.81 ohms. Then applying Ohm's Law:

$$I = \frac{V \text{ (volts)}}{R \text{ (ohms)}}$$

$$I = \frac{31.8}{8.81} = 3.61 \text{ amp}$$

Since the circuit elements are all in series, this same current flows through each element. At this time, we can compute the voltage across each resistance since a part of the total available voltage is used for each.

For Resistance $R_1$

$$V_1 = IR_1 \text{ volt}$$
$$V_1 = (3.61)(1.06) = 3.77 \text{ v}$$

For Resistance $R_2$

$$V_2 = (3.61)(3.50) = 12.64 \text{ v}$$

For Resistance $R_3$

$$V_3 = (3.61)(4.25) = 15.34 \text{ v}$$

As a check, the sum of the individual voltages across the resistances, frequently called the voltage drop across the resistance, can be obtained and should be the same as the original cell voltage, within slide rule accuracy.

$$V_1 + V_2 + V_3 = 31.75 \text{ v}$$

**Parallel Circuits**

Figure 16–71 is a sketch of a circuit containing resistances in parallel with the group connected in series with a cell.

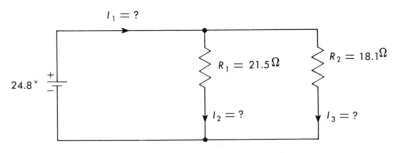

Figure 16–71. A parallel arrangement of resistances.

To solve for the currents in this circuit, first find the value of a single equivalent resistance that can replace the parallel set. This single equivalent can be found by the expression:

$$\frac{1}{R_{equiv}} = \frac{1}{R_1} + \frac{1}{R_2}$$

or

$$R_{equiv} = \frac{1}{\dfrac{1}{R_1} + \dfrac{1}{R_2}}$$

$$R_{equiv} = \frac{1}{\dfrac{1}{21.5} + \dfrac{1}{18.1}} = \frac{1}{0.0466 + 0.0553}$$

$$= \frac{1}{0.1019} = 9.83 \text{ ohm}$$

Using this equivalent resistance:

$$I_1 = \frac{V}{R_{equiv}}$$

$$I_1 = \frac{24.8}{9.83} = 2.52 \text{ amp}$$

Currents $I_2$ and $I_3$ can be found in several ways. For instance, since the currents will divide in inverse ratio to the resistances, a current ratio can be determined and since the total current (2.52 amp) is known, the individual currents can be found. A more universal method is to find the current in each resistance by using the *voltage drop* method. Since, in a parallel circuit, the same voltage appears across each resistance, an application of Ohm's Law to each branch will permit a solution for the current.

$$I_2 = \frac{V}{R_1}$$

$$I_2 = \frac{24.8}{21.5} = 1.152 \text{ amp}$$

and

$$I_3 = \frac{V}{R_2}$$

$$I_3 = \frac{24.8}{18.1} = 1.370 \text{ amp}$$

As a check, $I_2 + I_3$ should add to give the total current out of the cell

$$I_1 = I_2 + I_3$$
$$I_1 = 1.157 + 1.370 = 2.52 \text{ amp}$$

To summarize, for series circuits, the current in all parts is the same and the sum of the voltage drops across the resistances equals the available cell voltage. For parallel circuits, the voltage is the same across each parallel path, and the sum of the currents in each branch or path equals the total current supplied by the cell.

### Series-Parallel Circuits

If a problem involving a series-parallel combination of circuit elements is given, an application of the principles shown above will provide a means of solution.

*Example:*

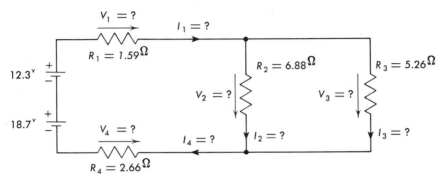

**Figure 16–72.** A series-parallel arrangement of resistances.

ANALYSIS: If the parallel arrangement of resistances $R_2$ and $R_3$ can be combined into a single equivalent resistance, the circuit then will be a single series circuit and a method of determining currents or voltages will be available as was used in a previous example.

SOLUTION: The equivalent resistance of $R_2$ and $R_3$ will be

$$\frac{1}{R_{\text{equiv}}} = \frac{1}{R_2} + \frac{1}{R_3}$$

$$\frac{1}{R_{\text{equiv}}} = \frac{1}{6.88} + \frac{1}{5.26}$$

$$= 0.1458 + 0.1902$$

$$= 0.3360$$

$$R_{\text{equiv}} = \frac{1}{0.3360} = 2.98 \text{ ohms}$$

This means that if the parallel combination were replaced by a single 2.98 ohm resistance, the current and voltage values in the remainder of the circuit would be unchanged. The circuit then can be redrawn substituting $R_{\text{equiv}}$ for $R_2$ and $R_3$ as shown in Figure 16–73 on the next page.

First, obtain the total voltage of the electric cells. This is simply the sum of the individual cell voltages.

$$V_{\text{total}} = 12.3 + 18.7$$

$$= 31.0 \text{ v}$$

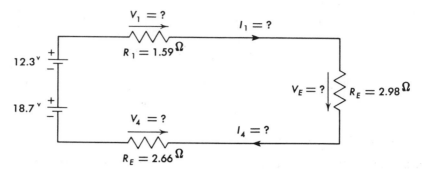

**Figure 16–73.** The equivalent circuit of figure 16–72.

Second, find the total circuit resistance. For this circuit, it is the sum of the individual resistances in series.

$$R_{total} = 1.59 + 2.98 + 2.66$$
$$= 7.23 \text{ ohm}$$

Third, find the total circuit current. This is found by an application of Ohm's Law using total voltage and total resistance.

$$I_{total} = \frac{V_{total}}{R_{total}}$$
$$= \frac{31.0}{7.23} = 4.28 \text{ amp}$$

Since, in a series circuit, the total current is the same as the current in each part, the current through each resistance also is 4.28 amp. From this, we can obtain the voltage drop across each resistance by applying Ohm's Law only to that part of the circuit.

$$V_1 = I_1 R_1$$
$$= (4.28)(1.59) = 6.80 \text{ v}$$
$$V_E = I_1 R_E$$
$$= (4.28)(2.98) = 12.78 \text{ v}$$
$$V_4 = I_1 R_4$$
$$= (4.28)(2.66) = 11.42 \text{ v}$$

As a check, the sum of $V_1$, $V_E$, and $V_4$ should be the same as the available voltage from the cells.

Fourth, referring back to Figure 16–72, we now can solve for the currents $I_2$ and $I_3$. Since the voltage across the equivalent resistance was 12.78 v, this will also be the voltage across each member of the parallel set. That is:

$$V_E = V_2 = V_3 = 12.78 \text{ volt}$$

The current $I_2$ and $I_3$ can be found by applying Ohm's Law only to that part of the circuit.

$$I_2 = \frac{V_2}{R_2}$$

and

$$= \frac{12.78}{6.88} = 1.858 \text{ amp}$$

$$I_3 = \frac{12.78}{5.26} = 2.43 \text{ amp}$$

As a check, $I_2 + I_3$ should equal $I_1$ or $I_4$.

More complicated circuits involving delta-wye transformations, applications of Kirchhoff's laws, or network theorems are not discussed here. However, the student may wish to investigate these additional methods of circuit solutions.

### Power

Electric power is determined in dc circuits by the product of current and voltage. That is

$$P = VI$$

where $P$ is the power in watts, $V$ is the voltage in volts, and $I$ is the current in amperes. This expression can be applied to a part of a circuit, but then only the current and voltage in that part can be used.

*Example:* Refer to Figure 16–72. Suppose it is required to determine the power used in Resistance $R_2$ and the total power supplied by the battery.

For the resistance $R_2$ power, use values only for that part.

$$P_R = V_2 I_2 \text{ (v)(amp)}$$
$$P_R = (12.78)(1.858)$$
$$= 23.7 \text{ w}$$

For the battery power, use total voltage and current values.

$$P_B = V_B I_1$$
$$= (12.3 + 18.7)(4.28)$$
$$= 133 \text{ w}$$

By algebra it can be shown that power also can be found by these expressions:

$$P = \frac{V^2}{R} \frac{(\text{volts})^2}{\text{ohm}}$$
$$P = I^2 R$$

In alternating current circuits, power expressions must be modified to account for the possibility of the maximum value of current and the maximum value of voltage not occurring at the same time. This phenomena usually is referred to as the current leading the voltage or the current lagging the voltage and is caused by the presence of capacitive or inductive components in the circuit. A detailed explanation of these effects is beyond the scope of this discussion, but this leading or lagging effect is a function of time and usually is written as

$$P = VI \cos \theta$$

where $P$ is the power in watts, $V$ is the voltage in volts, $I$ is the current in amperes, and $\theta$ is the angle called "phase angle" between a vector representing voltage and one representing current.

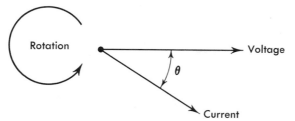

Figure 16–74. Vector representation of voltage and current in an alternating current circuit.

The diagram shown in Figure 16–74 is a vector system assumed to rotate counterclockwise and it generates sinusoidal traces on a linear time base. This figure represents current lagging in time behind the voltage. This can be caused by the presence of an inductance, usually a coil producing a magnetic field, in the alternating current circuit.

In making alternating current power measurements in a circuit having an inductance, the product of a voltmeter reading and an ammeter reading will be different from the reading of a wattmeter by the factor, cos $\theta$. Since the wattmeter reads power, the phase angle, $\theta$, can be found from the meter readings by the expression:

$$\cos \theta = \frac{P_{\text{wattmeter}}}{(V_{\text{voltmeter}})(I_{\text{ammeter}})}$$

The expression cos $\theta$, frequently is referred to as "power factor." It is possible to have a circuit condition of low power factor in which a large current is flowing but which actually involves relatively little actual power. This condition would occur if a very large capacitance or a large inductance having a very low resistance were connected in a circuit.

### Measurement of Electrical Quantities

The most common electrical measurements that are made are measurements of voltage, current, and resistance. Meters that contain a moving element and pointer together with a resistor or resistor network are the common indicating device for most measurements.

**Voltmeters.** A direct current voltmeter consists usually of a coil of very fine wire suspended but free to rotate in a permanent magnetic field. This is called a D'Arsonval movement. A typical meter contains this movement together with a series resistance of several thousand ohms in series with the coil to limit the flow of

Figure 16–75. A series resistance and millivoltmeter combination make up the basic parts of a voltmeter.

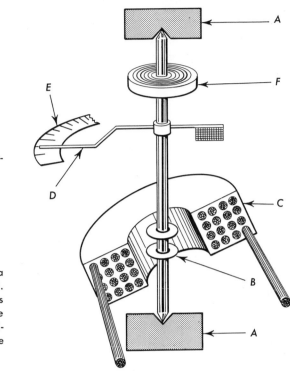

**Figure 16-76.** Iron vane type of alternating current meter.

A. Pivot bearings
B. Soft iron discs on pivot shaft
C. Cut away section of coil
D. Pointer
E. Scale
F. Controlling Spring

When current flows through the coil, a magnetic field is produced in the coil. The soft iron discs tend to line themselves along the lines of magnetism and the pivot assembly will turn until the controlling spring torque balances the torque due to magnetic effects.

current to a few milliamperes. See Figure 16–75. A scale graduated in appropriate units completes the readout assembly. It is not usable on alternating current circuits without additional circuit components.

An alternating current voltmeter usually will be one of two kinds. An iron vane type of instrument consists of a stationary coil of wire carrying a current proportional to the impressed voltage to which it is connected. The magnetic field produced by current in the coil reacts with a pivoted iron vane to which a pointer is affixed. The scale over which the pointer moves is graduated in voltage units, Figure 16–76.

A second type of alternating current voltmeter is made with two coils, one fixed and one moving. When current goes through the coils, a magnetic field is produced in each coil that reacts with each other coil to produce a torque. This is called the electrodynamometer type of instrument.

A D'Arsonval type of movement can be used to measure voltage in AC circuits if a rectifier system is used to convert the ac to dc.

**Ammeters.** A D'Arsonval movement meter can be used to measure direct currents by permitting most of the current to flow through a very low resistance device called a "shunt," Figure 16–77. When current flows through the shunt, a voltage drop is produced that can be read on a millivoltmeter. Most shunts will have a voltage drop of either 50 millivolts (mv) or 100 mv when full rated current flows through them.

An ac ammeter can be made using the iron vane or electrodynamometer type of construction. In addition, for high frequency current measurements, a hot wire type or a rectifier type of meter is sometimes used. The hot wire type of current

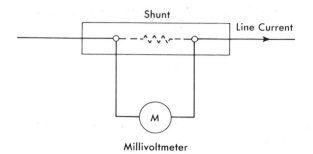

Figure 16–77. A millivoltmeter and a shunt making up an ammeter.

measuring instrument depends on the elongation of a straight wire due to the heat produced by current flowing through the wire. Its scale, like those of most ac meters, is nonlinear and is compressed at its low end.

**Wattmeters.** A common method of measuring electric power is to use a wattmeter. The usual form of wattmeter employs the dual coil construction of the electrodynamometer movement. With proper precautions, a wattmeter can be used to measure power either in dc or in ac circuits.

**Bridge Measurements.** A network of components arranged in a diamond shape is referred to as a bridge type of circuit. A typical resistive bridge is shown in Figure 16–78.

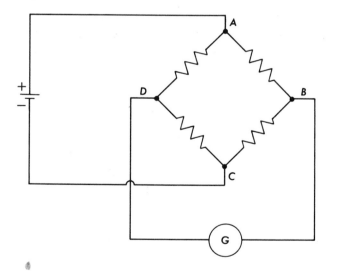

Figure 16–78. A typical resistive bridge circuit as used to indicate or measure resistance changes.

In this circuit, if the resistance path from $A$ to $B$ and $A$ to $D$ is the same resistance as the path from $B$ to $C$ and $D$ to $C$, no current flow will be shown by the galvanometer "$G$." A galvanometer is a very sensitive D'Arsonval type of movement that will respond to currents in the microampere range.

However, if any one of the four resistances is changed in resistance a very small amount, a current will flow and will be indicated by the movement of the galvanometer pointer. If one of the other resistances is changed a known amount, it is possible to rebalance the bridge to give no current flow in the galvanometer. This type of circuit measurement is called a "null-method" of measurement, since

it depends on balancing a known resistance against an unknown resistance to produce a zero or null deflection of the indicating instrument.

It can be shown that the ratio of resistance at null balances is as follows:

$$\frac{R_{AB}}{R_{AD}} = \frac{R_{BC}}{R_{DC}}$$

If we know the ratio $R_{AB}$ to $R_{AD}$ and know the amount of resistance in ohms of
$R_{DC}$, for example, then an unknown resistance $R_{BC}$ can be computed.

*Example:* The ratio of $R_{AB}$ to $R_{AD}$ is 1 to 10. At bridge balance (null) conditions, the value of $R_{DC}$ is 26.8 ohms. What is the value of $R_{BC}$?

SOLUTION:

$$R_{BC} = R_{DC}\left(\frac{R_{AB}}{R_{AD}}\right)$$
$$= 26.8\left(\frac{10}{1}\right)$$
$$= 268 \text{ ohms}$$

Note that the absolute values of $R_{AB}$ and $R_{AD}$ do not have to be known; only their
ratio must be known.

**Electron Tubes.** Following the discovery by Edison that electrical charges
could be transferred from a heated element in an evacuated space to another element in that space, DeForrest developed a device that could amplify electrical
currents. The essential parts are shown in Figure 16–79.

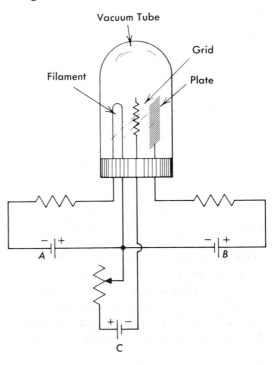

**Figure 16–79.** The essential parts of a
three-element (triode) vacuum tube.

In this simplified diagram, a cell or battery at *A* heats a filament of tungsten that frequently is coated with material such as cesium or thorium. The heat "boils off" electrons from the filament surface and produces a cloud of negatively charged particles around the filament. If the plate is made electrically positive with respect to the filament by the battery "*B*," it is possible for the charges to flow through the evacuated space from the filament area to the plate and constitute a current flow. If the positive voltage of the plate is below a certain level or if the polarity is reversed to make the plate negative, no current will flow.

These two elements in an evacuated space constitute a diode and can be used to rectify alternating currents—that is, charge the ac to pulsating direct current.

If a third electrode is introduced between the filament and plate and is connected so it is negative with respect to the filament, the voltage of this third element, called a "grid," can block the current flow, even though the positively charged plate is attempting to attract electrons. In fact, because the grid is near the filament, a very small change in its voltage will make a large change in the filament-to-plate current flow. This constitutes the amplifying capability of the vacuum tube.

### The Transistor

Shortly after the close of World War II, an announcement was made of the discovery of a solid state device requiring no heated filament that could be used as an amplifier. This discovery has in only a few years, revolutionized the electronics industry. Although the solid state diode as a rectifier had been in use for many years, the introduction of another element to permit amplification provided a tremendous opportunity for miniaturizing electronic components. This new device was called a *transistor* and, as it made its appearance almost at the same time that the computer was being developed, it was incorporated into almost all modern computers.

The theory of the transistor is fairly complex, but its action depends essentially on the presence of minute quantities of an "impurity" material such as arsenic in a crystal of pure material such as germanium permitting current to flow in one direction but not in the other. A proper assembly of three sections of negative carrier and positive carrier material permits a small voltage to control a much larger current flow in a manner similar to the way a vacuum tube behaves in a circuit.

The major advantages of the transistor as used in electronic circuits are light weight, small space, low power consumption, and long life. The modern integrated circuit described in Chapter 18 is made possible only by the use of semiconductor techniques, and permits a tiny chip of material to perform the same functions as a vacuum tube type of amplifier which would be thousands of times larger.

A fascinating new world of circuit design has been opened recently with the development of higher powered transistors, and now they can be used in all but the high current output stages of amplifiers.

### Problems

**16–135.** Using a small compass, verify experimentally the pattern of magnetic lines around a bar magnet or a horseshoe magnet.

**16–136.** List in order of increasing unit resistance, the ten best metallic conductors. In a word or two, give major advantages and disadvantages of using each as an electrical conductor for power circuits.

**16–137.** Sketch a simple circuit consisting of a crystal microphone, a vacuum tube or transistor used as an amplifier, and a loudspeaker. Explain briefly and concisely its features of operation in terms that might be used for a sales brochure.

**16–138.** A current of 5.5 ma flows from the filament to the plate of a vacuum tube. What is the approximate number of electrons flowing per second across the space?

**16–139.** A resistance of 3.65 kilohms is connected in series with 920 ohms. What is the combined resistance? If these two resistors are reconnected so they are in parallel, what will be the equivalent resistance?

**16–140.** Three resistors having values of 128 ohms, 144 ohms, and 98.2 ohms, respectively, are connected in series. What will be their combined resistance? If these three resistances are reconnected so they are in parallel with each other, what will their equivalent resistance be?

**16–141.** A current of 75.5 ma flows through a 1.80 kilohm resistance in a circuit containing a vacuum tube. What will be the voltage drop across the resistance? If the current is measured later and is found to have decreased to 48.1 ma, what things could have caused the decrease?

**16–142.** A circuit is suspected of having damaged insulation at some place in its installation on an aircraft. In order to check the insulation, a battery having a voltage of about 50 v is connected to the ship's metal structure and in series with the suspected circuit using a microammeter having an internal resistance of 100 ohms. If the microammeter reads 7.4 $\mu$a, what is the approximate resistance to ground of the circuit?

**16–143.** A battery having an internal resistance of 0.01 ohm and an open circuit voltage of 27.6 v is connected to a starter on an aircraft. If the starter resistance while not turning is 0.10 ohm and the line resistance of the connecting wires is 0.03 ohm, what maximum current can flow through the starter? What will be the voltage across the starter at the instant of closing the starting circuit?

**16–144.** Power in watts in a dc electric circuit is defined as the product of current in amperes and voltage in volts. If a 100 w lamp is connected to a 117 v line, what current will flow through the lamp? If a 40 w lamp is connected in parallel with the 100 w lamp, what total current will need to flow in the line supplying both lamps?

**16–145.** In the circuit of Figure 16–72, if the voltage of the cells is changed to an unknown amount but the current $I_1$ is measured to be 7.03 amp, what will be the values of $V_1$, $V_2$, $V_3$, $V_4$, $I_2$, $I_3$, $I_4$, and total cell voltages?

**16–146.** A dc voltage is to be measured which is known to be about 75 v. A voltmeter is not available, but a dc microammeter having a full scale of 100 $\mu$a and a resistance of 100 ohms is on hand. A large quantity of precision resistors is available. What series resistor should be chosen to make the meter show full scale deflection if 100 v is applied across it with a suitable resistor in series? (This will make the scale "direct reading.")

**16–147.** A dc shunt is to be made to permit the measurement of starting currents in an automotive starter. The expected current should not exceed 200 amp from a 12 v system. What should be the resistance of the shunt so that a current of 200 amp through it will produce a voltage drop of 50 mv across it?

**Problems (continued)**

**16–148.** A set of instructions accompanying an electrodynamic movement watt-meter says that a wattmeter should always have an ammeter and voltmeter in the circuit when the wattmeter is being used. Why is this desirable?

**16–149.** A Wheatstone bridge is set up with a ratio of 1:100 in the *AB* and *AD* sections of the bridge (see Figure 16–78). If the galvanometer shows no appreciable deflection when the resistance of *BC* is 157.1 ohms, what will be the resistance of *CD*? If there is a barely discernable deflection of the galvanometer when the resistance of *BC* is changed by ±0.3 ohms, what is the per cent uncertainty of the measurement of *CD*?

**16–150.** When using a Wheatstone bridge, what things might account for resistance measurements below 1 ohm being subject to considerable uncertainty?

**16–151.** If a change in plate voltage of 35.0 v in a vacuum tube produces a change in plate current of 2.20 ma and if a corresponding change of grid voltage of 1.7 voltage will produce the same change in plate current, what is the relative effectiveness of the change in plate voltage to change in grid voltage to produce the same change in each case of plate current? This ratio is known as amplification factor.

**16–152.** The life of an incandescent lamp varies inversely as the 12th power of the applied voltage. If the rated life of a lamp is 800 hr at 117 v, what would be the expected life if operated continuously at 120 v? What would be the expected life if operated at 110 v?

**16–153.** If energy cost is 2 cents per kw hr, what will be the approximate cost of operating a 100 w lamp an average of 5 hr per day for a month?

**16–154.** Four strain gages having a resistance of 350.0 ohms each, are cemented to a steel bar to measure surface strain. When the bar is strained and the bridge is slightly unbalanced by the strain, a galvanometer having a resistance of 30.5 ohms indicates a current flow of 12.3 $\mu$a. What would be the voltage between points *B* and *D* (see Figure 16–78) of the Wheatstone bridge network?

**16–155.** A series circuit is made up using a 10,000 ohm resistance, a 3000 ohm resistance and an ammeter having a resistance of 720 ohms all connected to a battery. If the ammeter shows a current flow of 3.03 ma, what voltage is supplied by the battery? What voltage drop would exist across the 3000 ohm resistance when this current is flowing?

**16–156.** A galvanometer used to measure small currents requires a connection to a circuit having an equivalent resistance of 350 ohms in order to help provide proper damping for reading oscillatory currents. If the strain gages making up a Wheatstone bridge to which the galvanometer is connected measure 120 ohms each, what resistance will need to be included in the circuit in order to provide proper matching resistance for the galvanometer?

**16–157.** A galvanometer used to measure small currents requires a connection to a circuit having an equivalent resistance of 120 ohms in order to help provide proper damping for reading oscillatory currents. If the strain gages making up a Wheatstone bridge to which the galvanometer is connected measure 350 ohms, what resistance will need to be included in the circuit in order to provide proper matching resistance for the galvanometer?

**16–158.** In the circuit of Figure 16–72 $R_1$ is 321 ohms, $R_2$ is 1080 ohms, $R_3$ is 844 ohms, $R_4$ is 112 ohms and $I_1$ is 39.5 ma. What will be the amount of the applied battery voltage, the voltage $V_2$, voltage $V_3$, currents $I_2$ and $I_3$ and voltage $V_4$?

**16–159.** By applications of Ohm's law show by derivation that $P = \dfrac{V^2}{R}$ and that $P = I^2R$ can be obtained from the expression $P = VI$.

**16–160.** The heating element of a cookstove is rated at 3000 w and 220 v. What current will flow when the element is turned on? To how many horse-power would 3000 w be equivalent?

**16–161.** If energy costs 2 cents per kw hr, what would be the approximate cost of operating a 100 w lamp for 1 hr?

**16–162.** In a circuit containing a large coil of wire, 60-cycle-per-second alternating current is applied and a wattmeter reads 866 w at the same time a volt-meter reads 114 v and an ammeter reads 10.1 amp. What is the phase angle in this circuit?

**16–163.** An electric iron is rated at 660 w, 110 v. What will be the approximate resistance of the heating element? Is it likely that copper wire is used for the heating element? Describe desirable properties that the heating element conductor should have.

**16–164.** A lantern type of dry cell has a voltage of 1.58 v when measured with a very high resistance voltmeter. When a very low resistance ammeter is connected across it, the current is 28.5 amp. Neglecting effects of the meter resistances on the readings, what is the internal resistance of the dry cell? Could this method be used successfully to measure the internal resistance of a 12 v automotive storage battery? Discuss.

**16–165.** A microammeter has an internal resistance of 3600 ohms and will show full scale deflection when a current of 100 $\mu$a flows through it. In order to use it as a voltmeter, a high resistance is placed in series with the micro-ammeter to limit the current through it. If it is desired that when connected to a 50 v line the microammeter and series resistor combination will be set to show full scale deflection of the pointer on the micro-ammeter, what value of series resistance should be used?

ANON. (n.d.) ... ... ... ... ... ... ... ... ... ... ... ... ... ...

# PART SIX

# INTRODUCTION TO THE
# DESIGN PROCESS

Creative and imaginative design by engineers is required to solve problems of undersea exploration. This cutaway shows a diving saucer which utilizes the principle of positive buoyance for operation down to 1,000 feet below the surface of the seas. (Courtesy Westinghouse Underseas Division.)

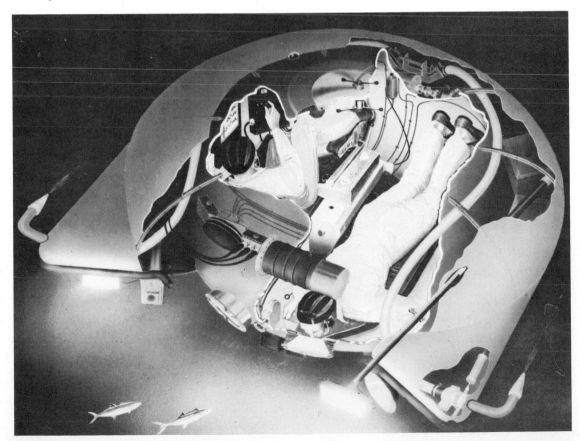

# Chapter 17

# The Engineer – A Creative Person

"In the beginning God created the heavens and the earth."[1] Thus as man counts time, the first act of recorded history was one of creation. When God created man, he endowed him with some of this ability to bring new things into being. Today the ability to think creatively is one of the most important assets that all men possess. The accelerated pace of today's technology emphasizes the need for conscious and directed creative behavior and imagination in the engineer's daily routine. However, this idea is not new.

For centuries primitive man fulfilled his natural needs by using the bounty nature placed about him. Since his choice was limited by terrain, climate, and accessibility, he was forced to choose from his environment those things which he could readily adapt to his needs. His only guide—trial and error—was a stern teacher. He ate whatever stimulated his sense of smell and taste, and he clothed himself and his family in whatever crude materials he could fashion to achieve warmth, comfort, and modesty. His mistakes often bore serious consequences, and he eventually learned that his survival depended upon his ability to think and to act in accordance with a plan. He learned the importance of imaginative reasoning in the improvement of his lot.

In recent years archaeologists have discovered evidences of early civilizations that made hunting weapons and agricultural tools, mastered the use of fire, and improvised fishing equipment from materials at hand—all at an advanced level of complexity. These remains are silent reminders of man's ingenuity. Only his cunning and imagination protected him from his natural enemies. The situation is much the same even today, centuries later. Many believe that in this respect man may not have improved his lot substantially over the centuries. The well being of our civilization still depends on how successfully we can mobilize our creative man-power. As a profession, engineering must rise to meet this challenge.

[1] *The Bible*, Revised Standard Version, Genesis I:1

PRIMITIVE TOOLS

**Illustration 17—1.** Archeologists have unearthed primitive tools which show evidence of man's creative and imaginative thought. (Courtesy E. I. DuPont de Nemours & Company.)

## WHAT IS CREATIVE BEHAVIOR?—CAN WE LEARN TO BE CREATIVE?

In recent years psychologists, philosophers, mathematicians, engineers, and others have attempted to define the characteristics of creative behavior, and particularly to describe the creative person's attributes. Although they do not agree completely, this chapter summarizes some conclusions which seem to have general consensus.

In scientific work the term *creativity* is often used interchangeably with *innovation*. However, the two should be distinguished. Both creativity and innovation refer to certain processes within an individual or system. *Innovation means producing a new, novel, or unusual idea or product (or both) by applying logic, experience, or artistry.* Innovation may come from (a) humans, (b) animals, or (c) engineered or natural phenomena. For example, some of today's high-speed digital computers have the remarkable ability to make certain decisions according to a programmed logic and to effect new and novel designs based upon the optimization of memory-stored experiences. This is innovation. As marvelous as modern computers are, some conditions do limit their usefulness. For instance, they are all slaves to some human master. They can make decisions only when they are told what criteria to use; but no computer can decide what decisions it *should* make, or on what basis. Also, as operating systems, they cannot imagine or dream. *Creativity* on the other hand, describes *a human mental process that can recognize there is a problem, and become motivated to formulate an imaginative solution, which is both valuable and innovational.* Thus, creativity assumes or presupposes human experience. Innovation may, or may not, imply human experience. Thus, an electronic computer might be programmed to innovate, but not to create. The person who programs the computer, however, might be either creative or innovative—or both.

Creativity is certainly one of the highest forms of mental activity. In addition to requiring innovation, creative behavior requires a peculiar insight set into action by a vivid but directed imagination—seemingly the result of a divine inspiration that some often call a "spark of genius." Indeed, the moment of inspiration is somewhat analogous to an electrical capacitor that has "soaked up" an electrical charge and then discharges it in a single instant. Sustained creative thought requires a large and ever increasing reservoir of innovations from which to feed.

Creative thought may be expressed in a suspension bridge, a musical composition, a painting, a poem, or a new type of machine or process. Much problem solving does not necessarily require creative thought. Many kinds of problems can be solved by careful, discriminating logic. A particular engineer then, may or may not, be a creative thinker, although all engineers should have mastered the basic techniques of problem solving. For problem solving, the engineer must be intelligent, well informed, and discerning, so that he can apply the principles of deductive reasoning to the various innovational alternatives, when he judges them.

Also, every new or original thought may not be a creative thought. A psychotic's hallucinations might well be unique even though they have no intrinsic value. Such thoughts are neither innovational nor creative. Although all creative thinkers must be innovators, it does not necessarily follow that all innovators have to be creative thinkers. Innovation occurs daily, on every hand and in every walk of life. True creative behavior is much rarer and usually requires the fulfillment of some deliberate contemplation.

All persons of normal intelligence possess some ability to think creatively and to engage themselves in imaginative and innovative effort. Unfortunately the vast majority of people are only partially aware of the range of their creative potential. This potential seldom is attained, even if recognized. This is true partially because one's social environment, home life, and educational experiences either stimulate or depress the urge to be creative. Even at a very early age, children are often urged to conform to group standards. Any deviations may bring immediate rebuke from the adult in charge. As an example, in the first grade little Johnny may be assigned to color inside the boundaries of his outlined and predrawn horse. He must color his horse brown—because the teacher likes brown horses. Black horses, white horses, green horses or other choices which might occur to Johnny are ruled out. The outline has been predrawn because, in this way, all of the children's work will appear to be reasonably good to the parents on PTA night. No child's work will have the obvious appearance of poor quality or extreme excellence—a very important item to please the majority of parents. Also the teacher will not be embarrassed by horses with horns or wings. And so it goes as Johnny grows up to assume his place in adult life. As a teenager he is considered "different" or an "odd ball" unless he always joins in with the majority. As a citizen, he is criticized as "anti-American" unless he affiliates with the political party that is in power at the moment. His neighbors "wonder" about him if he refuses to join a neighborhood drive to "achieve the Community Chest goal." His coworkers believe he is a "threat to our way of life" if he prefers independent action to letting some union speak in his behalf. And on and on we might continue. . . . It is no wonder that many well-informed persons today are creatively sterile, whereas others in former years (like Franklin and Edison) accomplished seemingly impossible results in spite of a poor formal education.

Years ago most American youths were accustomed to using innovative and imaginative design to solve their daily problems. Home life was largely one of rural experience. If tools or materials were not available, they quickly improvised some other scheme to accomplish the desired task. Most people literally "lived by their wits." Often it was not convenient, or even possible, to "go to town" to buy a clamp or some other standard device. Innovation was, in many cases, "the only way out." A visit to a typical midwestern farm or western ranch today, or to Peace Corps workers overseas, will show that these innovative and creative processes are still at work. However, today most American youths are city or suburb dwellers who do not have as many opportunities to solve real physical problems with novel ideas.

A person is not born with either a creative or noncreative mind, although some are fortunate enough to have exceptionally alert minds that literally feed on new experiences. Intellect is essential, but it is not a golden key to success in creative thinking. Intellectual capacity certainly sets the upper limits of one's innovative and creative ability; but nevertheless, motivation and environmental opportunities determine whether or not a person reaches this limit. Surprisingly, students with high I.Q.'s are not necessarily inclined to be creative. Recent studies reveal the fact that over 70 per cent of the most creative students do not rank in the upper 20 per cent of their class on traditional I.Q. measures.[2]

Everyone has some creative ability. For the average person (due to inactivity), this ability has probably been diminishing steadily since childhood. This is just another evidence of how natural laws operate in the universe. If we bind our hand or foot (as practiced in some parts of the Orient) and do not use it, it soon becomes paralyzed and ineffective. But unlike the hand or foot, which cannot recover full usefulness after long inactivity, the dormant instinct to think creatively may be revived through exercise and stimulated into activity after years of near suspended animation. Thus everyone can benefit from studying the creative and innovative processes and the psychological factors related to them.

Creative and imaginative thinking can be stimulated, and the basic principles of innovative and creative thinking can be mastered. Parnes and Meadow[3] have shown that deliberate education in creative thinking can significantly increase innovative and creative potential. In reporting this research, Osborn[4] notes that, for an experimental sample of 330 students, the subjects who enrolled in courses in creative problem solving produced 94 per cent more good ideas than subjects who did not get such training. Even if these results are somewhat optimistic, we certainly

[2] E. Paul Torrance, "Explorations in Creative Thinking in the Early School Years," in Calvin W. Taylor and Frank Barron (eds.), *Scientific Creativity,* Wiley, New York (1963), p. 182.
[3] Sidney J. Parnes and Arnold Meadow, "Development of Individual Creative Talent," *ibid.*
[4] Alex F. Osborn, *Applied Imagination,* Scribner's, New York (1963), xii.

cannot deny that even a 50 per cent improvement in our own individual creative abilities would be worth achieving. Many organizations—including DuPont, General Electric, Aluminum Company of America, Westinghouse, Aerojet General Corporation, General Motors, and the Armed Forces—believe the fundamental principles of creative thinking and problem solving can be taught, and give their personnel such training. Therefore, all young engineering students should profit from studying the principles used to spark innovation and creative effort.

### Exercises in Creative Thinking

**17–1.** How can engineering help solve some of the major world problems?

**17–2.** Discuss some of the inventions that have contributed to the success of man's first orbital space flight.

**17–3.** Write a paper not to exceed five hundred words, entitled "Fiction Today, Engineering Tomorrow."

**17–4.** You are the chief design engineer of a successful company that manufactures microelectronic devices. A local inventor proposes that your company manufacture his perpetual motion machine. Explain why you would or would not be interested in his proposition.

**17–5.** Propose a method and describe the general features of a value system whereby we could replace the use of money.

**17–6.** What procedures might be implemented to encourage more people to donate their blood to community blood banks?

**17–7.** Your engineering firm has been retained to design a relocation for the headquarters of our national government. List the states in which you would plan this new city-complex, and discuss your reasons for their selection.

**17–8.** List five problems that might now confront the city officials of your home town. Propose at least five solutions for each of these problems.

**17–9.** You have just been promoted to the vice presidency in charge of sales for a national company who manufactures hot water bottles. Give ten ways that the sale of hot water bottles may be stimulated.

**17–10.** Cut out five humorous cartoons from magazines. Recaption each cartoon such that the story told is completely changed. Attach a typed copy of your own caption underneath the original caption for each cartoon.

**17–11.** List what you believe to be the ten most important engineering achievements since the beginning of time and substantiate your selections.

**17–12.** Write a story about a mongoose, a duckling, and a crocodile that third grade children might like.

**17–13.** In one hundred words or less, provide transition statements between sentences *A* and *B* such that the total paragraph provides an interesting story with a surprise ending.

    *A*. There was an atmosphere of nostalgia surrounding John as he bid his parents farewell.

    *B*. After all, who would believe that engineering design could be that important?

**17–14.** Propose a title and theme for five new television programs.

**Exercises in Creative Thinking (continued)**

**17–15.** In the situations described below list as many consequences as you can, assuming that the changes take place suddenly.

    *a.* Earth is invaded by "beings" from outer space whose life can be sustained only by their being able to see a light at some time during the night.

    *b.* All women are forbidden by law to work, excluding those chores of housekeeping done in the home to provide for the individual needs of the family.

    *c.* The use and handling of paper in any form is forbidden.

    *d.* Electricity becomes unavailable everywhere.

    *e.* The 40-hour work week is reduced to a 20-hour work week.

**17–16.** Make a list of five common items that are used by the homeowner. Give as many suggestions for desirable design improvements as you can for each item.

**17–17.** List ten innovational uses that might be made of empty beverage cans.

**17–18.** List new items that might profitably be packaged and distributed in pressurized cans.

**17–19.** Describe the rules for play of a new athletic game suitable for high school or college students.

**17–20.** Door keys are frequently a nuisance and they can be easily misplaced. provide some means to do without them.

**17–21.** Suggest three new design features that might improve the chance of passenger survival for commercial airlines in the event of an inevitable crash.

**17–22.** Suggest solutions for each of the following predicaments:

    *a.* You desire to slowly compress a spring that is located in the entry hall of your home, and whose spring constant is 100 lb/in.

    *b.* the 50 ft high tower supporting a 10 lb television antenna has collapsed. Reception must be restored in three hours.

    *c.* You desire to measure exactly six gallons of water. You have only a four-gallon and a nine-gallon container.

**17–23.** The following series of five words are related such that each word has a meaningful association with the word adjacent to it. Supply the missing words.

    *a.* automobile   _____ _____ _____ green

    *b.* wristwatch   _____ _____ _____ Halloween

    *c.* teenager   _____ _____ _____ caboose

    *d.* football   _____ _____ _____ moon

    *e.* college   _____ _____ _____ highway

**17–24.** What things might be done in a dental office to improve patient comfort and reduce anxiety?

**17–25.** For what useful applications might solar radiant energy be efficiently utilized?

## DEVELOPMENT OF CREATIVE EFFORT

Associated with innovative and creative thought are imagination, curiosity, discovery, invention, and intuitive insight. As suggested above, the desire to use these faculties begins at an early age. Thwarting or suppressing this individuality of thought may change a child's personality. It is unfortunate that many of our mental resources are wasted in this way. Creative talent should be sought out, developed, and utilized wherever possible. But doing so is far from easy; although psychologists have described some general attributes and traits of the creative personality, it may be difficult to measure an individual's potential to perform creatively.

Although everyone has some capacity to be innovative and creative, "creative ability" is usually a scarce commodity. It need not be, however, because we can enumerate and measure the influence of the mental attitudes and thought processes that are most conducive to producing innovative and creative effort. Using some of these fundamental processes will certainly return valuable dividends. But first, one must have a proper mental attitude.

## AN ATTITUDE FOR INNOVATIVE AND CREATIVE THOUGHT

Unfortunately, there is no *one* set of ideal conditions that will always give the most effective imaginative and creative thought. The best conditions vary with personality and circumstances. However, it is important to approach all problems with an open mind—one as free from restrictions and preconceived limiting conditions as possible. Sentiments such as fear, greed, and hatred must be put aside. Try to approach problem situations with a clear mind that has been stimulated *but not restrained* by past experiences. In general, your thought processes are influenced by *how* and *what* you have already learned, but tradition may hinder rather than help, especially if you have made incorrect or irrelevant assumptions. This is particularly true where certain attitudes, convictions, or feelings have stimulated your emotions excessively. In such instances reasoning tends to be influenced so it will harmonize with these convictions. The engineer must learn to be receptive to new ideas, even though they may depart from conventional practices. He must always seek authenticity and truth, rather than trying to verify preconceived ideas or existing procedures.

The engineer must be *motivated* to use imaginative and innovative thought. Basically most creative persons—whether they are artists, musicians, poets, scientists, or engineers—are motivated to work at a particular task partly because of the exhilaration, thrill, special satisfaction, pride, and pleasure they get from completing a creative task. It is perhaps natural that man should emulate his Creator in this respect. For, in each case, after creating the heavens and the earth, after adorning the earth with plant and animal life, and again after creating man and woman, God gave expression of His pleasure.

"And God saw everything that he had made, and behold, it was very good."[5]

But besides the sense of satisfaction that comes from the creative process itself, other factors also stimulate and motivate the engineer toward creative design efforts.

[5] *The Bible,* Revised Standard Version, Genesis I:31.

These may be classified into two groups.

1. *Basic Motives:* food and preservation, faith, love, aspiration for fame or freedom.
2. *Secondary Motives:* competition, pride, loyalty

Motivation is the power source that drives all engineers forward in their role as problem solvers, innovators, and creators. Some factors and circumstances will reinforce and stimulate natural motive power. Others will weaken and depress motive power. Engineers should be acquainted with both positive and negative motivating factors.

## CONDITIONS THAT STIMULATE CREATIVE THINKING

There are a number of conditions and circumstances that stimulate creative thinking. Some of these are general *conditions of circumstance* that are related to individual *personality* and *philosophy* and are apart from any particular or specific action. Other conditions are related to the individual's *state of mind.* In addition, the engineer must have particular personal qualities and attitudes to achieve maximum motivational stimulation.

The engineer must understand both nature and his environment. He must learn to carefully evaluate the results and consequences of his work. Many times it will be easy for him to draw an incorrect, though seemingly obvious, conclusion. The story is told of a young biologist who was investigating the sensitivity of a frog's sensory system. He devised an experimental apparatus with blinking lights and screeching sirens and positioned his frog for testing. He reasoned that the frog would become frightened by the noise and lights and attempt to escape. Beginning with the right rear leg, he carefully severed each leg in turn, and noted how far the frog could jump. When the frog did not move after its fourth leg was severed, he noted the following in his laboratory report:

> All frogs are very sensitive to light and sound. However, at the moment the left foreleg is removed, they become deaf and blind.

We laugh at the young man's foolish statement, but daily we react in a similar manner as time after time we draw incorrect conclusions.

The engineer will devote a lifetime to changing and modifying his environment. His daily work will affect social and economic life. His actions and designs will be reflected in the lives of all people everywhere as their habits and customs change. He must recognize and assume a special responsibility in this regard because *all* of his innovate designs will probably not be used for the *betterment* of his fellow men and for uplifting their culture. He must recognize that the products of his imagination may, in fact, be used in ways that are detrimental to society. In addition, he must realize that his failures and his successes, all of the fruits of his labor, are always on public display. President Herbert Hoover, himself an engineer, stated these conditions well:

> *Engineering* training deals with the exact sciences. That sort of exactness makes for truth and conscience. It might be good for the world if more men had that sort of mental start in life, even if they did not pursue the profes-

sion. But he who would enter these precincts as a life work must have a test taken of his imaginative faculties, for engineering without imagination sinks to a trade.

It is a great profession. There is the fascination of watching a figment of the imagination emerge through the aid of science to a plan on paper. Then it moves to realization in stone or metal or energy. Then it brings jobs and homes to men. Then it elevates the standards of living and adds to the comforts of life. That is the engineer's high privilege.

The great liability of the engineer compared to men of other professions is that his works are out in the open where all can see them. His acts, step by step, are in hard substance. He cannot bury his mistakes in the grave like the doctors. He cannot argue them into thin air or blame the judge like the lawyers. He cannot, like the architect, cover his failures with trees and vines. He cannot, like the politicians, screen his shortcomings by blaming his opponents and hope that the people will forget. The Engineer simply cannot deny that he did it. If his works do not work, he is damned. That is the phantasmagoria that haunts his nights and dogs his days. He comes from the job at the end of the day resolved to calculate it again. He wakes in the night in a cold sweat and puts something on paper that looks silly in the morning. All day he shivers at the thought of the bugs which will inevitably appear to jolt its smooth consummation.

On the other hand, unlike the doctor, his is not a life among the weak. Unlike the soldier, destruction is not his purpose. Unlike the lawyer, quarrels are not his daily bread. To the engineer falls the job of clothing the bare bones of science with life, comfort and hope. . . .

The engineer performs many public functions from which he gets only philosophical satisfactions. Most people do not know it, but he is an economic and social force. Every time he discovers a new application of science, thereby creating a new industry, providing new jobs, adding to the standards of living, he also disturbs everything that is. New laws and regulations have to be made and new sorts of wickedness curbed. . . . But the engineer himself looks back at the unending stream of goodness which flows from his successes with satisfactions that few professions may know.[6]

No one, regardless of his profession, is likely to be motivated to creative effort unless he has a strong and undiminishing love for his work. With this love, each day's task becomes more than a means of providing a better standard of living. Each successfully accomplished design provides a special satisfaction that comes only to those who have a strong ambition to succeed. The habit of work will become a part of the individual's personality until even his subconscious mind becomes saturated with the problem. These general conditions and circumstances provide very important climates for creative and imaginative thought.

The proper attitudes or states of mind can also contribute much to creative and imaginative thought. To be most effective, a person should certainly have a healthy body and a clear, intelligent mind, although a high I.Q. or a strong physique by no means guarantees innovative or creative ideas. Psychological freedom, in which the mind is unrestricted by past or present evaluations and judgments, is also very important. In fact, where the "fear of being wrong" has been removed, innovative and

[6] Herbert Hoover, *Memoirs of Herbert Hoover,* Vol. 1, *Years of Adventure,* Macmillan, New York (1951), p. 132.

creative thought usually increases significantly, for groups of engineers working together as well as for individuals.

Significant and imaginative thought processes are usually rare when the conscious mind becomes fatigued or when there is intense emotion (joy, sorrow, or fear). The relationships between *effective creative behavior* and *physiological stress* might be illustrated in Figure 17–1. Each personality would have its own individual pattern or mathematical expression relating these variables.

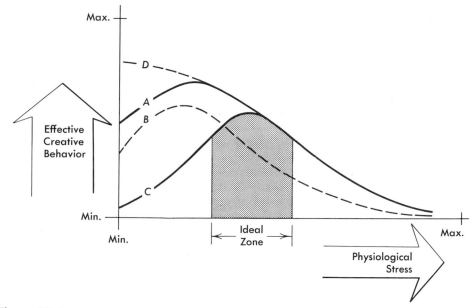

**Figure 17–1.**

The primary curve (A) indicates that, when the mind is without tension and the emotions are at rest, there is considerable possibility that imaginative and creative ideas can emerge. As supporting evidence for this conclusion, many creative people testify that their most novel ideas have appeared when they were engaged in such mild mental activities as bathing, listening to a musical concert, walking on the golf course, or riding the subway. Although this is not the usual case, such a situation might be represented by curve D. The secondary curves, B and C, indicate typical alternate paths that two different individuals might show. Thus there is an ideal condition or emotional zone for each individual; for him it is most conducive to creative thought.

Other mental states that contribute positively toward creative thought are (a) an inquiring and questioning mind, (b) abilities to concentrate and communicate, (c) ability to accept conflict and tension without becoming frustrated, and (d) willingness to consider a new idea *even though it may seem to be in conflict* with previous experience.

In addition, there are personal qualities which are frequently associated with creative individuals. Developing them will enhance the likelihood that the individual will express himself creatively. They are as follows:

1. Intellectual curiosity
2. Sensitivity to recognize that a problem exists
3. Acute powers of observation
4. Directed imagination
5. Initiative
6. Ability to think in analogies and images
7. Originality
8. Intuition
9. Memory
10. Being articulate in verbal response and alert in mental processes
11. Ability to analyze and synthesize
12. Patience, determination, and persistence
13. Intellectual integrity
14. Understanding of the creative process

## CONDITIONS THAT DEPRESS CREATIVE THINKING

Just as certain conditions stimulate creative thinking, certain conditions also depress creative thinking and creative behavior. Thus, though the engineer may have high creative potential and intellectual ability to analyze, synthesize, and evaluate, he still may not be creative and innovative. These "road blocks to creative behavior" may be classified into three categories: (a) barriers resulting from experience and perception, (b) emotional barriers, and (c) social and cultural barriers. Each of these will be considered briefly here.

### Barriers to Creative Behavior Resulting from Experience and Perception

A recent experiment vividly illustrates the limitations that can be imposed by habit. This experiment involved a problem solving situation where two groups were asked to extract a ping-pong ball from the bottom of a long, small-diameter pipe standing vertically. When the members of the first group entered the experimental room, they saw assorted objects, including a screwdriver, pliers, string, thumbtacks, and a bucket of dirty water. None of the tools seemed useful, but after some time, about half of the group realized that the ping-pong ball could be recovered by pouring water into the pipe until the ball floated to the top.

The second group attacked the same problem. The small articles were displayed again. In this case, however, the container of water was missing. In its place was a dinner table which had been set with china and silverware. On the table were a large pitcher of milk, and a bucket of ice cubes. No one was able to solve the problem because the subjects could not relate the liquid (milk), or "solid water" (ice) used for dining, to the totally different mechanical problem.

This experiment illustrates the danger of blind reliance on *restricted experience* in problem solving. In some instances, one may assume artificial restrictions that limit and bind his thought processes. As an example, consider the puzzle shown in Figure 17–2.

**Figure 17–2.**

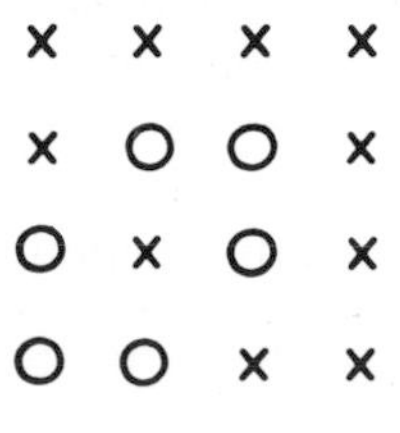

**Problem**

Six cows (shown as circles) are standing in a grove of trees (shown as X's). Draw three straight <u>connected</u> lines <u>to join</u> all of the trees without touching any of the cows.

Nothing in the problem statement implies that the lines represent fences or that the three lines must be restricted to the boundaries of the imaginary rectangular plot containing the cows and trees. However, most people automatically restrict themselves within this field and, under these artificial conditions, the problem becomes impossible to solve. This puzzle also illustrates the point that, in many instances, workable solutions to a problem are suggested by someone with minimal technical background related *directly* to the problem, but who has a broad fundamental understanding of the principles governing the situation.

Strange as it may seem, it is nevertheless true that the more original and novel an idea is, the more vulnerable it is to criticism. Often the people most apt to prejudge a situation and allow the past experiences to strangle a new idea are the ones whose analytical abilities have carried them to prior success. Certainly such skills *are essential* for minimum accomplishment in engineering. However, it sometimes seems easier to rely upon a previously successful mathematical model than to consider the problem anew. It may well be that the original conditions have changed. We are all familiar with this tendency to "overconfidence" which sometimes overcomes those who excel in their field. It is particularly evident in athletics, where a less-able person may be the eventual victor because he never recognizes that he is supposed to suffer defeat. The moral: Never prejudge; consider each situation on its own merits.

We are told that a man dying of thirst has little difficulty in seeing a mirage of a lake off in the distance. The image he *is* seeing seems to be affected in large measure by what his mind tells him that he *needs* to see. He is expectant and thirsty, therefore, it is easy for him to see the lake of water. In a sense, then, believing is seeing. The mind's recall of events and experiences also tends to influence one's observation, discernment, and judgment. For example, look at Figures 17–3 and 17–4. Note that there are two straight lines in each figure.

Do the two vertical lines in Figure 17–3 appear equal in length? Probably not. Are the two lines in Figure 17–4 parallel to each other? "No," you say. Most people will think that these two simple questions are strange indeed. The answers appear obvious in both cases. However, if we tell you that Figure 17–3 is actually a picture of two telephone poles standing in the desert sands, and that Figure 17–4 is a picture of a railroad track receding into the distance, you might quickly change your answers to "yes" or "maybe." In addition, the brief verbal descriptions that were added have given each picture a quality of depth that you did not recognize originally, demonstrating that we must sharpen our powers of observation, be alert to alternate explanations, and avoid the pitfalls of prejudgment and presumption that so often stifle our thought processes.

Another example might show how prior experience can artificially limit our thinking. Once two medical doctors were riding down the street together when they observed a "head-on" collision ahead. Upon arriving at the scene, they ran to the wrecked automobiles to render aid. After looking into one vehicle, the first physician moaned, "My wife and child!" Hearing this exclamation, the second physician pulled out a gun and killed the first physician. What is your analysis of the motive for this murder?

Writers of novels are skillful in maneuvering fiction plots so that the reader

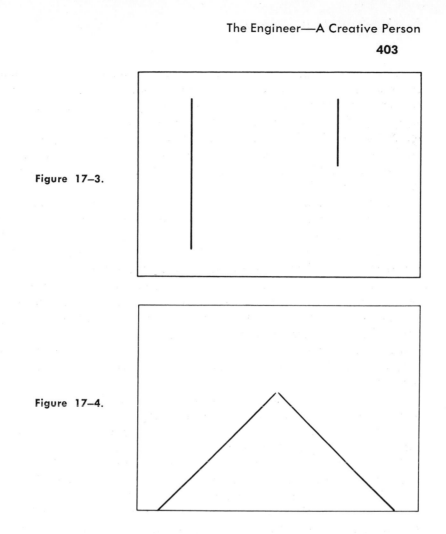

Figure 17–3.

Figure 17–4.

makes an invalid assumption. Perhaps you did this in the above example. Did you assume that both physicians were men? If both physicians were men, the story seems confused and no plausible explanation appears possible. However, the familiar triangular plot of secret love and consequential murder quickly unfolds when you realize that the second physician is a young woman.

Other barriers resulting from experience and perception are:

1. Limited scope of basic knowledge.
2. Failure to recognize all of the conditions relating to the problem—failure to get all of the facts.
3. Preconception and reliance upon the history of other events.
4. Failure to investigate both the obvious and the trivial.
5. Artificial restriction of the problem.
6. Failure to recognize the *real* problem.
7. Inclusion of extraneous environmental factors.
8. Failure to distinguish between cause and effect.
9. Inability to manipulate the abstract.

**Emotional Barriers**

The graph in Figure 17–1 illustrates that everyone's effective creative behavior diminishes to insignificance under high emotional stress. When under emotional strain, one is likely to narrow his field of observation, to make "snap judgments" that are not well thought out, and thus to disregard alternate and more valuable solutions. Overmotivated people are also likely to choose unrealistic and overambitious objectives. Emotional constraints are perhaps more damaging than other types because they can have such lasting influence upon one's personality. The emotional constraint most difficult to cope with is fear—fear of failure, of criticism, of ridicule, of embarrassment, or of loss of employment. The fear of social disapproval can stifle initiative and reduce the flow of imaginative ideas. Controlled psychological experiments have shown that groups produce up to 70 per cent more innovative and novel ideas when group members do not *judge and evaluate each other's ideas* until later, thus largely removing the fears of ridicule and criticism. Brainstorming, a technique developed in the advertising business to produce more imaginative ideas, is one type of group effort that receives its stimulus by deferring judgment. Ways to implement this technique will be discussed later.

An inferiority complex, resistance to change from the status quo, and a lack of reward stimulus can also be barriers to creative and innovative thought.

**Social and Cultural Barriers**

The history of civilization is essentially the record of man's creative behavior or lack thereof. Ancient cultures rose to great heights in Egypt (2700–1800 B.C.), Greece (600–300 B.C.), and Rome (400 B.C.–A.D. 400), but these civilizations eventually fell because of laxity of purpose, moral decay, and the people's overall lack of initiative. These conditions frequently arise when complacency, comfort, and luxury become primary objectives. When one must live or die by his wits, so to speak, his mind is stimulated to function more clearly than it would in a sheltered society. Younger generations who *inherit* the advantages of prosperity generally neither know nor appreciate the discipline of work. All these conditions reduce the motivation for creative thought.

Today, America faces a challenge much like those other cultures have faced in ages past. The physical frontiers that inspired our pioneer forefathers are fast disappearing from view. Fortunately, however, there are new frontiers such as outer space, ocean exploration, improved human relations and communications, disease eradication, new food and power sources, and waste elimination, which challenge our best and our maximum effort. These twentieth century goals are, in many ways, more challenging than the frontier-day obstacles of a few hundred years ago. Even more significant, perhaps, is the fact that these new frontiers cannot be conquered successfully by applying known procedures or processes routinely. Individual initiative and motivation must continue to be the keys that unlock new ideas and stimulate creative thought. However, as with other cultures, intellectual decay must inevitably result if we desire security too strongly, choose undirected leisure instead of work, or deviate from our fundamental ideals.

Man is a social being and, as such, he needs the companionship of other men. His emotions, habits, and thoughts are strongly affected by the cultural influences that surround him. At an early age, he learns that his associates disapprove some of his actions and reward others with accolades and commendation. Such rewards may motivate him to make supreme efforts to gain recognition, but condemnation may make him afraid of deviating from his comrades' "group opinion" and thus stifle his creative and imaginative thought.

Over conformity to a group seems especially unfortunate since a group or a committee as a discrete entity cannot, as such, produce creative thoughts. Creative thoughts come *only* from the minds of individuals. However, a committee or group can very definitely possess a unique personality that has strengths, weaknesses, and abilities—just as is the case for an individual. This fact does not discredit the accomplishments of teams, where the team members stimulate each other to produce novel and imaginative ideas. Not uncommonly, one team member's inspired idea will set off a chain reaction of ideas from other team members, whose subconscious memories have been awakened and stimulated into action. Team action is particularly effective in producing a large *volume* of ideas or getting a moderate course of action based on a *consensus*. Remember that hundreds of thousands of statues have been erected around the world . . . all to honor individuals. But so far, not one has been raised to honor a committee. It has been said, perhaps too harshly, that a committee never accomplishes anything unless it has three members one of whom is always absent and one of whom is always ill. Once Winston Churchill is said to have remarked that a committee was the organized result of a group of the incompetent who have been appointed by the uninformed to accomplish the unnecessary. Although his statement brings a smile to the lips of anyone who has served on very many committees, we must recognize that Churchill's own life showed there is no substitute for bold, imaginative, individual thought.

Cultural restraints may be intangible, but they are very real. For example, someone assigned to reduce hunger in India might logically begin by looking at the availability of edible and nourishing foodstuffs in India. He would soon discover that India has a higher ratio of cows to people than any other country. Many of these cows could be slaughtered to provide enough bouillon, or clear meat broth, to sustain millions of people. Yet Indian culture reinforced by the country's predominant religion, considers the cow a sacred animal that must not be harmed—certainly not killed and made into steaks and bouillon cubes.

In a modern society most people are reluctant to accept change. Generally they are either indifferent or negative to proposed ideas. This is why creative people like Leonardo da Vinci, Copernicus, Galileo, and Mozart never lived to see mankind accept the products of their imaginations. Modern civilizations have frequently been no more charitable to those who dared challenge contemporary mores. For example, John Kay was assaulted by weavers who feared his flying shuttle would destroy their means of livelihood; farmers scoffed at Charles Newbold's iron plow and insisted it would contaminate the soil; and the medical profession censured Dr. Horace Wells for using "gas" when extracting teeth.[7]

In more recent times when the motel was first proposed as a new concept in innkeeping, the idea was greeted with scorn by leading hotel executives. However, the test of time has shown the immense value of the idea. Because of this built-in

---

[7] Alex F. Osborn, *Applied Imagination*, Scribner's, New York (1963), p. 54.

resistance to change, many new developments must necessarily originate outside of the specialized area of endeavor.

But cultural blocks to creative behavior are not always as obvious as in these situations. For example, few of us would doubt the validity of a statement if we read it in a school textbook or in the daily newspaper. Under other circumstances, however, the same people might greet the same statement with considerable debate, for example, if it appears to be the casual observation of a friend or associate with equal or lower social or intellectual standing. Yesterday everyone admired the young person who showed initiative in thinking for himself. Unfortunately, today we may not. Too often teachers, parents, and friends value the young person's ability to adapt himself to associates' dictates and his willingness to think and act in accordance with crowd sentiments above everything else. These social constraints stifle and suppress our desire and ability to think independently and imaginatively and to behave creatively.

All of these constraints therefore are detrimental to creative thought processes.

### Exercises in Creative Thinking

**17–26.** What new products might make travel by private automobile more enjoyable?

**17–27.** Discuss the possibilities of using water as a fuel.

**17–28.** You have acquired 100,000 used tractor tubes. What might you do with them?

**17–29.** One million steel ball bearings one inch in diameter are available at a cost of 1¢ per 100. Would you purchase them? If so, how much profit might you anticipate?

**17–30.** What might be the consequences if:
   *a.* Water contracted instead of expanded on freezing?
   *b.* Everyone's thoughts were registered on a small TV screen on the forehead?
   *c.* The air temperature on the earth began to cool at the rate of one °F per year?
   *d.* All people were born without fingers or thumbs?
   *e.* All people were born with only one eye in the *back* of their heads?

**17–31.** You are assigned the task of dividing the United States into new State divisions. Show your solution on a map, and attach an explanation that describes your reasoning.

**17–32.** A new discovery has made it possible for man to live without eating. Discuss some consequences of this new discovery.

**17–33.** In one minute, list as many things as you can think of that are (*a*) black, (*b*) green, (*c*) round, (*d*) good to eat, (*e*) poison, and (*f*) sweet.

**17–34.** What are five ways in which you might accumulate a crowd of 100 people at the corner of Main Street and Central at 8 A.M. on Saturday?

**17–35.** Suggest several "highly desirable" alterations that would encourage personal travel by rail.

What might each of Figures 17–36 to 17–50 represent? List as many possibilities as you can. Modifications are encouraged.

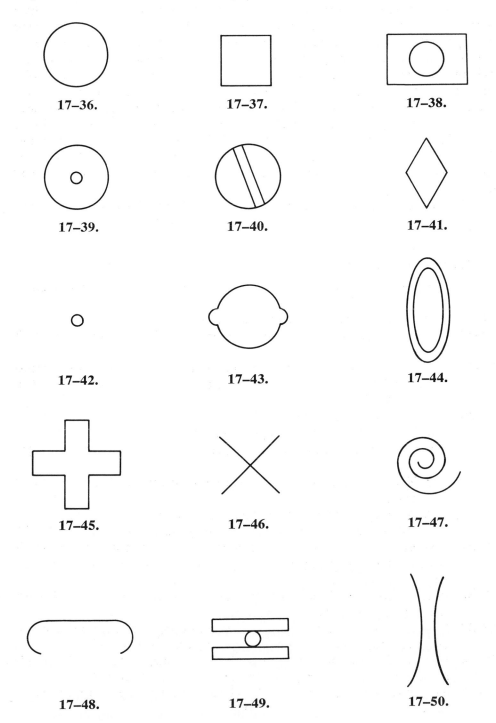

**17–36.**　　**17–37.**　　**17–38.**

**17–39.**　　**17–40.**　　**17–41.**

**17–42.**　　**17–43.**　　**17–44.**

**17–45.**　　**17–46.**　　**17–47.**

**17–48.**　　**17–49.**　　**17–50.**

## THE STIMULATION OF IDEAS

The engineer, as a professional man, must have keen analytical skill and the ability to synthesize. Without it he would be as handicapped as a boat without a rudder. His education must, necessarily, concentrate on this important part of the engineer's development. Both the engineer and his client must have confidence that his design calculations are both pertinent and accurate. However, an engineer who cannot produce a continuous flow of imaginative ideas is analogous to a boat without an engine. In the first case, he may wander aimlessly, stumbling over his errors. But in the second case, he will never get started at all. Therefore, engineering education must consider procedures for stimulating ideas. Certain of these procedures will work satisfactorily in one situation, yet at other times, other methods may be needed.

Previous paragraphs have shown how desirable it is to maintain the proper mental attitude toward the problem under study. High emotional stress, preconceived ideas based upon habit, or overemphasis on some assumed evaluation of an idea's ultimate value—all these are particularly damaging in the initial stages of idea development. Freedom of thought is essential. If freedom is restricted, whether the restricting agent is tangible or intangible makes little difference. The results will be the same: reduced imaginative effort. Ancient history reveals that, before 3000 B.C. societies allowed the individual considerable freedom; artisans worked to enhance their own well-being rather than to expand the dominion of some ruler, king, or god-king. Inventions, like the ax, the wheel, the plow, sail boats, writing, irrigation, the arch, pottery, spinning, and metallurgy, are all examples of new ideas that appeared first within this *free* type of environment. By about 1000 B.C., artisans found themselves working primarily to enhance the power of the ruler or king. Under these conditions, they produced considerably fewer new ideas than in the free environment. Customs may also block imaginative thought. For example, archaeologists now believe that the pyramid-shaped structures built to protect Egyptian tombs had been housed in oblong buildings whose walls were made of sun-dried bricks. Since rain deteriorated these walls, the Egyptians had learned to slope the walls inward at the top, thus improving drainage and increasing durability. This custom persisted some 2000 years later, when stone had long since replaced the primitive clay bricks. Even though the outside walls no longer needed to be sloped for protection against erosion, *custom* dictated that they should slope inward at the top.

Other examples have emphasized that the people who have imaginative ideas are the ones who "see with their minds" as well as their eyes. Therefore, the engineer must be continually sensitive to impressions and to their significance. It is said that Galileo was walking about a cathedral one day when he noticed a large lamp swinging from side to side. From this observation he conceived his idea of the pendulum. There are similar possibilities for imaginative thought today, and perhaps even more of them than in the ancient past.

Many times we will think of an idea that seems particularly exciting and innovative. When such a thought occurs, the substance of the idea should be recorded immediately so that it will not be lost. It is recommended therefore, that the engineer always have a small notebook or card that can be carried easily in a shirt or coat pocket and a pencil or pen.

The methods for deliberately stimulating ideas that are used most in industry today are: (a) reviewing of properties and alternatives and the use of check lists, (b) systematically searching design parameters, (c) brainstorming, and (d) synectics. These methods will be discussed briefly.

### Review of Properties and Alternatives and the Use of Check Lists

Most creative and innovative effort in industry today is the result of individual thought processes. Although some idea searches lend themselves to solution by a group effort, as will be discussed later, this is not usually so. Therefore, we should begin by considering the methods an individual can use to stimulate his own production of ideas.

Perhaps the most common procedure is considering how all of the various properties or qualities of a particular design solution might be changed or modified. First, the modifiable properties should be listed: weight, size, color, odor, taste, shape, or texture. Functions that are desirable for the item's intended use may also be listed: automatic, strong, or light weight. Then the engineer can consider each listed property or function individually.

As an example, consider redesigning a car jack. The listed properties might include (1) steel, (2) screw operated, (3) undercar type, (4) manual, (5) medium weight, and (6) black color. To devise a better jack, the engineer should consider other possibilities for each property. What other materials could we use? Can we reduce the weight? Would a hydraulic jack be better? How about a bumper jack? Would reflective paint help prevent accidents at night? Questions like these may suggest how the design could be improved. The properties of car jacks have changed many times. These changes have presumably made car jacks more efficient and easier to use.

Besides considering the product's various properties, the engineer must question, observe, and associate its functions. Can these functions be modified, rearranged, or combined? Or can the product even serve other functions? Can the product be adapted to other uses? Can it be substituted for another product? Can we change the shape (magnify or minify parts of the design)? With this type of questioning we can construct an individual check list of idea stimulators.

### Systematic Search of Design Parameters

Frequently it is advisable to investigate alternatives more thoroughly. A systematic search considers all possible combinations of given conditions or design parameters. This type of search is frequently called a "matrix analysis" or a "morphological synthesis" of alternatives[8,9]. Its success in stimulating ideas depends largely upon the engineer's identifying all of the significant parameters that affect the design. The necessary steps for implementing this type of idea search are:

1. *Describe the problem.* This description should be broad and general, so that it will not exclude possible solutions.

2. *Select the major independent-variable conditions* required in combination to describe the characteristics and functions of the problem under consideration.

---

[8] K. W. Norris, "The Morphological Approach to Engineering Design," in J. Christopher Jones, *Conference on Design Methods,* Macmillan, New York, (1963), p. 116.

[9] Myron S. Allen, *Morphological Synthesis,* Prentice Hall, Edgewood Cliffs, N.J., (1962).

3. *List several ways or methods that satisfy* each of the independent-variable conditions selected.

4. *Set up a matrix* with each of the independent-variable conditions as one axis of a rectangular array. Where more than three conditions are shown the display can be presented in parallel columns.[9]

5. *Consider, in turn, the feasibility of the combinations* of methods within the matrix.

Let us consider a specific example to see how this method can be applied.

1. *Problem Statement:* A continuous source of contaminate-free water is needed.
2. *Independent-Variable Conditions:*
   (1) Energy
   (2) Source
   (3) Process
3. *Methods of Satisfying Each Condition:*
   (1) *Types of Energy:*
       a. Solar
       b. Electrical
       c. Fossil
       d. Atomic
       e. Mechanical
   (2) *Types of Source:*
       a. Underground
       b. Atmosphere
       c. Surface supply
   (3) *Types of Process:*
       a. Distillation
       b. Transport
       c. Manufacture
4. *The Matrix:* (See Figure 17–5.)

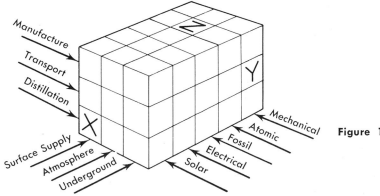

Figure 17–5.

5. *Combinations*

This particular matrix may be represented as an orderly arrangement of 45 small blocks stacked neatly to form a rectangular parallelepiped. Every block in each row or column on each of the major axes will be labeled with the unit designations selected previously. Thus block *x* suggests obtaining pure water by distilling a surface supply with a solar-energy power source. Block *y* means transporting water from an underground source by some mechanical means, and block *z* recommends manufacturing water from the atmosphere using atomic power. Obviously, some of the blocks represent well-known solutions, and others suggest absurd or impractical possibilities. Still others may represent untried combinations that deserve investigation.

Where more than three variables are to be considered the following method which has been developed by Dr. Myron S. Allen should be implemented:

*Step 1:* Get the feel of the general problem area. Read all available material concerning the problem, marking or otherwise identifying all ideas that appear to be of any possible significance—without any immediate evaluation. Talk with as many people as possible who are parts of the problem in any way. Take careful notes.

*Step 2:* Type all of the ideas collected in step one on 2.5 by 3-inch cards, with the 3-inch side horizontal.

*Step 3:* Lay the cards on a table in blocks of twelve—three cards wide and four cards high. Leave about one quarter of an inch between individual cards, and one inch between blocks of cards. This arrangement has worked out to be the best of many different plans.

*Step 4:* Read the cards over four or five times, as quickly as you can. All of the ideas presented will be retained in your mind permanently, most of them in your subconscious. We shall make intuitive use of these "submerged" ideas during the process of setting up the total problem.

*Step 5:* Go away from the cards for at least half an hour, taking great pains to occupy your conscious mind so completely that it will not be thinking about the cards. Your subconscious mind will continue to work diligently on the problem, and with much higher efficiency than it could if your conscious mind simultaneously is criticizing every new idea proposed by your intuition.

*Step 6:* Return to the cards and again study them. You will now notice that certain of the cards appear to be friendly to one another—just friendly—and may easily be collected into congenial groups. If you had started with 500 cards you might wind up with from 20 to 30 of these friendly groups. Now write a descriptive title card for each group (use a distinctive color) and place a rubber band around the group.

*Step 7:* Treating each of the groups of cards now as a single element, continue synthesizing the groups into a still smaller number of groups until you finally come to no more than seven groups. Again write a descriptive card for each of these final groups. These are the fundamental elements of the problem, which are commonly called parameters. (This number seven was not an arbitrary assumption, but is in recognition of the proven psychological fact that seven elements is the maximum that the human mind can consider efficiently at one time in a single group.)

*Step 8:* Analyze the cards of each parameter into not more than seven subgroups, called components. The original groupings as found in Step 6 will often turn out to be components, but sometimes other arrangements will appear more suitable.

*Step 9:* Type the parameters, and their components, in columns.

*Step 10:* Cut the pages up into strips of one parameter each. Then paste the strips on pieces of thin cardboard of the same size as the paper strips. Make a simple device to hold the slides. You are now ready to take a look at the real, the total, problem.[10]

Electronic computers also may be used to excellent advantage. After the matrix has been programmed, the computer can print a list of all the alternatives, and combinations thereof. Such a list is especially helpful when considering a large number of parameters.

The *review of properties and alternatives* and the *systematic search* are most useful for an individual engineer searching for new ideas. But often several designers may all be searching jointly for imaginative ideas about some particular product. Then it may be advantageous to use the procedures called brainstorming or synectics.

### Brainstorming

The term "brainstorming" was coined by Alex F. Osborn[11] to describe a particular type of organized group effort aimed at solving a problem by compiling all of the ideas the members of the group can contribute and deferring judgment concerning their worth. This is accomplished by (1) releasing the imagination of the participants from restraints such as fear, conformity, and judgment; and by (2) providing a means whereby the improvement and combination of ideas is encouraged at the moment that the ideas are expressed. Osborn points out that this collaborative group effort is not meant to replace individual ideative effort. Group brainstorming is used solely to supplement individual idea production. It is not recommended where the problem solution will depend primarily on judgment, rather than upon a new or novel design approach. Its use is also limited where the problem is vast, complex, vague, or controversial or in those situations where the people involved do not belong to a homogeneous status group. Sometimes, though, this method works very effectively for finding a large volume of alternative solutions. It has been particularly useful for stimulating imaginative ideas for new products or product development. A group of six to twelve persons seems to be best for stimulating ideas with this method. However, the United States Armed Forces have used a hundred or more participants effectively.

All of the panel members should be mentally alert individuals. Usually executives or other people mostly concerned with *evaluation* and *judgment* do not make good panel members. The group has only two officials: a chairman and a recorder. The chairman's responsibility is providing each panel member with a brief statement of the problem prior to the meeting. He also moderates the meeting. The recorder keeps a stenographic account of all of the ideas suggested during the brainstorming period.

[10] *Ibid.,* p. 182.
[11] Alex F. Osborn, *Applied Imagination,* Scribner's, New York (1963), p. 151.

The group leader or brainstorming chairman should make every effort to describe the problem in clear, concise terms. Some typical examples of ideas that might satisfy the problem statement may be included with the statement. The problem should be *specific,* rather than *general,* in nature. The entire period should be conducted in a free and informal manner. Before beginning the session, the chairman should review the rules of brainstorming with the panel. These principles, although few, are very important and may be summarized as follows:

1. *All ideas which come to mind are to be recorded.* No idea should be stifled. As Osborn says, "The wilder the idea, the better; it is easier to tame down than to think up." He recommends recording ideas on a chalkboard as they are suggested. Sometimes a tape recorder can be very valuable, especially when panel members suggest several different ideas in rapid succession.

2. *Suggested ideas must not be criticized or evaluated.* Judgments, whether adverse or laudatory, *must be withheld* until after the brainstorming session.

3. *Combine, modify, alter, or add to ideas as they are suggested.* Participants should consciously attempt to improve on other people's ideas, as well as contributing their own imaginative ideas. Modifying a previously suggested idea will often lead to other entirely new ideas.

4. *The group should be encouraged to think up a large quantity of ideas.* Research at the State University of New York at Buffalo[12] seems to indicate that when a brainstorming session produces more ideas, it will also produce higher-quality ideas. This may be because many ideas which are normally inhibited because of fear of ridicule and criticism are now brought out into the open. In many instances, ideas that would normally have been omitted turn out to be the best ideas.

The brainstorming chairman must always be alert to keep *evaluations* and *judgments* from creeping into the meeting. The spirit of enthusiasm that will permeate the group meeting is also very important to the success of the brainstorming session. It is most important to maintain, throughout the period, an environment where the group members are not afraid of seeming foolish. Both the speed of producing and recording ideas, and the number of ideas produced, help create this necessary artificial environment.

Some users suggest that each panel member should bring to the meeting a list of new ideas that he has thought up before the session. These ideas help to get the session started. In general, the entire brainstorming period should not last more than thirty minutes to an hour. However, team members may add ideas to the accumulated list for a 24-hour period. Later, the entire list of ideas should be rigorously evaluated, either by the original brainstorming group or preferably by a completely new team. Many of the ideas will be discarded quickly—others after some deliberation. Still others will likely show promise of success or at least suggest how the product can be improved.

Some specialists recommend that the brainstorming team should include a few persons who are broadly educated and alert but who are amateurs in the particular topic to be discussed. Thus new points of view usually emerge for later consideration. As suggested previously, particular care should be taken to confine the problem

[12] Sidney J. Parnes and Arnold Meadow, "Effects of Brainstorming Instructions on Creative Problem Solving by Trained and Untrained Subjects," *Journal of Educational Psychology,* Vol. 50, No. 4, 1959, p. 176.

statement within a narrow or limited range to assure that all team members direct their ideas toward a common target.

Brainstorming is no substitute for applying the fundamental mathematical and physical principles the engineer has at his command. It should be recognized that the objective of brainstorming is to stimulate ideas—not to effect a complete solution for a given problem. However, brainstorming is useful for directing a group's attention to a particular problem. Usually, it is more useful in the early stages of the design than in the final stages.

Although brainstorming has been described in terms of groups, its four general principles are equally applicable to *individual* idea production. . . . or actually to "solo brainstorming." This is an especially successful technique for the engineer to use.

Dr. William J. J. Gordon[13] has described a somewhat similar method of group therapy for stimulating imaginative ideas, which he calls "synectics."

### Synectics

This group effort is particularly useful to the engineer in eliciting a radically new idea or in improving products or developing new products. Unlike brainstorming, this technique does not aim at producing a large number of ideas. Rather, it attempts to bring about one or more solutions to a problem by drawing seemingly unrelated ideas together and forcing them to complement each other. This is a difficult and time consuming process. However, synectics has been used quite successfully in problem-solving situations in such diverse fields as military defense, the theatre, manufacturing, public administration, and education. Where most members of the brainstorming team are very knowledgeable about the problem field, synectics frequently draws the team members from diverse fields of learning, so that the group spans many areas of knowledge. Philosophers, artists, psychologists, machinists, physicists, geologists, biologists, as well as engineers, might all serve equally well in a synectics group. Synectics assumes that someone who is imaginative but not experienced in a particular field, may produce as many creative ideas as one who *is* experienced in that field. Unlike the expert, the novice can stretch his imagination. He approaches the problem with fewer preconceived ideas or theories, and he is thus freer from binding mental restrictions. (Obviously, this will not be true when the problem requires analysis or evaluation, where experience is a vital factor.) Where brainstorming emphasizes the team member's general intellectual background, synectics stresses his emotional constitution. There is always present in the synectics conference an expert in the particular problem field. The expert can use his superior technical knowledge to give the team missing facts, or he may even assume the role of "devil's advocate," pointing out the weaknesses of an idea the group is considering. *All* synectics sessions are tape recorded for later review and to provide a permanent record.

Synectics emphasizes the conscious, preconscious, and subconscious psychological states that are involved in all creative acts. In beginning, the group chairman leads the members to understand the problem and explore its *broad* aspects. For example, if a synectics group is seeking a better roofing material for traditional

[13] William J. J. Gordon, *Synectics,* Harper, New York (1961).

structures, the leader might begin a discussion on "coverings." He could also explore how the colors of coverings might enhance the overall efficiency (white in summer, black in winter). This might lead to a discussion of how colors are changed in nature. The group leader could then focus the group on more detailed discussion of how roofing materials could be made to change color automatically to correspond to different light intensities—like the biological action of a chameleon or a flounder. Similarly, the leader might approach the problem of devising a new type of can-opener by first leading a group discussion of the word "opening," or, he could begin considering a new type of lawnmower by first discussing the word "separation."

In general, synectics recommends viewing problems from various analogous situations. Paint that will not adhere to a surface might be viewed as analogous to water running off a duck's back. The earth's crust might be seen as analogous to the layer of ice over a pond. The problem of enabling army tanks to cross a 10-ft-wide, bottomless crevass might be made analogous to the problem that two ants have in crossing chasms wider than their individual lengths. In each case, the synectics participant tries to *imagine* himself as the "personality" of the inanimate object: "What would be my reaction *if I were that gear* (or drop of paint, or tank, or electron)? Thus, familiar objects take on strange appearances and actions, and strange concepts often become more comprehensible. A key part of this technique lies in the group leader's ability to make the team members "force-fit" or combine seemingly unrelated ideas into a new and useful solution.

Many believe that brainstorming comes to grips with the problem too abruptly while synectics delays too long. However, industry is using both methods successfully today.

## THE REAL WORLD

The engineer who masters the fundamental principles of mathematics and science is able to understand the laws of nature. If this were the total requirement, the task of the engineer would be simplified. However, he never operates in a free environment where he is limited only by the laws of nature. The engineer always must endeavor to bridge the span between the "desires of man" and the "realities of nature." He must work both with nature and with people. Because of these practical considerations he also is limited by artificial or man-made restrictions such as time, money, or personal preference. These latter restrictions necessitate compromises on the part of the engineer. But this is the real world, and the engineer must live and make his livelihood in it.

In the preceding pages, certain fundamental principles of creative thinking have been described. If the engineer implements them, he will enjoy an improved ability to innovate and, we hope, to create. However, consideration again must be given to living in the *real world*. Although the engineer may be able to produce a novel solution that is seemingly desirable and economically justified, it does not follow that his fellow man will always accept or implement it. In general, people of all civilizations have resisted change, and today is no exception. Although he will not suffer being thrown into jail, be whipped, shot, hung, burned at the stake, or crucified as he might have been years ago, the engineer with a radical idea might find that he is ignored, demoted, transferred to another part of the company, or even fired if he fails to observe some of the elementary rules of human relations. Such is life in the real world.

It is important, therefore, for the young engineer to recognize the importance of being able to sell his idea. Some suggestions to keep in mind are:

1. People resist change. The status quo is comfortable and familiar. Any alterations or modifications to existing patterns, therefore, must be "sold" to those who have the authority to approve decisions of change.

2. Never belittle a current practice or procedure in order to enhance the position of your own idea. Remember that your superior may have been responsible for implementing the technique that is now in use. Give him an opportunity to help you refine any improvement. If the idea is successful, there will be ample honor for all.

3. Present your design in a professional manner. Do not use sloppy sketches and poorly prepared commentary. Rather, take pride in your work. Remember that its worth may be judged solely upon its clarity and appearance.

4. Be prepared for all types of criticism. Try to think up as many reasons as you can why your idea *should not* be adopted. Prepare an answer for each objection.

5. Do not boast. It is better to minimize the overall effect of your idea and let others sell its virtue as a major contribution.

6. Do not allow yourself to become discouraged should you fail to sell your idea immediately. Time frequently acts as a healing ointment to injured pride.

## CONCLUSIONS

Since God created man in His own image, it is only *natural* for man to express himself in creative ways. The history of civilization is a history of man's creative efforts through the centuries. Man alone possesses the capacity for creative thought, and everyone has some capability for creative thinking. Hence, creative behavior is a function of the individual personality rather than of organization, luck, or happenstance. For this reason, it is important to understand the characteristics of the creative person and to develop the attributes basic to imaginative and creative thought. It is also important for one to realize that the real world is not always predictable, and that the art of compromise is in many cases the difference between success and failure. Instruction in the principles of creative thinking is particularly significant for the engineer.

### Exercises in Creative Thought

**17–51.** Suggest designs that might utilize the heat made available by the inefficiency of the automobile engine.

**17–52.** Propose some novel methods of illumination not involving fluorescent or incandescent lamps.

**17–53.** What new engineering developments that might help reduce traffic accidents might be contrived with our present state of technology?

**17–54.** Many cities today are faced with problems of air pollution. Suggest ways to eliminate or minimize this hazard.

**17–55.** Suggest five possible uses for soft drink bottle tops that might bring a profitable return.

**17–56.** Suggest as many possible uses as you can think of for the use of a laser.

**17–57.** "As inevitable as night after day"—using the word "inevitable," contrive six similar figures of speech. "As inevitable as. . . ."

**17–58.** Suggest as many novel and economically profitable uses as you can for worn automobile tires.

**17–59.** Name five waste products, and suggest ways in which these products may be reclaimed for useful purposes.

**17–60.** Using toothpicks, glue, and paper clips, design some useful device.

List as many possible uses as you can for each of these objects:

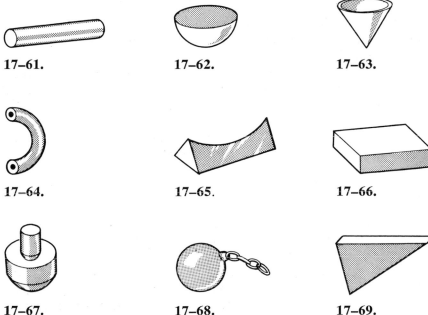

**17–61.**          **17–62.**          **17–63.**

**17–64.**          **17–65.**          **17–66.**

**17–67.**          **17–68.**          **17–69.**

**17–70.**

**17–71.** Select a common household item, and list its properties and functions.

**17–72.** Modify the functions of the item in Problem 17–71, and show the possible new types of products that might be described.

**17–73.** Select a common garden tool, and list its properties and functions.

## Exercises in Creative Thought (continued)

**17–74.** Modify the functions and alter the properties of the tool in Problem 17–73 so that new types of tools might be described.

**17–75.** Select a common piece of wearing apparel, and list its properties and functions.

**17–76.** Modify the functions and alter the properties of the piece of apparel in Problem 17–75, and describe the new types of garments that might result.

**17–77.** Select an automobile accessory, and list its properties and functions.

**17–78.** Alter or change the functions of the accessory in Problem 17–77, and show how new products can be described.

**17–79.** Using the principles of "solo" brainstorming, record as many ideas as you can in ten minutes with regard to solving the following problem:
"Devise a means of disposing of garbage for submarines while they are on secret submerged-alert missions."

**17–80.** In fifteen minutes make a list of all unsolved problems for which you would like to see solutions.

## BIBLIOGRAPHY

ALLEN, MYRON S., *Morphological Synthesis,* Prentice-Hall, Englewood Cliffs, N.J. (1962).

ANDERSON, HAROLD H. (ed.), *Creativity and Its Cultivation,* Harper, New York (1959).

ARMSTRONG, FRANK A., *Idea Tracking,* Criterion, New York (1960).

BEVERIDGE, W. I. B., *The Art of Scientific Investigation,* Vintage Books, New York (1957).

CLARK, CHARLES, *Brainstorming,* Doubleday, Garden City, N.Y. (1958).

CRAWFORD, ROBERT P., *The Techniques of Creative Thinking,* Hawthorn, New York (1954).

CRUTCHFIELD, RICHARD S., "Conformity and Creative Thinking," *Contemporary Approaches to Creative Thinking,* Atherton, New York (1963).

EASTON, WILLIAM H., "Creative Thinking and How to Develop It," *Creative Engineering,* The American Society of Mechanical Engineers, New York (1954).

FLESCH, RUDOLPH, *The Art of Clear Thinking,* Harper, New York (1951).

GHISELIN, BREWSTER (ed.), *The Creative Process,* University of California Press, Berkeley (1952).

GORDON, WILLIAM J. J., *Synectics,* Harper, New York (1961).

GUILFORD, J. P., "Creativity," *American Psychologist,* 1950, 5, p. 444–454.

HAEFELE, JOHN W., *Creativity and Innovation,* Reinhold, London (1962).

HUTCHINSON, E. D., *How to Think Creatively,* (rev. ed.), Abington-Cokeburg, New York (1949).

JEWKES, JOHN, DAVID SAWERS, and RICHARD STILLERMAN, *The Sources of Invention,* Macmillan, New York (1961).

JONES, J. CHRISTOPHER, and D. G. THORNLEY (eds.), *Conferences on Design Methods,* Macmillan, New York (1963).

LEFFORD, ARTHUR, "The Influence of Emotional Subject Matter on Logical Reasoning," *Journal of Psychology,* 1946, Vol. 34, p. 151.

OSBORN, ALEX F., *Applied Imagination,* Scribner's, New York (1963).

PARNES, SIDNEY J., and HAROLD F. HARDING (eds.), *A Sourcebook for Creative Thinking,* Scribner's, New York (1962).

PLATT, WASHINGTON, and ROSS A. BAKER, "The Relation of the Scientific Hunch to Research," *Journal of Chemical Education,* Vol. 8, No. 10, p. 1969.

ROSSMAN, JOSEPH, *The Psychology of the Inventor,* Inventors Pub. Co., Wash. D.C. (1931).

STEIN, MORRIS I., and SHIRLEY J. HEINZE, *Creativity and the Individual,* The Free Press of Glencoe, Chicago (1960).

TAYLOR, CALVIN W., and FRANK BARRON (eds.), *Scientific Creativity,* Wiley, New York (1963).

TAYLOR, JACK W., *How To Create New Ideas,* Prentice-Hall, Englewood Cliffs, N.J. (1961).

*Think,* A Special Issue: Man's Creative Mind, November-December, 1962.

TUSAK, C. D., *Inventors and Inventions,* McGraw-Hill, New York (1957).

VON FANGE, EUGENE K., *Professional Creativity,* Prentice-Hall, Englewood Cliffs, N.J. (1959).

WHITING, CHARLES S., *Creative Thinking,* Reinhold, London (1958).

# Chapter 18

# Engineering Systems

Today man has selected for himself many challenging goals that can be attained only by considerably revised methods of solution in contrast to conventional methods that have been used for many years. Not the least of the required changes is the appreciable increase in the *number of people* whose specialized contributions are necessary to the success of the designs. Other factors adding to the complexity of such design processes are the *enlarged scope* of the designs, the *variety of resources* required to support the designs, the necessity of *understanding interdisciplinary man-machine systems* and bringing them into harmonious relationships, the dependence upon *computerized* analyses to handle the enormous volumes of data resulting from computational and experimental procedures that are required for simulation studies and performance testing, the concept of *feedback* and the consequential *choices* or *alternatives* that result from the continuous refinement in the skillful art of *compromise,* and the *urgency* with which the selected goals must be achieved. Such complex problems are frequently referred to as "engineering systems" and the process of solving such problems is called "systems engineering."

The constituent parts of the solution of an "engineering system" are the same as the parts of the solution of any engineering design problem. However, systems engineering is concerned with the total, or overall, *success of the system* and the compatibility of its parts rather than in the arithmetic sum of the performances of the individual subsystems, when each is designed specifically for *its* ideal operation. Systems engineering also takes into account the interrelationships existing between subsystems and the consequential effects of these relationships upon the total system. A "system," in this context, is an aggregate of coordinated and cooperating, but sometimes diverse, components in some particular part of the universe that is reacting with its environment and that is identified and set apart for study at some point in time, Figure 18–1. This schematic drawing is representative of an *ideal* system and does not take into account the dynamic and variable interrelationships present

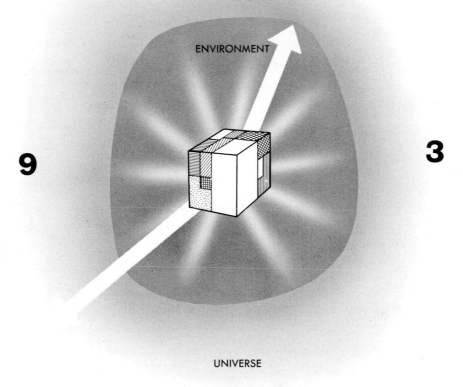

**Figure 18–1.** Schematic representation of a system.

in the subsystems and components. Also it should be recognized that engineering systems do not necessarily always operate in a state of equilibrium or balance. In fact, engineering systems commonly operate in a state of imbalance with self-correcting features being an integral part of the design.

Since a system is a defined quantity, its size may be any specified magnitude. Thus, an "engineering system" in one instance may revert to an "engineering sub-system" under other circumstances. Another way to explain this apparent contradiction is to recognize that all objects, when considered in interaction with their surrounding environment, are merely parts of a larger "order" or system.

The solutions to systems problems, as well as to engineering design problems in general, have several constituent parts as follows:

1. A recognition of a goal or objective that is desirable.

2. Identification, isolation, and formulation of a *specific* system or design whose solution is necessary before one can reach the objective.

3. Recognition and identification of the strategic subsystems or component parts of the design.

4. Construction of idealized models of the subsystems and of the system.

5. Manipulation of the idealized model configurations to achieve the most realistic conditions.

6. Exploratory research to identify unresolved problems and to find their solutions.

7. Testing of the system model and determining the compatibility of the subsystems and components.

8. Re-evaluation and judgment of the design in an iterative process to determine its value in satisfying the requirements specified by the original objective.

9. Fabrication, assembly, and testing of the system design.

10. Implementation (operation, use, maintenance) and re-evaluation of the design.

The concept of an engineering system is not new. Certainly the erection of the pyramids in Egypt was, for that particular time, a most complex problem. Men and materials were coordinated in such fashion that even today man stands in awe of the precision and durability of their construction. Evidences of complex engineering systems are evident—our communications networks, transportation systems, utility service, food distribution, weather forecasting, sewage disposal, the intercontinental ballistic missile, and the man-in-space program have become almost commonplace in our society.

Although engineering systems are not new, the systems engineering approach to obtain them is relatively new, dating to the World War II period. During this time the combined armed forces of Great Britain and the United States were concerned with evaluations of the management and operation of existing military systems and with the quick solution of difficult strategical and tactical problems. The scientific methods of analysis that developed out of these efforts were called Operations Research (O.R.), and this name has become standard nomenclature today. The essential difference between operations research and systems engineering is that methods of operations research are generally applied to procedural changes in existing organizations, whereas the principles of systems engineering are generally applied to new designs and equipment modifications.

A systems engineering problem is subdivided into subsystems and the subsystems are divided into components. It is important to know that an improvement made in one of the subsystems will not necessarily have a beneficial effect upon the total system. In fact, there are some situations where the imbalance which results from such an improvement would have a detrimental effect upon the total system.

As suggested in the schematic drawing, Figure 18–2, the effect of each sub-

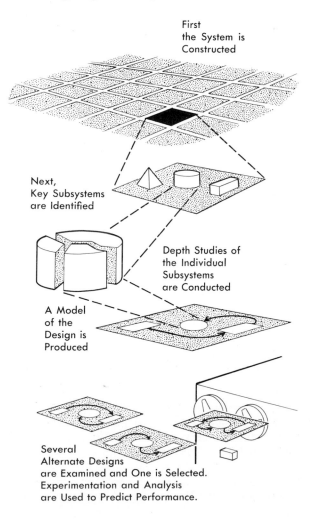

First the System is Constructed

Next, Key Subsystems are Identified

Depth Studies of the Individual Subsystems are Conducted

A Model of the Design is Produced

Several Alternate Designs are Examined and One is Selected. Experimentation and Analysis are Used to Predict Performance.

**Figure 18–2.** Major steps in the design of engineering systems. (Based upon a paper by Frederick A. Koomanoff and A. Alan B. Pritsker published in the March, 1962 issue of *Battelle Technical Review*. Used with permission.)

system must be considered in relation to the other subsystems as well as in relation to the total system. Also it is important that the design formulation first proceed from the total system to the subsystems and finally to the components. When this has been accomplished, the reverse order should be followed.

Two examples of the use of "systems engineering" principles in solving a complex "engineering system" follow. First, Paul E. Purser and Maxime A. Faget describe the free world's first attempt to achieve manned orbital flight.

Another example of the evolving solution of a complex engineering problem is presented in the Motorola story of man's attempt to miniaturize electronics: integrated circuit design. The most exciting aspect of this second account is that the desired objective has not yet been reached and that many of the engineering students who are reading this story will be able to contribute significantly to its achievement in the years ahead.

## DESIGN OF FIRST U.S. MANNED SPACECRAFT[1]
### Introduction

The history of transportation is the story of man's continual efforts to achieve increases in speed, range, and passenger or cargo capacity. This has also been a search for increased efficiency and effectiveness, and it has been apparent in essentially all forms of transportation—as evidenced by such diverse occurrences as the breeding of especially large draft horses to pull ever larger loads in wagons, the addition of steam power to ships to reduce transoceanic travel times, and the pattern of ever increasing speed, range, and size of transport aircraft.

Man's ever present desire to fly higher, faster, and farther when coupled with his natural inclination to explore the unknown in search of new knowledge led over the years to increasingly more serious consideration of the possibility of extending transportation capabilities to the realm of space. The dreams, calculations, and design work of such pioneers as Tsiolkovskii, Oberth, and Goddard all pointed toward the eventual achievement of manned flight through space when technology advanced to a stage where it became practical to design and build the necessary hardware. Essentially, the work of the spaceflight pioneers established the scientific possibility of spaceflight and also developed many of the engineering principles that could later be used in translating possibility into accomplishment. It remained, however, for engineering and manufacturing technology to develop and grow over many decades before this translation could occur.

During the decade of the 1950s, parallel advances in aviation and rocketry inspired by military (or defense) requirements in both the United States and the U.S.S.R. spurred the growth of technology to a stage such that the "scientific possibility" became an "engineering possibility." In this time period, various scientific groups around the world working through the International Council of Scientific Unions established plans for a concerted worldwide exercise in science investigation to be known as the International Geophysical Year (IGY). The IGY ran from July 1, 1957, to December 31, 1958; and both the U.S. and the U.S.S.R.

---

[1] Based on material furnished by Paul E. Purser and Maxime A. Faget of NASA Manned Spacecraft Center, Houston, Texas. Used with permission.

included in their planned investigations the use of instrumented earthorbiting satellites for making geophysical studies. This acceptance of the inevitability of spaceflight seemed to spur the efforts of engineering and scientific personnel on both sides of the world toward more serious consideration of achieving *manned* spaceflight. The actual accomplishment of earth-orbital flights of instrumented satellites by the U.S.S.R., on October 4, 1957, apparently served as a catalyst to arouse in the U.S. a national will to proceed with the development of the hardware necessary for man to fly in space.[2]

The following pages will describe in part how this national will for manned spaceflight has been translated into accomplishment. First, we shall look at the total problem, then we shall discuss the overall system design of the spacecraft chosen for this program; and finally we shall examine some of the multitude of detailed subsystems and component design problems that had to be solved.

### The Engineering System: Manned Orbital Flight

The solution of the total problem of achieving manned orbital flight involved a great deal more than the obvious necessity of enclosing the man in a suitable protective environment and then accelerating him by efficient use of rocket power to the velocity and altitude required for a stable orbit about the earth. Among the many questions that had to be answered were as follows:

1. When?
2. How many men at once?
3. Whether to take the approach of gradual development in which the speed and altitude capabilities of existing rocket aircraft were successively increased; or whether to take the direct approach of designing a new system specifically for orbital flight?

The pressure of international competition provided an answer of "As soon as practicable" to the first question. This time pressure, in turn, provided the answers of "one-man-crew" and "direct approach" to the next two questions. These questions were neither asked nor answered in any specific formal manner but rather were more or less intuitively asked and answered in each of many groups working on the problem in the laboratories and development facilities of the following agencies or institutions:

1. National Advisory Committee for Aeronautics
2. Army, Navy, and Air Force
3. Aerospace Industry
4. Universities and Research Institutes

During 1957 and 1958, research and advanced design teams in these varied organizations were also asking and answering successively more detailed questions about the approach to be taken. For example, the following paragraphs discuss

[2] More complete developments of the background events leading up to manned spaceflight may be found in the following books:
1. Eugene M. Emme, *A History of Space Flight*. Holt, Rinehart, and Winston, New York, 1965.
2. Maxime A. Faget, *Manned Space Flight*. Holt, Rinehart and Winston, New York, 1965.

uestions and the answers about the mission that evoived from a consider-
int of individual and team study.

### Orbital Altitude

At what altitude should the flight be made? The desire to avoid the newly discovered Van Allen radiation belts and to minimize the required propulsion energy
dictated a relatively low altitude.[3] The need to assure that the required number of
revolutions about the earth be attained without atmospheric drag causing premature
re-entry dictated a high altitude. Uncertainties in knowledge about the actual
density of the upper atmospheric also dictated a high altitude in order to prevent
inordinately large differences between the calculated and actual re-entry trajectories
and landing points. Many analyses and compromise or "trade-off" studies were
made; and these indicated that an approximately circular orbit at roughly 100 to
125 statute miles altitude would result in reasonable compromises among the various
conflicting requirements.

### Orbital Inclination

At what inclination to the plane of the equator should the flight be made?
Obviously, a directly eastward launch at the equator would take maximum advantage
of the earth's rotational speed and require the least expenditure of propulsive energy.
However, equatorial launching sites did not exist. The southernmost existing launching site was the Air Force Missile Test Range (now Eastern Test Range) at Cape
Canaveral, Florida. The tracking stations at AFMTR were laid out on a line that
was at an azimuth of about 120° (roughly SE) from the launch site. Powered flight
along this line of tracking stations would provide the maximum coverage by ground-
based instrumentation during this critical phase. However, the resulting orbital
plane would be such that successive passes would place the spacecraft in locations
not considered suitable for recovery. Again design analyses were made that resulted
in an orbital inclination of about 32.5°. Although this did not take maximum advantage of the range instrumentation during powered flight, it did mean that suitable
landing zones in temperate waters were available in the Atlantic for each of the first
three orbits.

### Re-entry Initiation

How should the de-orbit and re-entry maneuver be initiated? Various proposals
had been advanced for this phase of the flight, ranging from the extension of drag
brakes, through choosing an orbit altitude low enough so that the drag would limit
the number of revolutions to the desired number, to the firing of retrograde rockets
to start the re-entry. The problems of uncertainties about the upper atmospheric
density ruled out considerations of drag-initiated re-entry. In addition, the size of
drag brake required to de-orbit the spacecraft with any degree of accuracy would
have caused a prohibitive weight penalty as well as requiring a major development

[3] O'Brien, B. J., "Review of Studies of Trapped Radiation with Satellite-Borne Apparatus,"
*Space Science Reviews,* I, 1963, 415–484.

program in itself. Once the decision had been made to utilize retro rockets, there remained questions of how, when, and in what direction the rockets should be fired. It was decided to provide redundant means for retrofire: one, the pilot could fire the rockets by manually depressing a switch at a given time; or two, an automatic timing device incorporated in the spacecraft clock could fire the rockets at a pre-selected time. The time set into the clock could be manually changed by the pilot, and could also be changed by radio signals from a ground command station. The question of when, where, and in what direction to fire the retrorockets was answered by a series of analyses that balanced landingpoint dispersion against propellant weight for various orbital locations, spacecraft pitch angles, and pitch-angle errors at the firing point. The final decision was to fire the rockets about one third of a revolution before the intended landing point and at a pitch angle of 34° upward from the horizontal.

### Land vs. Water Landing

There was a natural desire to design the spacecraft for touchdown on land, but since the launch and powered flight were to be over water it had to be designed for at least emergency landing on water. This fact, coupled with the fact that on the orbital path chosen the spacecraft would be over water much more than over land, led to a choice of water landing as the primary mode. Similar considerations, incidentally, led to the Soviet choice of land landing as their primary mode, since they launched over land and were over land for much of their flight.

### Ground Tracking

The establishment of criteria for the ground tracking network and its subsequent detailed implementation was another complex phase of the overall design problem. The medical community at first wanted the capability of absolutely continuous voice communication and television coverage of the spacecraft crew. This was quickly shown to be prohibitive in cost and effort. After much consideration of emergency procedures, time required for re-entry and recovery, and possible physiological emergencies, it was finally decided that intervals of 10 to 15 minutes without communications would be satisfactory, and that television coverage really came under the heading of "nice to have" but not necessary. Other considerations involved in the network design were a choice of radio frequencies for communications, telemetry, and command equipment; choice of types of radars for spacecraft tracking; types of ground communications gear to bring the data to a central location; selection of a computing complex to control the data traffic flow and to transform the network data into usable form; and design of a central mission control center from which flight operations personnel could direct and monitor the flight.

### Mission Operations

The area of mission operations was also part of the total design problem. Part of this effort was included in the various trajectory studies required for establishing design parameters for orbital altitude and inclination, re-entry initiation, landing systems, and tracking network. Much additional mission analysis was required for establishing operational factors. Based on these studies, decisions were made on such questions as the organization of the operations team and the division of effort among NASA, Department of Defense, industry, and other agencies for the detailed operational tasks. In effect, the design of the spacecraft (a subsystem) and the design of the mission (a system) were concurrent and highly interrelated. Progress in each area both influenced, and was influenced by, progress in the other area.

### Spacecraft Design[4]

*Problem:* Design a spacecraft and mission for flying a man in earth orbit and accomplishing safe recovery.

*Given:* Atlas launch vehicle in advanced stage of development, large background of work in aeronautics and aircraft systems, and re-entry heat protection reaching a satisfactory state of technology.

*Approach:* Essentially, one had a launch vehicle and a man available, Figure 18–3, and the problem was to mount the man on the launch vehicle and protect him against:

1. Acceleration loads during powered flight,
2. Noise and vibration during powered flight,
3. Vacuum, ionizing radiation, micrometeoroids, and thermal radiation during space flight,
4. Acceleration loads during re-entry, and
5. Impact loads during landing.

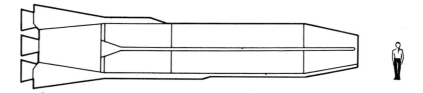

**Figure 18–3.** Transport a man into earth orbit with safe return.

### Environmental Protection

Among these various environments against which the man must be protected, it was intuitively felt that the acceleration loads would be the most critical. Prior experience in aircraft and on human centrifuges had shown that man's tolerance to external loads varied with time and with his position relative to the loads. For example, Figure 18–4 shows a summary of the data available in 1957 and 1958. It was obvious that the supine position provided greater protection for the man. The scanty data indicated that a supine man could safely withstand a maximum loading of 12 $g$ for the periods of powered flight and re-entry. However, in an abort from

[4] David S. Anderton, "How Mercury Design Evolved," *Aviation Week,* LXXVIII (May 22, 1961).
    Also see: "How Mercury Design Evolved," *Aviation Week,* LXX (Sept. 21, 1959).

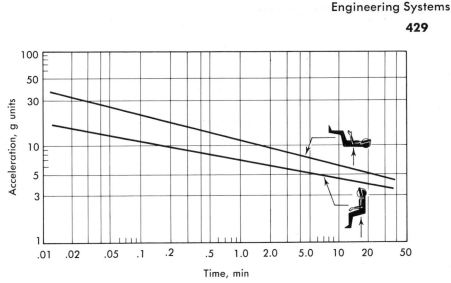

**Figure 18–4.** Man's tolerance to acceleration.

powered flight at intermediate speeds wherein the vehicle has attained a considerable altitude but somewhat less than orbital velocity, the re-entry trajectory can be quite steep; and the re-entry loads, therefore, quite high. In a ballistic vehicle like Mercury, for example, an abort at about 17,000 fps velocity could result in re-entry accelerations of 16 *g*, whereas a normal re-entry from orbit would create loads of only 8 *g*. The use of a lifting re-entry could modulate the trajectory and reduce the loads; but, as discussed later, the lifting re-entry body would require an additional propulsion stage on the launch vehicle. Accordingly, a solution was searched for in the human support system rather than in the vehicle design. During tests on the Navy centrifuge at Johnsville, Pennsylvania, R. Flanagan Gray and his associates had shown that submerging the body in water would increase human tolerance to acceleration. Faget and his associates reasoned that if the body were suspended in a form-fitting couch it would effectively "float" in the body fluids and react similarly to being submerged in water. To illustrate this, consider the cross-sectional views shown in Figure 18–5. This idea was tested on the Navy centrifuge at Johnsville in July 1958, and Lt. C. C. Collins withstood an acceleration of over 20 *g* without harm. Consequently, the Mercury program used the form-fitting couch as the means of pilot protection against the poweredflight and re-entry acceleration loads.

The noise and vibration, vacuum, ionizing and thermal radiation, and micrometeoroid protection were solved relatively simply by surrounding the pilot with a structurally sound spacevehicle cabin. A great deal of detail design work that involved the collection and analysis of much space environment data resulted in a

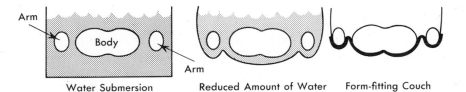

Water Submersion          Reduced Amount of Water      Form-fitting Couch

**Figure 18–5.** Considerations in couch design.

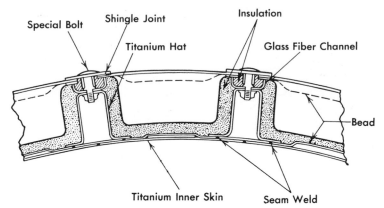

**Figure 18–6.** Design of spacecraft wall.

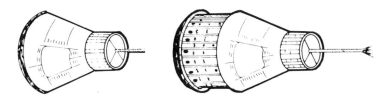

**Figure 18–7.** Design of the shock absorber.

spacecraft wall with the type of construction shown in Figure 18–6. The question of impact loads during landing was at first considered to have been solved by a combination of two means: first, a reduction of the overall loads by having the spacecraft land on water rather than on land; and second, by mounting the pilot-support couch on columns of crushable aluminum honeycomb that would serve to attenuate the remaining shock loads to tolerable values. As the detail design work progressed, it became apparent that some aborted flights might require land impacts and further that under certain conditions of waves, wind, and parachute swing, even a water landing could result in potentially intolerable impact loads. This problem was solved by use of a pneumatic shockabsorber formed by placing a glass-fabric curtain between the heat shield and the spacecraft pressure vessel, Figure 18–7. During most of the flight the curtain was folded between the heat shield and main pressure bulkhead. Upon deployment of the main parachute, the heat shield was released and its weight extended the curtain to form an impact bag. The detail design of the bag posed such problems as fatigue life under prolonged wave action after landing, but these problems were overcome in a development test program.

### External Configuration

Various shapes were considered for the external configuration of the spacecraft. Lifting bodies of varying degrees of bluntness ranging from Figure 18–8 to Figure 18–9 were ruled out because of structural weight and influences on launch vehicle stability and structural loads. A compact, blunt-face, nonlifting body was chosen as the best solution. A sphere would have been optimum from the standpoint of having a maximum volume for a minimum surface area, but its use would have created problems with stability during re-entry and with stowage for parachutes or other landing devices. A blunt-faced cone such as that shown in Figure 18–10 would be stable during re-entry and would have adequate space for stowage of parachutes but would require that the pilot's couch be rotated 180° so that both launch and re-entry accelerations would be applied in the same direction. Subsequent analyses and tests showed that a shape like Figure 18–11 would also be stable during re-entry and would not require a rotatable couch. The pointed end of the cone would also provide room for parachute stowage. Anderton[5] presents an excellent discussion of the development of the particular external configuration used in Project Mercury.

**Figure 18–8.** Shape considerations.

**Figure 18–9.**

**Figure 18–10.** Blunt-faced conical shape.

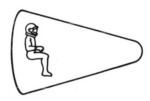

**Figure 18–11.** Pointed-end conical shape.

### Escape Provisions

The Atlas ICBM chosen as a launch vehicle was not designed originally as a man-carrying device, and its reliability against malfunction and breakup, therefore, did not have to be extremely high. As a missile, any degree of reliability between 0.51 and 1.00 would still require that at least two missiles be assigned to any one target; and thus, it was not economically feasible to strive for an ultimate goal of 0.99+ in reliability. As noted below, Figure 18–12, the reliability would naturally increase with the number of development vehicles flown as problems were discovered and corrected. Some degree of reliability could be added, as noted below, by special "man-rating" efforts such as increased quality control, parts selection, and redundancy in critical systems, but a deficit in reliability below 1.00 would still exist.

[5] *Ibid.,* p. 8.

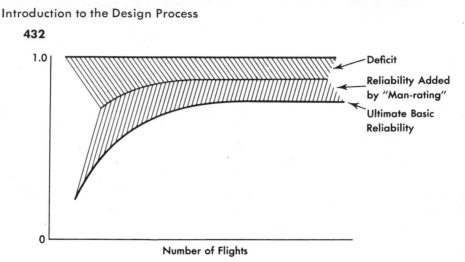

**Figure 18–12.** Reliability considerations.

A good discussion of the "man-rating" of the Atlas including the modifications necessary to provide warnings of impending malfunctions is given by Hohmann.[6]

Various means were considered to overcome the reliability deficit noted above. The most logical system seemed to be some means of removing the whole spacecraft from the vicinity of a potentially malfunctioning launch vehicle. This was considered necessary since the Atlas propellants, liquid oxygen and kerosene derivative, tend to form a gelatinous substance with many of the characteristics of TNT when mixed by a breakup of the tanks. A plan to use the retrorockets was discarded for two reasons: first, use of the retrorockets would require some form of automatic stabilization, since the center of gravity location must be such as to provide basic aerodynamic stability with the blunt heat shield forward; and second, the increased power that would be required if the retrorockets were to be used as escape rockets would mean that a much heavier weight would have to be carried into orbit. The solution chosen was to use a tractor rocket mounted on a pylon ahead of the spacecraft, Figure 18–13. This rocket could be used to pull the spacecraft away from an

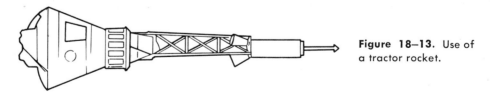

**Figure 18–13.** Use of a tractor rocket.

explosion if necessary. Since the danger from such an explosion exists primarily within the sensible atmosphere, the rocket could be jettisoned well below orbital altitude and speed. In fact, this early jettisoning meant that carrying an 800-pound escape rocket and tower created only about a 100-pound penalty in orbital weight.

### Escape System Design for Mercury

Once the general concept of an escape rocket was decided upon there were a

---

[6] Bernard A. Hohmann, "Pilot Safety and Mercury/Atlas," *Astronautics and Aerospace Engineering,* Vol. I, No. 1 (Feb., 1963), 40–43.

great many detail design problems associated with it that had to be studied. These fell into several categories as indicated in the following discussion.

**Aerodynamic.** The escape rocket approach generally provided good aerodynamic features. With the weight of the escape rocket well forward an aerodynamically stable configuration could be achieved. However, the degree of stability appeared marginal and aerodynamic considerations were an important element in the specific design solution. The shape and bulk of the rocket and tower had a major effect on the location of the aerodynamic center of pressure. Since an aerodynamically stable body must have the center of pressure behind the center of mass, it was important to minimize the aerodynamic side force (normal-force coefficient) generated by the elements of the escape rocket and tower. An open truss structure was used, since this would minimize the exposed lateral area ahead of the center of mass. The nose of the rocket was made flat, since a body that has a flat nose is known to have the least destabilizing force generated by the nose and forebody. Wind tunnel investigations showed that stability could further be improved by incorporation of a flow separation device at the base of the tower. A wedge-shaped cover over the attachment clamp-ring was found to be a satisfactory device for this purpose. An aerodynamic spike extending in front of the flat nose of the escape rocket was added to reduce the drag during launch.

Since the escape rocket was carried throughout that portion of launch flight where aerodynamic heating and loads were significant, its presence was used to protect the horizon scanners and the re-entry destabilization flap (used to prevent nose first re-entry) during this period. This was done by incorporation of suitable covers to protect these delicate devices.

**Propulsion.** The propulsive requirements for the escape rocket were set by two basic considerations. In the case of a launch pad abort sufficient altitude for safe parachute deployment (about 2500 ft) was needed. The rocket thrust was also expected to carry the spacecraft away from the launch vehicle during flight at a sufficiently rapid rate to minimize the hazard from the explosion that would follow the possible breaking-up of the failed launch vehicle. A rocket of 50,000 pounds of thrust with an action time of 1½ seconds was determined to be sufficient for these purposes. Since the rocket was to be used as a tractor, a special nozzle arrangement had to be designed. Three equal-size nozzles all fed from a common chamber were arranged so that the combined thrust vector was through the center line of the rocket motor. Each nozzle was made equal in size and with equal divergence angle. The nozzles were fitted with molybdenum throats to minimize erosion and, therefore, the possibility of the thrust direction changing due to unequal throat growth. The rocket mount on top of the tower allowed for adjustment of alignment. During the weight and balance process in the launch preparation phase, the rocket motor was purposely misaligned from the center of mass of the capsule by 0.8 inches in order to cause the escape path to turn to one side. This could prevent the launch vehicle from colliding with capsule subsequent to burnout of the escape rocket in the event the launch vehicle did not break up but continued to coast along its initial flight path.

A second, but much smaller, rocket was carried. This one was used to jettison the escape tower subsequent to an escape maneuver. It was also equipped with a triple nozzle. In the normal mission both the tower jettison rocket and main escape rocket were fired subsequent to staging the Atlas launch vehicle. Either rocket had sufficient energy to safely perform the jettisoning maneuver, thereby providing a desired redundancy.

**Structure.** The escape tower structure was made of 4130 tubular steel welded into an open truss structure. Aerodynamic heat transfer rates during the launch phase were sufficiently high that an ablating protective covering of fiberglass and plastic was used over the entire truss structure. Otherwise the steel tubing would have been heated sufficiently to reduce the strength of the structure to below the estimated stresses for worst-case load conditions. Rocket motor igniter wiring and instrumentation wiring were both routed through the tubular tower legs for protection. Where wiring had to be carried external of the frame, heat protected conduit was used.

One of the considerations that was given considerable thought was the attachment of the tower to the capsule. It was vital that the tower should separate reliably in every mission, since the tower structure covered the parachute compartment. If the tower were to fail to separate, the capsule and crew would certainly be lost. At the same time the escape rocket should be capable of pulling the capsule away at 20 g and sustaining aerodynamic loads that might be generated by an end-over-end tumble. Thus, a very rigid and strong attachment was necessary. The solution was to use a chevron-shaped clamp ring that was made of three 120° segments linked together by three explosive bolts. Each bolt had two charges in it, either one of which would sever the connection and allow the clamp ring to open. As a further precaution, the explosive charges were divided onto two firing circuits each with an independent electrical battery. Thus, each bolt could be severed by either circuit, and only one bolt need be severed to effect separation of the tower. As previously mentioned the clamp ring was covered by an aerodynamic fairing that also served the purpose of improving the aerodynamic stability by causing flow separation.

A final consideration was that a segment of the clamp ring might fall back upon the capsule or launch vehicle and damage it. In order to prevent such a collision, two retaining cables were loosely attached between each clamp ring segment and the adjacent tower legs, Figure 18–14. Thus, although the clamp ring segments were sufficiently free to fly open and allow a clean separation, they were retained and safely carried away with the tower.

Aerodynamic, propulsion, structural, mechanical, electrical, and materials engineers all contributed to the final design of the escape rocket and tower, and each worked on his element of the component or subsystem design to satisfy all criteria.

### Onboard Systems

In the early stages of design, the problem of onboard systems was considered to be essentially solved by specifying the use of "state-of-the-art" components. However, as the detail design proceeded various constraints were posed by limitations on weight, size, and reliability, and by the occurrence of failures during the various

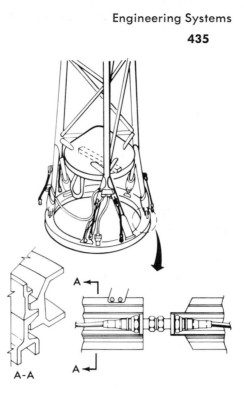

**Figure 18–14.** Design of the clamping.

A-A

development test programs. Typical of such constraints was the parachute problem. A survey of the literature and consultation with the country's leading parachute experts indicated that the "extended-skirt" cargo parachute was probably the most highly developed and reliable item available. Initial development tests wherein dummy spacecraft were dropped from high-flying aircraft showed that the "extended-skirt" parachute had a distressing habit of "streaming," or not opening fully, when deployed at the 10,000-foot altitude required by spacecraft stability considerations. Further investigation showed that almost all experience with large "extended-skirt" parachutes had been at altitudes of 5000 feet and lower. This realization resulted in a restudy of the problem, a selection of the "Ring-sail" type of parachute, and an extended development and qualification test program to insure that adequate reliability was achieved.

**Overall Development Program**

We have discussed some of the general design problems of a relatively simple manned spacecraft.[7] Solutions to the design problems came from many sources; some came from intuition based on sound engineering background, some came from detailed design studies by individuals or teams within the various government and industrial organizations involved, and some came as a result of new knowledge gained from test programs specifically devised for obtaining such solutions.

[7] Additional detailed information may be found in the following:

1. *Mercury Project Summary: Including Results of the Fourth Manned Orbital Flight, May 15 and 16, 1963.* Washington, D.C.: NASA SP-45, Oct. 1963.
2. P. E. Purser, M. A. Faget, N. F. Smith, *Manned Spacecraft: Engineering Design and Operation.* Fairchild Publications, New York, 1964.

It has not been possible to discuss in this limited treatment the overall development program. This program is summarized, however, in Figure 18–15. The summary refers to many other facets of the program and is intended to present an overall impression of the multidisciplinary scope of a major engineering effort.

**Figure 18–15.**

# PROJECT MERCURY HISTORY

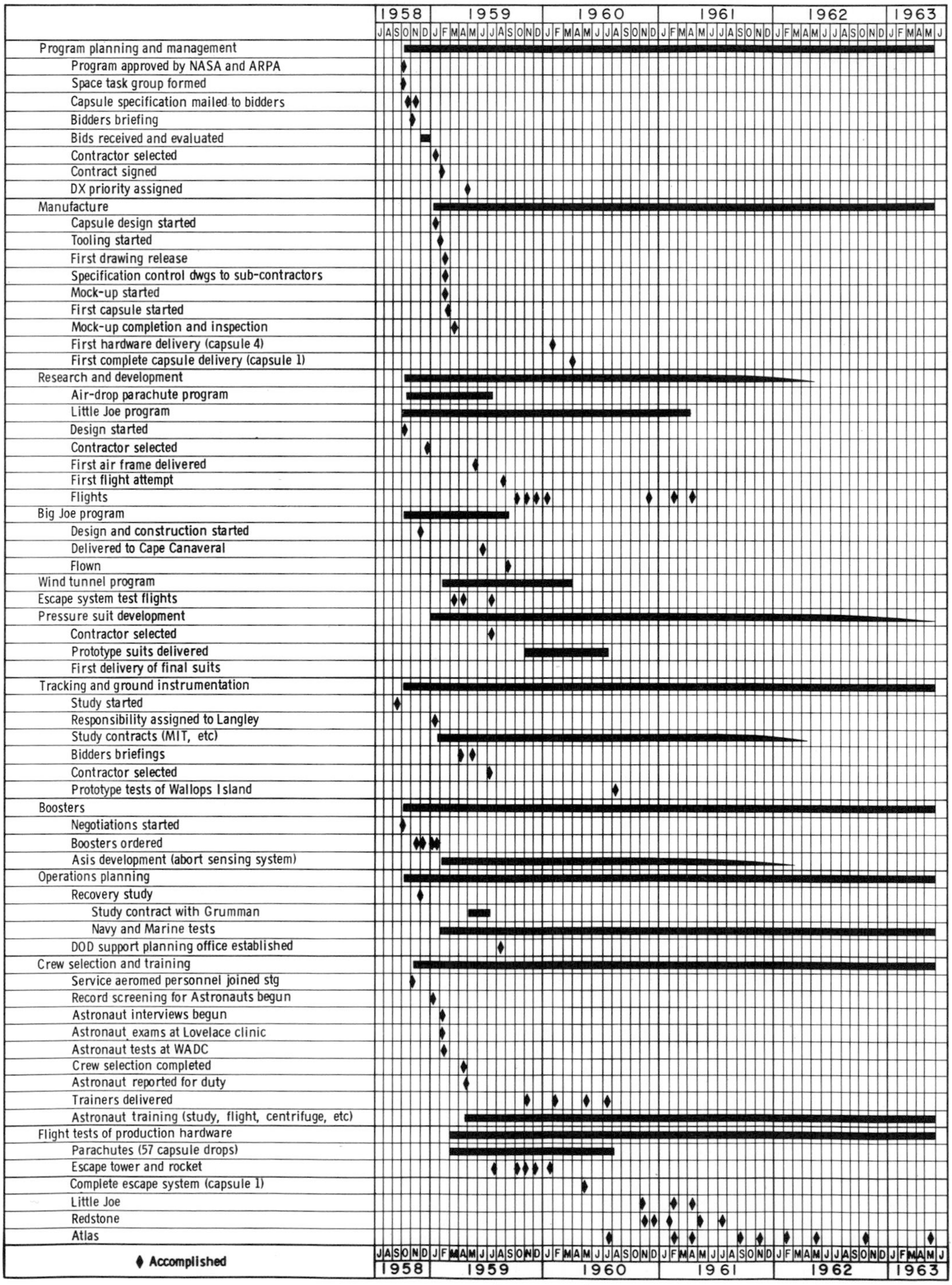

| | 1958 | 1959 | 1960 | 1961 | 1962 | 1963 |
|---|---|---|---|---|---|---|
| | J A S O N D | J F M A M J J A S O N D | J F M A M J J A S O N D | J F M A M J J A S O N D | J F M A M J J A S O N D | J F M A M J |

**Program planning and management**
- Program approved by NASA and ARPA
- Space task group formed
- Capsule specification mailed to bidders
- Bidders briefing
- Bids received and evaluated
- Contractor selected
- Contract signed
- DX priority assigned

**Manufacture**
- Capsule design started
- Tooling started
- First drawing release
- Specification control dwgs to sub-contractors
- Mock-up started
- First capsule started
- Mock-up completion and inspection
- First hardware delivery (capsule 4)
- First complete capsule delivery (capsule 1)

**Research and development**
- Air-drop parachute program
- Little Joe program
- Design started
- Contractor selected
- First air frame delivered
- First flight attempt
- Flights

**Big Joe program**
- Design and construction started
- Delivered to Cape Canaveral
- Flown

**Wind tunnel program**
**Escape system test flights**
**Pressure suit development**
- Contractor selected
- Prototype suits delivered
- First delivery of final suits

**Tracking and ground instrumentation**
- Study started
- Responsibility assigned to Langley
- Study contracts (MIT, etc)
- Bidders briefings
- Contractor selected
- Prototype tests of Wallops Island

**Boosters**
- Negotiations started
- Boosters ordered
- Asis development (abort sensing system)

**Operations planning**
- Recovery study
  - Study contract with Grumman
  - Navy and Marine tests
- DOD support planning office established

**Crew selection and training**
- Service aeromed personnel joined stg
- Record screening for Astronauts begun
- Astronaut interviews begun
- Astronaut exams at Lovelace clinic
- Astronaut tests at WADC
- Crew selection completed
- Astronaut reported for duty
- Trainers delivered
- Astronaut training (study, flight, centrifuge, etc)

**Flight tests of production hardware**
- Parachutes (57 capsule drops)
- Escape tower and rocket
- Complete escape system (capsule 1)
- Little Joe
- Redstone
- Atlas

♦ Accomplished

| | 1958 | 1959 | 1960 | 1961 | 1962 | 1963 |
|---|---|---|---|---|---|---|
| | J A S O N D | J F M A M J J A S O N D | J F M A M J J A S O N D | J F M A M J J A S O N D | J F M A M J J A S O N D | J F M A M J |

## THE DESIGN OF INTEGRATED CIRCUITS[8]

Over the past few years, the electronics industry has earned for itself the reputation of a glamour industry. It is "glamorous" not only because it represents one of the newest and fastest growing technologies, but also because the engineering applications of electronic principles have resulted in some of the most dramatic and exciting achievements of our civilization. In general, it is electronics that has liberated the field of communications from the boundaries previously set by the limited range of sound and light waves and has given us the media of radio and television. It is electronics that provides the means to unerringly guide space vehicles to the far reaches of the universe and send back the data that paves the way for interplanetary space travel. It is electronics that permits modern computers to solve, in minutes, complex problems that would require teams of experts many years to unravel. Yet, for all the progress that has been made, we stand today on the threshold of yet another new technology that will bring about a *new* era in electronics whose impact on the industry will possibly be greater than that of any new invention or innovation since the turn of the century: a technology called integrated circuits.

To understand the impact of integrated circuits on the industry, one must first examine the present state of the art and also the problem areas that this new technology is expected to resolve.

To begin with, it must be realized that for engineers who work with electronics today, the state of the art has reached a level of sophistication permitting the design of electronic systems with the capability to perform almost any desired communication, control, or arithmetic function. Although possible, there are some very practical reasons, however, why many technically feasible projects have not yet been attempted. Principally, these reasons are concerned with problems of size, weight, cost, and reliability. However, it is specifically these same problems that the technology of integrated circuits promises to solve.

### The Problem of Size and Weight Reduction

Conventionally, the building blocks of all electronic equipment have been the individual electronic components, such as transistors, diodes, resistors, and capacitors. The engineer uses these in various interconnected configurations to form basic circuits which, in turn, are interconnected to form subsystems and, finally, complete systems. Illustration 18–2 shows a handful of such components, consisting of 14 transistors, 10 resistors, and 2 capacitors. If he takes these components and hooks them together in the proper manner, either with hookup wire or with printed circuit wiring on a phenolic board, he can have an operating circuit for a computer, known as a J–K flip-flop.

However, through the use of integrated circuits, he can utilize the same number of components, with similar electrical characteristics, for the design of an electrically equivalent circuit—the total package to consist of a chip of silicon so tiny that it would take up little more space than the period at the end of this sentence. This tiny chip of silicon can contain not only the same 26 components, but also the components can all be properly interconnected and ready to operate as a functioning circuit. A greatly enlarged photograph of such a circuit is shown in Illustration 18–3.

[8] Based on material furnished by Motorola Semiconductor Products Division, Phoenix, Arizona. Used with permission.

**Illustration 18–2.** Entire handfuls of discrete electronic components, interconnected to perform complete circuit functions, can now be replaced by an integrated circuit fabricated on a tiny chip of silicon no larger than the head of a pin.

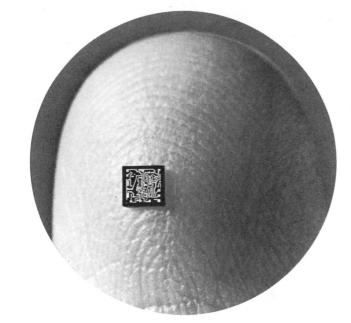

**Illustration 18–3.** Greatly enlarged view of a typical integrated circuit chip resting on a finger tip. (Courtesy Radio Corporation of America.)

**Illustration 18–4.** Chip transistors are very tiny as shown in this comparison with a sewing thimble. (Courtesy International Business Machines Corporation.)

All the engineer needs to connect to this chip is the proper input signal and an adequate power source.

This configuration presents some other problems for the engineer. Because the parts in this chip are so tiny, he cannot connect any external system to them directly. It is necessary, therefore, that the chip be placed in a larger package that has relatively thick lead wires, thus permitting him to interconnect one integrated circuit with another and with external signal and power sources, Illustration 18–4. Such connections from the package leads to the proper internal points in the circuit must be made with wires so fine that three thicknesses of wire would be approximately as thick as a human hair yet so strong that they can pass with ease the most stringent military shock, vibration, and centrifuge tests.

Even though the designed package is many times larger than one of the complete circuits, it is still miniscule compared with the conventional, discrete-component circuit. It is easy to visualize the impact of this new technology on the design of space equipment and other airborne equipment, where every inch of space and every ounce of weight is at a premium. When the space and weight savings for a single circuit is multiplied by the thousands of circuits that are used in modern, highly complex equipment, one can get some idea of its tremendous importance.

### The Problem of Cost Reduction

While reduced size and weight are the most obvious advantages of integrated circuits, they are not necessarily the most important. In a great many instances, it is the *cost-reducing potential* that may well be their most important feature. Already, in the brief time that integrated circuits have been on the market, some of these devices have been sold for less than the cost of discrete components needed to accomplish an identical function. The potential of such savings has not yet been fully realized. Let us investigate some related factors.

Illustration 18–5 shows a typical integrated circuit chip that is compared with

**Illustration 18–5.** Comparison between an integrated circuit chip, left, and the chip size of the smallest transistor being manufactured today—both greatly enlarged.

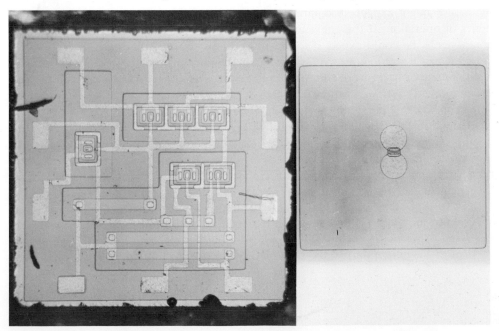

the size of the chip used for the construction of the smallest discrete transistor being made today. The integrated circuit chip is less than twice the size of the transistor. Yet, by utilizing all of the space available on the chip (and this does not necessarily represent the most efficient utilization of space) six transistors, and five resistors have been designed on the integrated circuit chip. It would be possible, in fact, to build an even larger number of parts into this chip, but, in this particular case, the engineer did not need a circuit with more components. From this example it is evident that for little more than the amount of material needed for a single transistor, one can get eleven or more components—all interconnected to form a complete, working circuit.

As another consideration, the package used for integrated circuits, except for a few extra package leads, is the same as that of some transistors, so comparable packaging costs are involved. Moreover, the integrated circuit is made by exactly the same processes as the transistor with the number of process steps being identical, except for one additional diffusion step. Therefore, in the time required to make a single transistor, and for approximately the same cost, it is possible for the engineer to design a complete and fully interconnected integrated circuit. And, if such a circuit utilizes, for example, a dozen transistors, it is obvious that the same circuit in discrete form would cost at least twelve times as much—even if one neglects the cost of diodes, resistors, and other parts, and all of the interconnections that are associated with the integrated circuit.

### The Problem of Improved Reliability

With present knowledge, it is possible for the engineer to design electronic equipment capable of performing almost every possible function that it might be called upon to do, yet which would be so complex and use so many parts that it would be impossible to keep it operating for any length of time.

To illustrate this concept, let us assume that we have a particular electronic component with a projected failure rate of 1 per cent per 1000 hours. (Actually, such a failure rate would be extremely high for semiconductor devices where more realistic values might be in the order of 0.0007 per cent.) Using this 1 per cent figure, we might expect an equipment using 100 such devices to fail within 1000 hours of operation. If the engineer designed a piece of equipment using 1000 such components, he could expect it to fail in 100 hours; and if he built it with 10,000 components, it would conceivably fail within 10 hours. Now, 10,000 components is a small number in terms of some of the large systems in use today, and even the use of components with as low a failure rate as 0.0007 per cent per 1000 hours leaves some considerable possibility for failure.

How does all this relate to integrated circuits? We have noted that integrated circuits, some of them at least, are made exactly like transistors, and transistors are among the most reliable devices available today. Now, if the processes and techniques for making an integrated circuit are identical to those for making a transistor, the engineer can reasonably expect that the reliability of such a circuit would be similar to that of the transistor. And, if a single circuit contains the equivalent of several dozen discrete components, he has reduced the number of "components" in his system several dozen times, with a corresponding increase in reliability.

But this is only a part of the story. Every electronic component requires at least two connections, each one with its built-in failure mechanism. In fact, the possibility of a failure in a solder joint interconnecting two components is at least as great as the possibility of a component failure. But by using integrated circuits, the engineer can eliminate a tremendous number of such interconnections, thereby making his equipment design even more reliable.

### Improved Performance

Integrated circuits can also improve the ultimate capability of equipment in which they are used. One of the most important potential improvements is in the area of system speed and response time. Engineers today have already made complex circuits whose propagation delay is in the order of only a few nanoseconds. A nanosecond is a thousandth of a millionth of a second, and propagation delay means the time it takes a signal applied to the input of a circuit to appear at the circuit output. This order of speed is extremely fast, especially when one considers that in one nsec an object traveling at the speed of light can cover only about a foot of distance. If we were to build a large computer where it might be necessary for a circuit at one point to energize a circuit located physically a few feet away, it would take longer, at such speeds, for the signal to travel from one circuit to the other along its conductive path, then it takes to do the actual work. The obvious answer to this problem is simply to put the circuits closer together—and therein lies one of the biggest advantages of integrated circuits. The extremely small size of these devices, and the microscopically small distance separating their inherent components, makes it possible to place the circuits in much closer relationship to each other than with discrete components, so that the system speed can be greatly increased. The small component size and spacing, moreover, reduces stray inductance and capacitance effects, thereby increasing potential high-frequency response of a circuit. The technical concepts of integrated circuits are based on transistor technology that has been well developed over the past two decades.

A transistor is an electronic component whose primary function is the amplification of an electrical signal. In this, it is like the vacuum tube, but it has the inherent advantages of smaller size, greater efficiency, and infinitely greater life expectancy. Its invention in 1948 has been hailed as one of the major milestones in the progress of engineering and science.

Basically, a transistor is a three-element device consisting of an emitter region, a base region, and a collector region, as shown in Illustration 18–6. Under proper operating conditions, a small electrical signal applied between the base and emitter elements will result in a greatly strengthened signal between the collector and emitter elements. Because many electronic signals at their origin are so weak that they cannot serve a useful function, such as driving a loudspeaker, a TV picture tube or a control mechanism, this signal-strengthening capability of tubes and transistors is fundamental to any electronic function.

Transistors are made by injecting controlled numbers of certain impurity atoms into selected portions of a semiconductor material (such as silicon) in order to differentiate the specific emitter, base, and collector regions and to give each of these the required electrical properties.

For all its capability, a transistor can be so tiny that if the engineer were to utilize only the minimum material necessary to achieve a transistor pattern, it would

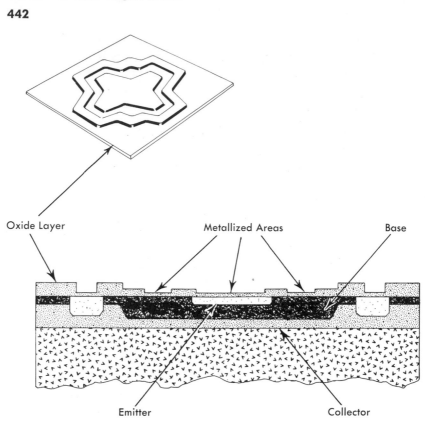

**Illustration 18—6.** Cross-section of a modern transistor showing internal structure.

be too small to be handled for processing. Therefore, as seen earlier in Illustration 18–4 the transistor structure itself occupies only a small portion of the minimum chip size needed to pick up and handle the device.

Logically, therefore, even a minimum sized chip of silicon can house many transistors, as well as accomodating a number of associated electronic parts. This, then, is the principle of integrated circuits. For, during the time used to design and fabricate the various elements of a single transistor on one part of the chip, the same processes can be utilized by the engineer to fashion additional transistors and other components in other regions of the same miniscule piece of silicon material.

### Integrated Circuits Today

In view of the many advantages of integrated circuits and because the manufacturing processes for such devices have been well developed for the transistor technology, it is not surprising that the progress in this new field has been rapid. Since the early 1960s, integrated circuits have been developed for many computer applications. This is not surprising, since computer technology, due to large-quantity requirements for identical circuits, lends itself particularly well to the cost reducing aspects of circuit integration described above. For military and space applications, where reliability improvements and space and weight savings are of prime concern, integrated circuits are being utilized as rapidly as the appropriate circuits can be designed and built. Even in the industrial and consumer electronic fields, the interest in this new technology is rising rapidly, although the urgency for the development of circuits in these areas has not been as intense, since the most compelling reason for switching to integrated circuits in these industries is reduced cost. The lack of circuit standardization for these latter applications has thus far prevented the full application of integrated-circuit bath-processing, so that the objective of drastically reduced prices has not yet been realized in these fields of electronics.

Furthermore, many of the circuit problems associated with some equipments for the industrial and consumer products industries have not yet been solved. For example, in today's technology of integrated circuits the required values of inductance are still beyond engineering capability. This eliminates automatically all forms of full integrated tuned amplifiers. Moreover, capacitance values above 0.001 microfarad would require too much space to be placed on a single chip along with other components. Therefore, low frequency amplifiers using resistance-capacitance are not available at present as fully integrated devices. Moreover, the number of parasitic parameters associated with integrated circuits (stray intercomponent coupling) is greater and more troublesome than in conventionally wired circuits. Thus, while tremendous strides have been made in the technology, many great engineering challenges still remain.

### The Engineering Challenge

Traditionally, the development of electronic equipment has involved three separate and distinct engineering disciplines. The focal point of this engineering effort is the *circuit design engineer* who, by blending theory and experience, develops circuit configuration of interconnected components to perform the needed functions. As his basic tools, the circuit designer uses the components designed by other engineers who have specialized in component design and whose intimate acquaintance with the properties of materials has enabled them to meet the circuit designer's needs, although they may not necessarily have a thorough knowledge of the end uses for their products. Finally, there is the systems engineer who utilizes the circuits in various ways to accomplish the desired objective of the *overall* equipment. He need not concern himself with circuit design so long as each particular circuit has the input-output characteristics compatible with his needs. In this technology, it has been quite possible for each of these three engineering disciplines to work independently, without a great deal of interdisciplinary coordination.

However, with integrated circuits, there is a definite need for coordination and synthesis of such activities. The development of an integrated circuit requires not only a considerable knowledge of circuit design theory, but also an intimate knowledge of materials and processes. The integrated circuit cannot be regarded as simply a collection of interconnected discrete components, but rather it must be recognized as an inseparable entity whose ultimate performance depends as much upon the proper utilization of materials and processes as it does upon circuit design. The successful development of integrated circuits, therefore, demands a high level of very carefully coordinated engineering, involving circuit theory, electronics, mathematics, physics, chemistry and metallurgy, as well as semiconductor processing and photography. While the integrated-circuit engineer need not be an expert in all of these fields, he must acquire a more-than-superficial acquaintance with each in order to effectively communicate with the various specialists involved. Thus, the engineers who work with electronics must acquire a broader base in many of the sciences than ever before, in order to become effective in this new technology.

The rewards for the successful engineer are great indeed. He will participate in a dynamic new field that will see the expansion of electronics into applications that, until now, have existed only in the imagination of the science-fiction writer. In communications, in medicine, in data processing, in consumer products for entertainment and recreation—in these fields and many more, integrated circuits are opening up vast new potentials and dramatic opportunities. And it is the engineer of today that will convert yesterday's dream into tomorrow's reality.

## SUMMARY

As can be seen from the foregoing examples, the solution to a systems engineering problem evolves through an *iterative* process, that is, a process composed of repetitions of designs and redesigns of the components and subsystems which compose the whole, until their cumulative effect is satisfactory. Frequently, a change in the design of one subsystem will necessitate a complete redesign of another subsystem.

It is also important to recognize the various categories of problems with which the engineer works. These may be generalized as follows:

1. Living systems
2. Information systems
3. Energy processes and transformations
4. Circuits
5. Machines
6. Structures

Finally, few design problems that can legitimately be classified as "engineering systems" are solved by an engineer working alone. Rather, a multidisciplined team effort is required to cope with both the complexity of the problem and with the span of time alloted for the problem solution.

## BIBLIOGRAPHY

EDER, ING. W. E., and W. GOSLING, *Mechanical System Design,* Pergamon, New York (1965).

GOODE, H. H., and R. E. MACHOL, *System Engineering,* McGraw-Hill, New York (1957).

GOSLING, W., *The Design of Engineering Systems,* Heywood, London (1962).

HALL, A. D., *A Methodology for Systems Engineering,* Van Nostrand, Princeton (1962).

KERSHNER, RICHARD B., "Proceedings of the Workshop on Systems Engineering," *IRE Transactions on Education,* vol. E-5, No. 2, June (1962).

PARKINSON, C. NORTHCOTE, *Parkinson's Law,* Houghton Mifflin, Boston (1957).

WILSON, WARREN E., *Concepts of Engineering System Design,* McGraw-Hill, New York (1965).

# Chapter 19

# The Engineering Design Process

Earlier in this text, we saw that much of the history of man has been influenced by the developments of engineering, science, and technology. When their progress was impeded, the culture of the era tended to stagnate and decline in desirable qualities. The converse also was true. Although many definitions have been given to "engineering," it can be generally agreed that *the basic purpose of the engineering profession is to bring into being technical devices, services, and systems for the use and benefit of mankind*. Regardless of the field of specialization or the complexity of the problem being considered, the process by which engineers "bring into being technical devices, services, and systems for the use and benefit of mankind" is the *engineering design process*. This is a creative and iterative process of problem solving (described more completely in Chapter 15) which is used by the engineer as a means of achieving his objective. His design is, in a sense, a bridge across the "unknown" between the *resources available* and the *needs of mankind*, Figure 19–1.

*Engineering design is a creative process* because it brings into being a multitude of new ideas and combinations of ideas that have never been in existence before. *Engineering design is an iterative process* because the cyclic process of problem solving, Figure 15–1, is applied over and over again as the scope of a problem becomes more completely defined and better understood.

For the design engineer, there are certain precepts and design methods which can be learned by study; however, the ability to do design work cannot be gained solely by reading books or studying methods. Rather, one must grapple with "real" problems and apply his abilities to effect their solutions. Just as an athlete requires rigorous practice, so the engineer needs practice on design situations as he attempts to gain proficiency in the art of engineering design. Although such experience must necessarily be gained over a period of years, now is a good time to begin acquiring some of the fundamental tools requisite for success in engineering design.

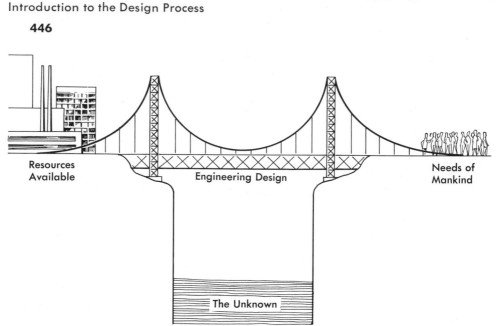

**Figure 19—1.**

## THE SIGNIFICANCE OF ENGINEERING DESIGN TODAY

Throughout history, good engineering design has been the lifeblood of prosperous nations. Today Switzerland, who must export or die, owes much of her strong financial position to the quality of her manufactured products. Other countries who were severely damaged by World War II, for example Germany and Japan, have made almost unbelievable recoveries through an emphasis on good engineering design. Although these statements are generally recognized as being true, their significance largely has been lost in a tension-filled world. However, the emphasis that has been placed recently upon engineering design by the United States and the U.S.S.R. has not gone unnoticed. In fact it is now being predicted that historians of the future may well select the development of "deliberate creative design" as the most significant development of this century.

Engineering design requires a compatibility of the forces of nature with the actions and desires of man. It is the means whereby man is able to take the resources about him and convert them so that they may serve a more useful purpose. Figure 19—2 illustrates how the engineer has used designs to solve various problems of mankind. In this context, engineering design involves the creation of a system whose parts function together so that their cumulative effect is desirable. Note in Figure 19—2 that the engineer begins his work with some *initial* condition or *state* and that he ends it at another condition, which we may call the *final state*. His design is responsible for the changes that take place between the initial and final states.

Today, a large majority of engineering projects are of such magnitude that they require the coordinated efforts of several engineers working together. Few design projects are handled by a single engineer who works alone from the inception to the completion of a design. Teamwork then is just as important a quality in engineering as it is in athletic contests. In basketball and football the individual athlete learns that generally he can accomplish much more if he is a "member" of the team.

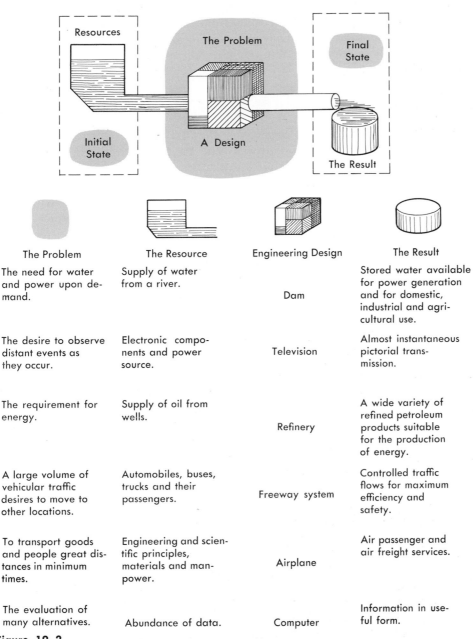

| The Problem | The Resource | Engineering Design | The Result |
|---|---|---|---|
| The need for water and power upon demand. | Supply of water from a river. | Dam | Stored water available for power generation and for domestic, industrial and agricultural use. |
| The desire to observe distant events as they occur. | Electronic components and power source. | Television | Almost instantaneous pictorial transmission. |
| The requirement for energy. | Supply of oil from wells. | Refinery | A wide variety of refined petroleum products suitable for the production of energy. |
| A large volume of vehicular traffic desires to move to other locations. | Automobiles, buses, trucks and their passengers. | Freeway system | Controlled traffic flows for maximum efficiency and safety. |
| To transport goods and people great distances in minimum times. | Engineering and scientific principles, materials and manpower. | Airplane | Air passenger and air freight services. |
| The evaluation of many alternatives. | Abundance of data. | Computer | Information in useful form. |

**Figure 19–2.**

However, in his instruction and preparatory work he is trained to be a "star." The most successful of all athletes are both "stars" and "team members." The same is true of engineers. Each engineer must become experienced in carrying a design through its various stages of development—from inception to completion. In addition, he must become proficient in assuming the responsibility for the completion of a design task that *was not* his own creation. Also he must be both able and willing to step into the problem solving cycle, (see Figure 15–1, page 322) at any point and carry it to the next step, or to completion. In addition there are personality traits and mental attitudes conducive *to good engineering* work. These are described more fully below. Possession of them will make the engineer's task easier to accomplish.

## THE DESIGN ENGINEER

When people speak of *good engineering,* they are usually referring to *good* design. These general references seem to have no limiting restrictions, such as size, complexity, or cost, and they may refer to the design of a transistor circuit for a television set, to the construction of a jet airliner, or to the design of a household mousetrap, Illustration 19–1. In each case the design has been achieved through a process of problem solving that follows closely the cyclic process described in Chapter 15. Also, each design usually has been the product of the inspirational

Illustration 19–1. Engineering designs may be complex or may be relatively simple, such as this toolset which was created for the use of astronauts and has more than 30 inflight uses. In either case the engineer must be certain that his design will produce the desired effect. (Courtesy North American Aviation, Inc.)

effort of one or more people. While these people's individual characteristics will vary, their qualities which have made the designs possible will be strikingly similar. Among these will be the following: (1) technical competence and an understanding of nature, (2) an active curiosity and a sensitivity to problems, (3) the capacity to synthesize, (4) initiative, (5) persistence and a sense of purpose, (6) the ability to observe with discernment, (7) confidence and willingness to "take a chance," (8) integrity, (9) a disposition to assume responsibility, and (10) a motivation to design for the "pleasure of accomplishment."

The design engineer must be a creative person—an idea man—and he must be able to try idea after idea without becoming discouraged. In general he will learn more from his failures than from his successes, and his designs will usually be compromises and departures from the "ideal" that he would like to achieve. Although he will find that, as a profession, engineering is often extreme in its requirements, he will also learn that engineering is most satisfying in its opportunities and rewards. There are, in fact, few satisfactons of man to match the thrill that comes to the engineer who has seen various ideas which were formed in his mind emerge into a real product or process both useful and acceptable to his fellowman.

## PHASES OF ENGINEERING DESIGN

The individual problem solving process that engineers use in designing is described in some detail in Chapter 15. However, in addition to *method* the engineer is also concerned with the *phases* of engineering design through which the design will move. These are:

1. The feasibility study phase
2. The preliminary design phase
3. The intermediate design phase
4. The detail design phase

### The Feasibility Study Phase

In general a design project will proceed through the various phases in the sequence indicated. The length of time spent on any phase, however, is a function of the complexity of the problem and the restrictions which are placed upon the engineer (time, money, or performance characteristics). The *feasibility study* is concerned with the following considerations:

1. A definiton of the elements of the problem
2. An identification of the factors that limit the scope of the design
3. An evaluation of the difficulties that can be anticipated as probable in the design process
4. A consideration of the consequences of the design
5. The problem formulation

The objective of the feasibility study is to discover the solutions to the problem that for one reason or another are not feasible and to identify the solutions that appear to have promise. It is good practice to prepare a block diagram showing the interrelationships of the component parts of the design. Once this has been completed, attention can be directed to the parts of the design that appear to be critical or the most difficult to solve. If it appears that these problems can be solved by reasonable means, the engineer can then move to the preliminary design phase, where closer approximations can be made with regard to each part of the design. It should be recognized that in such a study some nonfeasible designs may be allowed to proceed, since the feasibility of a design cannot really be known until it has been carried to completion. However, overall, much time and money can be saved by eliminating impractical designs at the outset.

In a feasibility study particular consideration should be given to the following:

1. Compatibility of the design with known principles of science and engineering
2. Compatibility of the design with the environment surrounding the overall system
3. Compatibility of the properties of the design with other parts of the system
4. A comparison of the design with other known solutions to the problem
5. Acceptability of the design in meeting the specifications set forth

Each alternative is examined to determine whether or not it can be physically achieved, whether its potential usefulness to the user is commensurate with the costs of making it available, and whether the return on the investment warrants its implementation. The feasibility study then is in effect a "pilot" effort whose primary purpose is to seek information pertinent to all possible solutions to the problem. After the information has been collected and evaluated and after the undesirable design possibilities have been discarded, the engineer may still have several alternatives to consider—all of which may be acceptable.

### The Preliminary Design Phase

The purpose of the *preliminary design phase* is to determine which of the remaining alternatives is the best solution to the problem. Some of the decision processes involving probabilities and expected outcomes that are most useful to the engineer are discussed in Chapter 20. Analog and digital simulations are particularly useful to the engineer in this phase in comparing one alternative with another. In some instances it will be more convenient for the engineer to compare the expected performance of the component parts of one design with the counterpart performances of the parts of another design. When this is done, the engineer must be very careful to consider the resultant effect of the optimized components, since it is frequently true that a simple combination of "seemingly ideal" parts will not produce an optimum condition for the overall design. It is not too difficult to list the advantages and disadvantages of each alternative being considered, but the proper evaluation of such lists may require the wisdom of Solomon.

In the preliminary design phase the engineer will work more with abstract, symbolic drawings and models, Figure 19–3, than with scale models. Mathematical models also are particularly useful in investigating the resultant effects of changes in the design criteria. Such models can be manipulated easily, they are less costly to construct in terms of money and time, and they usually are more reliable as a predictive instrument.

The consideration of *value* is very important in preliminary design work. From

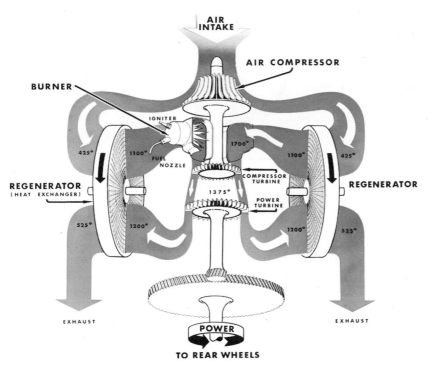

AIR
INTAKE

AIR COMPRESSOR

BURNER

IGNITER

425°

1100°

1700°

FUEL
NOZZLE

1100°

425°

REGENERATOR
(HEAT EXCHANGER)

COMPRESSOR
TURBINE

REGENERATOR

1375°

POWER
TURBINE

525°

1200°

1200°

525°

EXHAUST

EXHAUST

POWER

TO REAR WHEELS

**Figure 19–3.** Shown above is a schematic diagram of Chrysler Corporation's twin-regenerator gas turbine engine, which powers the new Turbine Car.

This illustration shows the direction of air flow and various temperatures from incoming fresh air to exhaust. Air enters the air intake and passes through the compressor where its pressure is increased four times. The air is heated as it passes through the regenerator passages in the front half of the regenerators (rotating heat-exchangers). It passes into the burner into which fuel is sprayed by the fuel nozzle and burned at a temperature of 1700 degrees. The hot gases pass through the compressor drive turbine and then through the power turbine to deliver power to the rear wheels. The gases are exhausted through the rear half of the regenerators, where they lose most of their remaining heat before being discharged through the exhaust ducts. The two rotating regenerator cores use the heat recovered from the exhaust to heat the incoming air, thus improving fuel economy and reducing exhaust temperature. (Courtesy Chrysler Corporation.)

whose point of view should a particular alternative be viewed? Performance characteristics that are viewed as being advantageous in one situation may be equally disadvantageous in another. As an example, steel might be substituted for aluminum as a basic structural material in the design of aircraft wings in order to gain a superior quality of strength per unit area. However, such a decision would also have serious consequences on the lift capability of the wing due to the increased weight of the steel members. In like manner the fuselage might be streamlined to achieve a higher range of speed. Such alterations might necessarily cause a corresponding decrease in the cargo carrying capacity of the plane. Which is the more important? Where the possible loss of human life is a consideration, the measurement of value becomes exceedingly difficult. In some parts of the world, human life is not highly valued. However, in the United States, for example, there is great reluctance to place a "cost" or value on the life of a human being. If the engineer assumes an infinite cost penalty, the design may be impossible. However, to ignore this factor

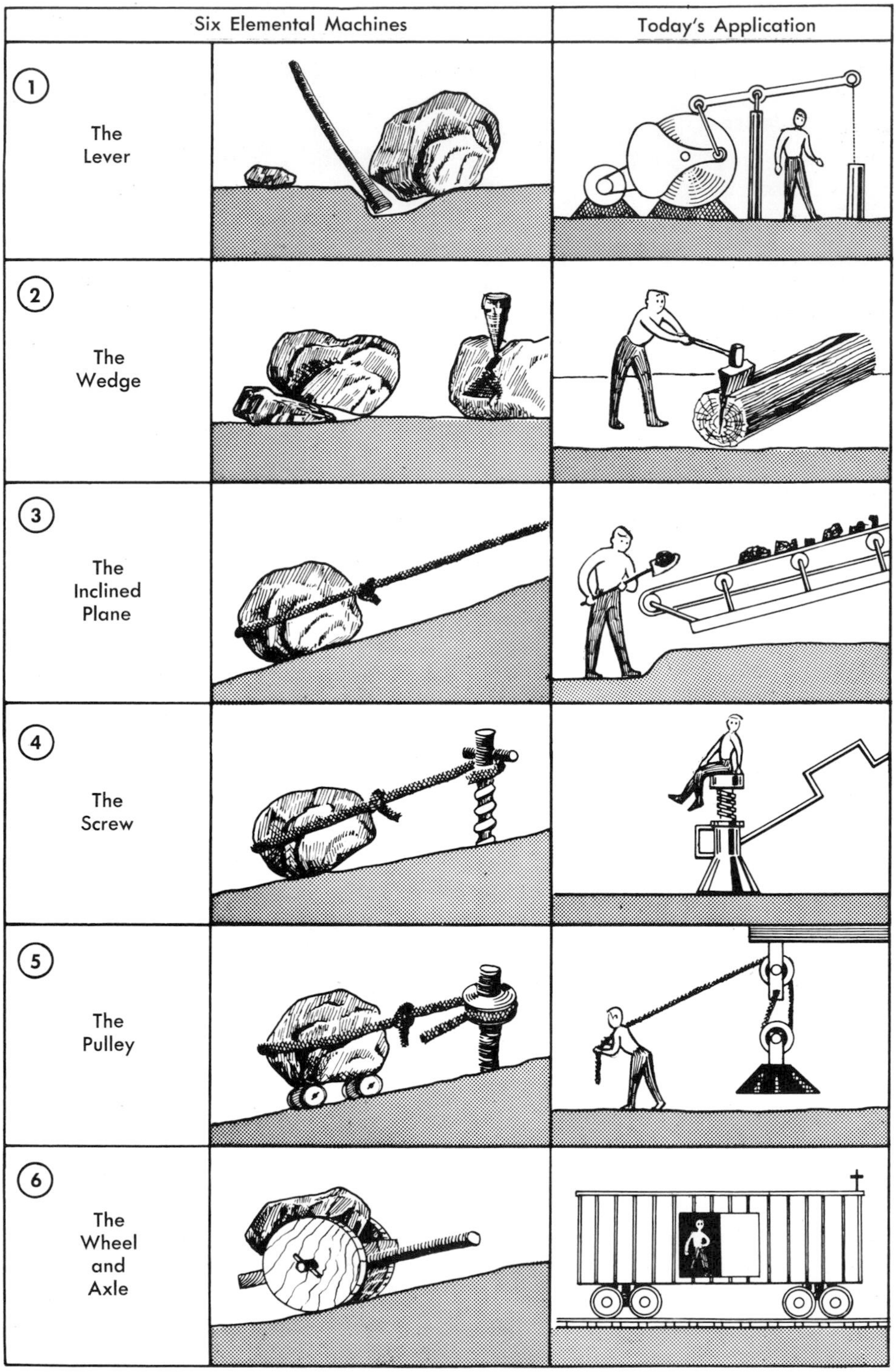

| | | Six Elemental Machines | Today's Application |
|---|---|---|---|
| ① | The Lever | | |
| ② | The Wedge | | |
| ③ | The Inclined Plane | | |
| ④ | The Screw | | |
| ⑤ | The Pulley | | |
| ⑥ | The Wheel and Axle | | |

**Figure 19—4.**

would, in effect, assign a cost factor of "zero" to the loss of a life. The engineer, then, must face his responsibilities with honesty and realism.

Engineers engaged in preliminary design must be able to project the future effectiveness of the alternative designs. In many cases the preliminary design stage of a product will precede the manufacture of the product by several years. Conditions change with time, and these changes too must be anticipated by the engineer. Many companies have become eminently successful, because of the quality of their preliminary design work, whereas others have been forced into bankruptcy.

The *human being* is one element common to a large majority of engineering systems. As such, the preliminary design phase must give consideration to the consequences of the design upon man's physical and mental well-being, and such factors as heat, noise, light, vibration, acceleration, air supply, and humidity must be anticipated.

In addition to selecting the best alternative to pursue, the engineer should make every effort to refine the chosen solution into its most elementary form. Simple solutions are usually the best solutions, but they also are the most difficult to achieve. However simplicity in design has long been recognized as a hallmark of quality and the engineer should work to this end. He should learn also that old ideas are not necessarily bad ideas. Figure 19–4 illustrates how some of the earliest inventions of man have been used in modern day applications.

### The Intermediate Design Phase

Once the feasibility study and preliminary design phases are complete, maximum effort can be placed upon development of the chosen solution. It must be remembered, however, that the chosen solution was selected originally because at *that* time it seemed best to meet the design criteria. Any alterations in these specifications could project another solution into the preferred category. The purpose of the *intermediate design phase* is to plan and implement the overall design concept of the chosen solution. Here the engineer is not concerned with "predictions of the future" but rather with the "reality of the moment." He is not concerned with an *estimated* budget but rather with an *actual* budget of dollars and hours based upon the recommendations of the previous studies made. In many instances the engineers who will be working on the intermediate design phase will not be the same individuals as those who worked on the feasibility study or on the preliminary design phase. If this is the case, certain problems of communication may occur.

Relatively speaking, commitments by management of money, manpower, and time were not great in the feasibility study or in the preliminary design phases. Such is not the case in the intermediate design phase. Much larger resources are now required. Large designs involve hundreds and sometimes thousands of technical people, and any miscalculation or mistake in judgment will have serious repercussions. Many engineers operating at various levels within the organization will be rendering design decisions that will vary widely in their significance and consequences. These efforts must be coordinated to form an overall design that meets the design criteria.

The intermediate design phase includes not only the design of the main subsystems that make up the overall design and an analysis of their cumulative effects, but also the design of the component parts of the subsystems, the budgeting of time

**Illustration 19–2.** The detail design phase demands close coordination between the engineer and his support personnel. Above, the engineer is explaining to his detail draftsman modifications which he has made in the design of a truck chassis. Note the miniaturized truck model. (Courtesy Chrysler Corporation.)

and money, the scheduling of the various tasks to be performed (see a more detailed explanation of this assignment later in this chapter), obtaining a realistic cost estimate of the product, and the assemblage of necessary technical and support manpower to accomplish the required tasks.

### The Detail Design Phase

As one moves through the design phases—from feasibility study to detail design—the tasks to be accomplished become less and less abstract and consequently more closely defined as to their expected functions. In the earlier phases, the engineer worked with the design of systems, subsystems, and components. In the detail design phase he will also work with the design of the parts and elementary pieces that will be assembled to form the components, Illustration 19–2.

In this final design phase all technical problems relating to the design solution must be solved. There is no other part of the design process remaining. Consequently questions pertaining to materials selection, tolerances, quality of workmanship required, production processes, and complete specifications regarding the design become critical and can no longer be avoided or delayed in consideration. They must be answered explicitly. Their complete definition is mandatory.

In the previous phase of engineering design, a large majority of the people involved were engineers. In the detail phase this is not necessarily the case. Many people—metallurgists, chemists, tool designers, detailers, draftsmen, technicians, checkers, estimators, manufacturing and shop personnel—will work together under the direction of engineers, Illustration 19–3. These technically trained support people will normally outnumber the engineers. In a sense then the engineer who works in this phase of design must be a "good manager" in addition to his other responsibilities, and his successes may be measured largely by his ability to bring forth their most capable efforts.

The detail design phase will include the completion of an operating physical model or prototype (a model having the correct layout and physical appearance but constructed by custom nonproduction line techniques), which may have been started in an earlier design phase. The first prototype will usually be incomplete and modifications and alterations will be necessary. This is to be expected. Problems heretofore unanticipated may be identified, undesirable characteristics may be eliminated, and performance under design conditions may be observed for the first time. This part of the design process is always a time of excitement for everyone, especially the engineer.

The final phase of design involves the checking of every detail, every component, and every subsystem. All must be compatible. Much testing may be necessary to prove theoretical calculations or to discover unsuspected consequences. Assump-

**Illustration 19–3.** The work of the engineer has only begun when he releases his detail design for fabrication. Here an engineer works with a technician to evaluate the results of his design. With this information he will continue to refine the design. (Courtesy Xerox Corporation.)

tions made in the earlier design phases should be re-examined and viewed with suspicion. Are they still valid? Would other assumptions now be more realistic? If so, what changes would be called for in the design?

The engineer should strive to produce a design which is the "obvious" answer to everyone who sees it, *once it is complete.* Such designs, simple and pleasing in appearance, are in a sense as beautiful as any painting, piece of sculpture, or poem penned from the hand of man . . . and they are considerably more useful to his well-being.

## DESIGN PHILOSOPHY

Design philosophy is an important factor with many industries, companies, and consulting firms. The aircraft industry, for example, generally would support a design philosophy that includes (a) components which are lightweight, (b) minimum safety factors, (c) a limited length service life, (d) particular attention to a wide range of loading conditions and temperature extremes, (e) consideration of vibration and fatigue, and (f) minimum attention to factors affecting cost. The automobile industry, on the other hand, would be more likely to support a design philosophy that would include (a) cost consciousness, (b) long life with minimum service and maintenance, (c) ease of maintenance, (d) customer appeal, (e) safety for the occupants, (f) design for mass production, and (g) a finished product that is durable under varying climatic conditions and that will withstand vibration and collision shock.

Some companies are more concerned that their products have a "familylike" image and that a responsiveness to customer appeal be designed into all of their products. In some instances the image is "safety," in some "efficiency," in some "quality." Public relations should be an important factor with all companies, and the engineer should not be insensitive to the effects that his design will have upon the total company image. The appearance of the product is particularly important in some industries. In such cases the engineer must take this into account in all phases of his design.

Any engineering design is but *one* answer to an identified problem. For this reason few designs have withstood the test of time without undergoing substantial revisions. One need but look at the continuous parade of modifications, alterations, changes, and complete redesigns that have taken place within the automobile industry since its inception to see how the product of a single industry has been changed thousands and thousands of times. Each change, it was believed at the time, was some improvement over the existing model. In some instances this assumption proved to be false and other modifications were quickly made.

In some situations the mounting pressure for a "quick solution" has led to the adoption of designs of minimum acceptability. However, the public tends to judge the quality of a device or machine by its performance, and generally the handicaps and financial and time pressures under which the engineer works are of little interest to the customer. This is perhaps as it should be. However, this emphasis on the product places an additional responsibility upon the shoulders of the engineer to release only those designs which he believes are good designs and designs to which he will have no hesitancy in affixing his signature. As a professional person he must be equally aware of his responsibilities to his fellowman and to his employer or client. He must perceive *when* he knows, he must realize *when he does not know,* and he must assume the final responsibility in either case.

## AN EXAMPLE OF THE DEVELOPMENT OF AN ENGINEERING DESIGN

There are many well-known engineering designs on the American scene that have, over a period of many years, almost become a "way of life." Although the authors of this text are reluctant to pick any one of these as being superior to another, they are eager that the students who study this text gain an appreciation for the concepts that "good ideas plus good engineering design practice equals success" and "all good engineering designs can be improved." For this reason the story of the developing design of the safety razor is given here.[1]

The idea for the safety razor that the American public knows today was the brainchild of a traveling salesman, King C. Gillette, who on a summer morning in 1895 became irritated and exasperated with his inability to shave with a dull straight razor. In an instant the idea of a replaceable flat blade secured in a holder for maximum safety was born. In Gillette's own words,

> I saw it all in a moment, and in that same moment many unvoiced questions were asked and answered more with the rapidity of a dream than by the slow process of reasoning. A razor is only a sharp edge and all back of that edge is but a support for that edge. Why do they spend so much material and time in fashioning a backing which has nothing to do with the shaving? Why do they forge a great piece of steel and spend so much labor in hollow grinding it when they could get the same result by putting an edge on a piece of steel that was only thick enough to hold an edge? At that time and in that moment it seemed as though I could see the way the blade could be held in a holder. Then came the idea of sharpening the two opposite edges on the thin piece of steel that was uniform in thickness throughout, thus doubling its service; and following in sequence came the clamping plates for the blade with a handle equally disposed between the two edges of the blade. All this came more in pictures than in thought as though the razor were already a finished thing and held before my eyes. I stood there before that mirror in a trance of joy at what I saw.

Previous to this time, men of wealth and influence of all nationalities frequented barber shops in which the customer was lathered from the community mug and shaved with an unsterilized razor, Illustration 19–4. Such a barber shop shave was a luxury that poor people could not afford, but many men of modest means did purchase their own straight razors. Ladies of respect would not think of using a razor to remove unsightly hair although it is reported that such practice was not uncommon for burlesque queens.

Several years previous to the inspirational moment of 1895, King Gillette was talking with a successful inventor friend who advised him:

> King, you are always thinking and inventing something; why don't you try to think of something like the Crown Cork, when used once, it is thrown away, and the customer keeps coming back for more—and with every additional customer you get, you are building a permanent foundation of profit.

---

[1] Much of the material presented here was made available by and is used with the permission of the Gillette Safety Razor Company, Boston, Massachusetts.

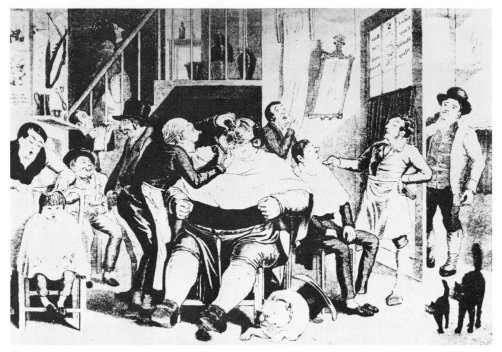

**Illustration 19–4.** The morning shave in 1568 was not without its difficulties, as shown in the above English woodcut. (Courtesy Gillette Safety Razor Company.)

Although Gillette often thought of this advice, he never was able to capitalize on it until that moment—holding in his hand a dull razor which was beyond the point of successful stropping and in need of honing—that the idea in his subconscious emerged to reinforce his need for a new and novel solution.

Gillette knew very little about razors and practically nothing about steel, and he could not foresee the trials and frustrations that were to come his way before the "safety razor" was a success. On the same day that he received the inspiration to devise a razor which could use interchangeable and disposable blades, and which were safe to use, Gillette went to a local hardware store and purchased several pieces of brass, some steel ribbon used for clock springs, and some hand tools. Using some rough pencil sketches and the recently purchased hand tools, he fashioned a crude model of his new design, Illustration 19–5. Gillette's invention did not consist primarily in a particular form of blade or design of a blade holder, but in the conception of a blade so cheap as to be discarded when dull. To obtain such a blade he abandoned the forged type and fashioned one of thin steel, so that it might be cut from a strip, avoiding the expense of forging or hollow grinding. Prior to this invention, razor makers produced an expensive blade that was expected to give service as long as possible, even a lifetime, and to be honed and stropped indefinitely. The new idea was a complete reversal of this practice and was a really unique invention.

In his new razor Gillette carried his theory to great completeness. The blade was to be made of relatively thin steel and thereby achieve economy through the

**Illustration 19–5.** King Gillette's moment of triumph came when he discovered that his idea could be made to work. (Courtesy Gillette Safety Razor Company.)

saving of both material and labor. It was to have two edges, one on each side, thus giving double shaving service. The adjustment of the blade edge in relation to the guard was to be obtained by flexing the blade so as to bring the edge nearer to or farther from the guard teeth, in order to obtain a finer or coarser cut, Figure 19–5.

However, all was not bright for this new idea. No one but Gillette had any faith in a razor the blades of which were to be used once and then wasted. Such a proposal did not seem to be within the bounds of reason, and even Gillette's friends looked upon it as a joke. Actually he had thought originally that the blades might be made very cheaply from a thin ribbon of steel, but he was, of course, aware that new machines and processes would need to be invented and developed before such "ribbon blades" could be manufactured cheaply. This did not seem to be a likely prospect. For more than five years Gillette clung tenaciously to his razor theories. He made a number of models with minor variations and sought through others to get blades made with shaving qualities. He got very little encouragement either from his helpers and advisers or from the results of his experiments. People who knew most about cutlery and razors in particular were most discouraging. Years later Gillette said, "They told me I was throwing my money away; that a razor was only possible when made from cast steel forged and fashioned under the hammer to give it density so it would take an edge. But I didn't know enough to quit. If I had

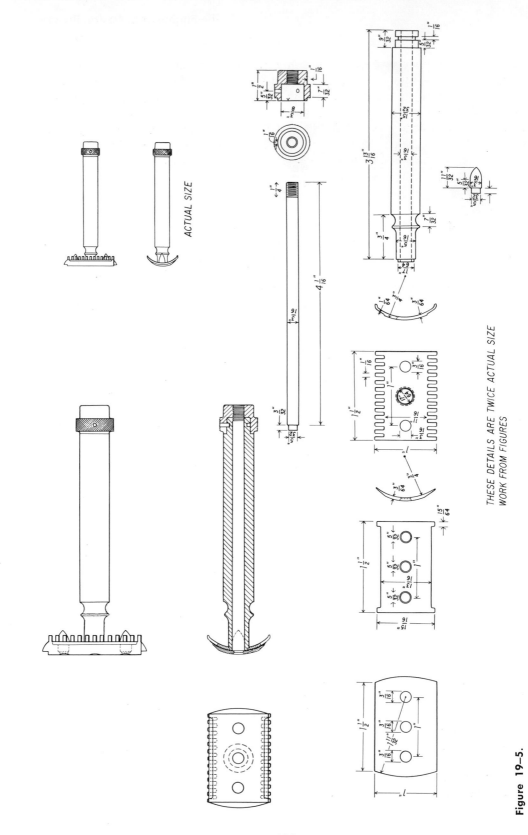

ACTUAL SIZE

THESE DETAILS ARE TWICE ACTUAL SIZE
WORK FROM FIGURES

Figure 19–5.

460

been technically trained, I would have quit or probably would never have begun." In spite of this discouragement, Gillette did not falter in his faith and persistence.

Faced with an inability to cope with the technical difficulties surrounding his idea, Gillette began to search for others to help him. He associated himself with several men, one of whom—W. E. Nickerson—was a mechanical engineering graduate of the Massachusetts Institute of Technology. The design capability of Nickerson soon became apparent. A notation from the Gillette Safety Razor Co. Silver Jubilee history relates the following:

> . . . after a very urgent plea, he [Nickerson] agreed to turn the problem over in his mind and give a decision within a month. On giving the problem serious thought, he began to see the proper procedure and felt that he could develop the razor into a commercial proposition. Things began to take definite shape in his mind, he could visualize the hardening process and sharpening machines, and definite ideas were developed as to the type of handle necessary to properly hold the blade.
>
> Hardening apparatus and sharpening machines could not be properly designed until the form and size of the blade were known, so the first step was to decide just what the blade and the handle were to be like. Mr. Gillette's models were amply developed to disclose the fundamental ideas, but there was left a wide range of choice in the matter of carrying out these ideas; and furthermore, the commercial success of the razor was sure to depend very much upon the judgment used in selecting just the right form and thickness of blade and the best construction in the handle.
>
> Mr. Nickerson's fundamental thought in relation to the remodeled razor was that the handle must have sufficient stability to make possible very great accuracy of adjustment between the edge of the blade and the protecting guard. Here is a point upon which he laid great stress, and which we are constantly endeavoring to drive home today: "No matter how perfect the blade is, you cannot get the best result unless the handle is perfect also." The Gillette handle is made to micrometric dimensions and is an extremely accurate instrument. If damaged or thrown out of alignment, poor shaves are likely to result. This idea of great stability led Mr. Nickerson to design a handle to be "machined" out of solid metal, in contra-distinction to one stamped from relatively thin sheet metal. To this fact much of the Gillette commercial success is due. In fact, it is doubtful if great success could have been achieved without it.
>
> The shape and thickness of the blade were determined as follows: Sheet steel thinner than six one-thousandths of an inch appeared to lack sufficient firmness to make a good blade, and a thickness greater than that seemed too difficult to flex readily; so six thousandths was chosen. In the matter of width, one inch was thought to be unnecessarily wide and three-quarters of an inch was found to be too narrow, especially when flexing was considered. Thus seven-eighths of an inch was adopted. As to contour, a circle one and three-quarters inches in diameter if symmetrically crossed by two parallel lines seven-eighths of an inch apart give chords corresponding to the cutting edges, one and one-half inches long, which was thought to be the right length for the edges. The rounded ends to the blade form thus produced strengthened the blade along the center where holes were to be and gave the blade its well-

known and pleasing shape. After twenty-five years of use nothing has transpired to cause regret that some other shape was not selected. These early decisions were of the utmost importance and almost seemed inspired.

On September 9, 1901, Mr. Nickerson sent a report of his findings and recommendations to Mr. Heilborn of which the following is an exact copy:

Boston, Mass., Sept. 9, 1901.

Jacob Heilborn, Esq.,
Boston, Mass.

Dear Sir:

I have had your proposition, in regard to the manufacture of the Gillette Safety Razor, under consideration for rather more than a month and desire to report as follows:

It is my confident opinion that not only can a successful razor be made on the principles of the Gillette patent, but that if the blades are made by proper methods a result in advance of anything known can be reached. On the other hand, to put out these razors with blades of other than the finest quality of temper and edge would be disastrous to their reputation and to their successful introduction.

With an almost unlimited market, and with such inducements as are offered by this razor, in the way of cheapness of manufacture and of convenience and effectiveness in use, I can see no reason why it cannot easily compete for popular favor with anything in its line ever put before the public.

I wish to reiterate that in my opinion the success of the razor depends very largely, if not almost wholly, on the production at a low price of a substantially perfect blade. This blade must possess an edge that shall, at least, be equal of any rival on the market, and should combine extreme keenness with a hardness and toughness sufficient to stand using a number of times without much deterioration.

For the past month I have been giving much thought to the subject of manufacturing these blades, and I now feel justified in offering to undertake the construction of machines and apparatus to that end. I am confident that I have grasped the situation and can guarantee, as far as such a thing can be guaranteed, a successful outcome. Your knowledge of my long experience with inventions and machine building will, perhaps, cause you to attach considerable weight to my opinion in this matter. You are of course aware that special machines will have to be designed and built for putting on the blades that delicate edge which is necessary for easy shaving. The problem is entirely different from that involved in the tempering and grinding of ordinary razors and other keen tools, not only on account of the thinness of the blades, but also on account of the cheapness with which it must be done. I believe that with the machines which I have in mind, an edge can be put upon these blades which will be unapproachable by ordinary hand sharpened razors. The machinery and methods for making the blades will naturally be of a novel character and admit of sound patents, which would become the property of the Company and would be of great advantage in disposing of foreign rights. It is not unlikely that the machines for honing these blades may be adapted for any of the present form of razors and do away with hand honing. I will also add that I have in mind a convenient and simple method of adjusting the position of the blade for different beards.

In reply to your questions as to the probable expense of fitting up to manufacture the razor on a scale suitable for a beginning on a commercial basis, I will make the following approximation:

| | |
|---|---|
| Drawings for machines for tempering, grinding, honing and stropping | $ 100 |
| Patterns for ditto | 250 |
| Materials for machines (one each) | 300 |
| Cost of building (one each) | 700 |
| Special dies and tools | 150 |
| Tools for making holders { Small turret lathe / Power punch / Small plain milling machine / Sensitive drill / Bench lathe / Bench tools, etc. | 1500 |
| Foreign patents: England, Germany, Belgium, France, Canada, Spain, Italy, Austria—about | 800 |
| Labor services, etc. | 1200 |
| | $5000 |

I have made what seems to me to be fairly liberal but by no means extravagant figures. It may cost considerably less or possibly a little more, but I think the sum given will not come out very far from the truth.

I should recommend that the machines for making the blades be built in some shop already established, and when they are completed, a suitable room be engaged and they and the holder tools set up in it. It is not easy to say just how long it would take to be ready for manufacturing, but if there are no serious delays it is possible that four months might cover it.

In conclusion let me add that so thoroughly am I satisfied that I can perfect machinery described on original lines which will be patentable, that I am ready to accept for my compensation stock in a Company which I understand you propose forming.

Very truly yours,
(Signed) Wm. E. Nickerson

Nickerson did design a machine for sharpening the blades and an apparatus for hardening the blades in packs. Thus through the application of fundamental engineering principles a successful new industry was born.

Success was not immediate because two years later, in 1903, when Gillette put his first razor on the market only 51 razors and 168 blades were sold. Barbers, who believed that their business would be ruined if this new fad caught on, were particularly scathing in their reproof. However, the new razor caught on, sales soared, and by 1905 manufacturing operations had to be moved to larger quarters. By 1917 razor sales had risen to over a million a year, and blade sales averaged

| Year | New Design | Improvements |
|------|-----------|--------------|
| 1932 | Gillette Blue Blade | Better shaving edge |
| 1934 | One-Piece Razor | Convenience, more exact edge exposure |
| 1938 | Thin Gillette Blade | Reduced cost by one-half |
| 1947 | Blade Dispenser | Blade edges protected, simplified blade-changing |
| 1957 | Adjustable Safety Razor | Variable cut, ease of adjustment |
| 1960 | Super Blue Blade | Longer life, first coated edge, less pull |
| 1963 | Stainless Steel Blade | Comfort, coated edge, durability |
| 1963 | Lady Gillette Razor | Designed expressly for women |
| 1965 | Super Stainless Steel Blade | Better steel, longer life, new coating |
| 1965 | Techmatic Razor with Razor Band | Cartridge load, convenience, no blades |

**Figure 19–6.**

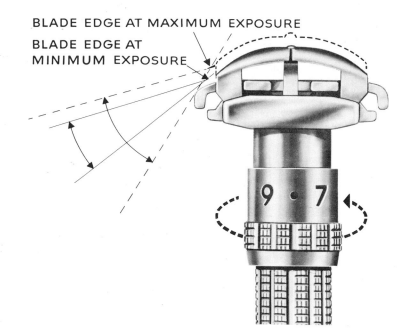

**Figure 19–7.** The adjustable safety razor. (Courtesy Gillette Safety Razor Company.)

150 million a year. As a result of World War I, self-shaving became widespread and returning servicemen carried the habit home with them. While World War I taught thousands of men the self-shaving habit, World War II introduced millions of men to daily shaving practice.

In the 62 years since Gillette razors first went on sale, the company has produced over one half billion razors and over one hundred billion blades. Throughout this period of time, however, many modifications and redesigns have been made, Figures 19–6 and 19–7.

The latest of these designs, the Techmatic Razor with razor band, Figure 19–8, is a complete departure from the blade-changing routine which has been so successfully sold to the American public. Interestingly enough the idea of shaving with

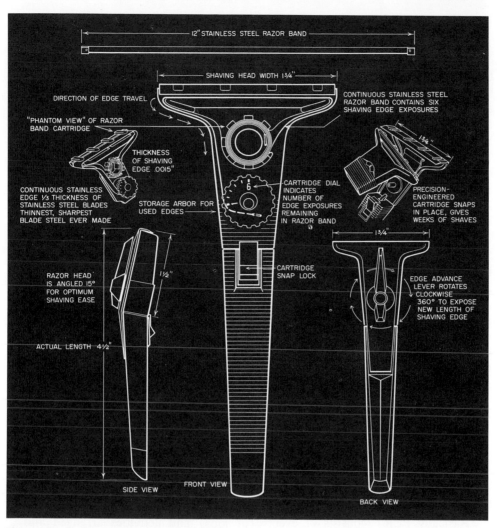

**Figure 19–8.** The Techmatic Razor with razor band. (Courtesy Gillette Safety Razor Company.)

a "ribbon of steel' is a simple adaption of the original material purchased by King Gillette on that summer day in 1895. It has, however, taken 70 years for engineering design to make possible mass produced "ribbon blades." Other improvements will undoubtedly follow in the years ahead.

Many other American industries have equally exciting engineering histories. In many respects the engineering students of today live in the most challenging period of history ever, and a *good idea,* together with the application of sound engineering design principles, will still produce *success.*

Today the planning of engineering projects has been given a larger and larger role of importance, and the following section is concerned with this aspect of engineering design.

## THE PLANNING OF ENGINEERING PROJECTS

In every walk of life, we notice and appreciate evidence of well-planned activities. You may have noticed that good planning involves more than "the assignment of tasks to be performed" although this frequently is the only aspect of planning that is given any attention. Planning in the broad sense must include the enumeration of all the activities and events associated with a project and a recognition and evaluation of their interrelationships and interdependencies. The assignment of tasks to be performed and other aspects of scheduling should follow.

Since "time is money," planning is a very important part of the implementation of any engineering design. Good planning is often the difference between success and failure, and the young engineering student would do well, therefore, to learn some of the fundamental aspects of planning as applied to the implementation of engineering projects.

In 1957 the United States Navy was attempting to complete the Polaris Missile System in record time. The estimated time for completion seemed unreasonably long. Through the efforts of an operations research team, a new method of planning and coordinating the many complex parts of the project was finally developed. The overall saving in time for the project amounted to more than eighteen months. Since that time a large percentage of engineering projects, particularly those which are complex and time consuming, have used this same planning technique to excellent advantage. It is called PERT (Program Evaluation and Review Technique). Other similar techniques or variations such as CPM (Critical Path Method) have also proved their usefulness in the economic utilization of time and money.

PERT enables the engineer-in-charge to view the total project as well as to recognize the interrelationships of the component parts of the design. Its utility is not limited to the beginning of the project but rather it continues to provide an accurate measure of progress throughout the work period. Pertinent features of PERT and CPM are combined in the following discussion.

### How Does PERT Work?

Basically PERT consists of events (or jobs) and activities arranged into a *time-oriented network* to show the interrelationships and interdependencies that exist. The network is also used to portray the events as they occur in the process of accomplishing missions or objectives, together with the activities that necessarily occur to interconnect the events. These relationships will be discussed more fully below.

**Events.** An event is the *start* or *completion* of a mental or physical task. It does not involve the actual performance of the task. Thus, events are *points in time* which require that action be taken or that decisions be made. Various symbols are used in industry to designate events, such as circles, squares, ellipses, or rectangles. In this book circles will be used, Figure 19–9.

Events are joined together to form a project network. It is important that the events be arranged within the network in logical or time sequence from left to right. If this is done, the completion of each event will occupy a discrete and identifiable

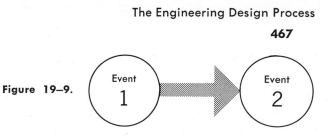

**Figure 19–9.**

point in time. An event cannot consume time and it cannot be considered to be completed until all activities leading to it have been completed. After all events have been identified and arranged within the network, they are assigned identification numbers. Since events and activities may be altered during the course of the project, the logical order of the events will not necessarily follow in exact numerical sequence 1, 2, 3, 4, 5, etc. The event numbers, therefore, serve only for identification purposes.

**Activities.** An activity is the actual performance of a task and, as such, it consumes an increment of time. Activities separate events. An activity cannot begin until all preceding activities have been completed. An arrow is used to represent the time span of an activity, with time flowing from the tail to the point of the arrow, Figure 19–10. In a PERT network an activity may indicate the use of time,

**Figure 19–10.**

**Figure 19–11.**

manpower, materials, facilities, space, or other resources. A *phantom* activity may also represent waiting time or "interdependencies." A phantom activity, represented by a dashed arrow, Figure 19–11, may be inserted into the network for clarity of the logic, although it represents no real physical activity. Waiting time would also be noted in this manner. Remember that events "happen or occur," and that activities are "started or completed."

**The Network.** A PERT network is one type of pictorial representation of a project. Bar charts, sometimes referred to as Gantt charts,[2] are also used for visualization purposes, Figure 18–15. Unfortunately, although the bar charts are useful for recognizing the occurrence of activities in series or parallel over some given time period, they do not show the interdependency and interrelationships of the activities. Also as shown in Figure 18–15, some bars are of such length that it is difficult to know for a given activity precisely what is being done at any given point in time. For this reason a PERT network would have decided advantages as a control device.

In PERT, events are connected by activities to form a project network. Progress from one event to another is made by completing the activity which connects them.

[2] Henry Gantt introduced the use of this type of planning chart near the turn of the century.

The case of Mr. Jones getting ready for work each morning can be examined as an example.

| EVENTS | ACTIVITIES |
|---|---|
| 1. The alarm rings | |
| | A. Jones lies in bed wishing that he didn't have to go to work |
| 2. Jones begins his morning toilet | |
| | B. Jones shaves, bathes, and dresses |
| 3. Jones starts to prepare breakfast | |
| | C. Jones cooks breakfast |
| 4. Jones begins to eat | |
| | D. Jones eats breakfast |
| 5. Jones realizes his bus is about to pass the corner | |
| | E. Jones jumps up, grabs his briefcase and runs for the corner |
| 6. Jones boards the bus | |

A PERT network can be drawn for Jones as follows, Figure 19–12.

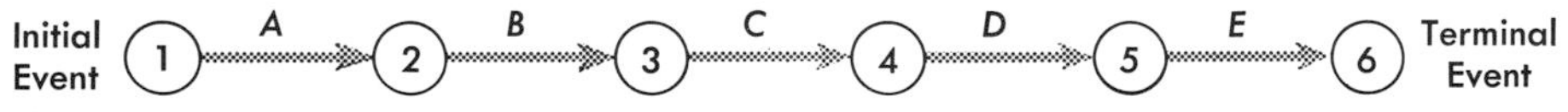

**Figure 19–12.**

After contemplating the situation Jones decides that he should get his wife's cooperation in helping him with his morning ordeal. He works out some additional parts of his program as follows:

| EVENTS | ACTIVITIES |
|---|---|
| 7. Jones awakens wife when alarm rings | |
| | F. Wife lies in bed wishing that it were Saturday |
| 8. Jones' wife gets up and begins breakfast | |
| | G. Wife cooks breakfast |
| | H. Wife eats breakfast |
| 9. Jones decides to walk to corner | |
| | J. Jones walks to corner |

His PERT network can now be shown as in Figure 19–13.

After trying his alternate plan Jones finds that it takes less total time because his wife is now preparing the breakfast while he is getting dressed for work. Although

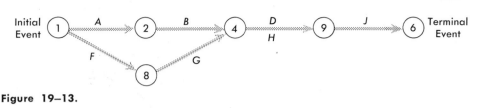

**Figure 19–13.**

this is a very elementary example, it does point up the constituent parts of a PERT network. Note that Jones and his wife must wait until he is dressed (B) and the breakfast is cooked (G) before they can eat.

In a PERT network each activity should be assigned a specified time for expected accomplishment. The time units chosen should be consistent throughout the network, but the size of the time unit (years, work-weeks, days, hours, etc.) should be selected by the engineer in charge of the project. The time value chosen for each activity should represent the mean (see p. 219) of the various times that the activity would take if it were repeated many times.

There are three types of time estimates that can be made for each activity. These are

1.  an *optimistic* time estimate $(t_o)$—the length of time required under the most favorable conditions and assuming that no unforeseen complications or difficulties arise. This might be the "one chance in a hundred" circumstance.

2.  the *most likely* time estimate $(t_m)$—the length of time in which the event is most likely to be completed under normal conditions and allowing for some unforeseen delays.

3.  a *pessimistic* time estimate $(t_p)$—The length of time required if everything goes wrong and if unusual difficulties and complications arise in carrying out the activity.

The expected time $(t_e)$ may be determined by the relationship

$$t_e = \frac{t_o + 4\,t_m + t_p}{6}$$

Statistical methods can also be used when these three time estimates are available to arrive at an expected time $(t_e)$ for each activity. However, for our purposes the *most likely* time estimates will be used as expected times. These times can be indicated in the network above or below the appropriate activity arrows.

By using the network of events and activities and by taking into account the times consumed by the various activities, a *critical path* can be established for the project. It is this path that controls the successful completion of the project, and it is important that the engineer be able to isolate it for study. Let us consider the

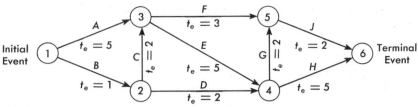

**Figure 19–14.**

PERT network in Figure 19–14 where the activity times are indicated in days. Activities represent the expenditure of time and effort. For example, Activity A (between event 1 and event 3) requires five days and is likely devoted to planning the project, while Activity B requires one day and may represent the procurement of basic supplies. Event 1 is the beginning of the project and Event 6 is the end of the project. The first step in locating the *critical path* is to determine the "earliest" event times $(T_E)$, the "latest" event times $(T_L)$, and the "slack" time $(T_L - T_E)$.

### Earliest Event Times $(T_E)$

The earliest expected time of an event refers to the time, $T_E$, when an event can be expected to be completed. $T_E$ for an event is calculated by summing all of the activity duration times $(t_e)$ from the beginning event to the event in question if the most time consuming route is chosen. To avoid confusion, the $T_E$ times of events are usually placed near the network in rectangular blocks. For reference purposes the beginning of the project is usually "time zero." In Figure 19–15 below $T_E$ for

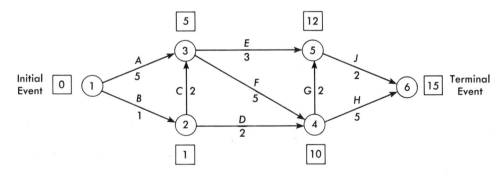

**Figure 19–15.**

Event 2 would be $0 + 1 = \boxed{1}$ and $T_E$ for Event 3 would be $0 + 5 = \boxed{5}$. However, there are two possible routes to Event 3 (A or B + C). The *maximum* of these event times should be selected as $T_E$ for Event 3. Summing the times we find:

$$\text{By Path A} \quad : \quad 0 + 5 = \boxed{5} \leftarrow \text{Select as } T_E$$

$$\text{By Path B + C:} \quad 0 + 1 + 2 = \boxed{3}$$

If we continue this summation process throughout the network we will arrive

at the earliest event times shown in Figure 19–15 and the final $T_E$ for Event 6 will be 15 days.

### Latest Event Times ($T_L$)

The latest expected time, $T_L$, of an event refers to the longest time which can be allowed for an event, assuming that the entire project is kept on schedule. $T_L$ for an event is determined by beginning at the terminal event and working backward through the various event circuits, subtracting the value $T_E$ at each event assuming the least time consuming route is chosen. The resulting values of $T_L$ are recorded in small ellipses located near the network. Thus, in Figure 19–16 $T_L$ for Event 4 would be the minimum of $\boxed{15} - 5 = \fbox{10}$ and $\boxed{15} - 2 - 2 = \fbox{11}$ ; for Event 2 $\boxed{15} - 5 - 5 - 2 = \fbox{3}$, and for Event 3 $\boxed{15} - 5 - 5 = \fbox{5}$. The final evaluations of latest event times are shown in Figure 19–16.

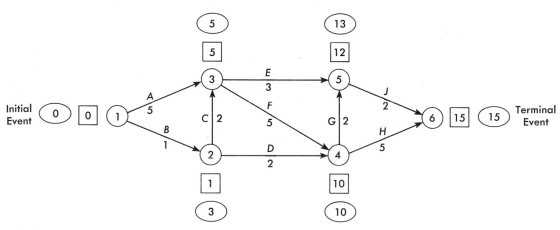

**Figure 19–16.**

Remember that $T_L$ is determined to be the minimum of the differences between the succeeding event $T_L$ and the intervening activity times. Also in calculating $T_L$ values one must proceed backward through the network—from the point of the arrows to the tail of the arrows.

### Slack Times

The slack time for each event is the difference between the earliest possible time for the proceeding event, $T_E$, and the latest allowable completion for the activity, $T_L$, minus the activity duration time. As an example, for $E$ the slack time would be as follows: $[ \bigcirc - \square ] - t_e = $ slack time

$$\left[ \enspace \fbox{13} \enspace - \enspace \fbox{5} \enspace \right] - 3 = 5$$

The value of slack can be either positive, negative, or zero, depending upon the relationship between $T_L$ and $T_E$. Positive slack is an indication that the project is "ahead of schedule" (excess resources). Zero slack is an indication that the project is "on schedule" (adequate resources). Negative slack is an indication of a "behind schedule" condition (lack of resources).

### The Critical Path

The *critical path* through a PERT network is drawn from the initial event of the network to the terminal event by connecting the events of minimum slack. The *critical path* is usually emphasized with a very heavy thick line. When color is used the *critical path* is drawn in red. In Figure 19–17 the *critical path* is shown connecting Events 1-3-4-6. Slack times for each activity are indicated adjacent to the activity.

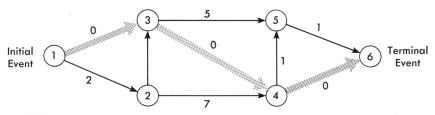

**Figure 19–17.**

Although these calculations have been done manually, it is conventional practice to program complex networks for solution by digital computer. In this way thousands of activities and events may be considered, and one or more critical paths located for further study.

Remember that the *critical path* is the path that controls the successful completion of the project. It is also the path that requires the most time to get from the initial event to the terminal event. Any event on the critical path that is delayed will cause the final event to be delayed by the same amount. Conversely putting an extra effort on noncritical activities will not speed up the project.

Finally, the PERT network should be periodically updated as the work on the project progresses.

### SUMMARY

Today, as has been the case throughout history, good engineering design is responsible for bringing into being technical devices, services, and systems for the use and benefit of mankind. The engineering design process is a creative and iterative process consisting of several phases, (a) the feasibility study, (b) the preliminary design, (c) the intermediate design, and (d) the detail design. Engineering students of today live in the most challenging period of history ever, and a good idea, together with the application of sound engineering design principles, *will produce success*.

Engineering design methods and processes will be studied in several courses over a period of several years. Consequently the engineering student should not expect to master the technique of engineering designing here. However, good design ability requires much practice and experience in addition to the learning of certain basic precepts. The design exercises and projects that follow are intended to supply some of this experience.

### Exercises in Design

**19–1.** Estimate the number of drug stores in the United States. Give reasons for your estimate.

**19–2.** Estimate the number of gallons of water of the Mississippi River that pass New Orleans every day. Show your analysis.

**19–3.** In 100 words or less describe how a household water softener works.

**19–4.** By the use of simple sketches and brief accompanying explanation describe the mechanical operation of a household toilet.

**19–5.** By the use of a diagrammatic sketch show how plumbing in a home might be installed so that hot water is always instantly available when the hot water tap is opened.

**19–6.** Analyze and discuss the economic problems involved in replacing ground level railroad tracks with a suspended monorail system for a congested urban area.

**19–7.** Discuss the feasibility of railroads offering a service whereby your automobile would be carried on a railroad car on the same train on which you are traveling so that you might have your car available for use upon arrival at your destination.

**19–8.** Discuss the desirability of assigning an identifying number to each person as soon as they are born. The number could, for example, be tattooed at some place on the body to serve as a social security number, military number, credit card number, etc.

**19–9.** Using local gas utility rates, electric utility rates, coal costs, fuel oil costs, and wood costs, what would be the comparative cost of heating a five room house in your home community for a winter season?

**19–10.** Discuss the advantages and disadvantages of having a channel of television show nothing but market quotations, except for brief commercials, during the time the New York stock market and the Chicago commodity market are open.

**19–11.** You are called to Alaska to consider the problem of public buildings that are sinking in permafrost due to warm weather. What might you do to solve this problem?

**19–12.** You are located on an ice cap. Ice and snow are everywhere but no water. Fuel and equipment are available. How can you prepare a well from which water can be pumped?

**19–13.** Assemble the following items: an ink bottle, a marble, a yardstick, an engineer's scale of triangular cross-section, five wooden matches, a pocket knife, a candle, a pencil, and a key. Now using as few of the objects as possible, balance the yardstick across the top "knife-edge" of the engineer's scale in such manner that soon after being released, and without being touched again, it unbalances itself.

**19–14.** Explain the operation of the rewind mechanism for the hand cord of a home gasoline lawnmower.

**Exercises in Design (continued)**

**19–15.** Devise a new method of feeding passengers on airplanes.

**19–16.** List the consequences of everyone being able to read everyone else's mind.

**19–17.** At current market values determine the number of years that would be necessary to regain the loss of money (lost salary plus college expense) if one stayed in college one additional year to obtain a Masters degree in engineering. What would be the number of years necessary to regain the loss by staying three years beyond the bachelor's degree to obtain a doctorate in engineering?

**19–18.** Estimate the number of policemen in (*a*) New York City, and (*b*) the United States.

**19–19.** Estimate the number of churches of all faiths in the United States.

**19–20.** Explain how the following work:
  *a*. An automobile differential
  *b*. A toggle switch
  *c*. An automatic cut-off on gasoline pumps
  *d*. A sewing machine needle when sewing cloth
  *e*. A refrigeration cycle which does not depend upon electricity.

**19–21.** With six equal-length sticks construct four equilateral triangles.

**19–22.** Estimate the number of aspirin tablets now available in the United States.

**19–23.** A cube whose surface area is six square miles is filled with water. How long will it take to empty this tank using a 1000 gal/min pump?

**19–24.** From memory sketch (*a*) a bicycle, (*b*) a reel-type lawnmower, (*c*) a coffee pot, (*d*) a salt-water fishing reel, and (*e*) a rifle.

**19–25.** Make something useful from the following items: a piece of corrugated cardboard 12 in. × 24 in., 6 ft of string, 3 pieces of chalk, 10 rubber bands, a small piece of gummed tape, 3 tongue depressors, 5 paper clips, and 7 tooth picks.

**19–26.** Propose some way to eliminate the need for bifocal glasses.

**19–27.** Design a device that can measure to a high degree of accuracy the wall thickness of a long tube whose ends are not accessible.

**19–28.** Design a man's compact travel kit that can be carried in the inside coat pocket.

**19–29.** Design a home-type sugar dispenser for a locality where the average rainfall is 100 in. per yr.

**19–30.** Design a new type of men's apparel to be worn around the neck in lieu of a necktie.

**19–31.** Design a new type of clothespin.

**19–32.** Design a new fastener for shirts or blouses.

**19–33.** Design a personal monogram.

**19–34.** Design a device to aid federal or civil officers in the prevention or suppression of crime.

**19–35.** Design a highway system and appropriate vehicles for a country where gasoline is not obtainable and where motive power must be supplied external to the vehicle.

**19–36.** Design an electrical system for a home that does not receive its energy from a power company or a storage battery.

**19–37.** Design a device for weighing quantities of food for astronauts who are enroute to the moon.

**19–38.** Design a machine or process to remove Irish potato peelings.

**19–39.** Design a "black-eyed pea" sheller.

**19–40.** Design a corn shucker.

**19–41.** Design a trap to snare mosquitoes alive.

**19–42.** Design the "ideal" bathroom, including new toilet fixtures.

**19–43.** Design a toothpaste dispenser.

**19–44.** Design a woozle.

**19–45.** Design a device that would enable paralyzed people to read in bed.

**19–46.** Design a jig-like device that an amateur "do-it-yourself" home workman could use to lay up an acceptably straight brick wall.

**19–47.** Design a device to retail for less than $10.00 to warn "tailgaters" that they are too close to your automobile.

**19–48.** Devise a system of warning lights connected to your automobile that will warn drivers in cars following you of the changes in speed of your car.

**19–49.** You live in a remote community near the Canadian border, and you have a shallow well near your home from which you can get a copious supply of water. Although the water is unfit for drinking or irrigation, its temperature is a constant 64°F. Design a system to use this water to help heat your home.

**19–50.** Design and build a prototype model of a small spot welder suitable for use by hobby craftsmen. Prepare working sketches and make an economic study of the advisability of producing these units in volume production.

**19–51.** Design some device that will awaken a deaf person.

**19–52.** Design a coin-operated hair-cutting machine.

**19–53.** Design a two-passenger battery powered Urbanmobile for use around the neighborhood, for local shopping center visits, to commute to the railway station, etc. The rechargeable battery should last for 60 mi, on each charge. Provide a complete report on the design including a market survey and economic study.

**19–54.** Design some means of visually determining the rate of gasoline consumption (mi/gal) at any time while the vehicle is in operation.

**19–55.** Design a device to continuously monitor and/or regulate automobile tire pressures.

**19–56.** Design a novel method of catching and executing mice that will not infringe the patent of any other known system now on the market.

**19–57.** Design a new toy for children ages 10 to 15.

**19–58.** Design a device to replace the conventional oarlocks used on all row boats.

**19–59.** Devise an improved method of garbage disposal for a "new" city that is to be constructed in its entirety next year.

**19–60.** Design and build a simple device to measure the specific heat of liquids. Use components costing less than $3.00.

**19–61.** Design for teenagers an educational hobby-kit that might foster an interest in engineering.

**Exercises in Design (continued)**

**19–62.** Design and build an indicator to tell when a steak is cooked as desired.

**19–63.** Design a device that would effectively eliminate wall outlets and cords for electrical household appliances.

**19–64.** Design the mechanism by which the rotary motion of a one-inch diameter shaft can be transferred around a 90° corner and imparted to a one-half inch diameter shaft.

**19–65.** Design a mechanism by which the vibratory translation of a steel rod can be transferred around a 90° corner and imparted to another steel rod.

**19–66.** Design a device or system to prevent snow accumulation on the roof of a mountain cabin. Electricity is available, and the owner is absent during the winter.

**10–67.** Using the parts out of an old springwound clock, design and fabricate some useful device.

**19–68.** Out of popsicle sticks build a pinned-joint structure that will support a load of 50 lb.

**19–69.** Design a new device to replace the standard wall light switch.

**19–70.** Design and build a recordchanger that will flip records as well as change them.

**19–71.** Design a wheelchair that can lift itself from street level to a level one foot higher.

**19–72.** Design a canopener that can be used to make a continuous cut in the top of a tin can whose top is of irregular shape.

**19–73.** Design and build for camping purposes a solar still that can produce one gallon of pure water per day.

**19–74.** A ban on the use of firearms in the United States has created the desirability of manufacturing some device suitable for use in hunting small game, such as squirrel and rabbit. The company for which you work has decided to compete for the market of small game hunters who will be seeking some replacement for their guns. You have been assigned the task of developing a blowgun and suitable projectiles for this purpose with the following provisions:

    *a.* The blow tube and five hunting darts must sell for $10.00 or less retail.

    *b.* No poison may be used to paralyze the animal.

    *c.* The technique of loading the blow tube and launching the dart must be simple enough for a 10-year-old boy to learn.

    *d.* The range of 100 ft with hunting accuracy is desirable.

Design and build a prototype tube and projectile. Detail the dimensions, tolerances, material, finish, and capability of the weapon system. Indicate the probable cost of one hunting set of tube and darts when manufactured in lots of 1000, 10,000 100,000, and 1,000,000.

**19–75.** The company for which you work has decided that altogether too large a percentage of the annual sales depend upon government defense contracts. A decision has been made to diversify and to add product lines that would appeal to individual citizens regardless of current world conditions. After some study it is decided that the manufacture of fishing lures might provide the desired market stability. You are assigned the task to design a new trout or bass lure under the following conditions:

  *a.* The lure must sell for $2.00 or less retail.
  *b.* The lure should be a design departure from existing lures on the market.

Design and build such a lure. Provide drawings giving dimensions, materials, and finish. Indicate the probable cost per lure when manufactured in lots of 1000, 10,000, and 100,000.

**19–76.** Few new musical instruments have been invented within the last 100 years. With the availability of modern materials and processes, many novel and innovative designs are now within the realm of possibility. To be marketable over an extended period of time such an instrument should utilize the conventional diatonic scale of eight tones to the octave. It could, therefore, be utilized by symphonies, in ensembles, or as a solo instrument using existing musical compositions. You are the chief engineer for a company whose present objective is to create and market such a new instrument. Design and build a prototype of a new instrument that would be salable. Prepare working drawings of your model together with cost estimates for volume production of the instrument.

**19–77.** Design some means of communicating with a deaf person who is elsewhere (such as by radio).

**19–78.** For a bicycle design an automatic transmission that will change gears according to the force applied.

**19–79.** Design a "decommercializer" that will automatically cut out all TV commercial sounds for 60 seconds.

**19–80.** Design a solar powered refrigerator.

**19–81.** Design a small portable means for converting sea water to drinking water.

**19–82.** Design a fishing lure capable of staying at any preset depth.

**19–83.** Design an educational toy that may be used to aid small children in learning to read.

**19–84.** Design some device to help a handicapped person.

**19–85.** Design a heating and cooling blanket.

**19–86.** Design an automatic pulse monitoring system for use in hospitals.

**19–87.** Design a portable solar cooker.

**19–88.** Design a carbon monoxide detector for automobiles.

**19–89.** Design a more effective method for prevention and/or removal of snow and ice from military aircraft.

**19–90.** Design a "practical" vehicle whose operation is based upon the "ground effect" phenomenon.

**19–91.** Design a neuter (neither male nor female) connector for quick connect and disconnect that can be used on the end of flexible hose to transport liquids.

**19–92.** Design an electric space heater rated from 10,000 BTU/hr to 50,000 BTU/hr for military use in temporary huts and enclosures.

### Exercises in Design (continued)

**19–93.** There is need for a system whereby one device emplaced in a hazardous area (minefield or other denial area) would interact with another device issued to each soldier, warn him of danger, and send guidance instructions for him to avoid or pass through the area of safety. Design such a system.

**19–94.** World communication and understanding would be greatly enhanced if there were available a system that would enable rapid translation from a language into a pictorial representation of what was communicated. Such a system would be helpful where there is a need for an exchange of information and where there is no common language between the parties involved. The system would therefore permit parties speaking different languages to rapidly portray in a TV-type picture the particular information that they are communicating or exchanging. Identify the problems that would need to be solved to make such a system feasible.

**19–95.** Various types of objects are in orbit around the earth. The problem of their identification is of concern to the government. Although locating them is not a problem, a suitable method for determining their *mass* has not yet been found. For example, some device might be mounted in an "inspector probe" or fly-by vehicle that could be used to apply a specific thrust to the suspect space object and also measure its resulting acceleration. Design the conceptual features of such a system. What are the apparent difficulties?

**19–96.** Man has long sought to identify groundwater (beneath the surface) supplies. "Water witching" and other techniques which have been tried have not proved to be reliable. Design an electronic system that would make possible the location of new groundwater supplies.

**19–97.** Develop some method to rate and/or identify the presence of rust spots when coatings fail to adequately protect metal. Present visual methods are unreliable and variable in results.

**19–98.** Develop a system whereby diseases of significance could be diagnosed rapidly and accurately.

**19–99.** Design an instrument that can be mounted on any vehicle and that will measure and record the distance traveled, the time elapsed, and the instantaneous speed of the vehicle when traveling at speeds between one and 70 mph.

**19–100.** Design an instrument that would have the capability of registering degrees of pain.

## BIBLIOGRAPHY

ALGER, JOHN R. M., and CARL V. HAYS, *Creative Synthesis in Design,* Prentice-Hall, Englewood Cliffs, N.J. (1964).

AZIMOW, MORRIS, *Introduction to Design,* Prentice-Hall, Englewood Cliffs, N.J. (1962).

BOURNE, JOHN, *Instructions for the Manufacture and Management of Every Species of Machine,* Appleton (1870).

BUHL, HAROLD R., *Creative Engineering Design,* Iowa State U. P., Ames (1960).

*Conference on Design Methods, London, England,* Macmillan, New York (1963).

DIXON, JOHN R., *Design Engineering,* McGraw-Hill, New York (1966).

EDER, ING. W. E., and W. GOSLING, *Mechanical System Design,* Pergamon, New York (1965).

GIBSON, JOHN E., *Introduction to Engineering Design,* Holt, Rinehart, and Winston, New York (1966).

KILLEFFER, D. H., *The Genius of Industrial Research,* Reinhold, New York (1948).

KRICK, EDWARD V., *An Introduction to Engineering and Engineering Design,* Wiley, New York (1965).

MATOUSEK, ROBERT, *Engineering Design, A Systematic Approach,* Blackie, London (1963).

STARR, MARTIN KENNETH, *Product Design and Decision Theory,* Prentice-Hall, Englewood Cliffs, N.J. (1963).

WOODSON, THOMAS T., *Introduction to Engineering Design,* McGraw-Hill, New York (1966).

# Chapter 20

## Decision Processes in Design

Throughout this text, attention has been directed to the quest for improved designs, improved methods, or what may be termed the "best" method under the circumstances. The implication made is that an *improved* design will be recognized readily to be an improvement over the existing design and will, therefore, be implemented. In other words it has been assumed that once all of the necessary data are available, a correct decision will be made. However, the truth is that relatively few contributions of man are of such a nature that they are recognized immediately as significant improvements. If the worth of a contribution is not obvious, how can the engineer decide whether or not to implement the new design? To answer this question completely one would need a detailed study of decision theory, which is beyond the scope of this text. However, in this chapter some of the conditions under which decisions are made and some of the basic principles of decision making will be discussed.

Human activity can be organized into two general classifications: those activities associated with *making decisions* and those associated with *implementing decisions*. Much of the work of an engineer is devoted to making decisions. An engineer's career may, in fact, be measured by the number and magnitude of the decisions he must make. This chapter will discuss briefly some decision processes used by the engineer in conjunction with his work. Early in his professional career he will be called upon to study a variety of situations and to recommend a solution that he has attained with the aid of his acquired skills and knowledge. Frequently he will not make the final decision but will contribute his findings to assist someone else who has this responsibility. The engineer will progress to positions of greater responsibility as he gains experience in the decision process. Thus, he will progress from an advisory capacity to a position where the most important and final decisions are his own responsibility.

It would be convenient if all decisions could be made on the basis of accurate engineering data and with the use of correct scientific methods. Much guesswork and intuitive reasoning could be eliminated. However, such a condition is not possible. In fact, there is some question as to whether many decisions can be made on a completely scientific basis. It does seem sensible, however, to proceed as far as possible using proven scientific methods to aid in making decisions. Fortunately the development of the high speed computer has brought about improvements in decision making that were not dreamed possible a few years ago.

An important factor in any decision process is the amount of accurate information available or, in other words, the extent to which scientific methods can be utilized. Many important decisions must be made under conditions of insufficient information. The future always remains unknown, and even the most sophisticated prediction techniques will sometimes give the wrong advice. Yet, the engineer always must strive to make the best decisions under any and all conditions. Let us define a *decision* as the selection of an alternative from a known set of alternatives. The selection of an alternative is made according to a *principle of choice*. There are three types of decisions:

1. decisions made under certainty
2. decisions made under risk
3. decisions made under uncertainty

**Illustration 20–1.** Design engineers evaluate ideas and select alternatives to improve the utility of their design. Conferences with other engineers aid them in reaching an optimum solution. (Courtesy Eastman Kodak Company.)

These types of decisions are shown in Figure 20–1 and they will be explained briefly below.

| Type of Decision | Principle of Choice |
|---|---|
| Certainty | Maximizing profit |
| Risk | Maximizing expectation |
| Risk | Most probable future |
| Risk | Aspiration level |
| Uncertainty | Equal probability |
| Uncertainty | Conservative |
| Uncertainty | Regret |

**Figure 20–1**

## THE GENERAL DECISION MATRIX

Before proceeding with an explanation of the types of decisions, some understanding of the general "decision matrix" would be helpful. A general decision matrix is a simple array constructed in such a manner that the rows represent the possible alternatives (controllable factors) available to the engineer in a decision situation. The alternatives are designated by $a_1, a_2, \ldots, a_i, \ldots a_m$, where $a_i$ represents the general expression; $i = 1, 2, \ldots m$. The column values represent possible future states that cannot be controlled by the engineer. The future states are designated $s_1, s_2, \ldots, s_j, \ldots s_n$, where $s_j$ is the general expression; $j = 1, 2, \ldots, n$. At the intersection of each column (possible future state) and each row (available alternative) is the result that occurs because alternative $a_i$ was selected and future state $s_j$ did, in fact, occur. The results are designated $R_{1-1}, R_{1-2}, \ldots, R_{i-j}, \ldots R_{m-n}$ where the first part of the subscript refers to the row (alternative) and the last part represents the column (future state). Thus, in Figure 20–2, $R_{2-3}$ is the result that occurs when alternative $a_2$ is selected and future state $s_3$ occurs.

**Possible Future States (Uncontrollable Factors)**

| | $s_1$ | $s_2$ | $s_3$ | $\cdots$ | $s_j$ | $\cdots$ | $s_n$ |
|---|---|---|---|---|---|---|---|
| $a_1$ | $R_{1-1}$ | $R_{1-2}$ | $R_{1-3}$ | $\cdots$ | $R_{1-j}$ | $\cdots$ | $R_{1-n}$ |
| $a_2$ | $R_{2-1}$ | $R_{2-2}$ | $R_{2-3}$ | $\cdots$ | $R_{2-j}$ | $\cdots$ | $R_{2-n}$ |
| $a_3$ | $R_{3-1}$ | $R_{3-2}$ | $R_{3-3}$ | $\cdots$ | $R_{3-j}$ | $\cdots$ | $R_{3-n}$ |
| $a_i$ | $R_{i-1}$ | $R_{i-2}$ | $R_{i-3}$ | $\cdots$ | $R_{i-j}$ | $\cdots$ | $R_{i-n}$ |
| $a_m$ | $R_{m-1}$ | $R_{m-2}$ | $R_{m-3}$ | $\cdots$ | $R_{m-j}$ | $\cdots$ | $R_{m-n}$ |

*Available Alternatives (Controllable Factors)*

**Figure 20–2.** General Decision Matrix

There is another very important consideration—the *probability* associated with the occurrence of a particular possible future state. The assignment of probability is an important and difficult task and will be covered in greater detail later in this chapter. The probability is designated $p_1$, $p_2$, . . $p_n$ as shown in Figure 20–3. It is important to note that for each future state $s_j$ there is a probability of occurrence $p_j$ where $j = 1, 2, \ldots n$ as before.

**Possible Future States**

| | $p_1$ | $p_2$ | $p_3$ | . . . | $p_j$ | . . . | $p_n$ |
|---|---|---|---|---|---|---|---|
| | $s_1$ | $s_2$ | $s_3$ | . . . | $s_j$ | . . . | $s_n$ |
| $a_1$ | $R_{1-1}$ | $R_{1-2}$ | $R_{1-3}$ | . . . | $R_{1-j}$ | . . . | $R_{1-n}$ |
| $a_2$ | $R_{2-1}$ | $R_{2-2}$ | $R_{2-3}$ | . . . | $R_{2-j}$ | . . . | $R_{2-n}$ |
| $a_3$ | $R_{3-1}$ | $R_{3-2}$ | $R_{3-3}$ | . . . | $R_{3-j}$ | . . . | $R_{3-n}$ |
| $a_i$ | $R_{i-1}$ | $R_{i-2}$ | $R_{i-3}$ | . . . | $R_{i-j}$ | . . . | $R_{i-n}$ |
| $a_m$ | $R_{m-1}$ | $R_{m-2}$ | $R_{m-3}$ | . . . | $R_{m-j}$ | . . . | $R_{m-n}$ |

*Alternatives*

**Figure 20–3**

By utilizing these probabilities, the engineer can gain greater insight into his problem, namely, the choice of alternatives. For example, in the manned space program there are many controllable alternatives which are made possible by known scientific principles and current technology. However, in every launch there are many unknown quantities and variables, errors, and other uncontrolled factors that will make themselves known. For each possible malfunction or instrumentation error, however, a probability exists that the event will occur, and a probability can be assigned for each of the possible occurrences.

## DECISIONS UNDER CERTAINTY

Decisions under certainty are made when it can be assumed that the engineer has complete and accurate knowledge concerning the result which will occur when he chooses any of the available alternatives. This assumption may be made when the amount of risk involved is so small that the decision maker feels safe in neglecting it or when the difficulty involved in including the risk makes it impractical to do so.

In terms of a decision model (a completed decision matrix for a given situation), if only one future state is possible, that future state will have a probability of occurrence of 1.00. A decision under certainty appears in matrix form as depicted in Figure 20–4. Note that the idea of a *value* $V(R_{i-j})$ associated with each result has been introduced. This is merely to generalize the matrix. For example, if the results are measurable in dollars, one can readily discuss the value involved. But what if the situation is military, and the results are losses in lives, equipment, and land? The value is then much more difficult to ascertain, and the discussion of the results becomes much more complex. The student of decision theory will recognize that this leads into the study of *utility,* a study beyond the scope of this material.

Future State

$$p_1 = 1.00$$
$$s_1$$

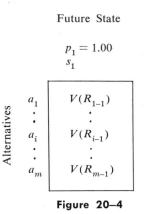

Figure 20–4

Decision matrix for a decision under certainty where the symbols are as previously defined.

A *principle of choice* is defined as a rule that can be applied to any decision matrix and that will lead to the selection of a particular alternative. In a decision under certainty there are as many rows in the matrix as there are alternatives, but *only one* possible future state. Therefore, the possible principles of choice are very simple: assuming the alternatives are equal in other respects, the engineer should (1) select the alternative that maximizes profit; or (2) select the alternative that minimizes cost. If it is not possible to evaluate the outcomes in terms of profit or cost, these principles must be modified or discarded (for example, where the loss of human lives may be involved).

### Exercises in Making Decisions

**20–1.** An electronics company is faced with a choice of purchasing one of two machines, either of which will accomplish the desired task satisfactorily. Some pertinent facts concerning the use of the two pieces of equipment are given below:

| | INITIAL COST | ANNUAL OPERATING COST | SERVICE LIFE | SALVAGE VALUE AT END OF 15 YR |
|---|---|---|---|---|
| Machine 1 | $40,000 | $5000 | 15 yr | $4000 |
| Machine 2 | $60,000 | $4000 | 15 yr | $6000 |

Which machine would you advise the company to purchase? Why?

**20–2.** What important assumptions have you made in your analysis in Problem 20–1?

**20–3.** Mr. Jones wants to buy a certain automobile which Mr. Smith owns. Mr. Smith has asked $1000 for the vehicle. Mr. Jones has countered with an offer of $1100 if Smith will wait a year for the money. Smith considers that he can invest his money at the rate of 6 per cent simple interest per year. What action would you advise Smith to take with regard to Jones' offer?

**20-4.** With regard to the situation described in Problem 20-3, what would you advise Smith to do if Jones offers $1050 to be paid at the end of one year?

**20-5.** The Niten-Day taxi-cab firm must purchase some new vehicles and they are considering two different types. One type uses conventional gasoline and the other type uses diesel fuel. Also, the following information has been obtained:

| | INITIAL COST | SERVICE LIFE | OPERATING COST PER MILE | EXPECTED MILES/YR | SALVAGE VALUE |
|---|---|---|---|---|---|
| Taxi A — Gasoline | $3000 | 5 yr | $0.08 | 30,000 | $300 |
| Taxi B — Diesel Fuel | $4000 | 5 yr | $0.06 | 30,000 | $400 |

Which type of vehicle would you recommend that they purchase? Why?

**20-6.** If the general conditions described in Problem 20-5 prevail, at what annual mileage would the choice be one of indifference?

**20-7.** Red and blue have declared war on each other. Each has three (3) strategies, designated $r_1$, $r_2$, $r_3$, and $b_1$, $b_2$, and $b_3$. A decision matrix may be drawn up as follows (entries represent values to *blue*):

| | $r_1$ | $r_2$ | $r_3$ |
|---|---|---|---|
| $b_1$ | win | lose | draw |
| $b_2$ | lose | draw | win |
| $b_3$ | draw | win | lose |

*a.* Blue's intelligence agents have brought back information that red is planning to employ strategy $r_2$. Which strategy should blue employ, assuming that total victory is the objective?

*b.* If blue's agents were wrong and red employs strategy $r_3$ instead of $r_2$, what will happen if blue employs strategy $b_3$?

## DECISIONS UNDER RISK

A decision to be made under risk differs from one to be made under certainty in that the engineer is concerned with the probabilities of occurrence of possible future states. Less information is available to the engineer than in a decision under certainty, but it is possible to assign probabilities to the various possible future states.

An automobile manufacturer is concerned about the quality of a brake lining that is used on his cars. Specifically, he wishes to make the most economical choice of replacing the defective lining in his products. The manufacturer concludes that he may follow one of three alternatives:

$a_1$: Do not inspect the linings. Those which fail in service will be replaced by the local dealer.

$a_2$: Inspect every lining utilizing a method which always detects the defectives.

$a_3$: Adopt an inspection policy which detects the defectives 75% of the time.

Suppose that the following costs have been determined:

The cost of replacing a defective lining in service is $25.00. The cost of inspecting using the method of $a_2$ is $2.00 per lining and the cost of inspecting using the method of $a_3$ is $1.00 per lining. Records indicate that 10% of all linings have the defect in question.

Let future state $s_1$ be that we have a perfect brake lining. Under $a_1$ there is no expense. Under $a_2$ there is an expense of $2.00 for the inspection and under $a_3$ the cost is $1.00 for the inspection. Consider a defective lining to be future state $s_2$. Policy $a_1$ results in a cost of $25.00 to replace the defect. Policy $a_2$ costs $2.00 for the inspection, and it always detects the defectives. Under $a_3$ there is a cost of $1.00 for the inspection, but 25% of the defective items are not discovered which later fail in service at a cost of $25.00 each. Therefore the average cost under $a_3$ is

$$(0.25)(\$26) + (0.75)(\$1) = \$7.25$$

The previous matrix notation gives us the matrix shown below.

**Figure 20–5.**

|  | $P_1 = 0.90$ | $P_2 = 0.10$ |
|---|---|---|
|  | $s_1$ = perfect | $s_2$ = defective |
| $a_1$ | 0 | $25.00 |
| $a_2$ | $2.00 | $ 2.00 |
| $a_3$ | $1.00 | $ 7.25 |

To obtain all of this information may be an expensive and inconvenient procedure. Also, the manufacturer still does not know which alternative to select. The most commonly used principle of choice is *"Expectation"* which calls for selecting the alternative that has the lowest expected cost. Expected costs are computed as the weighted sum of the costs associated with an alternative where the weight associated with each cost is the probability of that cost being incurred. Thus the expected costs for the three alternatives listed above are as follows:

$a_1$   $(0.90)(0) \ + (0.10)(\$25) \ = \$2.50$
$a_2$   $(0.90)(\$2) + (0.10)(\$2) \ = \$2.00$
$a_3$   $(0.90)(\$1) + (0.10)(\$7.25) = \$1.72$

Based on these values, alternative $a_3$ should be selected on the basis of having the lowest expected cost.

Another principle of choice used in risky situations is called *"Most Probable Future,"* in which case the decision maker considers only the future state that is most probable and behaves as though it were certain. Specifically, he finds the future state ($s_j$) for which the probability of occurrence ($p_j$) is the greatest, and for this state selects the alternative that has the lowest cost. In the example problem 90 per cent of the brake linings are perfect, therefore, only Column 1 is considered in making the decision using the Most Probable Future principle. In Column 1, the lowest cost is zero dollars and alternative $a_1$, do not inspect, is selected.

Many decisions are made based upon this principle. For example, most people will agree that there is a nonzero probability of World War III in any year, but the same people make *all* of their decisions as though eternal peace were certain.

Another important principle of choice is the *"Aspiration Level"* principle, a procedure widely used in management decision making. For a decision under risk, the aspiration level principle is as follows: for a given aspiration level, $L$, choose the alternative that has the highest probability that the cost will be less than or equal to $L$.

What type of situation might favor the use of an aspiration level? If the alternatives are expensive or difficult to discover, the *search* for alternatives should be continued *only* until one is found that gives a reasonable probability of achieving the aspiration level. This procedure may be more economical than searching for the alternative that minimizes the expected value.

In the example problem, if the manufacturer aspired *only* to keep his costs below $3.00, he would choose alternative $a_2$ because it will cost $2.00 with a probability of 1.00. Each of the other alternatives has a probability of 0.10 of exceeding $3.00.

### Exercises in Making Decisions

**20–8.** In an engineering design project you have tabulated some values (costs) in the following matrix:

|  | $p_1 = 0.60$ | $p_2 = 0.30$ | $p_3 = 0.10$ |
|---|---|---|---|
|  | $s_1$ | $s_2$ | $s_3$ |
| $a_1$ | $100 | $50 | $1000 |
| $a_2$ | $200 | $200 | $ 200 |
| $a_3$ | $150 | $500 | $ 100 |

Apply the "Expectation" principle to the matrix, and give your recommendation as to the preferred alternative.

**20–9.** Which alternative would you select in Problem 20–8 if the "Most Probable Future" principle is used?

**20–10.** If in Problem 20–8 you had established a level of aspiration of "keeping the cost below $400," which alternative would you choose?

**20–11.** Assume that the values shown in the decision matrix in Problem 20–8 are profits. Apply the "Expectation" principle to the matrix and give your recommendation as to the preferred alternative.

**20–12.** If the values in the decision matrix in Problem 20–8 are profits, which alternative would you recommend if you use the "Most Probable Future" principle?

**20–13.** If the values in the decision matrix in Problem 20–8 are profits, which alternative would you choose if your level of aspiration is *to make a profit of at least $400?*

**20–14.** Some outcomes are so difficult to evaluate that they can only be classified as "satisfactory" (s) or "unsatisfactory" (u). Consider the following matrix:

|  | $P_1 = 0.50$ | $P_2 = 0.30$ | $P_3 = 0.20$ |
|---|---|---|---|
|  | $s_1$ | $s_2$ | $s_3$ |
| $a_1$ | $s$ | $u$ | $u$ |
| $a_2$ | $s$ | $u$ | $s$ |
| $a_3$ | $u$ | $s$ | $s$ |

If you aspire to have an acceptable outcome, which alternative would you choose?

**20–15.** If you apply the "Expectation" principle to the decision matrix in Problem 20–14, which alternative should be selected?

**20–16.** Discuss briefly the assumptions involved when an engineer applies the "Expectation" principle to a decision matrix such as that in Problem 20–14.

**20–17.** Consider the following alternatives and future states concerning the purchase of fire insurance:

$a_1$ = Buy fire insurance.
$a_2$ = Do not buy fire insurance.
$s_1$ = A fire occurs.
$s_2$ = A fire does not occur.

The cell entries of your decision matrix will represent the costs to the prospective insurance purchaser. ($500 is the cost of the insurance; $45,000 is the cost of the fire.)

|  | $P_1 = 0.01$ | $P_2 = 0.99$ |
|---|---|---|
|  | $s_1$ | $s_2$ |
| $a_1$ | $500 | $500 |
| $a_2$ | $45,000 | 0 |

Apply the "Expectation" principle to the above matrix and give your recommendation with regard to purchasing insurance.

**20–18.** Discuss why the "Expectation" principle may not be an appropriate principle to apply when considering the purchase of insurance.

**20–19.** Apply the "Most Probable Future" principle to the decision matrix in Problem 20–17. Which alternative do you recommend?

**20–20.** In Problem 20–17, assume that you aspire to keep the cost below $1000.

Apply the "Level of Aspiration" principle, and make your recommendations concerning the best alternative to choose.

**20–21.** As plant engineer you have determined that without standby equipment a shutdown will cost an average of $250 a day. Over the past several years the plant has averaged three days per year lost due to shutdowns. A standby machine can be purchased for $5000 which has a service life of 10 years and a salvage value of $500 at that time. Its annual operating cost, including the three days of operation, would be $200. The president of the company has asked your opinion concerning the purchase of standby equipment. What would you advise him in this regard?

**20–22.** With regard to Problem 20–21, discuss the possible application of the "Level of Aspiration" principle.

**20–23.** A standard roulette wheel has 38 possible outcomes, 18 red, 18 black, and 2 green (0 and 00). For simplicity, consider wagering on the colors if the following decision matrix applies:

|  | $p_1 = 18/38$ | $p_2 = 18/38$ | $p_3 = 2/38$ |
|---|---|---|---|
|  | $s_1 = $ red | $s_2 = $ black | $s_3 = $ green |
| $a_1$ bet red | +1 | −1 | −1 |
| $a_2$ bet black | −1 | +1 | −1 |
| $a_3$ bet green | −1 | −1 | +17 |

Using the "Expectation" principle, compute the "best" bet, if one exists.

## DECISIONS UNDER UNCERTAINTY

Of the three classifications of decisions, perhaps the most realistic type is the decision made under uncertainty. This type of decision exists when the possible future states are known but the probabilities of occurrence of each are not available to the engineer. This type of decision making is particularly applicable in industry where a new type of work is being pioneered and no prior data exist, such as is the case for most research and development activities. In terms of the general decision matrix, a decision made under uncertainty appears to be much the same as a decision made under risk—except that the probabilities are missing.

### Decision Based Upon Dominance

In any situation where a decision is to be made and where several alternatives exist, all alternatives must be checked to see whether any one alternative *dominates* any of the other alternatives. If one alternative is always preferred to any other, regardless of which future state occurs, the preferred alternative is said to *dominate* the other alternative. When this condition exists, all dominated alternatives may be eliminated from consideration because they should never be selected.

For example, consider the problem faced by an engineer concerning his future career. He believes that his possible alternatives are as follows:

1. Go into business for himself.
2. Form a partnership.
3. Go to work for a small engineering firm.
4. Go to work for a large firm.

Assume that the future states with which he is concerned are three possible future economic conditions in the United States. For simplicity, we may classify them as follows:

1. Enter a recession
2. Continue under present economic conditions
3. Enter a booming economy

The cell entries in the matrix represent the profits associated with each situation as designated (by the engineer) on a scale from 0 to 100.

The decision matrix is as follows:

|  |  | $s_1$ | $s_2$ | $s_3$ |
|---|---|---|---|---|
|  |  | RECESSION | CONTINUE | BOOM |
| $a_1$ | Alone | 0 | 45 | 100 |
| $a_2$ | Partner | 10 | 30 | 60 |
| $a_3$ | Small firm | 20 | 40 | 70 |
| $a_4$ | Large firm | 10 | 70 | 70 |

Figure 20–6.

From the matrix it can be seen that no matter what the future holds, the engineer is better off going to work for a small firm than he is joining a partnership (in this example). Therefore, the alternative $a_2$ "form a partnership" should be eliminated from further consideration because alternative $a_3$ dominates it.

### Decisions Based Upon Equal Probability

If the engineer has no reason to suspect that the probability associated with any of the possible future states is different from that of any other future state, he may want to assume that the probabilities are all equal. Therefore, in the preceding example, we would assume that

$$p_1 = p_2 = p_3$$

since

$$p_1 + p_2 + p_3 = 1.00,$$

we have

$$p_1 = p_2 = p_3 = \tfrac{1}{3}$$

If the engineer uses the principle of assigning equal probabilities to the possible future states, then the decision may be treated as one to be made under risk. If he now *maximizes* his expected gain, the results would be as follows:

$$E(a_1) = \tfrac{1}{3}(0) + \tfrac{1}{3}(45) + \tfrac{1}{3}(100) = \frac{145}{3} = 48\tfrac{1}{3}$$

$$E(a_3) = \tfrac{1}{3}(20) + \tfrac{1}{3}(40) + \tfrac{1}{3}(70) = \frac{130}{3} = 43\tfrac{1}{3}$$

$$E(a_4) = \tfrac{1}{3}(10) + \tfrac{1}{3}(70) + \tfrac{1}{3}(70) = \frac{150}{3} = 50$$

Then, the engineer would choose alternative $a_4$ and accept employment with a large firm.

The use of this principle is predicated on the inability of an individual to estimate the likelihood of occurrence of each of the possible future economic states of the nation. In some cases, the "indicators" generally used to predict such occurrences will contradict each other. For such a situation the probabilities can be assumed to be equal. In most instances, however, the engineer will have *some* knowledge of the probable occurrence of the future states, even if it is only a subjective judgment. Methods for using these subjective judgments are currently being explored.

## DECISIONS BASED UPON CONSERVATISM

Another principle of choice is that of *Conservatism*. This principle calls for the engineer to examine the "smallest possible gain" associated with each alternative, then select that alternative which gives him the largest "minimum gain." In other words, the conservative approach says that the least desirable situation will occur and that the engineer should, therefore, choose accordingly the best of the worst. If the engineer decides that he should be concerned with costs instead of profits, he will examine the alternatives to determine the *largest* possible cost for each alternative, and then select the *smallest* cost of those maxima. In the example problem on page 490, the application of the conservative approach would result in the selection of alternative $a_3$, which is to go to work for a small firm.

Minimum Profit for $\quad a_1 = \quad 0$
Minimum Profit for $\quad a_3 = 20$
Minimum Profit for $\quad a_4 = 10$

The maximum of these minima is 20, therefore alternative $a_3$ should be selected using this principle of choice.

There are many decisions in which the application of this principle would lead to such conservatism that the conclusion would be counter to intuition. Consider the following example, where the values in the matrix again represent profits.

|       | $s_1$ | $s_2$     |
|-------|-------|-----------|
| $a_1$ | 0     | $10,000 |
| $a_2$ | $2  | $5      |

Figure 20–7.

---

The conservative principle would lead to the selection of $a_2$ because it has the greatest *minimum* gain, ($2). When, then, might such a conservative principle be applied? Perhaps the most common example is in the insurance industry, where one pays a (relatively) small cost to avoid a large loss.

## DECISIONS BASED UPON REGRET

One other principle of choice for making *Decisions Under Uncertainty* is the Savage Principle, named for L. J. Savage.[1] This principle suggests that the engineer construct a new matrix called the "regret" matrix, where regret is defined as the difference between the profit that will result and the maximum profit that could be obtained under that future state. That quantity is called the "regret." After the regret matrix is computed, select the alternative which minimizes the maximum regret. Consider the matrix on page 490. The regret matrix would be computed by subtracting each element in the matrix from the value indicated in the row labeled "Column Maximum Value" as shown in Figure 20–9.

**Profit Matrix**

|  | $s_1$ | $s_2$ | $s_3$ |
|---|---|---|---|
| $a_1$ | 0 | 45 | 100 |
| $a_3$ | 20 | 40 | 70 |
| $a_4$ | 10 | 70 | 70 |
| Column Maximum Values | 20 | 70 | 100 |

Figure 20–8.

**Regret Matrix**

|  | $s_1$ | $s_2$ | $s_3$ |
|---|---|---|---|
| $a_1$ | 20 | 25 | 0 |
| $a_3$ | 0 | 30 | 30 |
| $a_4$ | 10 | 0 | 30 |

Figure 20–9.

Now, the maximum regrets associated with each of the alternatives are as follows:

Maximum Regret for $a_1 = 25$
Maximum Regret for $a_3 = 30$
Maximum Regret for $a_4 = 30$

[1] Morris, W. T., *Engineering Economy*, Richard D. Irwin, Homewood, Ill., (1960), p. 315.

Since alternative $a_1$ has the minimum of the maximum regrets the decision to go into business alone would be selected.

The preceding discussion gives a cursory look at some of the more common principles of choice. It has been shown that the application of each principle of choice to the same situation may lead to the selection of different alternatives. There is no "one principle" that is always "best" because the final selection of a principle *must* remain a matter of individual preference. Perhaps the merit of utilizing a principle of choice, instead of applying judgment directly to the problem, lies in the fact that the use of a definite principle promotes consistency over a period of time and aids in the understanding of the decision making process.

### Exercises in Making Decisions

**20–24.** Consider the following cost matrix:

|       | $p_1$ | $p_2$ | $p_3$ |
|-------|-------|-------|-------|
|       | $s_1$ | $s_2$ | $s_3$ |
| $a_1$ | $100  | $140  | $200  |
| $a_2$ | $ 90  | $132  | $181  |
| $a_3$ | $ 92  | $135  | $185  |

Which alternative would you select? Why?

**20–25.** Consider the matrix in Problem 20–24 to be a profit matrix. Which alternative would you select? Why?

**20–26.** Consider the following profit matrix:

|       | $s_1$ | $s_2$ | $s_3$ | $s_4$ |
|-------|-------|-------|-------|-------|
| $a_1$ | $15   | $25   | $ 8   | $12   |
| $a_2$ | 0     | $25   | $12   | $12   |
| $a_3$ | $20   | $20   | $10   | $15   |
| $a_4$ | $15   | $15   | $15   | $15   |

a. Does any strategy (alternative) dominate any other?

b. Apply the principle of "Equal Probability." Which alternative should be selected?

**20–27.** Apply the principle of "Conservatism" to the profit matrix in Problem 20–26. Which alternative should be selected?

**20–28.** Which alternative would be selected in Problem 20–26 if the "Savage" principle is applied?

**20–29.** Consider the following cost matrix:

|  | $s_1$ | $s_2$ | $s_3$ |
|---|---|---|---|
| $a_1$ | $120 | $140 | $ 90 |
| $a_2$ | $150 | $130 | $100 |
| $a_3$ | $110 | $125 | $ 80 |
| $a_4$ | $115 | $135 | $ 95 |

Which alternative should be selected?

**20–30.** Your company is considering purchasing a safety device to protect the driver for all company cars. The device costs $100. You have evaluated the cost matrix for the company as follows:

$a_1$ = Buy the device.
$a_2$ = Do not buy the device.
$s_1$ = An accident occurs.
$s_2$ = No accident occurs.

|  | $s_1$ | $s_2$ |
|---|---|---|
| $a_1$ | $100 | $100 |
| $a_2$ | 0 | $V_{(injury)}$ |

If the principle of "Equal Probability" is applied, when would $a_2$ be selected?

**20–31.** Using the decision matrix of Problem 20–30, when would the "Conservatism" principle lead to the selection of $a_1$?

**20–32.** With regard to the decision matrix in Problem 20–30, when would the "Savage" principle lead to the selection of $a_1$?

**20–33.** With regard to the problem statement in Problem 20–30, which principle of choice would you apply in this instance? Why?

## PROBABILITY

Perhaps one wonders why there is so much emphasis on the difficulty and importance of assigning probabilities. It is an interesting fact that every man on the street thinks he knows what is meant by the term "probability," although mathematicians who have devoted their lives to a study of the subject cannot agree on a mathematical definition of the term. Needless to say, the controversy that has surrounded the subject of probability for centuries will not be resolved in these pages; however, a brief elementary discussion might be helpful.

There are two major types of probabilities: objective and subjective. An objective probability may be thought of as the mathematicians' definition of probability. For example, the probability of rolling a "two" on one roll of an "honest" die is ⅙ and the probability of pulling an ace out of a complete deck of 52 playing cards is 4/52, or 1/13. Now, let's put the decision maker into the middle of the picture.

A student has taken three tests in a particular subject during a semester. In each test he has received a grade of "C." Near the end of the course the professor offers the student the option of taking the grade he has earned to date (C for our student) for his final grade or taking a comprehensive final examination over the course material. The student feels that the C average he has earned to date is not a true indication of his knowledge; he therefore elects to take the final examination because he *believes* that there is a good probability of raising his grade to a B or an A. This is an example of subjective probability.

Although it may bother some people to use subjective probabilities, in the world of reality the successful engineer *must* use them. Is not the estimate of a qualified judge better than complete ignorance? The importance of the decision under consideration certainly influences the decision maker as to which type of probability he will accept or insist upon.

## OPTIMIZATION

To optimize means to minimize or maximize some function (a performance variable) by proper selection of design or controllable variables. Optimization often implies a mathematical relationship between the performance variable and the design variable. Such a relationship usually does not exist. Thus, "optimum" is an overused and often misused term. The same criticism could be leveled at the terms "maximum" and "minimum." For example, one often sees reference to a specification for a product design that achieves maximum reliability at minimum cost. These conditions can *never* be satisfied, since maximum reliability implies infinite cost and minimum cost, which is zero, implies zero reliability.

The more appropriate specification would be a reliability greater than .95 at a cost/unit not to exceed $1000. Alternatives would then be evaluated using the concepts presented in this chapter to meet these specifications.

In the rapidly changing world in which the engineer lives and works, it has become increasingly necessary for him to utilize scientific methods in making his decision. A *systems* approach to a problem is a very useful technique. Basically, as shown in Chapter 18, a system is a set of objects with relationships between the objects and between their attributes.[2] A system may be defined in any manner desired by the decision maker. The objects are the components of the system and the attributes are the properties of the objects. The relationships link the system together. The environment of a system is the set of all objects external to the system whose behavior affects the system and which are affected by the behavior of the system. For example, in one instance an Atlas missile may be the system, whereas in another instance one "black box" within the Atlas may be the system. Such a systems approach helps the decision maker to identify and isolate the problem under consideration.

The decision maker should always be alert for more information pertinent to his problem. In fact, he can often delay making a decision as long as possible in the hope that more information will become available. It must be remembered that the decision *not to decide* is also a valid decision.

[2] Hall, A. D., *A Methodology for Systems Engineering,* Van Nostrand, Princeton, (1962), p. 60.

Far *too much* money and efforts are expended by *too many* engineers and scientists today trying to devise an improvement which, even if developed, would be relatively insignificant. The implication, then, is that it is generally wiser to use a "Level of Aspiration" principle than to attempt to optimize. When the cost of the improvement exceeds the value of the modification, it is time to discard that project and proceed to others that hold more promise. This thought is very simply summed up in the Simon-March Hypothesis, which states: Most human decision making is concerned with the discovery and selection of satisfactory alternatives; only in exceptional cases is it concerned with the discovery and selection of optimal alternatives. This statement provides a key to the understanding and making of a wide variety of decisions.

## BIBLIOGRAPHY

BERNE, E., *Games People Play,* Grove Press, New York (1964).

CHERNOFF, H., and Moses, L. E., *Elementary Decision Theory,* John Wiley, New York (1959).

CHURCHMAN, C. W., and ACKOFF, R. L., "An Approximate Measure of Value," *Operations Research,* Vol. 2, 1954, pp. 172–187.

CHURCHMAN, C. W., *Decision and Value Theory,* Ch. 2 in Ackoff, R. L. (ed.), *Progress in Operations Research, Volume I,* John Wiley, New York (1961).

CHURCHMAN, C. W., *Prediction and Optimal Decision,* Prentice-Hall, Englewood Cliffs, N.J. (1961).

EDWARDS, W., "The Theory of Decision Making", *Psychological Bulletin,* Vol. 51, No. 4, 1954, pp. 380–417.

HALL, A. D., *A Methodology for Systems Engineering,* Van Nostrand, Princeton, 1962, p. 60.

LUCE, R. D., *Individual Choice Behavior,* Wiley, New York (1959).

LUCE, R. D., and RAIFFA, H., *Games and Decisions,* Wiley, New York (1957).

MORRIS, W. T., *Engineering Economy,* Irwin, Homewood, Ill., 1960, p. 315.

SAVAGE, L. J., *The Foundations of Statistics,* Wiley, New York (1954).

WILLIAMS, JOHN D., *The Compleat Strategyst,* McGraw-Hill, New York (1954).

# APPENDIXES

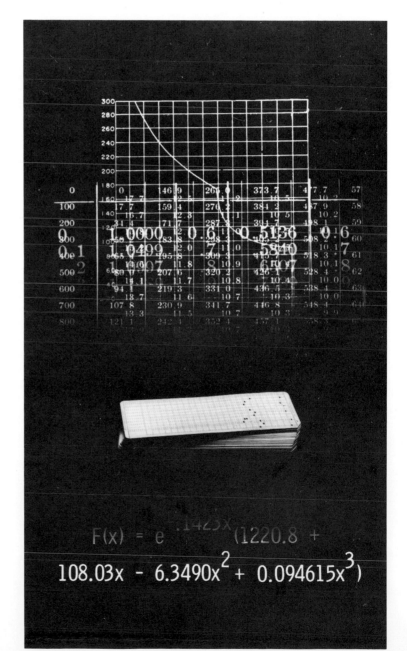

(Courtesy General Motors
Research Laboratories)

# Appendix I

# Logarithms – The Mathematical Basis for the Slide Rule

## LAWS OF LOGARITHMS

Since a logarithm is an exponent, all the laws of exponents should be reviewed. Let us examine a few of these laws.

**Exponential Law I:** $(a)^m(a)^n = a^{m+n}$

We can put the equation above in statement form, since we know that logarithms are exponents and therefore follow the laws of exponents.

**Law I.** The logarithm of a product equals the sum of the logarithms of the factors.

*Example:*
$$(5)(7) = ?$$
$$\log_{10} 5 + \log_{10} 7 = \log_{10} \text{ans.}$$
$$0.6990 + 0.8451 = \log \text{ans.}$$
$$1.5441 = \log \text{ans.}$$
$$\text{Answer} = (3.50)(10)^1$$

This is true because
$$5 = (10)^{0.6990}$$
$$7 = (10)^{0.8451}$$
$$\text{product} = (10)^{0.6990}(10)^{0.8451}$$
$$\text{product} = (10)^{0.6990+0.8451}$$
$$\text{product} = (10)^{1.5441}$$
$$\text{product} = (3.50)(10)^1$$

**Exponential Law II:** $\dfrac{a^m}{a^n} = a^{m-n}$

Putting the equation above in statement form, we obtain the following law.

**Law II.** The logarithm of a quotient equals the logarithm of the dividend minus the logarithm of the divisor.

*Example:*
$$\tfrac{5}{4} = ?$$
$$\log 5 - \log 4 = \log \text{ans.}$$
$$0.6990 - 0.6021 = \log \text{ans.}$$
$$0.0969 = \log \text{ans.}$$
$$\text{Answer} = 1.25$$

**Law III.** The logarithm of the $x$ power of a number equals $x$ times the logarithm of the number.

*Example:*
$$(5)^3 = ?$$
$$3(\log 5) = \log \text{ans.}$$
$$3(0.6990) = \log \text{ans.}$$
$$2.0970 = \log \text{ans.}$$
$$\text{Answer} = (1.25)(10)^2$$

**Law IV.** The logarithm of the $x$ root of a number equals the logarithm of the number divided by $x$.

*Example:*

$$\sqrt[3]{3375} = ?$$
$$\frac{\log 3375}{3} = \log \text{ans.}$$
$$\frac{3.5282}{3} = \log \text{ans.}$$
$$1.1761 = \log \text{ans.}$$
$$\text{Answer} = (1.50)(10)^1$$

NOTE: Law IV is actually a special case of Law III.
In some instances a combination of Law III and Law IV may be used.

*Example:*
$$(0.916)^{\frac{3}{4.15}} = ?$$
$$\frac{(\log 0.916)(3)}{4.15} = \log \text{ans.}$$
$$\frac{(9.9619 - 10)(3)}{4.15} = \log \text{ans.}$$

Perform multiplication first:
$$\frac{29.8857 - 30}{4.15} = \log \text{ans.}$$

To be divided by 4.15, the negative number must be divisible a whole number of times. Therefore, the characteristic (which is $-1$) is written as $414.0000 - 415$.

There are several values which could be chosen, such as $4149.0000 - 4150$, which would satisfy the condition that the characteristic be $-1$. Rewriting and dividing,

$$\frac{414.8857 - 415}{4.15} = \log \text{ ans.}$$

$$99.9725 - 100 = \log \text{ ans.}$$

$$\text{Answer} = (9.39)(10)^{-1}$$

**The Cologarithm.** Many times it is helpful to use the cologarithm of a number rather than the logarithm. The cologarithm of a number is the logarithm of the reciprocal of the number. The cologarithm is also the difference between the logarithm and the logarithm of unity.

*Example:*

$$\text{colog } 5 = \log \frac{1}{5}$$

$$= \log 1 - \log 5$$

$$= 0.0000 - 0.6990$$

$$= -0.6990$$

Since log 5 equals 0.6990, we see that the colog $x = -\log x$. Therefore:

    1. The logarithm of the quotient of two numbers equals the logarithm of the dividend plus the cologarithm of the divisor.

    2. The logarithm of the product of two numbers equals the logarithm of one number minus the cologarithm of the other number.

**Natural Logarithms.** When certain derivations of engineering formulas are made, a term may appear that contains a natural logarithm. For example, the magnetic field intensity near a current-carrying conductor varies with distance from the conductor according to a logarithmic pattern. In advanced texts it may be shown that a natural logarithm function, when plotted, gives an exponential curve whose slope at any point is equal to the ordinate at that point.

    In solving problems involving natural logarithms, tables of natural logarithms can be used if they are available, or the natural logarithm, frequently abbreviated as "ln," may be converted to a logarithm to the base 10. To perform this latter operation, an algebraic transformation called *change of logarithmic base* is used. This transformation can be performed as follows:

$$\text{Natural logarithm} = (\text{common log})(\log_\epsilon 10)$$

Since $\log_\epsilon 10 = 2.3026$, we may write:

$$\text{Natural logarithm} = (\text{common log})(2.3026)$$

If natural logarithms are computed, it must be remembered that the mantissa is not independent of the location of the decimal point. Therefore, the same sequence of significant figures does not have the same mantissa, as is the case with common logarithms.

*Example:* Find the natural logarithm of 245

$$\log_{10} 245 = 2.3892$$
$$\ln 245 = (2.3892)(2.3026)$$
$$= 5.5014$$

*Example:* Find the natural logarithm of 2.45

$$\log_{10} 245 = 0.3892$$
$$\ln 2.45 = (0.3892)(2.3026)$$
$$= 0.8961$$

The natural logarithm of a number less than 1 is a negative number.

*Example:* Find the natural logarithm of 0.245

$$\log_{10} 0.245 = 9.3892 - 10$$

Since the logarithm has a negative characteristic, we can solve by first finding the colog and then multiplying by $\log_e 10$.

$$\text{colog}_{10} 0.245 = -0.6108$$
$$\ln 0.245 = (-0.6108)(2.3026)$$
$$= -1.4064$$

# Appendix II

## Trigonometry

### RIGHT TRIANGLES

It can be shown by measurements and by formal derivations that for any given size of an angle at A or C, the ratio of the lengths of the sides to each other in a right triangle is a constant regardless of the numerical value of the lengths.

**Figure A II–1.**

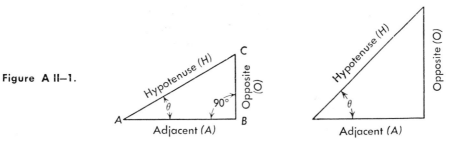

In Figure AII–1, the sides of a right triangle are named in reference to the angle under consideration. In these cases, the angle is designated as $\theta$ (theta).

Ratios of the sides are as follows:

$$\frac{\text{opposite side}}{\text{hypotenuse}} = \text{Sine } \theta \qquad \frac{O}{H} = \text{Sin } \theta \qquad \frac{\text{adjacent side}}{\text{opposite side}} = \text{Cotangent } \theta \qquad \frac{A}{O} = \text{Cot } \theta$$

$$\frac{\text{adjacent side}}{\text{hypotenuse}} = \text{Cosine } \theta \qquad \frac{A}{H} = \text{Cos } \theta \qquad \frac{\text{hypotenuse}}{\text{adjacent side}} = \text{Secant } \theta \qquad \frac{H}{A} = \text{Sec } \theta$$

$$\frac{\text{opposite side}}{\text{adjacent side}} = \text{Tangent } \theta \qquad \frac{O}{A} = \text{Tan } \theta \qquad \frac{\text{hypotenuse}}{\text{opposite side}} = \text{Cosecant } \theta \qquad \frac{H}{O} = \text{Csc } \theta$$

## METHODS OF SOLVING OBLIQUE TRIANGLE PROBLEMS

In order to solve an oblique triangle problem, at least three of the six parts of the triangle must be known, and at least one of the known parts must be a side. In the suggested methods listed below, only the most effective methods are given.

1. Given: two sides and an angle opposite one of them:
   a. Law of sines
   b. Right triangles
2. Given: two angles and one side:
   a. Law of sines
   b. Right triangles
3. Given: two sides and the included angle
   a. Law of cosines (answer is usually not dependable to more than three significant figures).
   b. Right triangles.
4. Given: three sides only:
   a. Tangent formula (half-angle solution)
   b. Sine formula (half-angle solution). This formula is not exact if the half-angle is near 90°.
   c. Cosine formula (half-angle solution). This formula is not exact if the half-angle is about 6° or less.
   d. Cosine formula (whole angle solution)
   e. Law of cosines (answer is usually not dependable to more than three significant figures).

## METHODS FOR FINDING AREAS OF OBLIQUE TRIANGLES

The area of an oblique triangle may be found by any of several methods. Some of the more common methods are given below:

1. Area = (½)(base)(altitude).
2. Area = $\sqrt{(S)(S-AB)(S-BC)(S-AC)}$, where $S$ = ½ perimeter of the triangle.
3. Area = ½ (product of two sides) (sine of the included angle).

## SINE LAW

In any triangle the ratio of the length of a side to the sine of the angle opposite that side is the same as the ratio of any other side to the sine of the angle opposite it. In symbol form:

$$\frac{AB}{\sin \angle C} = \frac{BC}{\sin \angle A} = \frac{AC}{\sin \angle B}$$

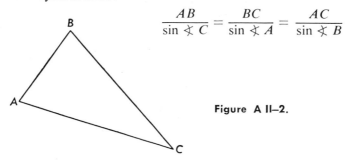

Figure A II–2.

This expression is called the *sine law*. The student is cautioned not to confuse the meanings of sine functions and sine law.

In the event one of the angles of a triangle is larger than 90°, a simple way to obtain the value of the sine of the angle is to subtract the angle from 180° and obtain the sine of this angle to use in the sine law expression.

The sine law can also be used if two sides and an angle ·f a triangle are known, provided the angle is not the one included between the sides. However, as explained in trigonometry texts, the product of the sine of the angle and the side adjacent must be equal to or less than the side opposite the angle; otherwise no solution is possible.

As an alternate method, the general triangle can be made into right triangles by adding construction lines. This method of using right triangle solutions is as exact as the sine law but usually will take more time than the sine law method.

## COSINE LAW

In an oblique triangle, the square of any side is equal to the sum of the squares of the other two sides minus twice the product of the other two sides times the cosine of the included angle. In symbol form:

$$(AB)^2 = (AC)^2 + (BC)^2 - (2)(AC)(BC)(\cos \measuredangle C)$$

This expression is called the *cosine law* and is useful in many problems, although it may not give an answer to the desired precision since we are adding and subtracting terms that have only three significant figures.

After the side $AB$ has been determined, the angles at $A$ and $B$ can be found by using the law of sines.

In the event that the angle used in the cosine law formula is larger than 90°, subtract the angle from 180°, and determine the cosine of this angle. Remember, however, that the cosine of an angle between 90° and 180° is negative. If the angle used in the formula is larger than 90°, the last term will add to the squared terms.

The problem above can also be solved by using construction lines and making right triangles from the figure. To do this, we construct the line $BD$ perpendicular to $AC$. This will form two right triangles, $ABD$ and $BCD$. In triangle $BCD$, side $BD$ may be found by using $BC$ and the sine of $\measuredangle C$. In a similar manner, by using the cosine of $\measuredangle C$, side $DC$ may be found. From this we can determine side $AD$ in triangle $ABD$.

Using the tangent function, the angle at $A$ can be found, and $AB$ can be determined by the use of the sine or cosine function or the Pythagorean theorem $(AB)^2 = (BD)^2 + (AD)^2$. The right triangle method, while it may take longer to solve, will in general give a more accurate answer.

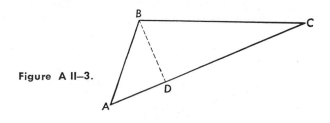

Figure A II–3.

## THREE SIDES LAWS

There are a number of formulas derived in trigonometry that will give the angles of an oblique triangle when only three sides are known. The formulas differ considerably in ease of application and precision, especially if logarithms are used. Of

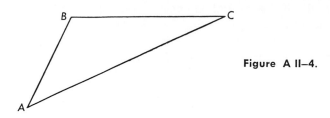

**Figure A II–4.**

all the formulas available, in general the half-angle (tangent) formula is better than others. The formula (half-angle solution) is as follows:

$$\tan \tfrac{1}{2} A = \frac{r}{S - BC}$$

where

$$r = \sqrt{\frac{(S - AB)(S - AC)(S - BC)}{S}}$$

and

$$S = \tfrac{1}{2} \text{ perimeter of triangle}$$

Other formulas that may be used are:

Sine formula (half-angle solution) $\sin \tfrac{1}{2} A = \sqrt{\dfrac{(S - AC)(S - AB)}{(AC)(AB)}}$

Cosine formula (half-angle solution) $\cos \tfrac{1}{2} A = \sqrt{\dfrac{(S)(S - BC)}{(AC)(AB)}}$

Cosine formula (whole angle solution) $\cos A = \dfrac{(2S)(S - BC)}{(AB)(AC)} - 1$

In the last formula, the quantity $(2S)(S - BC)/(AB)(AC)$ will usually be between 1 and 2 and can be read to four figures on the slide rule. Subtracting the 1 in the equation will leave the cosine of the angle correct to three figures. The formula has the advantage that it requires fewer operations. Also it is convenient to use if the slide rule is employed in solving problems.

After finding one angle, the remaining angles can be found by successive applications of the law, being careful to use the proper side of the triangle in the formula. The sine law can also be used after one angle is found. In order to have a check on the solution, it is better to solve for all three angles rather than solve for two angles, and then subtract their sum from 180°. If each angle is computed separately, their sum should be within the allowable error range of 180°.

As an incidental item in the tangent formula, the constant $r$ is equal to the length of the radius of a circle that can be inscribed in the triangle.

# Appendix III

## Geometric Figures

**Rectangle**

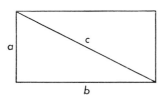

Area = (base)(altitude) = $ab$
Diagonal = $\sqrt{(\text{altitude})^2 + (\text{base})^2}$
$$C = \sqrt{a^2 + b^2}$$

**Right Triangle**

Angle $A$ + angle $B$ = angle $C$ = 90°
Area = ½ (base)(altitude)
Hypotenuse = $\sqrt{(\text{altitude})^2 + (\text{base})^2}$
$$C = \sqrt{a^2 + b^2}$$

**Any Triangle**

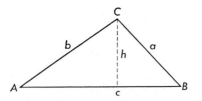

Angles $A + B + C$ = 180°
(Altitude $h$ is perpendicular to base $c$)
Area = ½ (base)(altitude)

**Parallelogram**

Area = (base)(altitude)
Altitude $h$ is perpendicular to base $AB$
Angles $A + B + C + D = 360°$

**Trapezoid**

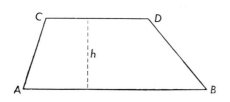

Area = ½ (altitude)(sum of bases)
(Altitude $h$ is perpendicular to sides $AB$ and
$CD$. Side $AB$ is parallel to side $CD$.)

**Regular Polygon**

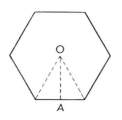

$$\text{Area} = \frac{1}{2}\left[\begin{array}{c}\text{length of}\\\text{one side}\end{array}\right]\left[\begin{array}{c}\text{Number}\\\text{of sides}\end{array}\right]\left[\begin{array}{c}\text{Distance}\\OA\text{ to}\\\text{center}\end{array}\right]$$

A regular polygon has equal angles and equal
sides and can be inscribed in or circum-
scribed about a circle.

**Circle**

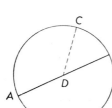

$AB$ = diameter, $CD$ = radius
Area $= \pi(\text{radius})^2 = \dfrac{\pi(\text{diameter})^2}{4}$
Circumference $= \pi(\text{diameter})$
$C = 2\pi(\text{radius})$
$\dfrac{\text{arc } BC}{\text{circumference}} = \dfrac{\text{angle } BDC}{360°}$
1 radian $= \dfrac{180°}{\pi} = 57.2958°$

**Sector of a Circle**

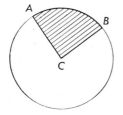

Area $= \dfrac{(\text{arc } AB)(\text{radius})}{2}$

$\qquad = \pi\dfrac{(\text{radius})^2(\text{angle } ACB)}{360°}$

$\qquad = \dfrac{(\text{radius})^2 \,(\text{angle } ACB \text{ in radians})}{2}$

## Segment of a Circle

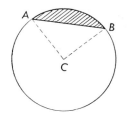

$$\text{Area} = \frac{(\text{radius})^2}{2}\left[\frac{\pi(\measuredangle ACB°)}{180} - \sin ACB°\right]$$

$$\text{Area} = \frac{(\text{radius})^2}{2}\left[\measuredangle ACB \text{ in radians} - \sin ACB°\right]$$

$$\text{Area} = \text{area of sector } ACB - \text{area of triangle } ABC$$

## Ellipse

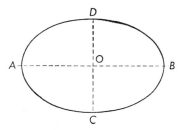

$$\text{Area} = \pi(\text{long radius } OA)(\text{short radius } OC)$$

$$\text{Area} = \frac{\pi}{4}(\text{long diameter } AB)(\text{short diameter } CD)$$

## Volume and Center of Gravity Equations*

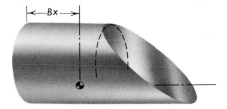

Volume equations are included for all cases. Where the equation for the CG (center of gravity) is not given, you can easily obtain it by looking up the volume and CG equations for portions of the shape and then combining values. For example, for the shape above, use the equations for a cylinder, Fig. 1, and a truncated cylinder, Fig. 10 (subscripts $C$ and $T$, respectively, in the equations below). Hence taking moments

$$B_x = \frac{V_C B_C + V_T(B_T + L_C)}{V_C + V_T}$$

$$\text{or} \quad B_x = \frac{\left(\frac{\pi}{4}D^2 L_C\right)\left(\frac{L_C}{2}\right) + \frac{\pi}{8}D^2 L_T\left(\frac{5}{16}L_T + L_C\right)}{\frac{\pi}{4}D^2 L_C + \frac{\pi}{8}D^2 L_T}$$

$$B_x = \frac{L^2_C + L_T\left(\frac{5}{16}L_T + L_C\right)}{2L_C + L_T}$$

* Courtesy of Knoll Atomic Power Laboratory, Schenectady, New York, operated by the General Electric Company for the United States Atomic Energy Commission. Reprinted from *Product Engineering*—Copyright owned by McGraw-Hill.

In the equations to follow, angle $\theta$ can be either in degrees or in radians.

Thus $\theta$ (rad) $= \pi\theta/180$ (deg) $= 0.01745\,\theta$ (deg).

For example, if $\theta = 30$ deg in Case 3, then $\sin\theta = 0.5$ and

$$B = \frac{2R\,(0.5)}{3\,(30)\,(0.01745)} = 0.637R$$

Symbols used are:

$B$ = distance from CG to reference plane,

$V$ = volume,

$D$ and $d$ = diameter,

$R$ and $r$ = radius,

$H$ = height,

$L$ = length.

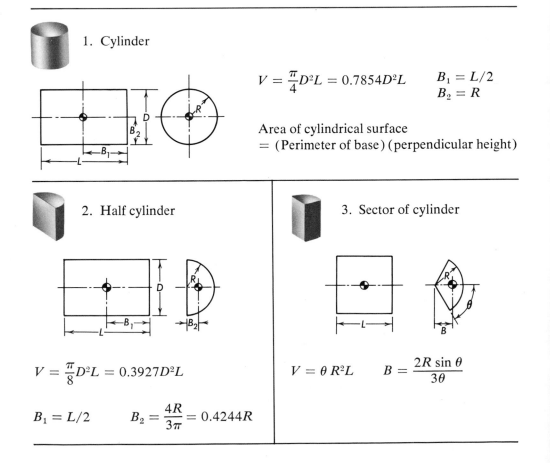

1. Cylinder

$$V = \frac{\pi}{4}D^2L = 0.7854D^2L \qquad \begin{aligned} B_1 &= L/2 \\ B_2 &= R \end{aligned}$$

Area of cylindrical surface
= (Perimeter of base) (perpendicular height)

2. Half cylinder

$$V = \frac{\pi}{8}D^2L = 0.3927D^2L$$

$$B_1 = L/2 \qquad B_2 = \frac{4R}{3\pi} = 0.4244R$$

3. Sector of cylinder

$$V = \theta\,R^2L \qquad B = \frac{2R\sin\theta}{3\theta}$$

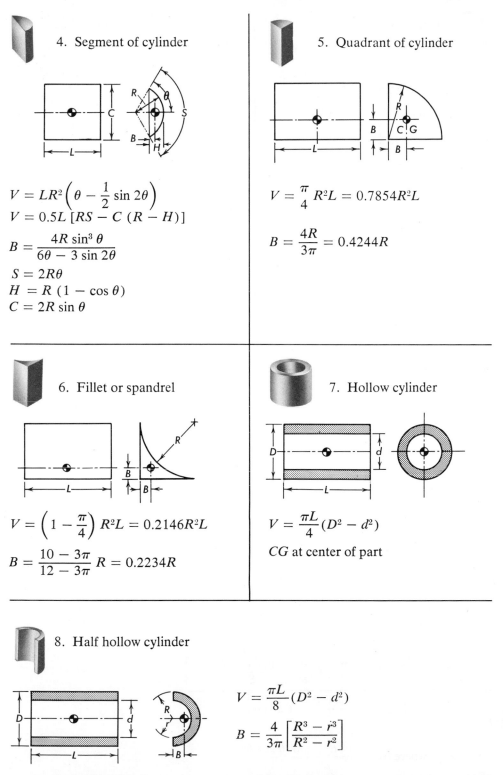

### 4. Segment of cylinder

$$V = LR^2\left(\theta - \frac{1}{2}\sin 2\theta\right)$$
$$V = 0.5L\left[RS - C\left(R - H\right)\right]$$

$$B = \frac{4R\sin^3\theta}{6\theta - 3\sin 2\theta}$$

$$S = 2R\theta$$
$$H = R\left(1 - \cos\theta\right)$$
$$C = 2R\sin\theta$$

### 5. Quadrant of cylinder

$$V = \frac{\pi}{4}R^2L = 0.7854R^2L$$

$$B = \frac{4R}{3\pi} = 0.4244R$$

### 6. Fillet or spandrel

$$V = \left(1 - \frac{\pi}{4}\right)R^2L = 0.2146R^2L$$

$$B = \frac{10 - 3\pi}{12 - 3\pi}R = 0.2234R$$

### 7. Hollow cylinder

$$V = \frac{\pi L}{4}(D^2 - d^2)$$

$CG$ at center of part

### 8. Half hollow cylinder

$$V = \frac{\pi L}{8}(D^2 - d^2)$$

$$B = \frac{4}{3\pi}\left[\frac{R^3 - r^3}{R^2 - r^2}\right]$$

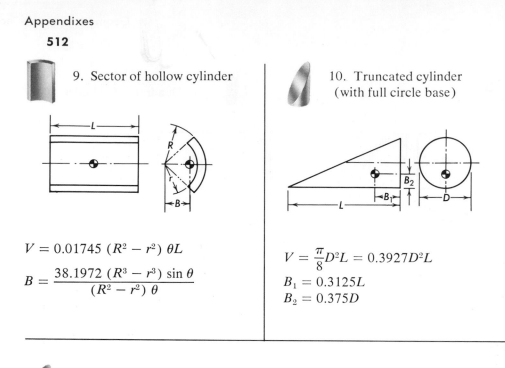

9. Sector of hollow cylinder

10. Truncated cylinder
(with full circle base)

$$V = 0.01745 \, (R^2 - r^2) \, \theta L$$

$$B = \frac{38.1972 \, (R^3 - r^3) \sin \theta}{(R^2 - r^2) \, \theta}$$

$$V = \frac{\pi}{8} D^2 L = 0.3927 D^2 L$$

$$B_1 = 0.3125L$$

$$B_2 = 0.375D$$

11. Truncated cylinder (with partial circle base)

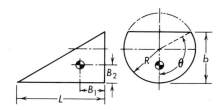

$$b = R \, (1 - \cos \theta)$$

$$V = \frac{R^3 L}{b} \left[ \sin \theta - \frac{\sin^3 \theta}{3} - \theta \cos \theta \right]$$

$$B_1 = \frac{L \left[ \dfrac{\theta \cos^2 \theta}{2} - \dfrac{5 \sin \theta \cos \theta}{8} + \dfrac{\sin^3 \theta \cos \theta}{12} + \dfrac{\theta}{8} \right]}{\left[ 1 - \cos \theta \right]\left[ \sin \theta - \dfrac{\sin^3 \theta}{3} - \theta \cos \theta \right]}$$

$$B_2 = \frac{2R \left[ -\dfrac{\theta \cos \theta}{2} + \dfrac{\sin \theta}{2} - \dfrac{\theta}{8} + \dfrac{\sin \theta \cos \theta}{8} - N \right]}{\left[ \sin \theta - \dfrac{\sin^3 \theta}{3} - \theta \cos \theta \right]}$$

$$\text{where } N = \frac{\sin^3 \theta}{6} - \frac{\sin^3 \theta \cos \theta}{12}$$

12. Oblique cylinder
(or circular hole at oblique angle)

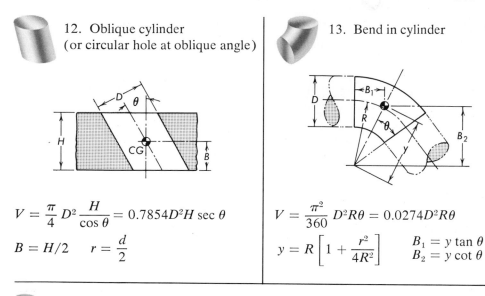

$$V = \frac{\pi}{4} D^2 \frac{H}{\cos \theta} = 0.7854 D^2 H \sec \theta$$

$$B = H/2 \qquad r = \frac{d}{2}$$

13. Bend in cylinder

$$V = \frac{\pi^2}{360} D^2 R\theta = 0.0274 D^2 R\theta$$

$$y = R \left[ 1 + \frac{r^2}{4R^2} \right] \qquad \begin{array}{l} B_1 = y \tan \theta \\ B_2 = y \cot \theta \end{array}$$

14. Curved groove in cylinder

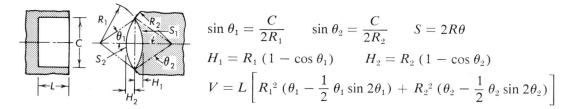

$$\sin \theta_1 = \frac{C}{2R_1} \qquad \sin \theta_2 = \frac{C}{2R_2} \qquad S = 2R\theta$$

$$H_1 = R_1 (1 - \cos \theta_1) \qquad H_2 = R_2 (1 - \cos \theta_2)$$

$$V = L \left[ R_1^2 \left( \theta_1 - \frac{1}{2} \theta_1 \sin 2\theta_1 \right) + R_2^2 \left( \theta_2 - \frac{1}{2} \theta_2 \sin 2\theta_2 \right) \right]$$

Compute *CG* of each part separately

15. Slot in cylinder

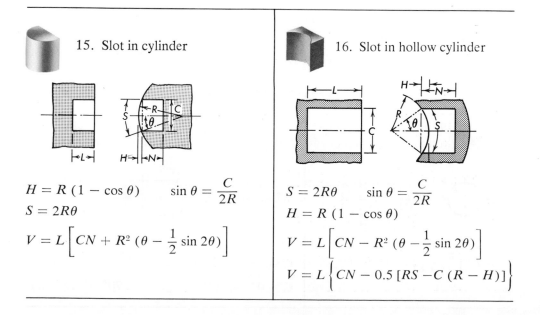

$$H = R (1 - \cos \theta) \qquad \sin \theta = \frac{C}{2R}$$

$$S = 2R\theta$$

$$V = L \left[ CN + R^2 \left( \theta - \frac{1}{2} \sin 2\theta \right) \right]$$

16. Slot in hollow cylinder

$$S = 2R\theta \qquad \sin \theta = \frac{C}{2R}$$

$$H = R (1 - \cos \theta)$$

$$V = L \left[ CN - R^2 \left( \theta - \frac{1}{2} \sin 2\theta \right) \right]$$

$$V = L \left\{ CN - 0.5 [RS - C (R - H)] \right\}$$

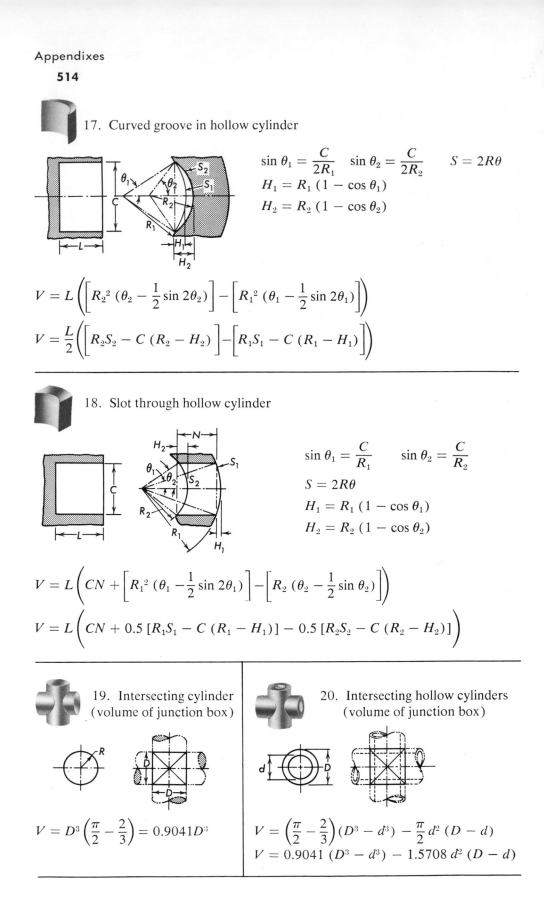

17. Curved groove in hollow cylinder

$$\sin \theta_1 = \frac{C}{2R_1} \quad \sin \theta_2 = \frac{C}{2R_2} \quad S = 2R\theta$$
$$H_1 = R_1 (1 - \cos \theta_1)$$
$$H_2 = R_2 (1 - \cos \theta_2)$$

$$V = L\left(\left[R_2^2\left(\theta_2 - \frac{1}{2}\sin 2\theta_2\right)\right] - \left[R_1^2\left(\theta_1 - \frac{1}{2}\sin 2\theta_1\right)\right]\right)$$

$$V = \frac{L}{2}\left(\left[R_2 S_2 - C(R_2 - H_2)\right] - \left[R_1 S_1 - C(R_1 - H_1)\right]\right)$$

18. Slot through hollow cylinder

$$\sin \theta_1 = \frac{C}{R_1} \quad \sin \theta_2 = \frac{C}{R_2}$$
$$S = 2R\theta$$
$$H_1 = R_1 (1 - \cos \theta_1)$$
$$H_2 = R_2 (1 - \cos \theta_2)$$

$$V = L\left(CN + \left[R_1^2\left(\theta_1 - \frac{1}{2}\sin 2\theta_1\right)\right] - \left[R_2\left(\theta_2 - \frac{1}{2}\sin \theta_2\right)\right]\right)$$

$$V = L\left(CN + 0.5\left[R_1 S_1 - C(R_1 - H_1)\right] - 0.5\left[R_2 S_2 - C(R_2 - H_2)\right]\right)$$

19. Intersecting cylinder (volume of junction box)

$$V = D^3\left(\frac{\pi}{2} - \frac{2}{3}\right) = 0.9041 D^3$$

20. Intersecting hollow cylinders (volume of junction box)

$$V = \left(\frac{\pi}{2} - \frac{2}{3}\right)(D^3 - d^3) - \frac{\pi}{2}d^2(D - d)$$
$$V = 0.9041(D^3 - d^3) - 1.5708 d^2(D - d)$$

21. Intersecting parallel cylinders
$(M < R_1)$

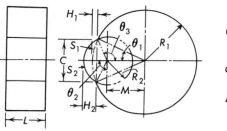

$$\theta_2 = 180° - \theta_3 \qquad \cos \theta_3 = \frac{R_2{}^2 + M^2 - R_1{}^2}{2MR_2}$$

$$\cos \theta_1 = \frac{R_1{}^2 + M^2 - R_2{}^2}{2MR_1}$$

$$H_1 = R_1 (1 - \cos \theta_1)$$
$$S_1 = 2R_1\theta_1$$

$$V = L\left( \pi R_1{}^2 + \left[ R_2{}^2 \left(\theta_2 - \frac{1}{2} \sin 2\theta_2\right) \right] - \left[ R_1{}^2 \left(\theta_1 - \frac{1}{2} \sin 2\theta_1\right) \right] \right)$$

22. Intersecting parallel cylinders $(M > R_1)$

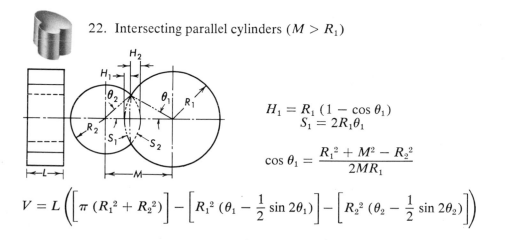

$$H_1 = R_1 (1 - \cos \theta_1)$$
$$S_1 = 2R_1\theta_1$$

$$\cos \theta_1 = \frac{R_1{}^2 + M^2 - R_2{}^2}{2MR_1}$$

$$V = L\left( \left[ \pi (R_1{}^2 + R_2{}^2) \right] - \left[ R_1{}^2 \left(\theta_1 - \frac{1}{2} \sin 2\theta_1\right) \right] - \left[ R_2{}^2 \left(\theta_2 - \frac{1}{2} \sin 2\theta_2\right) \right] \right)$$

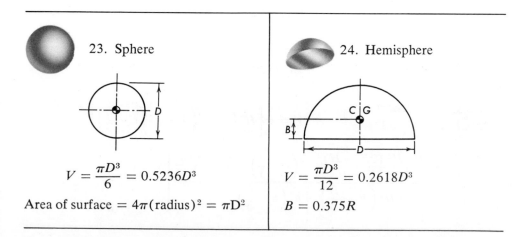

23. Sphere

$$V = \frac{\pi D^3}{6} = 0.5236D^3$$

Area of surface $= 4\pi(\text{radius})^2 = \pi D^2$

24. Hemisphere

$$V = \frac{\pi D^3}{12} = 0.2618D^3$$

$$B = 0.375R$$

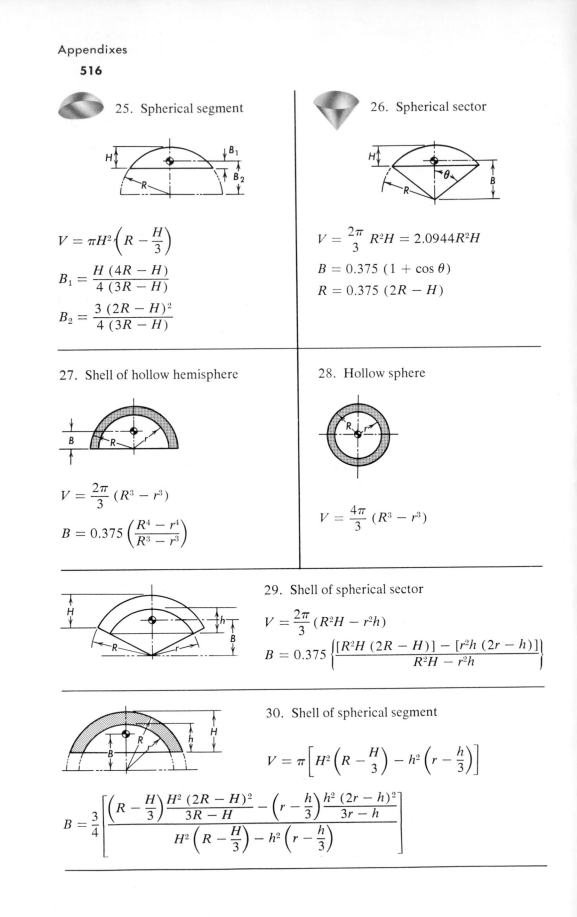

25. Spherical segment

$$V = \pi H^2 \left( R - \frac{H}{3} \right)$$

$$B_1 = \frac{H\,(4R - H)}{4\,(3R - H)}$$

$$B_2 = \frac{3\,(2R - H)^2}{4\,(3R - H)}$$

26. Spherical sector

$$V = \frac{2\pi}{3}\,R^2 H = 2.0944R^2 H$$

$$B = 0.375\,(1 + \cos\theta)$$

$$R = 0.375\,(2R - H)$$

27. Shell of hollow hemisphere

$$V = \frac{2\pi}{3}\,(R^3 - r^3)$$

$$B = 0.375 \left( \frac{R^4 - r^4}{R^3 - r^3} \right)$$

28. Hollow sphere

$$V = \frac{4\pi}{3}\,(R^3 - r^3)$$

29. Shell of spherical sector

$$V = \frac{2\pi}{3}\,(R^2 H - r^2 h)$$

$$B = 0.375 \left\{ \frac{[R^2 H\,(2R - H)] - [r^2 h\,(2r - h)]}{R^2 H - r^2 h} \right\}$$

30. Shell of spherical segment

$$V = \pi \left[ H^2 \left( R - \frac{H}{3} \right) - h^2 \left( r - \frac{h}{3} \right) \right]$$

$$B = \frac{3}{4} \left[ \frac{\left( R - \dfrac{H}{3} \right) \dfrac{H^2\,(2R - H)^2}{3R - H} - \left( r - \dfrac{h}{3} \right) \dfrac{h^2\,(2r - h)^2}{3r - h}}{H^2 \left( R - \dfrac{H}{3} \right) - h^2 \left( r - \dfrac{h}{3} \right)} \right]$$

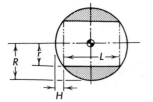

### 31. Circular hole through sphere

$$V = \pi \left[ r^2 L + 2H^2 \left( R - \frac{H}{3} \right) \right]$$

$$H = R - \sqrt{R^2 - r^2}$$
$$L = 2(R - H)$$

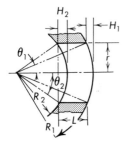

### 32. Circular hole through hollow sphere

$$V = \pi \left\{ r^2 L + H_1 \left( R_1 - \frac{H_1}{3} \right) - H_2^2 \left( R_2 - \frac{H_2}{3} \right) \right\}$$

$$\sin \theta_1 = r/R_1 \qquad \sin \theta_2 = r/R_2 \qquad H = R(1 - \cos \theta)$$

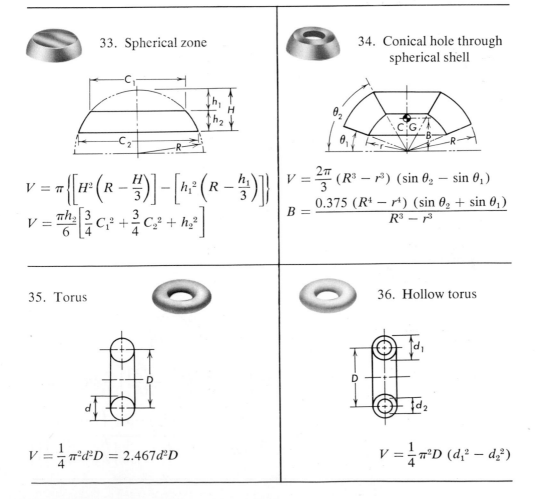

### 33. Spherical zone

$$V = \pi \left\{ \left[ H^2 \left( R - \frac{H}{3} \right) \right] - \left[ h_1^2 \left( R - \frac{h_1}{3} \right) \right] \right\}$$

$$V = \frac{\pi h_2}{6} \left[ \frac{3}{4} C_1^2 + \frac{3}{4} C_2^2 + h_2^2 \right]$$

### 34. Conical hole through spherical shell

$$V = \frac{2\pi}{3} (R^3 - r^3)(\sin \theta_2 - \sin \theta_1)$$

$$B = \frac{0.375 (R^4 - r^4)(\sin \theta_2 + \sin \theta_1)}{R^3 - r^3}$$

### 35. Torus

$$V = \frac{1}{4} \pi^2 d^2 D = 2.467 d^2 D$$

### 36. Hollow torus

$$V = \frac{1}{4} \pi^2 D (d_1^2 - d_2^2)$$

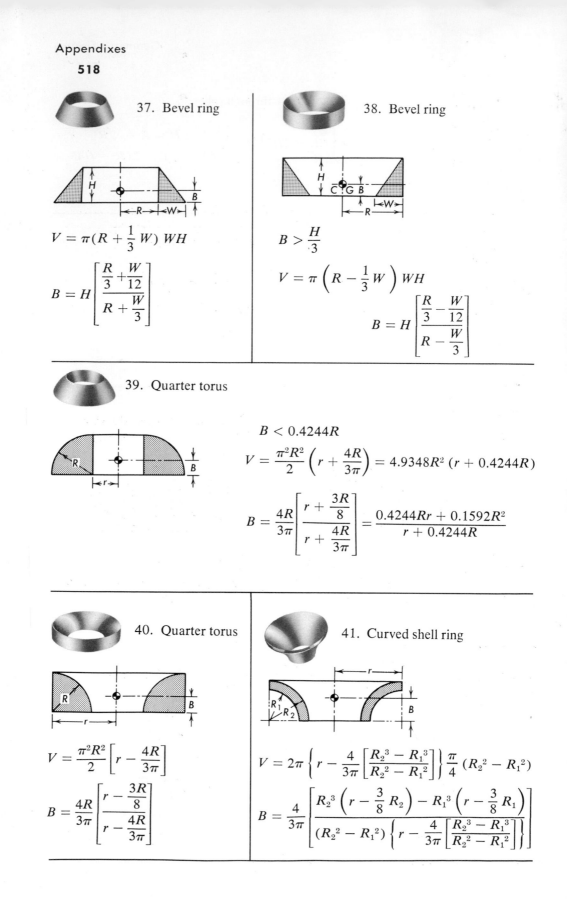

37. Bevel ring

$$V = \pi\left(R + \frac{1}{3}W\right)WH$$

$$B = H\left[\frac{\dfrac{R}{3} + \dfrac{W}{12}}{R + \dfrac{W}{3}}\right]$$

38. Bevel ring

$$B > \frac{H}{3}$$

$$V = \pi\left(R - \frac{1}{3}W\right)WH$$

$$B = H\left[\frac{\dfrac{R}{3} - \dfrac{W}{12}}{R - \dfrac{W}{3}}\right]$$

39. Quarter torus

$$B < 0.4244R$$

$$V = \frac{\pi^2 R^2}{2}\left(r + \frac{4R}{3\pi}\right) = 4.9348R^2\,(r + 0.4244R)$$

$$B = \frac{4R}{3\pi}\left[\frac{r + \dfrac{3R}{8}}{r + \dfrac{4R}{3\pi}}\right] = \frac{0.4244Rr + 0.1592R^2}{r + 0.4244R}$$

40. Quarter torus

$$V = \frac{\pi^2 R^2}{2}\left[r - \frac{4R}{3\pi}\right]$$

$$B = \frac{4R}{3\pi}\left[\frac{r - \dfrac{3R}{8}}{r - \dfrac{4R}{3\pi}}\right]$$

41. Curved shell ring

$$V = 2\pi\left\{r - \frac{4}{3\pi}\left[\frac{R_2{}^3 - R_1{}^3}{R_2{}^2 - R_1{}^2}\right]\right\}\frac{\pi}{4}\,(R_2{}^2 - R_1{}^2)$$

$$B = \frac{4}{3\pi}\left[\frac{R_2{}^3\left(r - \dfrac{3}{8}R_2\right) - R_1{}^3\left(r - \dfrac{3}{8}R_1\right)}{(R_2{}^2 - R_1{}^2)\left\{r - \dfrac{4}{3\pi}\left[\dfrac{R_2{}^3 - R_1{}^3}{R_2{}^2 - R_1{}^2}\right]\right\}}\right]$$

42. Curved shell ring

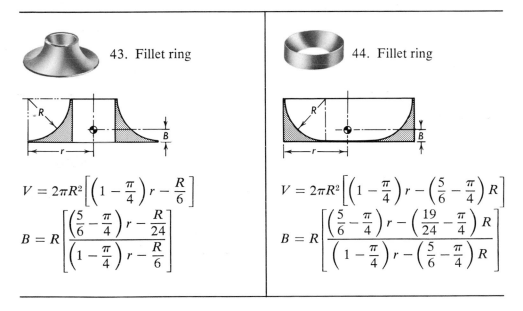

$$V = \frac{\pi^2}{2}\left[r(R_2{}^2 - R_1{}^2) + \frac{4}{3\pi}(R_2{}^3 - R_1{}^3)\right]$$

$$B = \frac{2}{\pi}\left[\frac{\frac{2r}{3}(R_2{}^3 - R_1{}^3) + \frac{1}{4}(R_2{}^4 - R_1{}^4)}{r(R_2{}^2 - R_1{}^2) + \frac{4}{3\pi}(R_2{}^3 - R_1{}^3)}\right]$$

43. Fillet ring

$$V = 2\pi R^2\left[\left(1 - \frac{\pi}{4}\right)r - \frac{R}{6}\right]$$

$$B = R\left[\frac{\left(\frac{5}{6} - \frac{\pi}{4}\right)r - \frac{R}{24}}{\left(1 - \frac{\pi}{4}\right)r - \frac{R}{6}}\right]$$

44. Fillet ring

$$V = 2\pi R^2\left[\left(1 - \frac{\pi}{4}\right)r - \left(\frac{5}{6} - \frac{\pi}{4}\right)R\right]$$

$$B = R\left[\frac{\left(\frac{5}{6} - \frac{\pi}{4}\right)r - \left(\frac{19}{24} - \frac{\pi}{4}\right)R}{\left(1 - \frac{\pi}{4}\right)r - \left(\frac{5}{6} - \frac{\pi}{4}\right)R}\right]$$

45. Curved-sector ring

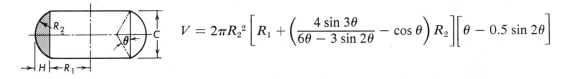

$$V = 2\pi R_2{}^2\left[R_1 + \left(\frac{4\sin 3\theta}{6\theta - 3\sin 2\theta} - \cos\theta\right)R_2\right]\left[\theta - 0.5\sin 2\theta\right]$$

46. Ellipsoidal cylinder

$$V = \frac{\pi}{4}AaL$$

47. Ellipsoid

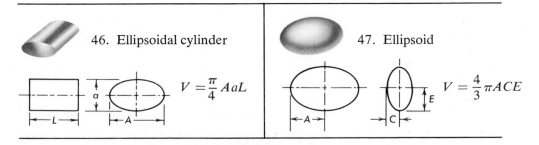

$$V = \frac{4}{3}\pi ACE$$

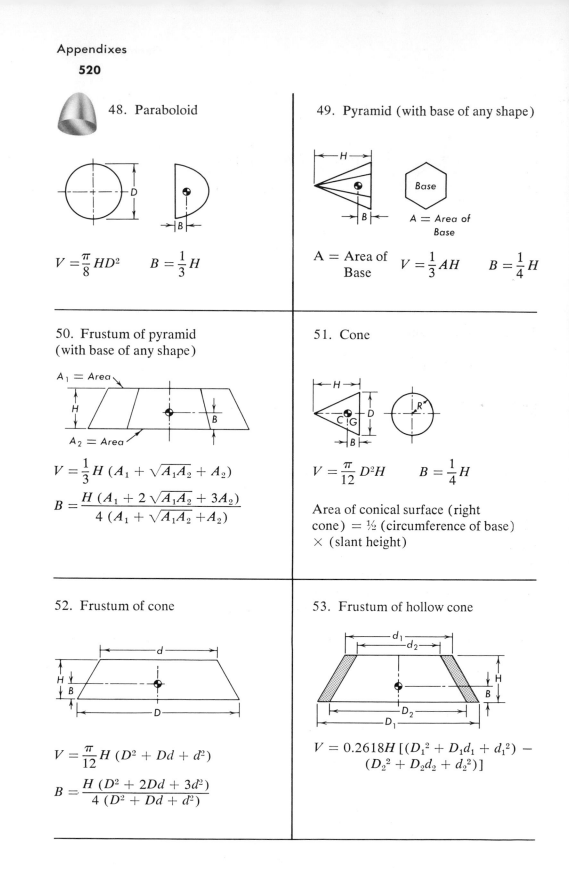

48. Paraboloid

$$V = \frac{\pi}{8} HD^2 \qquad B = \frac{1}{3} H$$

49. Pyramid (with base of any shape)

Base

$A$ = Area of Base

$A$ = Area of Base $\qquad V = \frac{1}{3} AH \qquad B = \frac{1}{4} H$

50. Frustum of pyramid (with base of any shape)

$A_1$ = Area

$A_2$ = Area

$$V = \frac{1}{3} H (A_1 + \sqrt{A_1 A_2} + A_2)$$

$$B = \frac{H (A_1 + 2\sqrt{A_1 A_2} + 3A_2)}{4 (A_1 + \sqrt{A_1 A_2} + A_2)}$$

51. Cone

$$V = \frac{\pi}{12} D^2 H \qquad B = \frac{1}{4} H$$

Area of conical surface (right cone) = ½ (circumference of base) × (slant height)

52. Frustum of cone

$$V = \frac{\pi}{12} H (D^2 + Dd + d^2)$$

$$B = \frac{H (D^2 + 2Dd + 3d^2)}{4 (D^2 + Dd + d^2)}$$

53. Frustum of hollow cone

$$V = 0.2618H \left[ (D_1^2 + D_1 d_1 + d_1^2) - (D_2^2 + D_2 d_2 + d_2^2) \right]$$

## 54. Hexagon

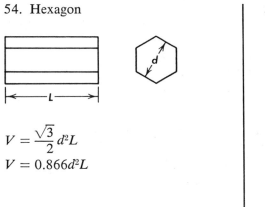

$$V = \frac{\sqrt{3}}{2}\, d^2 L$$

$$V = 0.866 d^2 L$$

## 55. Closely packed helical springs

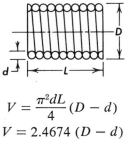

$$V = \frac{\pi^2 dL}{4}(D - d)$$

$$V = 2.4674\,(D - d)$$

## 56. Rectangular prism

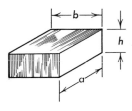

Volume = length × width × height
Volume = area of base × altitude

## 57. Any prism

(Axis either perpendicular or inclined to base)

Volume = (area of base) (perpendicular height)

Volume = (lateral length) (area of perpendicular cross-section)

# Appendix IV

## Tables

### WEIGHTS AND MEASURES

#### Avoirdupois Weight

| | |
|---|---|
| 1 grain (avdp) | 1 grain         1 grain (troy) |
| 27 11/32 grain | 1 dram |
| 16 dram | 1 ounce (oz) |
| 16 ounces | 1 pound (lb) |
| 100 pounds | 1 hundredweight (cwt) |
| 2000 pounds | 1 short ton (T) |
| 2240 pounds | 1 long ton |

#### Metric Weight

| | |
|---|---|
| 10 milligram (mg) | 1 centigram (cg) |
| 10 centigram | 1 decigram (dg) |
| 10 decigram | 1 gram (g) |
| 10 gram | 1 dekagram (Dg) |
| 10 dekagram | 1 hectogram (hg) |
| 10 hectogram | 1 kilogram (kg) |

#### Mass and Force Equivalents

| | | |
|---|---|---|
| 1 gram | 0.03527 ounce | 980.6 dynes |
| 1 kilogram | 2.2046 pound | $(6.852)(10^{-2})$ slug 9.807 newton |
| 1 metric ton | 2205 pound | |
| 1 pound | 453.6 gram | 0.4536 kilogram   4.448 newton |
| 1 ounce | 28.35 gram | |
| 1 newton | $10^5$ dynes | 0.2248 pounds |

## Dry Measure

| | |
|---|---|
| 2 pints | 1 quart (qt)     67.2 cubic inches (in.³) |
| 8 quarts | 1 peck |
| 4 pecks | 1 bushel (bu) |

## Liquid Measure

| | |
|---|---|
| 4 gill | 1 pint (pt)     16 fluid ounces   2 cups |
| 2 pints | 1 quart |
| 4 quarts | 1 gallon (gal)   231 cubic inches |
| 7.48 gallons | 1 cubic foot (ft³) |
| 31½ gallons | 1 barrel (bbl) |
| 1 British Imperial gallon | 1.200 U.S. gallons |

## Linear Measure

| | | | |
|---|---|---|---|
| 1 mil | 0.001 inch (in.) | | |
| 12 inches | 1 foot (ft) | | |
| 3 feet | 1 yard (yd) | | |
| 5½ yards | 1 rod | | |
| 40 rods | 1 furlong | | |
| 320 rods | 1 mile | 5280 ft | 1760 yards |
| 3 miles | 1 league | | |

## Linear Measure Equivalents

| | |
|---|---|
| 6.08 feet | 1 fathom |
| 6080.2 feet | 1 nautical mile |
| 1 nautical mile | 1.15 statute mile |

1 knot is a speed of 1 nautical mile per hour

## Metric Linear Measure

| | |
|---|---|
| 10 millimeter (mm) | 1 centimeter (cm) |
| 10 centimeter | 1 decimeter (dm) |
| 10 decimeter | 1 meter (m) |
| 10 meter | 1 dekameter (Dm) |
| 10 dekameter | 1 hectometer (hm) |
| 10 hectometer | 1 kilometer (km) |

## Metric Linear Equivalents

| | | | |
|---|---|---|---|
| 1 centimeter | 0.3937 inch | $10^{-5}$ kilometer | |
| 1 meter | 39.37 inches | 1.0936 yard | 3.281 feet |
| 1 kilometer | 0.62137 mile (approximately ⅝ mile)   3281 feet | | |
| 1 inch | 2.540 centimeter | | |
| 1 foot | 30.48 centimeter | 0.3048 meter | |
| 1 mile | 1.6093 kilometer | | |
| 1 Angstrom | $10^{-10}$ meter | | |
| 1 micron ($\mu$) | $10^{-6}$ meter | | |

## Area Measure

| | |
|---|---|
| 144 square inches (in.$^2$) | 1 square foot (ft$^2$) |
| 9 square feet | 1 square yard (yd$^2$) |
| 30¼ square yards | 1 square rod |
| 160 square rods | 1 acre    4840 square yards   43,560 square feet |
| 640 acres | 1 square mile   1 section |
| 2.47 acres | 1 hectare (metric) |
| 0.7854 square mils | 1 circular mil   7.854($10^{-7}$) square inches |

## Volume Measure

| | |
|---|---|
| 1728 cubic inches | 1 cubic foot (ft$^3$) |
| 27 cubic feet | 1 cubic yard (yd$^3$) |
| 231 cubic inches | 1 standard gallon (U.S.) |
| 2150.42 cubic inches | 1 standard bushel |
| 144 cubic inches | 1 board foot |
| 61.02 cubic inches | 1 liter (metric) |

## Conversion Equivalents

| | |
|---|---|
| 1 atmosphere | 14.69 pounds per square inch (psi) |
| | 29.92 inches of mercury |
| | 406.8 inches of water |
| 1 British thermal unit | 252 calories (gram, at 15°C) |
| 1 British thermal unit | 778 foot-pounds (ft-lb)  0.00039 horsepower-hour |
| 1 calorie | 0.003968 British thermal unit |
| 1 cubic inch | 16.39 cubic centimeters  0.01639 liters |
| 1 foot-pound per second | 0.001818 horsepower (hp) |
| 1 horsepower | 746 watts       33,000 foot-pounds per minute |
| | 550 foot-pounds per second |
| 1 kilowatt | 1.34 horsepower |

Hydrostatic water pressure in pounds per square inch = (height in feet) (0.4332)

| | |
|---|---|
| 1 inch Hg (mercury) | 0.491 pound per square inch |
| 1 Joule | 1 watt second  0.737 foot-pound  $10^7$ ergs |
| | 9.48($10^{-4}$) Btu |
| 1 kilowatt-hour | 3413 British thermal unit |
| | 1.341 hp-hr |
| | 3.6($10^6$) Joule |
| 1 radian | 57.2958 degrees |
| 1 million electron volts (Mev) | 1.602($10^{-13}$) joule |

# COEFFICIENTS OF FRICTION

### Average Values

| SURFACES | STATIC | KINETIC |
|---|---|---|
| Metals on wood | 0.4 —0.63 | 0.35—0.60 |
| Wood on wood | 0.3 —0.5 | 0.25—0.4 |
| Leather on wood | 0.38—0.45 | 0.3 —0.35 |
| Iron on iron (wrought) | 0.4 —0.5 | 0.4 —0.5 |
| Glass on glass | 0.23—0.25 | 0.20—0.25 |
| Leather on glass | 0.35—0.38 | 0.33—0.35 |
| Wood on glass | 0.35—0.40 | 0.28—0.31 |
| Wood on sheet iron | 0.43—0.50 | 0.38—0.45 |
| Leather on sheet iron | 0.45—0.50 | 0.35—0.40 |
| Brass on wrought iron | 0.35—0.45 | 0.30—0.35 |
| Babbitt on steel | 0.35—0.40 | 0.30—0.35 |
| Steel on ice | 0.03—0.04 | 0.03—0.04 |

# THE GREEK ALPHABET

| A | $\alpha$ | Alpha | N | $\nu$ | Nu |
|---|---|---|---|---|---|
| B | $\beta$ | Bēta | Ξ | $\xi$ | Xī |
| Γ | $\gamma$ | Gamma | O | $o$ | Omicron |
| Δ | $\delta$ | Delta | Π | $\pi$ | Pī |
| E | $\epsilon$ | Epsilon | P | $\rho$ | Rhō |
| Z | $\zeta$ | Zēta | Σ | $\sigma\varsigma$ | Sigma |
| H | $\eta$ | Eta | T | $\tau$ | Tau |
| Θ | $\theta$ | Thēta | Υ | $\upsilon$ | Upsilon |
| I | $\iota$ | Iōta | Φ | $\phi$ | Phī |
| K | $\kappa$ | Kappa | X | $\chi$ | Chī |
| Λ | $\lambda$ | Lambda | Ψ | $\psi$ | Psī |
| M | $\mu$ | Mu | Ω | $\omega$ | Omega |

# DIMENSIONAL PREFIXES

| SYMBOL | PREFIX | MULTIPLE |
|---|---|---|
| T | tera units | $10^{12}$ |
| G | giga units | $10^9$ |
| M | mega units | $10^6$ |
| k | kilo units | $10^3$ |
| h | hecto units | $10^2$ |
| da | deca units | $10^1$ |
|  | units | $10^0$ |
| d | deci units | $10^{-1}$ |
| c | centi units | $10^{-2}$ |
| m | milli units | $10^{-3}$ |
| $\mu$ | micro units | $10^{-6}$ |
| n | nano units | $10^{-9}$ |
| p | pico units | $10^{-12}$ |
| f | femto units | $10^{-15}$ |
| a | atto units | $10^{-18}$ |

## SPECIFIC GRAVITIES AND SPECIFIC WEIGHTS (Average Values)

| Material | Specific Gravity | Average Specific Weight in $LB_f/FT^3$ | Material | Specific Gravity | Average Specific Weight in $LB_f/FT^3$ |
|---|---|---|---|---|---|
| Alcohol, ethyl | 0.792 | 49.6 | Limestone, crushed | 1.4—1.6 | 95 |
| Aluminum, cast | 2.65 | 166 | Marble | 2.5—2.8 | 166 |
| Air, S.T.P. | 0.001293 | 0.0806 | Mercury | 13.56 | 845 |
| Babbitt metal, soft | 9.75—10.65 | 625 | Nickel | 8.90 | 558 |
| Brass, cast, red | 8.4—8.7 | 530 | Oil, lubricating | 0.91 | 57 |
| Brick, common | 1.8—2.0 | 119 | Paraffin | 0.90 | 56 |
| Cement, portland, bags | 1.44 | 90 | Petroleum, crude | 0.88 | 55 |
| Chalk | 2.25 | 140 | Rubber | 1.25 | 78 |
| Clay, loose, wet | 1.7—1.8 | 110 | Sand, loose, wet | 1.9 | 120 |
| Coal, anthracite, solid | 1.4—1.8 | 95 | Sandstone, solid | 2.3 | 144 |
| Coal, bituminous, solid | 1.2—1.5 | 85 | Sea water | 1.03 | 64 |
| | | | Silver | 10.5 | 655 |
| Concrete, gravel, sand | 2.2—2.4 | 142 | Steel, structural | 7.9 | 490 |
| Copper, wire | 8.93 | 560 | Sulfur | 1.9—2.1 | 125 |
| Cork | 0.18—0.25 | 12.5 | Tin | 7.3 | 456 |
| Earth | 1.45—2.2 | 90—130 | Turpentine | 0.865 | 54 |
| Gasoline | 0.68—0.72 | 44 | Water, 4°C (39.2°F) | 1.000 | 62.43 |
| Glass, crown | 2.5—2.7 | 161 | Water, 100°C (212°F) | 0.96 | 59.83 |
| Glass, flint | 3.0—3.6 | 205 | Wood seasoned: | | |
| Glycerine | 1.25 | 78 | Cedar | 0.35—0.65 | 31 |
| Gold | 19.3 | 1205 | Cypress | 0.48—0.57 | 32 |
| Granite, solid | 2.5—3.0 | 172 | Ebony | 1.2—1.3 | 78 |
| Gravel, loose, wet | 1.45—1.90 | 105 | Fir | 0.51—0.60 | 35 |
| Ice | 0.911 | 57 | Hickory | 0.70—0.93 | 51 |
| Iron, gray cast | 7.00—7.12 | 450 | Mahogany | 0.56—0.85 | 44 |
| Iron, wrought | 7.6—7.9 | 480 | Maple | 0.68—0.80 | 45 |
| Kerosene | 0.8 | 50 | Oak | 0.70—0.90 | 50 |
| Lead | 11.34 | 710 | Pine, white | 0.38—0.48 | 28 |
| Limestone, solid | 2.5—2.9 | 168 | Pine, yellow | 0.65—0.75 | 44 |
| | | | Walnut | 0.60—0.70 | 41 |
| | | | Zinc | 7.14 | 445 |

NOTE: The value for the specific weight of water, which is usually used in problem solutions, is 62.4 $lb_f/ft^3$ or 8.34 $lb_f$ per gallon.

## TRIGONOMETRIC FUNCTIONS

$\sin(-\alpha) = -\sin\alpha$

$\cos(-\alpha) = \cos\alpha$

$\tan(-\alpha) = -\tan\alpha$

$\sin^2\alpha = \frac{1}{2} - \frac{1}{2}\cos 2\alpha$

$\cos^2\alpha = \frac{1}{2} + \frac{1}{2}\cos 2\alpha$

$\sin^2\alpha + \cos^2\alpha = 1$

$\sec^2\alpha = 1 + \tan^2\alpha$

$\csc^2\alpha = 1 + \operatorname{ctn}^2\alpha$

$\sin 2\alpha = 2\sin\alpha\cos\alpha$

$\cos 2\alpha = \cos^2\alpha - \sin^2\alpha = 1 - 2\sin^2\alpha = 2\cos^2\alpha - 1$

$$\sin\alpha = \alpha - \frac{\alpha^3}{3!} + \frac{\alpha^5}{5!} - \frac{\alpha^7}{7!} + \frac{\alpha^9}{9!} \cdots$$

$$\cos\alpha = 1 - \frac{\alpha^2}{2!} + \frac{\alpha^4}{4!} - \frac{\alpha^6}{6!} + \frac{\alpha^8}{8!} \cdots$$

$\sin(\alpha \pm \theta) = \sin\alpha\cos\theta \pm \cos\alpha\sin\theta$

$\cos(\alpha \pm \theta) = \cos\alpha\cos\theta \mp \sin\alpha\sin\theta$

## DIFFERENTIALS AND INTEGRALS

$$\frac{dx^n}{dx} = nx^{n-1}$$

$$\frac{d(uv)}{dx} = U\frac{dv}{dx} + V\frac{du}{dx}$$

$$\frac{d(u/v)}{dx} = \frac{V(du/dx) - U(dv/dx)}{v^2}$$

$$\int x^n dx = \frac{x^{n+1}}{n+1} + C$$

$$\int u\,dv = uv - \int v\,du$$

$$\int \frac{dx}{x} = \log_\epsilon x + C$$

$$\int \sin x\,dx = -\cos x + C$$

$$\int \cos x\,dx = \sin x + C$$

$$\int \sin^2 x\,dx = \frac{x}{2} - \frac{\sin 2x}{4} + C$$

$$\int \cos^2 x\,dx = \frac{x}{2} + \frac{\sin 2x}{4} + C$$

## SPECIAL PURPOSE FORMULAS USEFUL IN SOLVING UNIFORM MOTION PROBLEMS

### Legend

| | | | |
|---|---|---|---|
| $V$—velocity | $V_2$—final velocity | $S$—distance | $a$—acceleration |
| $V_1$—initial velocity | $V_{av}$—average velocity | $t$—time | |

| GIVEN | TO FIND | SUGGESTED FORMULAS |
|---|---|---|
| $V_1$, $V_2$, $t$ | $S$ | $S = \left( \dfrac{V_1 + V_2}{2} \right) t$ |
| $V_1$, $V_2$, $a$ | $S$ | $S = \dfrac{V_2^2 - V_1^2}{2a}$ |
| $V_1$, $a$, $t$ | $S$ | $S = V_1 t + \dfrac{at^2}{2}$ |
| $V_1$, $V_2$ | $V_{av}$ | $V_{av} = \dfrac{V_1 + V_2}{2}$ |
| $S$, $t$ | $V_{av}$ | $V_{av} = \dfrac{S}{t}$ |
| $V_2$, $a$, $t$ | $V_1$ | $V_1 = V_2 - at$ |
| $V_2$, $a$, $S$ | $V_1$ | $V_1 = \sqrt{V_2^2 - 2aS}$ |
| $S$, $a$, $t$ | $V_1$ | $V_1 = \dfrac{S}{t} - \dfrac{at}{2}$ |
| $V_1$, $a$, $t$ | $V_2$ | $V_2 = V_1 + at$ |
| $V_1$, $a$, $S$ | $V_2$ | $V_2 = \sqrt{V_1^2 + 2aS}$ |
| $V_1$, $S$, $t$ | $V_2$ | $V_2 = \dfrac{2S}{t} - V_1$ |
| $V_1$, $V_2$, $S$ | $t$ | $t = \dfrac{2S}{V_1 + V_2}$ |
| $V_1$, $a$, $S$ | $t$ | $t = \dfrac{-V_1 \pm \sqrt{V_1^2 + 2aS}}{a}$ |
| $V_1$, $V_2$, $a$ | $t$ | $t = \dfrac{V_2 - V_1}{a}$ |
| $V_1$, $V_2$, $t$ | $a$ | $a = \dfrac{V_2 - V_1}{t}$ |
| $V_1$, $V_2$, $S$ | $a$ | $a = \dfrac{V_2^2 - V_1^2}{2S}$ |
| $V_1$, $S$, $t$ | $a$ | $a = \dfrac{2S}{t^2} - \dfrac{2V_1}{t}$ |

## LOGARITHMS

| Natural Numbers | 0 | 1 | 2 | 3 | 4 | 5 | 6 | 7 | 8 | 9 | PROPORTIONAL PARTS | | | | | | | | |
|---|---|---|---|---|---|---|---|---|---|---|---|---|---|---|---|---|---|---|---|
| | | | | | | | | | | | 1 | 2 | 3 | 4 | 5 | 6 | 7 | 8 | 9 |
| 10 | 0000 | 0043 | 0086 | 0128 | 0170 | 0212 | 0253 | 0294 | 0334 | 0374 | 4 | 8 | 12 | 17 | 21 | 25 | 29 | 33 | 37 |
| 11 | 0414 | 0453 | 0492 | 0531 | 0569 | 0607 | 0645 | 0682 | 0719 | 0755 | 4 | 8 | 11 | 15 | 19 | 23 | 26 | 30 | 34 |
| 12 | 0792 | 0828 | 0864 | 0899 | 0934 | 0969 | 1004 | 1038 | 1072 | 1106 | 3 | 7 | 10 | 14 | 17 | 21 | 24 | 28 | 31 |
| 13 | 1139 | 1173 | 1206 | 1239 | 1271 | 1303 | 1335 | 1367 | 1399 | 1430 | 3 | 6 | 10 | 13 | 16 | 19 | 23 | 26 | 29 |
| 14 | 1461 | 1492 | 1523 | 1553 | 1584 | 1614 | 1644 | 1673 | 1703 | 1732 | 3 | 6 | 9 | 12 | 15 | 18 | 21 | 24 | 27 |
| 15 | 1761 | 1790 | 1818 | 1847 | 1875 | 1903 | 1931 | 1959 | 1987 | 2014 | 3 | 6 | 8 | 11 | 14 | 17 | 20 | 22 | 25 |
| 16 | 2041 | 2068 | 2095 | 2122 | 2148 | 2175 | 2201 | 2227 | 2253 | 2279 | 3 | 5 | 8 | 11 | 13 | 16 | 18 | 21 | 24 |
| 17 | 2304 | 2330 | 2355 | 2380 | 2405 | 2430 | 2455 | 2480 | 2504 | 2529 | 2 | 5 | 7 | 10 | 12 | 15 | 17 | 20 | 22 |
| 18 | 2553 | 2577 | 2601 | 2625 | 2648 | 2672 | 2695 | 2718 | 2742 | 2765 | 2 | 5 | 7 | 9 | 12 | 14 | 16 | 19 | 21 |
| 19 | 2788 | 2810 | 2833 | 2856 | 2878 | 2900 | 2923 | 2945 | 2967 | 2989 | 2 | 4 | 7 | 9 | 11 | 13 | 16 | 18 | 20 |
| 20 | 3010 | 3032 | 3054 | 3075 | 3096 | 3118 | 3139 | 3160 | 3181 | 3201 | 2 | 4 | 6 | 8 | 11 | 13 | 15 | 17 | 19 |
| 21 | 3222 | 3243 | 3263 | 3284 | 3304 | 3324 | 3345 | 3365 | 3385 | 3404 | 2 | 4 | 6 | 8 | 10 | 12 | 14 | 16 | 18 |
| 22 | 3424 | 3444 | 3464 | 3483 | 3502 | 3522 | 3541 | 3560 | 3579 | 3598 | 2 | 4 | 6 | 8 | 10 | 12 | 14 | 15 | 17 |
| 23 | 3617 | 3636 | 3655 | 3674 | 3692 | 3711 | 3729 | 3747 | 3766 | 3784 | 2 | 4 | 6 | 7 | 9 | 11 | 13 | 15 | 17 |
| 24 | 3802 | 3820 | 3838 | 3856 | 3874 | 3892 | 3909 | 3927 | 3945 | 3962 | 2 | 4 | 5 | 7 | 9 | 11 | 12 | 14 | 16 |
| 25 | 3979 | 3997 | 4014 | 4031 | 4048 | 4065 | 4082 | 4099 | 4116 | 4133 | 2 | 3 | 5 | 7 | 9 | 10 | 12 | 14 | 15 |
| 26 | 4150 | 4166 | 4183 | 4200 | 4216 | 4232 | 4249 | 4265 | 4281 | 4298 | 2 | 3 | 5 | 7 | 8 | 10 | 11 | 13 | 15 |
| 27 | 4314 | 4330 | 4346 | 4362 | 4378 | 4393 | 4409 | 4425 | 4440 | 4456 | 2 | 3 | 5 | 6 | 8 | 9 | 11 | 13 | 14 |
| 28 | 4472 | 4487 | 4502 | 4518 | 4533 | 4548 | 4564 | 4579 | 4594 | 4609 | 2 | 3 | 5 | 6 | 8 | 9 | 11 | 12 | 14 |
| 29 | 4624 | 4639 | 4654 | 4669 | 4683 | 4698 | 4713 | 4728 | 4742 | 4757 | 1 | 3 | 4 | 6 | 7 | 9 | 10 | 12 | 13 |
| 30 | 4771 | 4786 | 4800 | 4814 | 4829 | 4843 | 4857 | 4871 | 4886 | 4900 | 1 | 3 | 4 | 6 | 7 | 9 | 10 | 11 | 13 |
| 31 | 4914 | 4928 | 4942 | 4955 | 4969 | 4983 | 4997 | 5011 | 5024 | 5038 | 1 | 3 | 4 | 6 | 7 | 8 | 10 | 11 | 12 |
| 32 | 5051 | 5065 | 5079 | 5092 | 5105 | 5119 | 5132 | 5145 | 5159 | 5172 | 1 | 3 | 4 | 5 | 7 | 8 | 9 | 11 | 12 |
| 33 | 5185 | 5198 | 5211 | 5224 | 5237 | 5250 | 5263 | 5276 | 5289 | 5302 | 1 | 3 | 4 | 5 | 6 | 8 | 9 | 10 | 12 |
| 34 | 5315 | 5328 | 5340 | 5353 | 5366 | 5378 | 5391 | 5403 | 5416 | 5428 | 1 | 3 | 4 | 5 | 6 | 8 | 9 | 10 | 11 |
| 35 | 5441 | 5453 | 5465 | 5478 | 5490 | 5502 | 5514 | 5527 | 5539 | 5551 | 1 | 2 | 4 | 5 | 6 | 7 | 9 | 10 | 11 |
| 36 | 5563 | 5575 | 5587 | 5599 | 5611 | 5623 | 5635 | 5647 | 5658 | 5670 | 1 | 2 | 4 | 5 | 6 | 7 | 8 | 10 | 11 |
| 37 | 5682 | 5694 | 5705 | 5717 | 5729 | 5740 | 5752 | 5763 | 5775 | 5786 | 1 | 2 | 3 | 5 | 6 | 7 | 8 | 9 | 10 |
| 38 | 5798 | 5809 | 5821 | 5832 | 5843 | 5855 | 5866 | 5877 | 5888 | 5899 | 1 | 2 | 3 | 5 | 6 | 7 | 8 | 9 | 10 |
| 39 | 5911 | 5922 | 5933 | 5944 | 5955 | 5966 | 5977 | 5988 | 5999 | 6010 | 1 | 2 | 3 | 4 | 5 | 7 | 8 | 9 | 10 |
| 40 | 6021 | 6031 | 6042 | 6053 | 6064 | 6075 | 6085 | 6096 | 6107 | 6117 | 1 | 2 | 3 | 4 | 5 | 6 | 8 | 9 | 10 |
| 41 | 6128 | 6138 | 6149 | 6160 | 6170 | 6180 | 6191 | 6201 | 6212 | 6222 | 1 | 2 | 3 | 4 | 5 | 6 | 7 | 8 | 9 |
| 42 | 6232 | 6243 | 6253 | 6263 | 6274 | 6284 | 6294 | 6304 | 6314 | 6325 | 1 | 2 | 3 | 4 | 5 | 6 | 7 | 8 | 9 |
| 43 | 6335 | 6345 | 6355 | 6365 | 6375 | 6385 | 6395 | 6405 | 6415 | 6425 | 1 | 2 | 3 | 4 | 5 | 6 | 7 | 8 | 9 |
| 44 | 6435 | 6444 | 6454 | 6464 | 6474 | 6484 | 6493 | 6503 | 6513 | 6522 | 1 | 2 | 3 | 4 | 5 | 6 | 7 | 8 | 9 |
| 45 | 6532 | 6542 | 6551 | 6561 | 6571 | 6580 | 6590 | 6599 | 6609 | 6618 | 1 | 2 | 3 | 4 | 5 | 6 | 7 | 8 | 9 |
| 46 | 6628 | 6637 | 6646 | 6656 | 6665 | 6675 | 6684 | 6693 | 6702 | 6712 | 1 | 2 | 3 | 4 | 5 | 6 | 7 | 7 | 8 |
| 47 | 6721 | 6730 | 6739 | 6749 | 6758 | 6767 | 6776 | 6785 | 6794 | 6803 | 1 | 2 | 3 | 4 | 5 | 5 | 6 | 7 | 8 |
| 48 | 6812 | 6821 | 6830 | 6839 | 6848 | 6857 | 6866 | 6875 | 6884 | 6893 | 1 | 2 | 3 | 4 | 4 | 5 | 6 | 7 | 8 |
| 49 | 6902 | 6911 | 6920 | 6928 | 6937 | 6946 | 6955 | 6964 | 6972 | 6981 | 1 | 2 | 3 | 4 | 4 | 5 | 6 | 7 | 8 |
| 50 | 6990 | 6998 | 7007 | 7016 | 7024 | 7033 | 7042 | 7050 | 7059 | 7067 | 1 | 2 | 3 | 3 | 4 | 5 | 6 | 7 | 8 |
| 51 | 7076 | 7084 | 7093 | 7101 | 7110 | 7118 | 7126 | 7135 | 7143 | 7152 | 1 | 2 | 3 | 3 | 4 | 5 | 6 | 7 | 8 |
| 52 | 7160 | 7168 | 7177 | 7185 | 7193 | 7202 | 7210 | 7218 | 7226 | 7235 | 1 | 2 | 2 | 3 | 4 | 5 | 6 | 7 | 7 |
| 53 | 7243 | 7251 | 7259 | 7267 | 7275 | 7284 | 7292 | 7300 | 7308 | 7316 | 1 | 2 | 2 | 3 | 4 | 5 | 6 | 6 | 7 |
| 54 | 7324 | 7332 | 7340 | 7348 | 7356 | 7364 | 7372 | 7380 | 7388 | 7396 | 1 | 2 | 2 | 3 | 4 | 5 | 6 | 6 | 7 |

## LOGARITHMS (continued)

| Natural Numbers | 0 | 1 | 2 | 3 | 4 | 5 | 6 | 7 | 8 | 9 | PROPORTIONAL PARTS | | | | | | | | |
|---|---|---|---|---|---|---|---|---|---|---|---|---|---|---|---|---|---|---|---|
| | | | | | | | | | | | 1 | 2 | 3 | 4 | 5 | 6 | 7 | 8 | 9 |
| 55 | 7404 | 7412 | 7419 | 7427 | 7435 | 7443 | 7451 | 7459 | 7466 | 7474 | 1 | 2 | 2 | 3 | 4 | 5 | 5 | 6 | 7 |
| 56 | 7482 | 7490 | 7497 | 7505 | 7513 | 7520 | 7528 | 7536 | 7543 | 7551 | 1 | 2 | 2 | 3 | 4 | 5 | 5 | 6 | 7 |
| 57 | 7559 | 7566 | 7574 | 7582 | 7589 | 7597 | 7604 | 7612 | 7619 | 7627 | 1 | 2 | 2 | 3 | 4 | 5 | 5 | 6 | 7 |
| 58 | 7634 | 7642 | 7649 | 7657 | 7664 | 7672 | 7679 | 7686 | 7694 | 7701 | 1 | 1 | 2 | 3 | 4 | 4 | 5 | 6 | 7 |
| 59 | 7709 | 7716 | 7723 | 7731 | 7738 | 7745 | 7752 | 7760 | 7767 | 7774 | 1 | 1 | 2 | 3 | 4 | 4 | 5 | 6 | 7 |
| 60 | 7782 | 7789 | 7796 | 7803 | 7810 | 7818 | 7825 | 7832 | 7839 | 7846 | 1 | 1 | 2 | 3 | 4 | 4 | 5 | 6 | 6 |
| 61 | 7853 | 7860 | 7868 | 7875 | 7882 | 7889 | 7896 | 7903 | 7910 | 7917 | 1 | 1 | 2 | 3 | 4 | 4 | 5 | 6 | 6 |
| 62 | 7924 | 7931 | 7938 | 7945 | 7952 | 7959 | 7966 | 7973 | 7980 | 7987 | 1 | 1 | 2 | 3 | 4 | 5 | 6 | 6 | 6 |
| 63 | 7993 | 8000 | 8007 | 8014 | 8021 | 8028 | 8035 | 8041 | 8048 | 8055 | 1 | 1 | 2 | 3 | 3 | 4 | 5 | 5 | 6 |
| 64 | 8062 | 8069 | 8075 | 8082 | 8089 | 8096 | 8102 | 8109 | 8116 | 8122 | 1 | 1 | 2 | 3 | 3 | 4 | 5 | 5 | 6 |
| 65 | 8129 | 8136 | 8142 | 8149 | 8156 | 8162 | 8169 | 8176 | 8182 | 8189 | 1 | 1 | 2 | 3 | 3 | 4 | 5 | 5 | 6 |
| 66 | 8195 | 8202 | 8209 | 8215 | 8222 | 8228 | 8235 | 8241 | 8248 | 8254 | 1 | 1 | 2 | 3 | 3 | 4 | 5 | 5 | 6 |
| 67 | 8261 | 8267 | 8274 | 8280 | 8287 | 8293 | 8299 | 8306 | 8312 | 8319 | 1 | 1 | 2 | 3 | 3 | 4 | 5 | 5 | 6 |
| 68 | 8325 | 8331 | 8338 | 8344 | 8351 | 8357 | 8363 | 8370 | 8376 | 8382 | 1 | 1 | 2 | 3 | 3 | 4 | 4 | 5 | 6 |
| 69 | 8388 | 8395 | 8401 | 8407 | 8414 | 8420 | 8426 | 8432 | 8439 | 8445 | 1 | 1 | 2 | 2 | 3 | 4 | 4 | 5 | 6 |
| 70 | 8451 | 8457 | 8463 | 8470 | 8476 | 8482 | 8488 | 8494 | 8500 | 8506 | 1 | 1 | 2 | 2 | 3 | 4 | 4 | 5 | 6 |
| 71 | 8513 | 8519 | 8525 | 8531 | 8537 | 8543 | 8549 | 8555 | 8561 | 8567 | 1 | 1 | 2 | 2 | 3 | 4 | 4 | 5 | 5 |
| 72 | 8573 | 8579 | 8585 | 8591 | 8597 | 8603 | 8609 | 8615 | 8621 | 8627 | 1 | 1 | 2 | 2 | 3 | 4 | 4 | 5 | 5 |
| 73 | 8633 | 8639 | 8645 | 8651 | 8657 | 8663 | 8669 | 8675 | 8681 | 8686 | 1 | 1 | 2 | 2 | 3 | 4 | 4 | 5 | 5 |
| 74 | 8692 | 8698 | 8704 | 8710 | 8716 | 8722 | 8727 | 8733 | 8739 | 8745 | 1 | 1 | 2 | 2 | 3 | 4 | 4 | 5 | 5 |
| 75 | 8751 | 8756 | 8762 | 8768 | 8774 | 8779 | 8785 | 8791 | 8797 | 8802 | 1 | 1 | 2 | 2 | 3 | 3 | 4 | 5 | 5 |
| 76 | 8808 | 8814 | 8820 | 8825 | 8831 | 8837 | 8842 | 8848 | 8854 | 8859 | 1 | 1 | 2 | 2 | 3 | 3 | 4 | 5 | 5 |
| 77 | 8865 | 8871 | 8876 | 8882 | 8887 | 8893 | 8899 | 8904 | 8910 | 8915 | 1 | 1 | 2 | 2 | 3 | 3 | 4 | 4 | 5 |
| 78 | 8921 | 8927 | 8932 | 8938 | 8943 | 8949 | 8954 | 8960 | 8965 | 8971 | 1 | 1 | 2 | 2 | 3 | 3 | 4 | 4 | 5 |
| 79 | 8976 | 8982 | 8987 | 8993 | 8998 | 9004 | 9009 | 9015 | 9020 | 9026 | 1 | 1 | 2 | 2 | 3 | 3 | 4 | 4 | 5 |
| 80 | 9031 | 9036 | 9042 | 9047 | 9053 | 9058 | 9063 | 9069 | 9074 | 9079 | 1 | 1 | 2 | 2 | 3 | 3 | 4 | 4 | 5 |
| 81 | 9085 | 9090 | 9096 | 9101 | 9106 | 9112 | 9117 | 9122 | 9128 | 9133 | 1 | 1 | 2 | 2 | 3 | 3 | 4 | 4 | 5 |
| 82 | 9138 | 9143 | 9149 | 9154 | 9159 | 9165 | 9170 | 9175 | 9180 | 9186 | 1 | 1 | 2 | 2 | 3 | 3 | 4 | 4 | 5 |
| 83 | 9191 | 9196 | 9201 | 9206 | 9212 | 9217 | 9222 | 9227 | 9232 | 9238 | 1 | 1 | 2 | 2 | 3 | 3 | 4 | 4 | 5 |
| 84 | 9243 | 9248 | 9253 | 9258 | 9263 | 9269 | 9274 | 9279 | 9284 | 9289 | 1 | 1 | 2 | 2 | 3 | 3 | 4 | 4 | 5 |
| 85 | 9294 | 9299 | 9304 | 9309 | 9315 | 9320 | 9325 | 9330 | 9335 | 9340 | 1 | 1 | 2 | 2 | 3 | 3 | 4 | 4 | 5 |
| 86 | 9345 | 9350 | 9355 | 9360 | 9365 | 9370 | 9375 | 9380 | 9385 | 9390 | 1 | 1 | 2 | 2 | 3 | 3 | 4 | 4 | 5 |
| 87 | 9395 | 9400 | 9405 | 9410 | 9415 | 9420 | 9425 | 9430 | 9435 | 9440 | 0 | 1 | 1 | 2 | 2 | 3 | 3 | 4 | 4 |
| 88 | 9445 | 9450 | 9455 | 9460 | 9465 | 9469 | 9474 | 9479 | 9484 | 9489 | 0 | 1 | 1 | 2 | 2 | 3 | 3 | 4 | 4 |
| 89 | 9494 | 9499 | 9504 | 9509 | 9513 | 9518 | 9523 | 9528 | 9533 | 9538 | 0 | 1 | 1 | 2 | 2 | 3 | 3 | 4 | 4 |
| 90 | 9542 | 9547 | 9552 | 9557 | 9562 | 9566 | 9571 | 9576 | 9581 | 9586 | 0 | 1 | 1 | 2 | 2 | 3 | 3 | 4 | 4 |
| 91 | 9590 | 9595 | 9600 | 9605 | 9609 | 9614 | 9619 | 9624 | 9628 | 9633 | 0 | 1 | 1 | 2 | 2 | 3 | 3 | 4 | 4 |
| 92 | 9638 | 9643 | 9647 | 9652 | 9657 | 9661 | 9666 | 9671 | 9675 | 9680 | 0 | 1 | 1 | 2 | 2 | 3 | 3 | 4 | 4 |
| 93 | 9685 | 9689 | 9694 | 9699 | 9703 | 9708 | 9713 | 9717 | 9722 | 9727 | 0 | 1 | 1 | 2 | 2 | 3 | 3 | 4 | 4 |
| 94 | 9731 | 9736 | 9741 | 9745 | 9750 | 9754 | 9759 | 9763 | 9768 | 9773 | 0 | 1 | 1 | 2 | 2 | 3 | 3 | 4 | 4 |
| 95 | 9777 | 9782 | 9786 | 9791 | 9795 | 9800 | 9805 | 9809 | 9814 | 9818 | 0 | 1 | 1 | 2 | 2 | 3 | 3 | 4 | 4 |
| 96 | 9823 | 9827 | 9832 | 9836 | 9841 | 9845 | 9850 | 9854 | 9859 | 9863 | 0 | 1 | 1 | 2 | 2 | 3 | 3 | 4 | 4 |
| 97 | 9868 | 9872 | 9877 | 9881 | 9886 | 9890 | 9894 | 9899 | 9903 | 9908 | 0 | 1 | 1 | 2 | 2 | 3 | 3 | 4 | 4 |
| 98 | 9912 | 9917 | 9921 | 9926 | 9930 | 9934 | 9939 | 9943 | 9948 | 9952 | 0 | 1 | 1 | 2 | 2 | 3 | 3 | 4 | 4 |
| 99 | 9956 | 9961 | 9965 | 9969 | 9974 | 9978 | 9983 | 9987 | 9991 | 9996 | 0 | 1 | 1 | 2 | 2 | 3 | 3 | 3 | 4 |

## TRIGONOMETRIC FUNCTIONS

| Angle $\theta$ Degrees | Radians | $\cos \theta$ | $\sin \theta$ | $\tan \theta$ | $\sec \theta$ | $\csc \theta$ | $\cot \theta$ | | |
|---|---|---|---|---|---|---|---|---|---|
| 0° 00′ | .0000 | 1.0000 | .0000 | .0000 | 1.000 | No value | No value | 1.5708 | 90° 00′ |
| 10 | 029 | 000 | 029 | 029 | 000 | 343.8 | 343.8 | 679 | 50 |
| 20 | 058 | 000 | 058 | 058 | 000 | 171.9 | 171.9 | 650 | 40 |
| 30 | 087 | 1.0000 | 087 | 087 | 000 | 114.6 | 114.6 | 621 | 30 |
| 40 | 116 | .9999 | 116 | 116 | 000 | 85.95 | 85.94 | 592 | 20 |
| 50 | 145 | 999 | 145 | 145 | 000 | 68.76 | 68.75 | 563 | 10 |
| 1° 00′ | .0175 | .9998 | .0175 | .0175 | 1.000 | 57.30 | 57.29 | 1.5533 | 89° 00′ |
| 10 | 204 | 998 | 204 | 204 | 000 | 49.11 | 49.10 | 504 | 50 |
| 20 | 233 | 997 | 233 | 233 | 000 | 42.98 | 42.96 | 475 | 40 |
| 30 | 262 | 997 | 262 | 262 | 000 | 38.20 | 38.19 | 446 | 30 |
| 40 | 291 | 996 | 291 | 291 | 000 | 34.38 | 34.37 | 417 | 20 |
| 50 | 320 | 995 | 320 | 320 | 001 | 31.26 | 31.24 | 388 | 10 |
| 2° 00′ | .0349 | .9994 | .0349 | .0349 | 1.001 | 28.65 | 28.64 | 1.5359 | 88° 00′ |
| 10 | 378 | 993 | 378 | 378 | 001 | 26.45 | 26.43 | 330 | 50 |
| 20 | 407 | 992 | 407 | 407 | 001 | 24.56 | 24.54 | 301 | 40 |
| 30 | 436 | 990 | 436 | 437 | 001 | 22.93 | 22.90 | 272 | 30 |
| 40 | 465 | 989 | 465 | 466 | 001 | 21.49 | 21.47 | 243 | 20 |
| 50 | 495 | 988 | 494 | 495 | 001 | 20.23 | 20.21 | 213 | 10 |
| 3° 00′ | .0524 | .9986 | .0523 | .0524 | 1.001 | 19.11 | 19.08 | 1.5184 | 87° 00′ |
| 10 | 553 | 985 | 552 | 553 | 002 | 18.10 | 18.07 | 155 | 50 |
| 20 | 582 | 983 | 581 | 582 | 002 | 17.20 | 17.17 | 126 | 40 |
| 30 | 611 | 981 | 610 | 612 | 002 | 16.38 | 16.35 | 097 | 30 |
| 40 | 640 | 980 | 640 | 641 | 002 | 15.64 | 15.60 | 068 | 20 |
| 50 | 669 | 978 | 669 | 670 | 002 | 14.96 | 14.92 | 039 | 10 |
| 4° 00′ | .0698 | .9976 | .0698 | .0699 | 1.002 | 14.34 | 14.30 | 1.5010 | 86° 00′ |
| 10 | 727 | 974 | 727 | 729 | 003 | 13.76 | 13.73 | 981 | 50 |
| 20 | 765 | 971 | 756 | 758 | 003 | 13.23 | 13.20 | 952 | 40 |
| 30 | 785 | 969 | 785 | 787 | 003 | 12.75 | 12.71 | 923 | 30 |
| 40 | 814 | 967 | 814 | 816 | 003 | 12.29 | 12.25 | 893 | 20 |
| 50 | 844 | 964 | 843 | 846 | 004 | 11.87 | 11.83 | 864 | 10 |
| 5° 00′ | .0873 | .9962 | .0872 | .0875 | 1.004 | 11.47 | 11.43 | 1.4835 | 85° 00′ |
| 10 | 902 | 959 | 901 | 904 | 004 | 11.10 | 11.06 | 806 | 50 |
| 20 | 931 | 957 | 929 | 934 | 004 | 10.76 | 10.71 | 777 | 40 |
| 30 | 960 | 954 | 958 | 963 | 005 | 10.43 | 10.39 | 748 | 30 |
| 40 | .0989 | 951 | .0987 | .0992 | 005 | 10.13 | 10.08 | 719 | 20 |
| 50 | .1018 | 948 | .1016 | .1022 | 005 | 9.839 | 9.788 | 690 | 10 |
| 6° 00′ | .1047 | .9945 | .1045 | .1051 | 1.006 | 9.567 | 9.514 | 1.4661 | 84° 00′ |
| 10 | 076 | 942 | 074 | 080 | 006 | 9.309 | 9.255 | 632 | 50 |
| 20 | 105 | 939 | 103 | 110 | 006 | 9.065 | 9.010 | 603 | 40 |
| 30 | 134 | 936 | 132 | 139 | 006 | 8.834 | 8.777 | 573 | 30 |
| 40 | 164 | 932 | 161 | 169 | 007 | 8.614 | 8.556 | 544 | 20 |
| 50 | 193 | 929 | 190 | 198 | 007 | 8.405 | 8.345 | 515 | 10 |
| 7° 00′ | .1222 | .9925 | .1219 | .1228 | 1.008 | 8.206 | 8.144 | 1.4486 | 83° 00′ |
| 10 | 251 | 922 | 248 | 257 | 008 | 8.016 | 7.953 | 457 | 50 |
| 20 | 280 | 918 | 276 | 287 | 008 | 7.834 | 7.770 | 428 | 40 |
| 30 | 309 | 914 | 305 | 317 | 009 | 7.661 | 7.596 | 399 | 30 |
| 40 | 338 | 911 | 334 | 346 | 009 | 7.496 | 7.429 | 370 | 20 |
| 50 | 367 | 907 | 363 | 376 | 009 | 7.337 | 7.269 | 341 | 10 |
| 8° 00′ | .1396 | .9903 | .1392 | .1405 | 1.010 | 7.185 | 7.115 | 1.4312 | 82° 00′ |
| | | $\sin \theta$ | $\cos \theta$ | $\cot \theta$ | $\csc \theta$ | $\sec \theta$ | $\tan \theta$ | Radians | Degrees |
| | | | | | | | | Angle $\theta$ | |

## TRIGONOMETRIC FUNCTIONS (continued)

| Angle θ Degrees | Radians | cos θ | sin θ | tan θ | sec θ | csc θ | cot θ | | |
|---|---|---|---|---|---|---|---|---|---|
| 8° 00′ | .1396 | .9903 | .1392 | .1405 | 1.010 | 7.185 | 7.115 | 1.4312 | 82° 00′ |
| 10 | 425 | 899 | 421 | 435 | 010 | 7.040 | 6.968 | 283 | 50 |
| 20 | 454 | 894 | 449 | 465 | 011 | 6.900 | 827 | 254 | 40 |
| 30 | 484 | 890 | 478 | 495 | 011 | 765 | 691 | 224 | 30 |
| 40 | 513 | 886 | 507 | 524 | 012 | 636 | 561 | 195 | 20 |
| 50 | 542 | 881 | 536 | 554 | 012 | 512 | 435 | 166 | 10 |
| 9° 00′ | .1571 | .9877 | .1564 | .1584 | 1.012 | 6.392 | 6.314 | 1.4137 | 81° 00′ |
| 10 | 600 | 872 | 593 | 614 | 013 | 277 | 197 | 108 | 50 |
| 20 | 629 | 868 | 622 | 644 | 013 | 166 | 6.084 | 079 | 40 |
| 30 | 658 | 863 | 650 | 673 | 014 | 6.059 | 5.976 | 050 | 30 |
| 40 | 687 | 858 | 679 | 703 | 014 | 5.955 | 871 | 1.4021 | 20 |
| 50 | 716 | 853 | 708 | 733 | 015 | 855 | 769 | 1.3992 | 10 |
| 10° 00′ | .1745 | .9848 | .1736 | .1763 | 1.015 | 5.759 | 5.671 | 1.3963 | 80° 00′ |
| 10 | 774 | 843 | 765 | 793 | 016 | 665 | 576 | 934 | 50 |
| 20 | 804 | 838 | 794 | 823 | 016 | 575 | 485 | 904 | 40 |
| 30 | 833 | 833 | 822 | 853 | 017 | 487 | 396 | 875 | 30 |
| 40 | 862 | 827 | 851 | 883 | 018 | 403 | 309 | 846 | 20 |
| 50 | 891 | 822 | 880 | 914 | 018 | 320 | 226 | 817 | 10 |
| 11° 00′ | .1920 | .9816 | .1908 | .1944 | 1.019 | 5.241 | 5.145 | 1.3788 | 79° 00′ |
| 10 | 949 | 811 | 937 | .1974 | 019 | 164 | 5.066 | 759 | 50 |
| 20 | .1978 | 805 | 965 | .2004 | 020 | 089 | 4.989 | 730 | 40 |
| 30 | .2007 | 799 | .1994 | 035 | 020 | 5.016 | 915 | 701 | 30 |
| 40 | 036 | 793 | .2022 | 065 | 021 | 4.945 | 843 | 672 | 20 |
| 50 | 065 | 787 | 051 | 095 | 022 | 876 | 773 | 643 | 10 |
| 12° 00′ | .2094 | .9781 | .2079 | .2126 | 1.022 | 4.810 | 4.705 | 1.3614 | 78° 00′ |
| 10 | 123 | 775 | 108 | 156 | 023 | 745 | 638 | 584 | 50 |
| 20 | 153 | 769 | 136 | 186 | 024 | 682 | 574 | 555 | 40 |
| 30 | 182 | 763 | 164 | 217 | 024 | 620 | 511 | 526 | 30 |
| 40 | 211 | 757 | 193 | 247 | 025 | 560 | 449 | 497 | 20 |
| 50 | 240 | 750 | 221 | 278 | 026 | 502 | 390 | 468 | 10 |
| 13° 00′ | .2269 | .9744 | .2250 | .2309 | 1.026 | 4.445 | 4.331 | 1.3439 | 77° 00′ |
| 10 | 298 | 737 | 278 | 339 | 027 | 390 | 275 | 410 | 50 |
| 20 | 327 | 730 | 306 | 370 | 028 | 336 | 219 | 381 | 40 |
| 30 | 356 | 724 | 334 | 401 | 028 | 284 | 165 | 352 | 30 |
| 40 | 385 | 717 | 363 | 432 | 029 | 232 | 113 | 323 | 20 |
| 50 | 414 | 710 | 391 | 462 | 030 | 182 | 061 | 294 | 10 |
| 14° 00′ | .2443 | .9703 | .2419 | .2493 | 1.031 | 4.134 | 4.011 | 1.3265 | 76° 00′ |
| 10 | 473 | 696 | 447 | 524 | 031 | 086 | 3.962 | 235 | 50 |
| 20 | 502 | 689 | 476 | 555 | 032 | 4.039 | 914 | 206 | 40 |
| 30 | 531 | 681 | 504 | 586 | 033 | 3.994 | 867 | 177 | 30 |
| 40 | 560 | 674 | 532 | 617 | 034 | 950 | 821 | 148 | 20 |
| 50 | 589 | 667 | 560 | 648 | 034 | 906 | 776 | 119 | 10 |
| 15° 00′ | .2618 | .9659 | .2588 | .2679 | 1.035 | 3.864 | 3.732 | 1.3090 | 75° 00′ |
| 10 | 647 | 652 | 616 | 711 | 036 | 822 | 689 | 061 | 50 |
| 20 | 676 | 644 | 644 | 742 | 037 | 782 | 647 | 032 | 40 |
| 30 | 705 | 636 | 672 | 773 | 038 | 742 | 606 | 1.3003 | 30 |
| 40 | 734 | 628 | 700 | 805 | 039 | 703 | 566 | 1.2974 | 20 |
| 50 | 763 | 621 | 728 | 836 | 039 | 665 | 526 | 945 | 10 |
| 16° 00′ | .2793 | .9613 | .2756 | .2867 | 1.040 | 3.628 | 3.487 | 1.2915 | 74° 00′ |

| | sin θ | cos θ | cot θ | csc θ | sec θ | tan θ | Radians | Degrees |
|---|---|---|---|---|---|---|---|---|
| | | | | | | | Angle θ | |

## TRIGONOMETRIC FUNCTIONS (continued)

| Angle Degrees | Radians | $\cos \theta$ | $\sin \theta$ | $\tan \theta$ | $\sec \theta$ | $\csc \theta$ | $\cot \theta$ | | |
|---|---|---|---|---|---|---|---|---|---|
| 16° 00′ | .2793 | .9613 | .2756 | .2867 | 1.040 | 3.628 | 3.487 | 1.2915 | 74° 00′ |
| 10 | 822 | 605 | 784 | 899 | 041 | 592 | 450 | 886 | 50 |
| 20 | 851 | 596 | 812 | 931 | 042 | 556 | 412 | 857 | 40 |
| 30 | 880 | 588 | 840 | 962 | 043 | 521 | 376 | 828 | 30 |
| 40 | 909 | 580 | 868 | .2944 | 044 | 487 | 340 | 799 | 20 |
| 50 | 938 | 572 | 896 | .3026 | 045 | 453 | 305 | 770 | 10 |
| 17° 00′ | .2967 | .9563 | .2924 | .3057 | 1.046 | 3.420 | 3.271 | 1.2741 | 73° 00′ |
| 10 | .2996 | 555 | 952 | 089 | 047 | 388 | 237 | 712 | 50 |
| 20 | .3025 | 546 | .2979 | 121 | 048 | 357 | 204 | 683 | 40 |
| 30 | 054 | 537 | .3007 | 153 | 048 | 326 | 172 | 654 | 30 |
| 40 | 083 | 528 | 035 | 185 | 049 | 295 | 140 | 625 | 20 |
| 50 | 113 | 520 | 062 | 217 | 050 | 265 | 108 | 595 | 10 |
| 18° 00′ | .3142 | .9511 | .3090 | .3249 | 1.051 | 3.236 | 3.078 | 1.2566 | 72° 00′ |
| 10 | 171 | 502 | 118 | 281 | 052 | 207 | 047 | 537 | 50 |
| 20 | 200 | 492 | 145 | 314 | 053 | 179 | 3.018 | 508 | 40 |
| 30 | 229 | 483 | 173 | 346 | 054 | 152 | 2.989 | 479 | 30 |
| 40 | 258 | 474 | 201 | 378 | 056 | 124 | 960 | 450 | 20 |
| 50 | 287 | 465 | 228 | 411 | 057 | 098 | 932 | 421 | 10 |
| 19° 00′ | .3316 | .9455 | .3256 | .3443 | 1.058 | 3.072 | 2.904 | 1.2392 | 71° 00′ |
| 10 | 345 | 446 | 283 | 476 | 059 | 046 | 877 | 363 | 50 |
| 20 | 374 | 436 | 311 | 508 | 060 | 3.021 | 850 | 334 | 40 |
| 30 | 403 | 426 | 338 | 541 | 061 | 2.996 | 824 | 305 | 30 |
| 40 | 432 | 417 | 365 | 574 | 062 | 971 | 798 | 275 | 20 |
| 50 | 462 | 407 | 393 | 607 | 063 | 947 | 773 | 246 | 10 |
| 20° 00′ | .3491 | .9397 | .3420 | .3640 | .1064 | 2.924 | 2.747 | 1.2217 | 70° 00′ |
| 10 | 520 | 387 | 448 | 673 | 065 | 901 | 723 | 188 | 50 |
| 20 | 549 | 377 | 475 | 706 | 066 | 878 | 699 | 159 | 40 |
| 30 | 578 | 367 | 502 | 739 | 068 | 855 | 675 | 130 | 30 |
| 40 | 607 | 356 | 529 | 772 | 069 | 833 | 651 | 101 | 20 |
| 50 | 636 | 346 | 557 | 805 | 070 | 812 | 628 | 072 | 10 |
| 21° 00′ | .3665 | .9336 | .3584 | .3839 | 1.071 | 2.790 | 2.605 | 1.2043 | 69° 00′ |
| 10 | 694 | 325 | 611 | 872 | 072 | 769 | 583 | 1.2014 | 50 |
| 20 | 723 | 315 | 638 | 906 | 074 | 749 | 560 | 1.1985 | 40 |
| 30 | 752 | 304 | 665 | 939 | 075 | 729 | 539 | 956 | 30 |
| 40 | 782 | 293 | 692 | .3973 | 076 | 709 | 517 | 926 | 20 |
| 50 | 811 | 283 | 719 | .4006 | 077 | 689 | 496 | 897 | 10 |
| 22° 00′ | .3840 | .9272 | .3746 | .4040 | 1.079 | 2.669 | 2.475 | 1.1868 | 68° 00′ |
| 10 | 869 | 261 | 773 | 074 | 080 | 650 | 455 | 839 | 50 |
| 20 | 898 | 250 | 800 | 108 | 081 | 632 | 434 | 810 | 40 |
| 30 | 927 | 239 | 827 | 142 | 082 | 613 | 414 | 781 | 30 |
| 40 | 956 | 228 | 854 | 176 | 084 | 595 | 394 | 752 | 20 |
| 50 | 985 | 216 | 881 | 210 | 085 | 577 | 375 | 723 | 10 |
| 23° 00′ | .4014 | .9205 | .3907 | .4245 | 1.086 | 2.559 | 2.356 | 1.1694 | 67° 00′ |
| 10 | 043 | 194 | 934 | 279 | 088 | 542 | 337 | 665 | 50 |
| 20 | 072 | 182 | 961 | 314 | 089 | 525 | 318 | 636 | 40 |
| 30 | 102 | 171 | .3987 | 348 | 090 | 508 | 300 | 606 | 30 |
| 40 | 131 | 159 | .4014 | 383 | 092 | 491 | 282 | 577 | 20 |
| 50 | 160 | 147 | 041 | 417 | 093 | 475 | 264 | 548 | 10 |
| 24° 00′ | .4189 | .9135 | .4067 | .4452 | 1.095 | 2.459 | 2.246 | 1.1519 | 66° 00′ |
| | | $\sin \theta$ | $\cos \theta$ | $\cot \theta$ | $\csc \theta$ | $\sec \theta$ | $\tan \theta$ | Radians | Degrees |
| | | | | | | | | Angle $\theta$ | |

## TRIGONOMETRIC FUNCTIONS (continued)

| Degrees | Radians | cos θ | sin θ | tan θ | sec θ | csc θ | cot θ | | |
|---|---|---|---|---|---|---|---|---|---|
| 24° 00' | .4189 | .9135 | .4067 | .4452 | 1.095 | 2.459 | 2.246 | 1.1519 | 66° 00' |
| 10 | 218 | 124 | 094 | 487 | 096 | 443 | 229 | 490 | 50 |
| 20 | 247 | 112 | 120 | 522 | 097 | 427 | 211 | 461 | 40 |
| 30 | 276 | 100 | 147 | 557 | 099 | 411 | 194 | 432 | 30 |
| 40 | 305 | 088 | 173 | 592 | 100 | 396 | 177 | 403 | 20 |
| 50 | 334 | 075 | 200 | 628 | 102 | 381 | 161 | 374 | 10 |
| 25° 00' | .4363 | .9063 | .4226 | .4663 | 1.103 | 2.366 | 2.145 | 1.1345 | 65° 00' |
| 10 | 392 | 051 | 253 | 699 | 105 | 352 | 128 | 316 | 50 |
| 20 | 422 | 038 | 279 | 734 | 106 | 337 | 112 | 286 | 40 |
| 30 | 451 | 026 | 305 | 770 | 108 | 323 | 097 | 257 | 30 |
| 40 | 480 | 013 | 331 | 806 | 109 | 309 | 081 | 228 | 20 |
| 50 | 509 | .9001 | 358 | 841 | 111 | 295 | 066 | 199 | 10 |
| 26° 00' | .4538 | .8988 | .4384 | .4877 | 1.113 | 2.281 | 2.050 | 1.1170 | 64° 00' |
| 10 | 567 | 975 | 410 | 913 | 114 | 268 | 035 | 141 | 50 |
| 20 | 596 | 962 | 436 | 950 | 116 | 254 | 020 | 112 | 40 |
| 30 | 625 | 949 | 462 | .4986 | 117 | 241 | 2.006 | 083 | 30 |
| 40 | 654 | 936 | 488 | .5022 | 119 | 228 | 1.991 | 054 | 20 |
| 50 | 683 | 923 | 514 | 059 | 121 | 215 | 977 | 1.1025 | 10 |
| 27° 00' | .4712 | .8910 | .4540 | .5095 | 1.122 | 2.203 | 1.963 | 1.0996 | 63° 00' |
| 10 | 741 | 897 | 566 | 132 | 124 | 190 | 949 | 966 | 50 |
| 20 | 771 | 884 | 592 | 169 | 126 | 178 | 935 | 937 | 40 |
| 30 | 800 | 870 | 617 | 206 | 127 | 166 | 921 | 908 | 30 |
| 40 | 829 | 857 | 643 | 243 | 129 | 154 | 907 | 879 | 20 |
| 50 | 858 | 843 | 669 | 280 | 131 | 142 | 894 | 850 | 10 |
| 28° 00' | .4887 | .8829 | .4695 | .5317 | 1.133 | 2.130 | 1.881 | 1.0821 | 62° 00' |
| 10 | 916 | 816 | 720 | 354 | 134 | 118 | 868 | 792 | 50 |
| 20 | 945 | 802 | 746 | 392 | 136 | 107 | 855 | 763 | 40 |
| 30 | .4974 | 788 | 772 | 430 | 138 | 096 | 842 | 734 | 30 |
| 40 | .5003 | 774 | 797 | 467 | 140 | 085 | 829 | 705 | 20 |
| 50 | 032 | 760 | 823 | 505 | 142 | 074 | 816 | 676 | 10 |
| 29° 00' | .5061 | .8746 | .4848 | .5543 | 1.143 | 2.063 | 1.804 | 1.0647 | 61° 00' |
| 10 | 091 | 732 | 874 | 581 | 145 | 052 | 792 | 617 | 50 |
| 20 | 120 | 718 | 899 | 619 | 147 | 041 | 780 | 588 | 40 |
| 30 | 149 | 704 | 924 | 658 | 149 | 031 | 767 | 559 | 30 |
| 40 | 178 | 689 | 950 | 696 | 151 | 020 | 756 | 530 | 20 |
| 50 | 207 | 675 | .4975 | 735 | 153 | 010 | 744 | 501 | 10 |
| 30° 00' | .5236 | .8660 | .5000 | .5774 | 1.155 | 2.000 | 1.732 | 1.0472 | 60° 00' |
| 10 | 265 | 646 | 025 | 812 | 157 | 1.990 | 720 | 443 | 50 |
| 20 | 294 | 631 | 050 | 851 | 159 | 980 | 709 | 414 | 40 |
| 30 | 323 | 616 | 075 | 890 | 161 | 970 | 698 | 385 | 30 |
| 40 | 352 | 601 | 100 | 930 | 163 | 961 | 686 | 356 | 20 |
| 50 | 381 | 587 | 125 | .5969 | 165 | 951 | 675 | 327 | 10 |
| 31° 00' | .5411 | .8572 | .5150 | .6009 | 1.167 | 1.942 | 1.664 | 1.0297 | 59° 00' |
| 10 | 440 | 557 | 175 | 048 | 169 | 932 | 653 | 268 | 50 |
| 20 | 469 | 542 | 200 | 088 | 171 | 923 | 643 | 239 | 40 |
| 30 | 498 | 526 | 225 | 128 | 173 | 914 | 632 | 210 | 30 |
| 40 | 527 | 511 | 250 | 168 | 175 | 905 | 621 | 181 | 20 |
| 50 | 556 | 496 | 275 | 208 | 177 | 896 | 611 | 152 | 10 |
| 32° 00' | .5585 | .8480 | .5299 | .6249 | 1.179 | 1.887 | 1.600 | 1.0123 | 58° 00' |
| | | sin θ | cos θ | cot θ | csc θ | sec θ | tan θ | Radians | Degrees |
| | | | | | | | | | Angle θ |

## TRIGONOMETRIC FUNCTIONS (continued)

| Angle θ Degrees | Angle θ Radians | cos θ | sin θ | tan θ | sec θ | csc θ | cot θ | | |
|---|---|---|---|---|---|---|---|---|---|
| 32° 00' | .5585 | .8480 | .5299 | .6249 | 1.179 | 1.887 | 1.600 | 1.0123 | 58° 00' |
| 10 | 614 | 465 | 324 | 289 | 181 | 878 | 590 | 094 | 50 |
| 20 | 643 | 450 | 348 | 330 | 184 | 870 | 580 | 065 | 40 |
| 30 | 672 | 434 | 373 | 371 | 186 | 861 | 570 | 036 | 30 |
| 40 | 701 | 418 | 398 | 412 | 188 | 853 | 560 | 1.0007 | 20 |
| 50 | 730 | 403 | 422 | 453 | 190 | 844 | 550 | .9977 | 10 |
| 33° 00' | .5760 | .8387 | .5446 | .6494 | 1.192 | 1.836 | 1.540 | .9948 | 57° 00' |
| 10 | 789 | 371 | 471 | 536 | 195 | 828 | 530 | 919 | 50 |
| 20 | 818 | 355 | 495 | 577 | 197 | 820 | 520 | 890 | 40 |
| 30 | 847 | 339 | 519 | 619 | 199 | 812 | 511 | 861 | 30 |
| 40 | 876 | 323 | 544 | 661 | 202 | 804 | 501 | 832 | 20 |
| 50 | 905 | 307 | 568 | 703 | 204 | 796 | 492 | 803 | 10 |
| 34° 00' | .5934 | .8290 | .5592 | .6745 | 1.206 | 1.788 | 1.483 | .9774 | 56° 00' |
| 10 | 963 | 274 | 616 | 787 | 209 | 781 | 473 | 745 | 50 |
| 20 | .5992 | 258 | 640 | 830 | 211 | 773 | 464 | 716 | 40 |
| 30 | .6021 | 241 | 664 | 873 | 213 | 766 | 455 | 687 | 30 |
| 40 | 050 | 225 | 688 | 916 | 216 | 758 | 446 | 657 | 20 |
| 50 | 080 | 208 | 712 | .6959 | 218 | 751 | 437 | 628 | 10 |
| 35° 00' | .6109 | .8192 | .5736 | .7002 | 1.221 | 1.743 | 1.428 | .9599 | 55° 00' |
| 10 | 138 | 175 | 760 | 046 | 223 | 736 | 419 | 570 | 50 |
| 20 | 167 | 158 | 783 | 089 | 226 | 729 | 411 | 541 | 40 |
| 30 | 196 | 141 | 807 | 133 | 228 | 722 | 402 | 512 | 30 |
| 40 | 225 | 124 | 831 | 177 | 231 | 715 | 393 | 483 | 20 |
| 50 | 254 | 107 | 854 | 221 | 233 | 708 | 385 | 454 | 10 |
| 36° 00' | .6283 | .8090 | .5878 | .7265 | 1.236 | 1.701 | 1.376 | .9425 | 54° 00' |
| 10 | 312 | 073 | 901 | 310 | 239 | 695 | 368 | 396 | 50 |
| 20 | 341 | 056 | 925 | 355 | 241 | 688 | 360 | 367 | 40 |
| 30 | 370 | 039 | 948 | 400 | 244 | 681 | 351 | 338 | 30 |
| 40 | 400 | 021 | 972 | 445 | 247 | 675 | 343 | 308 | 20 |
| 50 | 429 | .8004 | .5995 | 490 | 249 | 668 | 335 | 279 | 10 |
| 37° 00' | .6458 | .7986 | .6018 | .7536 | 1.252 | 1.662 | 1.327 | .9250 | 53° 00' |
| 10 | 487 | 966 | 041 | 581 | 255 | 655 | 319 | 221 | 50 |
| 20 | 516 | 951 | 065 | 627 | 258 | 649 | 311 | 192 | 40 |
| 30 | 545 | 934 | 088 | 673 | 260 | 643 | 303 | 163 | 30 |
| 40 | 574 | 916 | 111 | 720 | 263 | 636 | 295 | 134 | 20 |
| 50 | 603 | 898 | 134 | 766 | 266 | 630 | 288 | 105 | 10 |
| 38° 00' | .6632 | .7880 | .6157 | .7813 | 1.269 | 1.624 | 1.280 | .9076 | 52° 00' |
| 10 | 661 | 862 | 180 | 860 | 272 | 618 | 272 | 047 | 50 |
| 20 | 690 | 844 | 202 | 907 | 275 | 612 | 265 | .9018 | 40 |
| 30 | 720 | 826 | 225 | .7954 | 278 | 606 | 257 | .8988 | 30 |
| 40 | 749 | 808 | 248 | .8002 | 281 | 601 | 250 | 959 | 20 |
| 50 | 778 | 790 | 271 | 050 | 284 | 595 | 242 | 930 | 10 |
| 39° 00' | .6807 | .7771 | .6293 | .8098 | 1.287 | 1.589 | 1.235 | .8901 | 51° 00' |
| 10 | 836 | 753 | 316 | 146 | 290 | 583 | 228 | 872 | 50 |
| 20 | 865 | 735 | 338 | 195 | 293 | 578 | 220 | 843 | 40 |
| 30 | 894 | 716 | 361 | 243 | 296 | 572 | 213 | 814 | 30 |
| 40 | 923 | 698 | 383 | 292 | 299 | 567 | 206 | 785 | 20 |
| 50 | 952 | 679 | 406 | 342 | 302 | 561 | 199 | 756 | 10 |
| 40° 00' | .6981 | .7660 | .6428 | .8391 | 1.305 | 1.556 | 1.192 | .8727 | 50° 00' |
| | | sin θ | cos θ | cot θ | csc θ | sec θ | tan θ | Radians | Degrees |
| | | | | | | | | Angle θ | |

## TRIGONOMETRIC FUNCTIONS (continued)

| Angle $\theta$ Degrees | Angle $\theta$ Radians | cos $\theta$ | sin $\theta$ | tan $\theta$ | sec $\theta$ | csc $\theta$ | cot $\theta$ | | |
|---|---|---|---|---|---|---|---|---|---|
| 40° 00′ | .6981 | .7660 | .6428 | .8391 | 1.305 | 1.556 | 1.192 | .8727 | 50° 00′ |
| 10 | .7010 | 642 | 450 | 441 | 309 | 550 | 185 | 698 | 50 |
| 20 | 039 | 623 | 472 | 491 | 312 | 545 | 178 | 668 | 40 |
| 30 | 069 | 604 | 494 | 541 | 315 | 540 | 171 | 639 | 30 |
| 40 | 098 | 585 | 517 | 591 | 318 | 535 | 164 | 610 | 20 |
| 50 | 127 | 566 | 539 | 642 | 322 | 529 | 157 | 581 | 10 |
| 41° 00′ | .7156 | .7547 | .6561 | .8693 | 1.325 | 1.524 | 1.150 | .8552 | 49° 00′ |
| 10 | 185 | 528 | 583 | 744 | 328 | 519 | 144 | 523 | 50 |
| 20 | 214 | 509 | 604 | 796 | 332 | 514 | 137 | 494 | 40 |
| 30 | 243 | 490 | 626 | 847 | 335 | 509 | 130 | 465 | 30 |
| 40 | 272 | 470 | 648 | 899 | 339 | 504 | 124 | 436 | 20 |
| 50 | 301 | 451 | 670 | .8952 | 342 | 499 | 117 | 407 | 10 |
| 42° 00′ | .7330 | .7431 | .6691 | .9004 | 1.346 | 1.494 | 1.111 | .8378 | 48° 00′ |
| 10 | 359 | 412 | 713 | 057 | 349 | 490 | 104 | 348 | 50 |
| 20 | 389 | 392 | 734 | 110 | 353 | 485 | 098 | 319 | 40 |
| 30 | 418 | 373 | 756 | 163 | 356 | 480 | 091 | 290 | 30 |
| 40 | 447 | 353 | 777 | 217 | 360 | 476 | 085 | 261 | 20 |
| 50 | 476 | 333 | 799 | 271 | 364 | 471 | 079 | 232 | 10 |
| 43° 00′ | .7505 | .7314 | .6820 | .9325 | 1.367 | 1.466 | 1.072 | .8203 | 47° 00′ |
| 10 | 534 | 294 | 841 | 380 | 371 | 462 | 066 | 174 | 50 |
| 20 | 563 | 274 | 862 | 435 | 375 | 457 | 060 | 145 | 40 |
| 30 | 592 | 254 | 884 | 490 | 379 | 453 | 054 | 116 | 30 |
| 40 | 621 | 234 | 905 | 545 | 382 | 448 | 048 | 087 | 20 |
| 50 | 650 | 214 | 926 | 601 | 386 | 444 | 042 | 058 | 10 |
| 44° 00′ | .7679 | .7193 | .6947 | .9657 | 1.390 | 1.440 | 1.036 | .8029 | 46° 00′ |
| 10 | 709 | 173 | 967 | 713 | 394 | 435 | 030 | .7999 | 50 |
| 20 | 738 | 153 | .6988 | 770 | 398 | 431 | 024 | 970 | 40 |
| 30 | 767 | 133 | .7009 | 827 | 402 | 427 | 018 | 941 | 30 |
| 40 | 796 | 112 | 030 | 884 | 406 | 423 | 012 | 912 | 20 |
| 50 | 825 | 092 | 050 | .9942 | 410 | 418 | 006 | 883 | 10 |
| 45° 00′ | .7854 | .7071 | .7071 | 1.000 | 1.414 | 1.414 | 1.000 | .7854 | 45° 00′ |

| | | sin $\theta$ | cos $\theta$ | cot $\theta$ | csc $\theta$ | sec $\theta$ | tan $\theta$ | Radians | Degrees |
|---|---|---|---|---|---|---|---|---|---|
| | | | | | | | | Angle $\theta$ | |

# ABBREVIATIONS FOR ENGINEERING TERMS[1]

| | | | | |
|---|---|---|---|---|
| absolute | abs | cord | cd |
| acre | spell out | cosecant | csc |
| acre-foot | acre-ft | cosine | cos |
| air horsepower | air hp | cosine of the amplitude, an elliptic | |
| alternating-current (as adjective) | a-c | function | cn |
| ampere | amp | cotangent | cot |
| ampere-hour | amp-hr | coulomb | spell out |
| amplitude, an elliptic function | am. | cubic | cu |
| Angstrom unit | Å | cubic centimeter | cu cm, cm³ |
| antilogarithm | antilog | cubic feet per minute | cfm or ft³/min |
| atmosphere | atm | cubic feet per second | cfs or ft³/sec |
| atomic weight | at. wt | cubic foot | cu ft or ft³ |
| average | avg | cubic inch | cu in. or in.³ |
| avoirdupois | avdp | cubic meter | cu m or m³ |
| azimuth | az or $\alpha$ | cubic micron | cu $\mu$ or cu mu or $\mu^3$ |
| | | cubic millimeter | cu mm or mm³ |
| barometer | bar. | cubic yard | cu yd or yd³ |
| barrel | bbl | cylinder | cyl |
| Baumé | Bé | | |
| board feet (feet board measure) | fbm | decibel | db |
| boiler pressure | spell out | degree | deg or ° |
| boiling point | bp | degree Celsius | C |
| brake horsepower | bhp | degree Fahrenheit | F |
| brake horsepower-hour | bhp-hr | degree Kelvin | K |
| Brinell hardness number | Bhn | degree Réaumur | R |
| British thermal unit | Btu or B | diameter | diam |
| bushel | bu | direct-current (as adjective) | d-c |
| | | dollar | $ |
| calorie | cal | dozen | doz |
| candle | c | dram | dr |
| candle-hour | c-hr | dyne | spell out |
| candlepower | cp | | |
| cent | c or ¢ | efficiency | eff |
| center to center | c to c | electric | elec |
| centigram | cg | electromotive force | emf |
| centiliter | cl | elevation | el |
| centimeter | cm | equation | eq |
| centimeter-gram-second (system) | cgs | external | ext |
| chemical | chem | | |
| chemically pure | cp | farad | spell out or f |
| circular | cir | feet board measure (board feet) | fbm |
| circular mils | cir mils | feet per minute | ft/min or fpm |
| coefficient | coef | feet per second | ft/sec or fps |
| cologarithm | colog | fluid | fl |
| conductivity | cond | foot | ft |
| constant | const | foot-candle | ft-c |

[1] This list of abbreviations is revised from *Abbreviations for Scientific and Engineering Terms*, approved by the American Standards Association, and published by the American Society of Mechanical Engineers, New York City.

## ABBREVIATIONS FOR ENGINEERING TERMS (continued)

foot-Lambert . . . . . . . . . . . . . . . . . . . ft-L
foot-pound . . . . . . . . . . . . . . . . . . . . ft-lb
foot-second (see cubic feet per second)
freezing point . . . . . . . . . . . . . . . . . . . fp
fusion point . . . . . . . . . . . . . . . . . . . . fnp

gallon . . . . . . . . . . . . . . . . . . . . . . . . gal
gallons per minute . . . . . gal/min or gpm
gallons per second . . . . . . . gal/sec or gps
gram . . . . . . . . . . . . . . . . . . . . . . . . . g
gram-calorie . . . . . . . . . . . . . . . . . . . g-cal

haversine . . . . . . . . . . . . . . . . . . . . . hav
hectare . . . . . . . . . . . . . . . . . . . . . . . ha
henry . . . . . . . . . . . . . . . . . . . . . . . . h
high-pressure (adjective) . . . . . . . . . . h-p
hogshead . . . . . . . . . . . . . . . . . . . . . hhd
horsepower . . . . . . . . . . . . . . . . . . . . hp
horsepower-hour . . . . . . . . . . . . . . . hp-hr
hour . . . . . . . . . . . . . . . . . . . . . . . . hr
hundred . . . . . . . . . . . . . . . . . . . . . . C
hundredweight (112 lb) . . . . . . . . . . . cwt
hyperbolic cosine . . . . . . . . . . . . . . . cosh
hyberbolic sine . . . . . . . . . . . . . . . . . sinh
hyperbolic tangent . . . . . . . . . . . . . . tanh

inch . . . . . . . . . . . . . . . . . . . . . . . . in.
inch-pound . . . . . . . . . . . . . . . . . . . in.-lb
inches per second . . . . . . . . in./sec or ips
indicated horsepower . . . . . . . . . . . . ihp
indicated horsepower-hour . . . . . . . ihp-hr
inside diameter . . . . . . . . . . . . . . . . . ID
internal . . . . . . . . . . . . . . . . . . . . . . int

joule . . . . . . . . . . . . . . . . . . . . . . . . j

kilocalorie . . . . . . . . . . . . . . . . . . . . kcal
kilogram . . . . . . . . . . . . . . . . . . . . . kg
kilogram-calorie . . . . . . . . . . . . . . . kg-cal
kilogram-meter . . . . . . . . . . . . . . . . kg-m
kilograms per cubic meter
. . . . . . . . . . . . . . kg per cu m or kg/m³
kilograms per second . . . . kg/sec or kgps
kiloliter . . . . . . . . . . . . . . . . . . . . . . kl
kilometer . . . . . . . . . . . . . . . . . . . . . km
kilometers per second . . . . . . . . . . . kmps
kilovolt . . . . . . . . . . . . . . . . . . . . . . kv
kilovolt-ampere . . . . . . . . . . . . . . . . kva
kilowatt . . . . . . . . . . . . . . . . . . . . . . kw
kilowatthour . . . . . . . . . . . . . . . . . . kwhr

latitude . . . . . . . . . . . . . . . . . . lat or $\phi$
linear foot . . . . . . . . . . . . . . . . . . lin ft
liter . . . . . . . . . . . . . . . . . . . . . . . . l
logarithm (common) . . . . . . . . . . . . . log
logarithm (natural) . . . . . . . . . $\log_\varepsilon$ or ln
longitude . . . . . . . . . . . . . . . long. or $\lambda$
low-pressure (as adjective) . . . . . . . . l-p
lumen . . . . . . . . . . . . . . . . . . . . . . . l
lumen-hour . . . . . . . . . . . . . . . . . . . l-hr
lumens per watt . . . . . . . . . . . . . . . lpw

mass . . . . . . . . . . . . . . . . m or spell out
maximum . . . . . . . . . . . . . . . . . . . max
mean effective pressure . . . . . . . . . . mep
melting point . . . . . . . . . . . . . . . . . mp
meter . . . . . . . . . . . . . . . . . . . . . . . m
meter-kilogram . . . . . . . . . . . . . . . . m-kg
microampere . . . . . . . . . . $\mu$a or mu a
microfarad . . . . . . . . . . . . . . . . . . $\mu$f
microinch . . . . . . . . . . . . . . . . . . $\mu$in.
micromicrofarad . . . . . . . . . . . . . . $\mu\mu$f
micromicron . . . . . . . . . . $\mu\mu$ or mu mu
micron . . . . . . . . . . . . . . . $\mu$ or mu
microvolt . . . . . . . . . . . . . . . . . . . $\mu$v
microwatt . . . . . . . . . . . $\mu$w or mu w
mile . . . . . . . . . . . . . . . mi or spell out
miles per hour . . . . . . . . . mi/hr or mph
miles per hour per second
. . . . . . . . . . . . . . . mi/hr/sec or mphps
milliampere . . . . . . . . . . . . . . . . . . ma
milligram . . . . . . . . . . . . . . . . . . . . mg
millihenry . . . . . . . . . . . . . . . . . . . mh
millilambert . . . . . . . . . . . . . . . . . . mL
milliliter . . . . . . . . . . . . . . . . . . . . ml
millimeter . . . . . . . . . . . . . . . . . . . mm
millimicron . . . . . . . . . . $m\mu$ or m mu
million . . . . . . . . . . . . . . . . . . spell out
million gallons per day . . . . . . . . . . mgd
millivolt . . . . . . . . . . . . . . . . . . . . mv
minute . . . . . . . . . . . . . . . . . . . . . min
minute (angular measure) . . . . . . . . . . '
mole . . . . . . . . . . . . . . . . . . . spell out
molecular weight . . . . . . . . . . . . mol. wt
month . . . . . . . . . . . . . . . . . . spell out

National Electrical Code . . . . . . . . NEC
newton . . . . . . . . . . . . . . . . . . . . . . n

ohm . . . . . . . . . . . . . . . spell out or $\Omega$
ohm-centimeter . . . . . . . . . . . . ohm-cm

| | |
|---|---|
| ounce | oz |
| ounce-foot | oz-ft |
| ounce-inch | oz-in. |
| outside diameter | OD |
| | |
| parts per million | ppm |
| peck | pk |
| penny (pence) | d |
| pennyweight | dwt |
| pint | pt |
| pound | lb |
| pound-foot | lb-ft |
| pound-inch | lb-in. |
| pound sterling | £ |
| pounds per brake horsepower-hour | lb/bph-hr or lb per bhp-hr |
| pounds per cubic foot | lb/ft³ or lb per cu ft |
| pounds per square foot | lb/ft² or psf |
| pounds per square inch | lb/in.² or psi |
| pounds per square inch absolute | lb/in. abs. or psia |
| power factor | spell out or pf |
| | |
| quart | qt |
| | |
| radian | rad or spell out |
| revolutions per minute | rev/min or rpm |
| revolutions per second | rev/sec or rps |
| rod | spell out |
| root mean square | rms |
| | |
| secant | sec |
| second | sec |
| second (angular measure) | ″ |

| | |
|---|---|
| shaft horsepower | shp |
| shilling | s |
| sine | sin |
| specific gravity | sp gr |
| specific heat | sp ht |
| square | sq |
| square centimeter | sq cm or cm² |
| square foot | ft² or sq ft |
| square inch | in.² or sq in. |
| square kilometer | sq km or km² |
| square meter | sq m or m² |
| square micron | sq μ or sq mu or μ² |
| square millimeter | sq mm or mm² |
| square root of mean square | rms |
| standard | std |
| | |
| tangent | tan |
| temperature | temp |
| thousand | M |
| thousand pound | kip |
| ton | spell out |
| | |
| versed sine | vers |
| volt | v |
| volt-ampere | va |
| volt-coulomb | spell out |
| | |
| watt | w |
| watthour | whr |
| watts per candle | wpc |
| week | spell out |
| weight | wt |
| | |
| yard | yd |
| year | yr |

# Appendix V

## Answers to Selected Problems

### Chapter 9

**9–1.** *e.* $x = 5$
  *j.* $x = -3$
  *o.* $x = 4$
  *t.* $x = 12$
**9–2.** *e.* 318.3
  *j.* 702.25
**9–3.** *e.* $-8.961$
  *j.* 0.851

**9–4.** *e.* $5.6856(10)^4$
  *j.* $-5.345(10)^2$
  *o.* $5.2(10)^1$
**9–5.** *e.* 1.55
  *j.* $-3.064(10)^{-6}$
  *o.* 1.6
**9–6.** *e.* $7(10)^{-2}\%$
  *j.* $1(10)^2\%$

**9–7.** *e.* $\pm 2(10)^{-4}$
  *j.* $\pm 10^{-1}$
**9–10.** *a.* 7.47 ft
  *b.* 1.89 ft
  *c.* 0.7% error

### Chapter 10

**10–1.** *e.* 2.781
  *j.* 7.772
  *o.* 6.822
  *t.* 3.644
  *y.* 7.857
**10–45.** $8.51(10)^6$
**10–50.** $8.75(10)^1$
**10–55.** $3.79(10)^3$
**10–60.** $8.37(10)^5$
**10–65.** $4.35(10)^5$
**10–70.** $1.202(10)^6$
**10–75.** 1.095
**10–80.** $8.32(10)^3$
**10–85.** $6.06(10)^6$
**10–90.** $1.619(10)^6$
**10–135.** $2.53(10)^1$
**10–140.** $4.59(10)^{-1}$
**10–145.** $4.25(10)^4$

**10–150.** $5.91(10)^2$
**10–155.** $2.77(10)^{-1}$
**10–160.** $3.88(10)^{-3}$
**10–165.** $1.275(10)^8$
**10–170.** 1.278
**10–175.** $2.21(10)^3$
**10–180.** $5.96(10)^3$
**10–225.** $1.350(10)^1$
**10–230.** $1.524(10)^{-2}$
**10–235.** $9.54(10)^{-1}$
**10–240.** $1.099(10)^{-1}$
**10–245.** $2.87(10)^{-6}$
**10–250.** $1.437(10)^{-3}$
**10–255.** $2.93(10)^{-7}$
**10–260.** $2.96(10)^{-4}$
**10–265.** $5.07(10)^{-1}$
**10–270.** 5.64
**10–355.** $1.430(10)^2$

**10–360.** $4.46(10)^{-3}$
**10–365.** $2.02(10)^9$
**10–370.** $9.98(10)^{-1}$
**10–375.** 1.772
**10–380.** $5.27(10)^{-1}$
**10–385.** $3.62(10)^3$
**10–390.** $2.53(10)^1$
**10–445.** $1.079(10)^5$
**10–450.** $1.357(10)^6$
**10–455.** $8.12(10)^{-7}$
**10–460.** 2.08
**10–465.** $3.26(10)^1$
**10–470.** $3.68(10)^2$
**10–475.** $5.36(10)^2$
**10–480.** $1.138(10)^7$
**10–560.** 0.978
**10–565.** 0.407
**10–570.** 0.669

**10–575.** 1.397

**10–580.** 1.028

**10–585.** 0.719

**10–590.** 1.034

**10–595.** 1.856

**10–600.** 1.061

**10–605.** 88.36°

**10–610.** 7.25°

**10–615.** 0.999

**10–620.** 31.8°

**10–625.** 29.55°

**10–630.** 0.602

**10–635.** 0.235

**10–640.** 0.897

**10–645.** 1.513

**10–650.** 1.569

**10–655.** 1.168

**10–660.** $b = 15.97$

$B = 23.5°$

**10–665.** $c = 4.09$

$B = 15°$

**10–670.** $a = 599$

$b = 1807$

**10–675.** $a = 677$

$c = 678$

**10–730.** $1.11(10)^2$

**10–735.** 1.331

**10–740.** 0.1048

**10–745.** 1.0352

**10–750.** $6.89(10)^{11}$

**10–755.** 0.492

**10–760.** 1.433

**10–765.** 1.0006

**10–770.** 0.386

**10–775.** 0.8728

**10–780.** 0.044

**10–785.** 36

**10–790.** 3.89

**10–795.** 0.925

**10–800.** 1.018

**10–805.** $-0.250$

**10–810.** 3.51

**10–815.** $-6.70$

**10–820.** 4.495

**10–825.** $-0.0026$

**10–830.** $3.11(10)^1$

**10–835.** $2.73(10)^{-2}$

**10–840.** $3.97(10)^4$

**10–845.** $-1.230(10)^3$

**10–850.** $1.706(10)^5$

**10–855.** $8.53(10)^3$

**10–860.** $8.98(10)^7$

**10–865.** $9.41(10)^{-2}$

**10–870.** $5.62(10)^1$

**10–875.** $5.43(10)^3$

**10–880.** $2.75(10)^{-3}$

**10–885.** 1.776

**10–890.** $3.26(10)^3$

**10–895.** $2.45(10)^{12}$

**10–900.** $7.39(10)^4$

**10–905.** 1.049

**10–910.** $1.071(10)^{-1}$

**10–915.** $3.34(10)^1$

**10–920.** $3.24(10)^{-1}$

**10–925.** $1.071(10)^{-9}$

**10–930.** *a.* 1.039

*b.* 1.579

*c.* 3.69

*d.* 5.395

*e.* 17.61

*f.* 28.42

*g.* 74.21

**10–935.** *a.* $4.81 + j\,3.90$

*b.* $2.97 + j\,2.68$

*c.* $8.58 + j\,3.36$

*d.* $0.88 + j\,2.56$

**10–940.** *a.* 218 /317.4°

*b.* 100.5 /332.6°

*c.* 0.00803 /320.5°

*d.* 3.65 /327.4°

**Chapter 11**

**11–5.** $k = \dfrac{R^8\,T^3}{G^4\,JN}$

**11–10.** $k = \dfrac{Y\,C^2}{R^{1/2}\,M^3}$

**11–15.** $M = FL$

**11–20.** $r = L$

**11–25.** $1.326(10)^7$ ft³

**11–30.** *a.* $6.66(10)^4$ mi/hr

*b.* $9.77(10)^4$ ft/sec

*c.* $2.98(10)^4$ m/sec

*d.* $1.788(10)^3$ km/min

**11–35.** *a.* $\sigma = 1160$ $\text{lb}_f$/in.²

*b.* $A = 9.48(10)^{-3}$ ft²

*c.* $l = 4.12$ ft

*d.* $R = 9.96(10)^6$ lb/in.²

**11–40.** *a.* $F = 4.915$ n

*b.* 5.01 kg

**11–45.** $F = 4.57(10)^9$ dynes

**11–50.** $m_1 = 5.97(10)^{24}$ kg

**11–60.** 2.24 kg

**11–65.** *a.* $1.56(10)^{-1}$ amp/m

*b.* 95.1 volt/m

**Chapter 12**

**12–1.** $X = 2.01913$g

$s = \pm0.0016$ g

$s_m = \pm4.25(10)^{-4}$ g

Wt. $= 2.0191 \pm 0.0004$ g

**12–7.** $\overline{X} = 6.804$ in.

Tolerance $\pm$ 6.794 to 6.814 in.

## Chapter 16

**16–5.** Wt. $= 1.50(10)^4$ lb$_f$

**16–10.** $V = 430$ ft$^3$

**16–15.** $t = 9.04$ hr

**16–20.** $V = 525$ yd$^3$

**16–25.** Wt. $= 1.170(10)^3$ lb$_f$

**16–30.** $V = 21.9$ gal

**16–35.** $A = 54.1$ ft

**16–40.** $A = 51.3$ acres
  $L = 7405$ ft

**16–45.** $L = 18.4$ ft

**16–50.** $AB = 272$ ft

**16–55.** $V = 1737$ ft$^3$

**16–60.** $p_2 = 34.3$ psig

**16–65.** *a.* $R = 3110$ lb at $20°$
  *b.* $R = 1490$ lb at $130°$

**16–70.** $R = 425$ mi/hr
  at S $77°$ E

**16–75.** $M_1 = 40.5$ lb
  $M_2 = 66$ lb

**16–80.** $T_1 = 296$ lb
  $T_2 = 296$ lb

**16–85.** $F_3 = 74.6$ lb
  at S $52° 50'$ E

**16–90.** $R = 333$ lb
  at N $58.6°$ E

**16–95.** $A = 930$ lb
  $B = 1315$ lb

**16–100.** $M_A = 231$ lb ft

**16–105.** $P = 92.3$ lb

**16–110.** $R_r = 7.37$ ft from
  right end

**16–115.** Wt. $= 37.6$ lb

**16–120.** $BC = 1.714(10)^3$ lb
  $R_A = 1.715(10)^3$ lb
  at $33.6°$

**16–125.** $CB = 1885$ lb T
  $AB = 1709$ lb C

**16–130.** $AC = 1750$ lb
  $R_B = 1405$ lb at
  S $72.4°$ E

**16–140.** $R_s = 370.2\Omega$
  $R_E = 40.1\Omega$

**16–145.** $V_1 = 10.0$ v
  $V_2 = 21.0$ v
  $V_3 = 21.0$ v
  $V_4 = 18.78$ v
  $I_2 = 3.05$ amp
  $I_3 = 3.99$ amp
  $I_4 = 7.03$ amp
  $V_c = 50.9$ v

**16–155.** $V_B = 41.5$ v
  $V_3 = 9.09$ v

**16–160.** $I = 13.62$ amp
  $H_p = 4.02$ hp

**16–165.** $R_s = 4.964(10)^5\Omega$

## Chapter 20

**20–5.** Purchase taxi "B"

**20–10.** Choose $a_2$

**20–15.** Choose $a_2$

**20–20.** Choose $a_1$

**20–25.** $a_1$ dominates

**20–30.** Select $a_2$ when
  ½ $V_{injury}$ is greater
  than $100

# INDEX

**545**